NATIONAL GEOGRAPHIC SOCIETY

Research Reports

NATIONAL GEOGRAPHIC SOCIETY

Research Reports

VOLUME 13

On research and exploration projects
supported by the National Geographic Society,
the initial grant for which
as made in the year

1971 or 1972

Compiled and edited by
Paul H. Oehser, John S. Lea, and Nancy Link Powars
under the direction of the
Committee for Research and Exploration

NATIONAL GEOGRAPHIC SOCIETY
WASHINGTON, D. C.

• • •

Copyright © 1981 National Geographic Society
International Standard Book No. ISBN 0-87044-422-0
Library of Congress Catalog Card No. 68-26794

iv

Statement by the Chairman

The National Geographic Society was founded in 1888 by a group, composed largely of Washington scientists, to increase and diffuse geographic knowledge and to promote research and exploration. The Society's activities toward achieving its second objective date from 1890, when the society sponsored a geographic and geologic expedition to study the Mount St. Elias Range of Alaska. Since then it has made more than 2,300 grants in support of approximately 1,750 projects in research and exploration. The work has encompassed the broad scope of geography, including such scientific disciplines as geology, paleontology, astronomy, geophysics, oceanography, biology, anthropology, archeology, ethnology, and geographic exploration. The research program has increased as the Society has grown, until today the budget of the Society provides $2,500,000 annually in support of the program.

To assist in the task of selecting from among the hundreds of applicants those best qualified to continue the high standards of accomplishment set by recipients of grants during the past nine decades, the Society has assembled the panel of distinguished scientists and scholars listed above.

This is the thirteenth in a series of volumes presenting summary reports on the results of all the research and exploration projects sponsored by the Society since it was established. These are being published volume by volume, as rapidly as the material can be assembled. The present volume contains 3 accounts covering work for which the initial grant was made in 1971 and 69 for which the initial grant was made in 1972. In instances when a continuing research program has been supported by grants over a number of years, and a breakdown of results by year is impracticable, it has seemed best to report on the subsequent grants in one résumé, with cross references to the main account inserted in other volumes as appropriate. The volumes now in print, and the grant years covered in them, are listed in the Editor's Note that follows.

In presenting the reports, no attempt has been made to standardize the style and specific approach of the investigator, other than to confine each account to reasonable space limitations. In many cases fuller but scattered reports on the work have been, or will be, published elsewhere—in technical and scientific journals, occasionally in the *National Geographic,* or in book form. Published accounts emanating from the research projects are included in the literature references, which each author has been encouraged to supply.

Although the editors of these Reports make every reasonable effort to obtain a timely report from every grantee, so that the results of all projects supported in a given year will be accounted for in one volume, circumstances occasionally interfere. In these instances the delayed report will be published in a later volume. Grantees generally have been most cooperative in this publication project. The Committee for Research and Exploration takes this opportunity to thank them for their support, and we solicit their continued help.

Experience with the preceding volumes of this series has convinced us that the presentation of research findings as given in these books is of significant value to the scientific community. Scholars the world over find this record of the accumulating results of National Geographic Society research grants of real assistance in their own investigations and in the preparation of scientific publications. The general reader also gains new and important knowledge about the current state of research related to geography from each of these volumes.

MELVIN M. PAYNE

Editor's Note

The accounts in this volume are arranged alphabetically under the name of the principal investigator, who is not necessarily the senior author named in the Table of Contents. A full list of the 1972 grants on which these are based is to be found in the Appendix (p. 313) of *National Geographic Society Research Reports*, vol. 8 *(1967 Projects)*, published in 1974.

The following accounts published in *National Geographic Society Research Reports*, vol. 10 *(1969 Projects)*, vol. 11 *(1970 Projects)*, and vol. 12 *(1971 Projects)* deal with research that continued into 1972 and was supported by grants in that year. Since these accounts cover this 1972 research, no further treatment of it is required here.

"Petrology and Origin of the Mount Stuart Batholith, Cascade Mountains, Washington," by Erik H. Erikson, Jr., *1971 Projects*, pp. 175-184.

"The 'Acropolis' of Aphrodisias in Caria: Investigations and Excavations of the Theater and the Prehistoric Mounds, 1971-1977," by Kenan T. Erim, *1971 Projects*, pp. 185-204.

"Excavations at Rattlers Bight—A Late Maritime Archaic Settlement and Cemetery in Hamilton Inlet, Labrador," by William W. Fitzhugh, *1971 Projects*, pp. 223-231.

"Mountain Gorilla Research, 1971-1972," by Dian Fossey, *1971 Projects*, pp. 237-255.

"Archeological Investigations at Chalcatazingo, 1972, 1973," by David C. Grove, *1971 Projects*, pp. 287-304.

"Stratigraphy, Age, and Environmental Interpretation of the Olduvai Beds, Tanzania," by Richard L. Hay, *1970 Projects*, pp. 259-260.

"Archeological and Paleoecological Investigations at Guadalupe Pueblo, Sandoval County, New Mexico: A Preliminary Report," by Cynthia Irwin-Williams and Lonnie C. Pippin, *1970 Projects*, pp. 309-330.

"Population Ecology of the Flamingos of the World," by M. Philip Kahl, *1971 Projects*, pp. 407-415.

"Lower Pleistocene Hominids from Lake Turkana, North Kenya, 1970-1972," by Richard E. F. Leakey, *1970 Projects*, pp. 363-376.

"Breeding Biology of Cackling Geese and Associated Species on the Yukon-Kuskokwim Delta, Alaska," by Peter G. Mickelson, *1970 Projects*, pp. 399-404.

"Behavior and Ecology of Feral Asses *(Equus asinus)*," by Patricia D. Moehlman, *1970 Projects*, pp. 405-411.

"The Chan-Chan-Moche Valley Archeological Project, Peru," by Michael E. Moseley, *1970 Projects*, pp. 413-425.

"Behavior of the Reef Sharks of Rangiroa, French Polynesia," by Donald R. Nelson and Richard H. Johnson, *1971 Projects*, pp. 479-499.

"Research on the Behavior of Various Species of Whales," by Roger S. Payne, *1971 Projects*, pp. 551-564.

"Excavation of the Phoenician and Roman Cities at Sarepta (Modern Sarafand, Lebanon)," by James B. Pritchard, *1969 Projects*, pp. 455-472.

"Archeological Research on the Island of Cozumel, Mexico," by Jeremy A. Sabloff and William L. Rathje, *1971 Projects*, pp. 595-599.

"Excavation of Oligocene Marine Fossil Beds Near Charleston, South Carolina," by Albert E. Sanders, *1971 Projects*, pp. 601-621.

"Ecology and Behavior of High-Altitude Mammals in South Asia," by George B. Schaller, *1970 Projects*, pp. 461-478.

"Archeological Surveys in Southwest Mississippi," by Stephen Williams, *1970 Projects*, pp. 581-590.

Reports on the 1972 grants listed below were not available at the time this volume went to press. They will appear in later volumes as they are received.

1084: To Dr. William J. L. Sladen, Johns Hopkins University, Baltimore, Maryland, for study of the migration of the whistling swan between Alaska and its wintering grounds.

1095: To Dr. Paul B. Kannowski, University of North Dakota, Grand Forks, North Dakota, for a feasibility study of expansion of Theodore Roosevelt National Memorial Park.

Libraries and institutions regularly receiving copies of these reports will note that this one bears the volume number 13 and that this practice of numbering is now being used to identify the volumes. For their convenience, the earlier ones may be considered to bear numbers (shown in parentheses) as follows:

Vol. no.	Covering grant years	Date issued
(1)	1890-1954	1975
(2)	1955-1960	1972
(3)	1961-1962	1970
(4)	1963	1968
(5)	1964	1969
(6)	1965	1971
(7)	1966	1973
(8)	1967	1974
(9)	1968	1976
(10)	1969	1978
(11)	1970	1979
12	1971	1980

To aid researchers, the Society's grants made from 1966 onward are listed numerically in the Appendix of *Research Reports* volumes as indicated below:

Grants (year made)		In volume	(project year)
550 - 600	(1966)	(4)	1963
601 - 670	(1967)	(5)	1964
671 - 743	(1968)	(5)	1964
744 - 822	(1969)	(6)	1965
823 - 917	(1970)	(6)	1965
918 - 1036	(1971)	(7)	1966
1037 - 1136	(1972)	(8)	1967
1137 - 1285	(1973)	(9)	1968
1286 - 1421	(1974)	(10)	1969
1422 - 1568	(1975)	(11)	1970
1569 - 1701	(1976)	(11)	1970
1702 - 1844	(1977)	12	(1971)
1845 - 1974	(1978)	12	(1971)
1975 - 2130	(1979)	13	(1971, 1972)

Contents

xi

Wild Orangutan Studies at Tanjung Puting Reserve, Central Indonesian Borneo, 1971-1977

Principal Investigators: Biruté M. F. Galdikas, Adjunct Associate Professor of Anthropology, University of New Mexico, Albuquerque, New Mexico.

Grant Nos. 988, 1227, 1351, 1393, 1502, 1645,1772.   For study of the behavior and ecology of the wild orangutan at Tanjung Puting Reserve, in Borneo.

The following is a brief summary report on the wild orangutan (*Pongo pygmaeus*) research carried out from November 1971 through November 1977 at the Tanjung Puting Reserve in coastal Central Borneo (Kalimantan Tengah), Indonesia (see fig. 1), under National Geographic grants 988, 1227, 1351, 1393, 1502, 1645, and 1772. Until the recent field studies of John McKinnon (1971, 1974, and 1979), David Horr (1972, 1975, and 1977), Peter Rodman (1973, 1977, and 1979), and Herman Rijksen (1978), orangutans were considered to be the most enigmatic of the great apes. Nonetheless, although these recent studies greatly expanded our knowledge of wild orangutans, a paucity of detailed, long-term data on orangutan adaptation still remained. The purpose of the Tanjung Puting work was to examine intensively the social behaviors, mating, foraging, and ranging patterns observed among a wild orangutan population and to assess the adaptive significance of these patterns over the long term.

Over six years Rod M. C. Brindamour and I, assisted by several local workmen and biology students from Universitas Nasional, Jakarta (each of whom served for six months: Suharto Djojosudarmo, Jaumat Dulhajah, Benny Djaya, Dadang Kusmana, and Richard Pattan), amassed over ten thousand hours of direct observation[1] on wild orangutans in a 35-square-kilometer tropical rain forest study area consisting of several habitat types: dry ground Dipterocarp Forest (63%), Peat Swamp Forest (27%), Tropical Heath Forest (5%) and abandoned dry rice fields, young secondary forest and shallow lakes (5%). Observations were carried out on approximately 70 individually recognized orangutans as well as some others who were not named or recognized. In

---

[1] An observation hour was defined as one hour of direct observation of one target orangutan, regardless of the number of observers or the number of orangutans present.

1

addition to orangutans, other ape and monkey species found in the study area forests included: gibbons *(Hylobates agilis)*,[2] red leaf-eating monkeys *(Presbytis rubicundus)*, proboscis monkeys *(Nasalis larvatus)*, long-tailed macaques *(Macaca fascicularis)*, and (infrequently) pig-tailed macaques *(Macaca nemestrina)*.

A large area of forest was initially chosen for this orangutan study so that (1) the home ranges of at least several adult members of each sex would be partially encompassed, and (2) data on a representative sample of the population could be gathered, enabling us to observe interactions between a variety of individuals of different age/sex classes as well as to make ecological and other comparisons among classes.

The entire study area was covered with a grid of small transects, initially placed 500 meters apart, running north-south and east-west. The combined length of all transects and trails exceeds 125 kilometers. The transect system was surveyed and staked every 25 meters with small posts bearing metal tags indicating distance from datum point. This allowed for the accurate mapping of orangutan daily movements and home ranges.

The principal difficulty in studying orangutans is simply locating them. Once located, an animal was followed, if at all possible, until it nested for the night. The next morning the observer(s) would arrive at the nest before dawn. The bulk of our data consisted of whole days (when the animals were followed continuously as they left their night nest in the morning to the time they made a nest for the following night). Since only one orangutan (or one adult and dependent offspring) was usually present, sampling of behavior was automatically limited to the "focal" individual or target (Altmann, 1974). Target individuals were observed for periods ranging from one minute to 65 consecutive days. However, we normally attempted to obtain at least two or three whole days of consecutive observations before releasing an individual from our scrutiny.

Since orangutan movement is slow, it was usually possible to monitor accurately the behavior of a target individual throughout the day, to log the occurrence of each major activity (resting, feeding, traveling, nesting, displaying, fighting, chasing, allogrooming, and mating), and to record times for bout initiation and termination. With the exception of very infrequent events such as allogrooming, the smallest observation interval utilized was one minute. In addition, the food type eaten (if known), any vocalization

---

[2] Other Universitas Nasional biology students, Sugardjito, Endang Soekara, Barita Manulang, Yatna Supriatna, Dwi Sutanto, Natasudradjat Amban, and Mahfudz Markaya, each conducted research on red leaf-eating monkeys or gibbons for six-month periods.

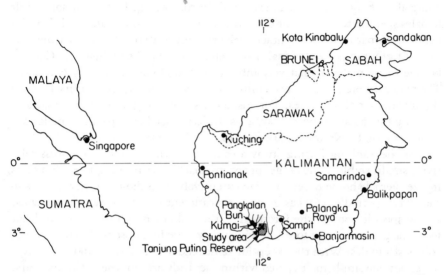

FIG. 1.   Map showing location of the wild orangutan study area in Borneo (from
Galdikas, 1979, p. 197).

made or heard, drastic changes in the target animal's height in the canopy (in
5-meter intervals), the target's descent to the ground, duration on the
ground, and the presence of other orangutans, primates, or large animals in
the vicinity were always noted. Descriptive notes on the behaviors involved in
activity bouts as well as on postures, locomotory and feeding techniques, self-
grooming, and playing were made but were not always consistent in quality
throughout the day, owing to observer fatigue.

In addition, time-point sampling was used (since 1974) for at least one
hour per whole day to record the behavior of mother and offspring every minute on the minute. The distance between mother and infant, the occurrence of
suckling, approaches, and leaves were among the events recorded.

Other studies (McKinnon, 1971, 1974; Horr, 1972, 1975; Rodman,
1973) have confirmed the fact that orangutan populations, unlike those of
other monkeys and apes, are basically structured in terms of incomplete reproductive units. With the exception of dependent offspring accompanying their
mothers, both adult male and female orangutans are essentially solitary.

The first four years of Tanjung Puting data, consisting of 6,804 hours of
direct observation, were analyzed in some detail; they demonstrate that Tanjung Puting adult male orangutans are the most asocial of age-sex classes,

being almost entirely solitary, except when consorting. In comparison, adult females spend 5 to 17 percent of their time with other orangutans while independent immatures are in contact with other units 40 percent of the time. Almost all groupings involve males and females or females exclusively. Contact between lone males is relatively infrequent and almost invariably nonsocial. The major differences between chimpanzee and orangutan sociability lie with the males, not the females. For instance, some orangutan adult females at Tanjung Puting are almost as social as the least social chimpanzee females observed at Gombe National Park (Galdikas, 1978; Halperin, 1979).

At the Tanjung Puting study area adult females seemed to possess relatively small, stable home ranges of approximately five to six square kilometers in size. Female home ranges overlap extensively with those of other females so that over a period of years as many as six different females have been observed at one specific spot in the forest. As far as is known, adult females did not leave the general area of forest in which they were first observed. This was not true of the males. With the exception of dependent immatures and large juveniles, not one single male stayed within the study area for the entire six years, indicating that male home ranges were considerably larger than the 35-square-kilometer study area. Occasional adult males temporarily resided in smaller home ranges equivalent in size to female home range but this was never for more than a few years at a time.

Considerable data on reproductive behavior were collected. During six years over 90 copulatory bouts (attempted and/or completed) were witnessed. Although nonconsort rape occurs, consortships seem to represent the effective mechanism of orangutan reproduction. Since orangutan females are less conspicuous than males and locate males to initiate consortship, female selection seems to play a very important role in the orangutan mating system. A very high degree of male vs. male competition, augmented by female selection of consort partners, seems to exclude some males from reproduction. While avoidance or mild aggression characterizes encounters between lone adult males, violent chases and combats occur when males contact each other in the presence of an adult female. Three combats between adult males were witnessed; all involved the presence of a consorting (and thus, presumably estrous) adult female. Combats consisted of furious grappling with males biting each other's head, shoulders, and extremities. Two combats lasted approximately half an hour while the third lasted less than one minute. In this case an adult male drew blood by biting the cheekpad of the other. Although relatively few combats were actually witnessed, the fact that most adult males observed in the study area sported old wounds, or missing, stiff, or gibbled digits, and/or other physical anomalies indicated that direct aggression between adult males was not an uncommon occurrence.

Over six years we observed more than 16,000 foraging bouts. Of these, 11,338 foraging bouts occurring in the first four years (1971-1975) were analyzed. Orangutans spent an average of 60 percent of their waking hours foraging. They spent approximately 61 percent of this time foraging on fruit although they fed on young leaves, bark, and termites as well (see Table 1).

Frugivorous diet and the distribution of fruit resources in Southeast Asian tropical rain forests seem to enforce the isolation of individual orangutans from one another and to lead to an ecological separation of the sexes, in line with differential roles in reproduction (Galdikas, 1978). At Tanjung Puting adult males and females utilize significantly different proportions of resources in their diets. The primary difference between habituated adult males and females (fig. 2) is that the males spend significantly less time eating bark (Mann-Whitney $U=2$, $n_1=5$, $n_2=5$, $p<.05$), and young leaves (Mann-Whitney $U=3$, $n_1=5$, $n_2=5$, $p<.05$) and more time eating termites than adult females (Mann-Whitney $U=4$, $n_1=5$, $n_2=5$, $p=.056$). Males also spent more time foraging on other foods such as the young shoots of ground plants.

Male-female differences involved differential utilization of the ground, with adult males spending 66 minutes per mean day on the ground and adult

TABLE 1.   Percentages of Foraging Time Spent on Food Categories by Tanjung Puting Orangutans, 1971-1975

Food category	Foraging time		Percent of total foraging time
	Hours/Minutes	*Minutes*	
Fruit	2,318/16	139,096	60.93
Flowers	149/10	8,950	3.92
Leaves	558/27	33,507	14.68
Bark	434/52	26,092	11.43
Termites	163/49	9,829	4.31
Fungus	2/55	175	0.07
Other Foods	138/26	8,306	3.64
Not Known/ Poor Observations	38/44	2,324	1.02
TOTALS	3,804/39	228,279	100.00

females only three minutes. Adult males also have longer mean-day ranges with prime adult males traveling an average of 850 meters per day and prime adult females 710 meters. Comparisons between Tanjung Puting orangutans and Gombe National Park chimpanzees (both populations being frugivorous) indicate that mean distance between food sources is considerably less for orangutans than chimpanzees, a fact that may help account for their differential adaptations (Wrangham, 1977; Galdikas, 1978).

In addition to the systematic collection of large amounts of data for quantitative analysis, occasional single observations proved to be of exceptional interest. One such observation involved tool use. In the past the only instances of tool use reliably reported from wild orangutan studies invariably involved agonistic displays (breaking and dropping of branches, pushing over of snags, etc.) and nesting/covering behaviors. The Tanjung Puting data indicate that this is not merely an artifact of sampling, as only once in six years was an indisputable instance of tool use observed in another context. A mature male, while sitting 10 to 12 meters up in a small ironwood *(Eusideroxylon zwageri)* tree, broke off the end from a dead branch and, with the left hand, reached under his left thigh and for 30 to 35 seconds rhythmically scratched himself with the stick somewhere in the vicinity of his anus.

Another observation of unusual interest involved a primiparous female giving birth. This is probably the first time that orangutan parturition has been observed in the wild. It was particularly significant since we knew the identity of this female's mother who, thus, became the first known wild orangutan grandmother. In fact, when we initially observed "Fern" in 1972 she was riding on her mother's back while her mother carried a small infant. We estimated that the adolescent "Fern" was approximately nine or ten years old at the time. Over the years we followed her progress. Although occasionally in association with her mother, she also traveled alone or with other orangutans. In September 1976 when she was approximately fourteen years of age we first noticed that she was displaying the swollen genitals indicative of pregnancy.

We followed her almost continuously from the afternoon of January 8, 1977, until February 27 when we lost her in the rain. She was alone when she gave birth during the late afternoon of February 5 although we did not actually see the infant until the morning of February 6. Birth took place in a tree nest approximately 22 meters up (as later measured with a tape-rule). Since the nest was so high and since it was raining much of the time, observation was extremely difficult. Most of the time the female's body was hidden from view although we could occasionally glimpse limbs or hair protruding from the nest.

FIG. 2.   Wild orangutan female and infant eating inner bark of *Gironniera nervosa*.

   The sequence of events surrounding the birth lasted about two and a half hours. Fern's agitation, probably corresponding to labor, may have lasted up to two hours. Observation was difficult during the first hour owing to heavy rain. During the second hour she was observed twisting and turning in the nest. She occasionally had both arms wrapped around the tree trunk against which her nest was made. There was a 1-meter-long squirt of fluid at the height of the agitation. Three quarters of an hour later she seemed to have calmed down and was observed lying on her back. Twenty minutes later she was seen licking her fingers. The next morning we observed the infant for the first time when one of our workmen climbed a vine some distance away. Fern moved up 1 meter above her nest holding the infant on her right breast near her face. The umbilical cord with the placenta was hanging under her right thigh still attached to the infant. These only separated from the infant on the third morning after parturition, and were left behind in the night nest.

   Observations at the Tanjung Puting study area continue. One of the goals of the long-term collection of data is to eventually accumulate life-histories for a relatively large sample of individuals. Only when this is done will we be able truly to explicate wild orangutan adaptation.

REFERENCES

ALTMAN, J.
   1974.   Observational study of behavior sampling methods.   Behaviour, vol. 49, pp. 227-267.
GALDIKAS, BIRUTÉ M. F.
   1978.   Orangutan adaptation at Tanjung Puting Reserve, Central Borneo.   Ph.D. thesis, University of California at Los Angeles, 334 pp., illus.
HALPERIN, S. D.
   1979.   Temporary association patterns in free ranging chimpanzees: An assessment of individual grouping preferences.   Pp. 491-499 *in* "The Great Apes," D. A. Hamburg and E. R. McCown, eds.   Benjamin/Cummings Publishing Company, Menlo Park.
HORR, D. A.
   1972.   The Borneo orang-utan.   Borneo Res. Bull., vol. 4, pp. 46-50.
   1975.   The Borneo orang-utan: Population structure and dynamics in relationship to ecology and reproductive strategy.   Primate Behavior, vol. 4, pp. 307-323.
   1977.   Orang-utan maturation: Growing up in a female world.   Pp. 289-321 *in* "Primate Bio-Social Development: Biological, Social and Ecological Determinants," S. Chevalier-Skolnikoff and F. E. Poirier, eds.   Garland Publishing Inc., New York.

McKINNON, J. R.
1971.   The orang-utan in Sabah today.   Oryx, vol. 11, pp. 141-191.
1974.   The behavior and ecology of wild orangutans *(Pongo pygmaeus)*.   Animal
         Behaviour, vol. 22, pp. 3-74.
1979.   Reproductive behavior in wild orangutan populations.   Pp. 257-273 *in*
         "The Great Apes," D. A. Hamburg and E. R. McCown, eds.   Benja-
         min/Cummings, Menlo Park.
RIJKSEN, H. D.
1978.   A field study on Sumatran orangutans *(Pongo pygmaeus abelii* Lesson
         1927): Ecology, behaviour and conservation.   H. Veenman and B. V.
         Zonen, Wageningen, 420 pp., illus.
RODMAN, P. S.
1973.   Population composition and adaptive organization among orang-utans
         of the Kutai Nature Reserve.   Pp. 171-209 *in* "Comparative Ecology
         and Behaviour of Primates," R. P. Michael and J. H. Crook, eds.   Aca-
         demic Press, London.
1977.   Feeding behaviour of orang-utans of the Kutai Nature Reserve, East Ka-
         limantan.   Pp. 383-413 *in* "Primate Ecology: Studies of Feeding and
         Ranging Behaviour in Lemurs, Monkeys and Apes," T. H. Clutton-
         Brock, ed.   Academic Press, London.
1979.   Individual activity patterns and the solitary nature of orangutans.   Pp.
         235-255 *in* "The Great Apes," D. A. Hamburg and E. R. McCown,
         eds.   Benjamin/Cummings, Menlo Park.
WRANGHAM, R. W.
1977.   Feeding behaviour of chimpanzees in Gombe National Park, Tanzania.
         Pp. 503-538 *in* "Primate Ecology: Studies of Feeding and Ranging Be-
         haviour in Lemurs, Monkeys and Apes," T. H. Clutton-Brock, ed.
         Academic Press, London.

Other Publications Resulting from Tanjung Puting
Orangutan Studies

GALDIKAS, BIRUTÉ M. F.
1975.   Orangutans, Indonesia's "people of the forest."   National Geographic,
         vol. 148, no. 4 (Oct.), pp. 444-473.
1977.   Orang Hutan Penduduk Hutan.   Kehutanan Indonesia, vol. 10-12,
         pp. 13-16.
1978.   Orangutans and hominid evolution.   Pp. 287-309 *in* "Spectrum, Es-
         says Presented to Sutan Takdir Alisjahbana on his Seventieth Birthday,"
         S. Udin, ed.   Dian Rakyat, Jakarta, Indonesia.
1978.   Orangutan death and scavenging by pigs.   Science, no. 4337, pp. 68-
         70.
1979.   Orangutan adaptation at Tanjung Puting Reserve: Mating and ecolo-
         gy.   Pp. 195-233 *in* "The Great Apes," D. A. Hamburg and E. R.
         McCown, eds.   Benjamin/Cummings, Menlo Park.

1979.   Orangutan dan Evolusi Bangsa Manusia.   Ilmu dan Budaya, vol. 1, pp.
         5-28.   (Translation of Spectrum article.)
1980.   Living with the great orange apes.   National Geographic, vol. 157, no.
         6 (June), pp. 830-853.
_____. Wild orangutan reproduction.   *In* "Reproductive Biology of the Great
         Apes: Biomedical and Comparative Perspectives."   C. E. Graham,
         ed.   Academic Press, New York. (In press.)
GALDIKAS, B.M.F., and TELEKI, G.
_____. Variations in the subsistence activities of female and male pongids:
         New perspectives on the origins of hominid labor division.   Current
         Anthropology.   (In press.)
STAFFORD, E. E.; GALDIKAS-BRINDAMOUR, B.; and BEAUDOIN, R. L.
1978.   Hepatocystis in the orangutan, *Pongo pygmaeus*.   Trans. Roy. Soc.
         Trop. Med. Hyg., vol. 72, pp. 107-108.

                                                        BIRUTÉ M. F. GALDIKAS

Lower Amazonian Forest Bird Communities

Principal Investigator: Thomas E. Lovejoy, World Wildlife Fund, Washington, D. C.

Grant No. 946: For ecological studies of Amazon forest birds.

Studies of bird communities in forests in the vicinity of Belém, Brazil, conducted over a 7-year period from 1965 to 1972 constitute the first long-term studies of Amazon forest bird communities by any means. Birds were mist-netted, banded, and measured or examined in a variety of ways before release in four major forest types. One type was classic high-ground forest, represented by Mocambo Island, already famous for studies of its tree populations (Cain et al., 1956), as well as by other, more disturbed high-ground forest. Two types of swamp forest, the *várzea* forest, flooded twice daily by tidally induced changes in river level, and *igapó* forest (here referring to permanent swamp forest with black water, but vide Prance, 1979), were studied. A fourth type studied was high-ground, second-growth forest, known locally as *capoeira*.

These bird communities proved to have the highest diversity (as measured by the information theory index $H' = -\Sigma p_i(\log p_i)$) ever recorded for any organisms. Subsequently bird communities in the western Amazon have been found to be a bit higher. Some of the diversity in the tropics stemmed from frugivory and nectarivory being possible on a round-the-year basis. Increased diversity was also based on additional resources such as a large lizard fauna. Army ants *(Eciton)*, while not themselves fed on, provide resources by flushing out insects and other cryptic animals of the rain-forest floor, enabling their capture by species of birds specialized in following army ants. Many of the bird as well as tree species are very rare, often represented by single individuals even in large samples such as these (hundreds and thousands of captures).

Hummingbirds make up a significant proportion (in individuals) of the bird community. It is hard to estimate how large (perhaps 10 percent) because their feet are too small to carry ordinary bird bands. An attempt to mark hummingbirds with special bands did not, over a 2-month period, succeed in saturating the population sufficiently to provide an answer.

One very interesting aspect of the research was that the most abundant bird species, although specialists of various sorts, tended to be the same ones

11

in all the different forest types. It showed that a niche can be specialized yet very large (Hutchinson, 1978).

Another interesting aspect is that despite the bewildering diversity there tended to be a strong relationship between bird species composition and tree species composition in these forests. The former changed more rapidly than the latter across the gradients involved, because the major gradients were ones of soil moisture. Nonetheless the more similar the tree species around two sets of nets, the more similar were the bird species caught in the nets.

These forests are among the best studied in the Amazon and will provide an important base for future studies and for the growing problems of national park design and management.

REFERENCES

CAIN, S. A.; DE OLIVEIRA CASTRO, G. M.; PIRES, J. M.; and DA SILVA, N. J.
    1956.   Applications of some phytosociological techniques to Brazilian rain forest. Amer. Journ. Bot., vol. 43, pp. 911-941.
HUTCHINSON, G. E.
    1978.   An introduction to population ecology, xi + 260 pp. Yale University Press, New Haven and London.
LOVEJOY, THOMAS E.
    1972.   Bird species diversity and composition in Amazonian rain forests. Amer. Zoologist, vol. 12, pp. 711-712.
    1975.   Bird diversity and abundance in Amazon forest communities. Living Bird, vol. 12, pp. 127-191.
PRANCE, G. T.
    1979.   Notes on the vegetation of Amazonia III. The terminology of Amazonian forest types subject to inundation. Brittonia, vol. 31, pp. 26-38.

THOMAS E. LOVEJOY

Archeology of Coxcatlán, Puebla, Mexico

Principal Investigator: Edward B. Sisson, R. S. Peabody Foundation for Archeology, Andover, Massachusetts, and the University of Mississippi

Grant Nos. 955,   In support of an archeological investigation of Coxcatlán,
1070, 1188.   Puebla, Mexico.

At the time of the Spanish Conquest, the Tehuacán Valley was controlled locally by four native "cacicazogos"—Tehuacán, Cutha, Coxcatlán, and Teotitlán del Camino. These "cacicazogos" had been tributaries of the Triple Alliance since the 1460's. The "principales" of one of these, Coxcatlán, traveled to Tepeaca (Segura de la Frontera) in 1520, met Cortes, and offered themselves as loyal allies and faithful subjects of the Spanish Crown. In 1534, the second "audencia" made Coxcatlán the "cabecera" of a "corregimiento." In spite of Coxcatlán's new political status, effective local government remained in the hands of a native royal lineage and native nobility. This situation prevailed until at least 1559. Coxcatlán was also a "cabecera de doctrina" with a resident vicar who, in 1569, spoke Nahuatl. According to the "Relación Geográfica" of 1580 (Paso y Troncoso, 1905-1906, vol. 5, pp. 46-54), Coxcatlán had eleven subject towns located within the Tehuacán Valley, in the pine-oak forests of the mountains east of the valley, and in the rain forest of the foothills along the present day Veracruz-Puebla border. Through its subject towns, Coxcatlán had access to the resources of highly contrasting ecological zones.

Acknowledgments

From June 1971 until September 1974, the R. S. Peabody Foundation for Archeology, with financial assistance from the National Geographic Society, conducted an investigation of the pre-Conquest and immediate post-Conquest development of the "cacicazogo" of Coxcatlán. Richard S. MacNeish, director of the Robert S. Peabody Foundation for Archaeology, assumed administrative responsibility for the project and provided valuable advice based on his previous fieldwork in the Tehuacán Valley. Edward B. Sisson, curator of the Peabody Foundation, directed the fieldwork and laboratory analyses. The following individuals contributed to the success of the project by their work as field and laboratory supervisors—Stuart Baldwin, William

13

Dobbs, William Doelle, Brian Gannon, Paul Healy, René Péron, Richard Peterson, Raymond Potvin, Larry Remmel, Deborah Scheraga, Penny Sisson, Jonathan Stein, and Pat Stein. Lawrence Feldman of the University of Missouri identified the excavated mollusk remains; and Elizabeth Wing of the University of Florida identified all other animal remains. Lauro Gonzalez Quintero, Instituto Nacional de Antropología e Historia, has studied the carbonized plant remains. A small sample of obsidian blades was analyzed for trace element composition by Frank Asaro and Fred Stross of the Berkeley Radiation Laboratory.

The Coxcatlán research would not have been possible without the assistance and friendly cooperation of federal, state, and local authorities in Mexico. The research was conducted in accordance with the terms of an archeological concession granted by the Departamento de Monumentos Prehispanicos, Arq. Ignacio Marquina, director, and Argo. Eduardo Matos M., subdirector, of the Instituto Nacional de Antropología e Historia, Arq. Luis Ortiz Macedo (1970) and Dr. Guillermo Bonfil B. (1972) director general, of the Secretaría de Educación Pública, Ing. Victor Bravo Ahuja, secretary.

Two preliminary reports describing the results of the project have been published by the Robert S. Peabody Foundation for Archaeology (Sisson, 1973a, 1974). More limited aspects of the project are described in a series of unpublished reports and articles (Dobbs, 1972; Doelle, 1972a, 1972b; Gannon, 1973; Péron, 1974; Sisson, 1971, 1972b); published articles (Sisson, 1975; Sisson and Doelle, 1974); papers given at national and international meetings (Sisson, 1972a, 1973b, 1973c, 1979; Sisson and Doelle, 1971); and a master's thesis (Scheraga, 1973). A monograph and additional short articles are currently in preparation.

The Peabody Foundation continued its support of archeological research in the Tehuacán Valley after the end of fieldwork on the Coxcatlán Project by initiating in 1975 the Palo Blanco Project. This project focuses on the Late and Terminal Formative and the Early Classic. See Drennan, 1977, 1978, and 1979.

Objectives

The background and objectives of the Coxcatlán Project have been described in detail elsewhere (Sisson, 1973, pp. 4-6). Briefly, the project grew out of the Peabody Foundation's previous research in the Tehuacán Valley, which had concentrated on the origins of New World agriculture and settled village life. See Byers, 1967a and 1967b; MacNeish, 1970, 1972, and 1974; and Johnson, 1972.

The archeological research was designed to be part of an interdisciplinary project integrating data from archeology, ethnohistory, and social anthropology in an analysis of social and cultural adaptation and change in the Tehuacán Valley and its "sierra" hinterland from the beginning of the Postclassic (ca. A.D. 700) until the present. Unfortunately, illness and other research commitments prevented the development of the ethnohistoric and social anthropological aspects of the project. The absence of the anticipated feedback and interdisciplinary stimulation from ethno-history and social anthropology adversely affected the archeological research. This research has focused primarily on the economic and social organization of Coxcatlán and its subject towns around the time of the Spanish Conquest. The principal methods employed include intensive systematic surface survey of known sites; surveys to locate additional sites; excavation of selected plaza complexes, households, salt production facilities, and other miscellaneous features; and analyses of recovered materials.

Archeological Phases

As a result of the Coxcatlán Project, it is possible to divide the Postclassic, Venta Salada Phase into four chronologically sequential subphases or periods. The earliest corresponds to the Early Venta Salada Phase as established by MacNeish and his associates (MacNeish, 1970) and dates from approximately A.D. 700 to 1000. Components of this time period were not represented in the excavations of the Coxcatlán Project. Ceramically, the period is characterized by a continuation of many Classic, Palo Blanco Phase pottery types and by the introduction of such types as Coxcatlán Brushed, Coxcatlán Red/Orange, and perhaps Teotitlán Incised. The addition of spindle whorls, new figurine types, and god effigy censers also distinguishes this period from the preceding (MacNeish, 1970, p. 17).

The second period corresponds to the early part of the Late Venta Salada Phase and is estimated to date from A.D. 1000 to 1200. Excavations and systematic surface collection from the Venta Salada site (Tr57) supplement our knowledge of this period from previously excavated components and surface collections. The most striking new ceramic feature of this period is a red to metallic gray ware with broad, curvilinear, preslip incised decoration on the exterior of bowls and jars. MacNeish (1970, figs. 124 and 127) illustrates sherds which share form and decorative modes with this ware and assigns the sherds to the types Teotitlán Incised and Cholula Incised (?). Similar forms and decorative modes occur at Tula on "naranja pulida" (Cobean, 1974, fig. 15A). It is tempting to argue that the appearance of this ware in the Tehuacán

Valley marks the arrival of the Nonoalcas from Tula, but the archeological data in hand are too sparse to support this argument. It remains a possibility worth further study. This period can be distinguished from the fourth and final period by its projectile point types which include Tehuacán, Salado, Ensor, Morhiss, Texcoco, and Palmillas points; by its spindle whorls; by its ceramic types; and by its obsidian sources.

With respect to its material culture, the third period is transitional between the second and fourth periods. Excavation at the San Pedro site (Tr205) revealed two components falling within the estimated A.D. 1200 to 1465 time span of this period. The projectile point types are those of the final period, with its preponderance of Teotihuacan and Harrell points. The obsidian sources include ones represented in both the second and the fourth periods. Ceramically, neither the red to metallic gray ware of the second period nor the more characteristic types of the final period are represented.

The fourth period begins around A.D. 1465 and persists until sometime after the Conquest. Formal use of the ceremonial precincts of the Coxcatlán Viejo site (Tr62) had probably ceased by 1540 when Motolinia (1950, p. 141) reports that Indians from the towns surrounding Tehuacán brought their idols to the Franciscan monastery of Santa Maria de la Concepción. Informal use of the ceremonial precincts continued after they were no longer maintained. Cremation burials in temple ruins indicate that traditional burial practices were conducted surreptitiously even after the native temples were abandoned in favor of Catholic churches. Since there was a vicar residing in Coxcatlán by at least 1569, even this informal use may have ceased by that time. Farther north, at Tehuacán Viejo, the native ceremonial precincts probably were abandoned even earlier, since Santa Maria de la Concepción was established there in the mid 1530's. Households at Coxcatlán Viejo and Tehuacán Viejo were occupied after the ceremonial precincts were abandoned; and in these individual residences, there is ample evidence of the worship of native deities.

A handwrought nail and a few pieces of glass are the only European artifacts recovered from components of this period, and these may be intrusive. A few sherds of Aztec Black/Orange from Coxcatlán Viejo which were identified as post-Conquest by Thomas Charlton and five bones of European domesticates (Equus, Bovid, Suid) of questionable provenience at Coxcatlán Viejo and Tlacuchcalco (Tr65) are the only other definite indications of a post-Conquest occupation.

Although there are a few Tehuacán, Palmillas, and Salado points from components of this last period, Harrell points of a white, translucent, cryptocrystalline material and obsidian Teotihuacan points comprise 80 percent of the identified projectile points. The spindle whorls of this period are completely different from those of preceding periods. Not only do they differ in size and decoration, but they are also much smaller, suggesting a shift to finer cotton threads in woven materials. There is also a major shift in obsidian sources with the Pachuca source now heavily represented. The presence at this time of large amounts of Pachuca obsidian in the Coxcatlán area suggests direct or indirect economic ties with the Valley of Mexico. The existence of such ties is further suggested by ceramic evidence. During this period, there is a large influx into Coxcatlán of ceramic types characteristic of the Valley of Mexico. Of 5,186 sherds from the surface of Coxcatlán Viejo, 10.1 percent are either Texcoco Black/Red or Texcoco Black and White/Red. In addition to these and other rarer exotic types, the local types, Coxcatlán Polychrome and Coxcatlán Red/Cream, are characteristic of this last period.

Most of the excavated components belong to this final period. In the discussion which follows, the time reference unless otherwise specified should be understood to be from approximately A.D. 1465 until sometime in the early to mid-16th century. Excavation at Tehuacán Viejo or in modern Coxcatlán might help better define the terminal date for this period and separate the pre-Conquest and immediately post-Conquest components.

Subsistence

Excavation was limited to open sites where there was either no preservation or poor preservation of plant and animal remains. Flotation was not employed. The only recovered plant remains are carbonized corncobs and chupandilla seeds.

Recovered animal remains are more common, and small collections were obtained from the Venta Salada (Tr57), Coxcatlán Viejo, Tlacuchcalco, and San Pedro sites. These remains have been identified by Elizabeth Wing, but further analysis remains to be completed. Qualitatively, there are few surprises. The species represented are by and large the same as those reported by Flannery (1967) from the earlier Tehuacán excavations. Four genera and a species not previously reported from archeological sites in the Tehuacán Valley are *Mazama* sp., *Dasypus* sp., *Dermatemys* sp., *Chrysemys* sp., and *Chrysemys* cf. *scripta*. As a group, these genera are more typical of the Gulf Coastal lowlands than they are of the dry, highland Tehuacán Valley. In addition to the animal remains identified by Wing, Lawrence Feldman identified 28 species of marine mollusks from the four sites. Of these, 75 percent are Caribbean species and were used as raw material for artifacts rather than as food sources. The animal remains and certain classes of artifacts discussed below document procurement of foodstuffs, raw materials, and manufactured goods from as far away as the Gulf Coast and Coastal Lowlands. This is not surprising since two of Cox-catlán's subject towns, Mazateopan and Petlapa, were located across the mountains in the Gulf Coastal Lowlands.

Reliable estimates of the relative quantities of the different faunal species in the diet are not now available. It is clear, however, that the collections from the four open sites (Venta Salada, Coxcatlán Viejo, Tlacuchcalco, and San Pe-dro) contain relatively larger quantities of turtle, dog, and turkey than do the collections from the previous Tehuacán excavations. The implied dietary dif-ferences are not surprising when one considers that samples from rock shelters and a small open site are being compared with samples from four large open sites. In both sets of collections, deer would have provided the greatest quan-tity of meat by weight. Keeping in mind the above exceptions and Eric Cal-len's (1967) warning that the diet of the people living in rock shelters may not be typical of the general population, MacNeish's (1967) reconstruction of Venta Salada Phase sustenance and subsistence activities remains the best available.

Occupational Specialization

In addition to the farmers and hunters who supplied foodstuffs and raw materials, Late Postclassic states in central highland Mexico had a plethora of occupational specialists. Some specialists can be recognized archeologically by their tools, their wastes, and/or their finished products. Systematic, intensive surface collection and excavation led to the identification of occupational spe-cialists at Coxcatlán Viejo, Tlacuchcalco, and other sites. The easiest special-ities to recognize were salt production and pottery manufacture.

Salt production occurred at special industrial sites near sources of saline water. Saline water from springs was collected in small holding basins. From the holding basin, the saline solution was carried by a small canal to shallow solar evaporation pan. In the pan, solar evaporation concentrated the solution until salt crystals formed. The salt was removed from the pan as a slurry and placed in conical ceramic molds over an open fire. Firing drove off the remain-ing water and produced a hard conical salt cake. These conical cakes were a critical commodity in Coxcatlán's regional and long distance trade. (Sisson, 1972a, 1973a; Doelle, 1972a, 1972b.)

Systematic surface collection of Tlacuchcalco revealed that 95 percent of the convex molds for making pottery came from a cluster of five structures. This cluster represents the residence of a group of potters specializing in the production of god effigy censers, "cajetes," "molcajetes," and "cantaros" of the ceramic type Coxcatlán Brushed. Surface survey at Coxcatlán Viejo also revealed concentrations of pottery molds. Here, however, there were multiple concentrations more widely distributed about the site. Two contiguous terraces with concentrations of molds were excavated. This material has not been analyzed, and it is impossible to specify exactly which ceramic types were being produced. It is clear, however, that the inventory differs from that of the production center at Tlacuchcalco. In addition to ceramic vessels, figurines were manufactured on one of the terraces. A small kiln located on the upper terrace is similar to those still in use in Altepexi, Puebla, today. An Olmec figurine discovered in situ on the floor of a room on the lower terrace illustrates archeological serendipity.

Marine and freshwater shell occur in small quantities at both Coxcatlán Viejo and Tlacuchcalco. An unusually large concentration of shell scrap and shell artifacts including a bracelet, "buttons," a worked columella, and perforated olivella shells from the upper terrace described above indicates that shell artifacts were also being manufactured locally as an occupational speciality. Most shell artifacts were made from marine shell imported from the Caribbean and the Pacific Coasts.

Two molds believed to be for small copper "hachas" were found beneath a household altar at Tlacuchcalco. These molds may indicate that there were metalworkers residing locally. Copper bells, tweezers, rings, and needles have been recovered.

Stone quarries occur in the Tehuacán Valley; but they are not located in the Coxcatlán area. Manos and metates of basalt were imported as finished objects. Obsidian was imported as polyhedral cores. The differential distribution of obsidian cores on the surface at Coxcatlán Viejo suggests that there may have been either centralized control over their distribution or perhaps knappers who specialized in the production of obsidian blades, points, and end of blade scrapers.

Spinning and presumably the weaving of cotton cloth was practiced in every household. There were spindle whorls in every residential structure extensively tested. Spindle whorls also occurred in several pyramid-plaza complexes. The largest number were associated with Group D Plaza where there was a concentration around a circular altar.

Exchange Systems

Of the various occupational specialists, the saltmakers may have well been the most important. With the exception of land and water, salt was the most valuable natural resource of the Tehuacán Valley in the second half of the 16th century. Salt was the basic commodity in exchange systems that included both raw materials and manufactured goods and involved localities as far away as Guatemala to the south and Pachuca to the north. Salt circulated as tribute from the local producers to the "cacique" and as an item of commercial exchange. See Sisson, 1973a, for an extended discussion of the crucial role of salt in the 16th century.

An idea of the intricacies in the trade of salt can be gained from the "Relación Geográfica" of Teotitlán del Camino (Pasco y Troncoso, 1905-1906, vol. 4, pp. 213-231). Salt, collected from the subject towns of San Gabriel and San Antonio, was exchanged in the Veracruz lowlands for cotton. The cotton was returned to Teotitlán where it was spun into thread and woven into cloth. Cloth "mantas" were then taken to the Xoconusco where they were exchanged for cacao beans. Unfortunately, the "Relación" does not tell us who controlled or who engaged in each transaction. Control of these transactions may have been conducted by a professional merchant class.

This scenario is probably applicable to 16th-century Coxcatlán as well. Coxcatlán's subject towns of Petlapa and Mazateopan in the Veracruz lowlands would have functioned as entry ports for lowland tropical products obtained as tribute or in exchange for salt. Assuming that salt was the crucial commercial commodity in pre-Conquest Coxcatlán, what items were received in exchange? Cotton is one possibility. Actual bolls of cotton were found in Coxcatlán Cave. In addition, spindle whorls stylistically similar to those of the Veracruz Gulf Coast and with bitumen paint are quite common. Other Gulf Coast imports known archeologically include a fine paste, red and orange on cream polychrome, and marine shells. Salt from Coxcatlán may have been exchanged in the Veracruz lowlands for cotton, spindle whorls, decorated pottery, and marine shell. Some of the tropical fruits from MacNeish's excavations may have been imported from the lowlands as well. Subject towns in the neighboring "sierra" probably supplied beans and timber in exchange for salt.

Polyhedral obsidian cores were imported from the Orizaba and Pachuca sources. In the 16th-century Tepeaca to the north was an important redistribution center for salt from the Tehuacán Valley. The presence at Coxcatlán Viejo of polychrome pottery similar to that found on the surface at Tepeaca, Tecali, and Tecamachalco suggests that this economic relationship may have been pre-Conquest in origin. Orizaba obsidian may have entered Coxcatlán from Tepeaca along with this pottery in exchange for salt. Pachuca obsidian and such Valley of Mexico ceramic types as Texcoco Black/Red and Texcoco Black and White/Red may not have entered Coxcatlán Viejo via the Tepeaca route since these ceramic types do not appear to be as common in the Tepeaca area. Pachuca obsidian and ceramics may have been imported directly from the Valley of Mexico.

Finally, at Coxcatlán Viejo there is pottery imported from the Mixteca Alta. Once again there is evidence that Coxcatlán supplied the Mixteca Alta with salt during the Colonial Period.

Thus, there is considerable archeological data indicating the existence of trade in various artifact categories over great distances. Who controlled this trade? The large amount of major building activity at the center of Coxcatlán Viejo indicates that someone or some group in the "cabecera" had surplus capital to invest. This individual or group of individuals was almost certainly the "cacique" and/or the native nobility. In the 16th century, much of their wealth came directly from tribute. Since the tribute from at least three subject towns was salt, the early Colonial and pre-Conquest "cacique" may have reinvested this capital by supplying traders with salt to exchange for raw materials and manufactured goods. Tribute and the profits from trade provided the "cacique" and his relatives with the capital necessary for major construction programs. This reconstruction based on 16th-century data and analogy with the Aztec situation is consistent with the archeological data.

Residential and "Barrio" Organization

During three field seasons, portions of 15 small residential complexes were excavated at three different sites. Some of these may have begun as nuclear family residences; but, they were all extended or compound family residences in their final form. One of the mechanisms integrating the members of each residential complex was religious ritual at a centrally located household shrine. There may have been an element of ancestor worship in the religious rituals since burials were common beneath these household shrines. Invariably, a god effigy censer was placed in the household shrine. Members of some residences may have also engaged in the same occupation. At Coxcatlán Viejo and Tlacuchcalco these residential complexes cluster in what may have been wards or "barrios." We know that during the Colonial period large civic and ceremonial centers in the neighboring Mixteca Alta were divided into "barrios." Spores (1967, pp. 91-92) reports that ". . . barrios . . . were more or less contiguous districts comprising the compact pueblo center . . . Some of the wards were occupied by families devoted to the service of the community ruler; others were taken over by free commoners who were farmers, merchants, or artisans; also residing in the center were the hereditary ruler and his family and members of the local nobility. . . . The documents make frequent mention of barrios as residential and political units but . . . there is at present no good evidence that the Mixtec barrios constituted discrete kinship or corporate property-holding units. . . ." The "barrios" were ". . . governed by a noble appointed by the ruler-cacique." Similarly, in Tenochtitlán there was ". . . a certain amount of correlation . . . between territorial divisions and the division of labor and the social stratification" (Carrasco, 1971, p. 363).

At Tlacuchcalco structures cluster on four ridges. The ridges and their architectural clusters are separated by small seasonal arroyos. After the first field season, William Doelle and I (Sisson and Doelle, 1971) suggested that these clusters were "barrios" occupied by occupational specialists. Subsequent excavation blurred the distinctions which we so clearly saw between the clusters after a single season. A good case can only be made for the localized production of pottery.

Residential structures at Coxcatlán Viejo cluster on terraced ridges which rise above the Arroyo Soyolapa. On each ridge, there is an architectural complex consisting of a small plaza with a pyramid on the east, a second pyramid or a small platform mound on the west, and a much larger, low platform mound on the south and/or on the north. Temples were built atop the pyramids; shrines or small temples were located on the smaller platform mounds; and residential structures occupied the low, larger platforms. These plaza-pyramid complexes always occur at the highest occupied point on the ridge and dominate lower terraces with residential complexes. The two exceptions to this spatial arrangement are two very large plaza-pyramid complexes which are located at the base of the ridges along the Soyolapa and which together form the civic-ceremonial focus for the entire site. In discussing Tenochtitlán, Carrasco (1971, p. 365) suggests that there may have been a correspondence between priest's houses and "barrios." The distribution of plaza-pyramid complexes and of residential structures described above suggests that the same may have been true of Coxcatlán Viejo.

During the 1973 season, four plaza-pyramid complexes were excavated. Our experience in residential complexes led us to believe that we would recover numerous god effigy censers. If the site were divided into wards and these were represented archeologically by the ridges with their plaza-pyramid complexes, we expected the sets of god effigies to be "barrio" specific much in the same way that the "barrios" of a contemporary town have their patron saint. If there were a correlation between "barrio" residence and occupation, we expected the effigies of the tutelary gods of different occupations to cluster by plaza-pyramid complex. Unfortunately, rather extensive excavation failed to recover a single god effigy from any of the plaza-pyramid complexes. One possibility is that they had all been removed after the Franciscan arrival in Tehuacán. Another possibility is that they had all been removed by looters. In either case, it seems rather unlikely that we would not have recovered sherds from broken effigies. The god effigy censer appears therefore to have been primarily a household representation. Effigies also occur in shrines atop isolated hills. It is still possible that an analysis of god effigy censers and figurines from residential areas will yield the expected clusters of gods.

One characteristic of the ward temple in Tenochtitlán was that it was frequently the burial place for the cremated remains of deceased ward members (Anderson and Dibble, 1952, p. 43). In all four of the plaza-pyramid complexes which we excavated, vessels containing cremated human remains were discovered beneath aprons at the bases of pyramids and small raised platforms. The favored location was on the axis of the pyramid on the east side of the plaza. The archeological evidence from Coxcatlán Viejo reflects Sahagun's description of funeral rituals in Tenochtitlán even down to the types of offerings included in the vessels with the cremated remains.

If subsequent analysis reveals systematic variation among the residential and plaza-pyramid complexes, areas of specialized activities as reflected in artifact distribution, and religious differences as reflected in the distribution of effigy censers and figurines, we will have a strong argument for regarding the ridges with their architectural components as wards with overlapping residential, occupational, and religious functions.

Social Class

Coxcatlán, one of four locally autonomous states which controlled the Tehuacán Valley, consisted of twelve residential communities. Power was centralized in the hands of the "cacique" who resided in the "cabecera" and of the native nobility, relatives of the "cacique," who resided in the "cabecera" and in the smaller, politically dependent subject towns. As late as 1559, there were three distinct social classes in Coxcatlán—the "tlatoque," or lineage of the "cacique"; the "pipiltin," or nobility; and the "macehaultin," or free commoners (Spores, 1967, p. 124). These classes were distinguished from one another by access to power, tribute, and strategic goods and by codes of dress and behavior. Data from the Cuicatec and the Valley of Mexico suggest that additional social classes were also recognized.

Archeologically, social stratification in Coxcatlán was tested with three sets of data—the size, complexity, and location of residences; the content of residences; and the differential distribution of grave goods. It was assumed that the elite classes lived near the center of the "cabecera," the "barrio," or the subject town. If this were true, then it was expected that residences near the center would be larger, more complex, and would contain more exotic artifacts.

With one exception, the size and complexity of residences at Coxcatlán Viejo and at Tlacuchcalco do not vary greatly as one moves away from the center. The single exception is a poorly preserved structure on the first terrace above the principal plaza-pyramid complex at Coxcatlán Viejo. This structure does tend to have more massive walls. Exotic artifacts such as pottery from the Valley of Mexico; marine shell bracelets, etc.; and Pachuca obsidian are more common at Coxcatlán Viejo than at Tlacuchcalco and tend to become more common as one approaches the center of Coxcatlán Viejo. These differences in distribution may reflect class differences between and within sites.

Burials display considerable variation with respect to body preparation (cremation, flexed on side, or seated), to grave location (in sealed rooms, beneath floors and shrines in residences, beneath plaza floors in front of pyramids and small platforms), and to the quality and quantity of grave goods (nothing; jade or greenstone beads; obsidian blades; spindle whorls; copper bells, tweezers, and needles; miniature vessels; figurines). Judging by the archeological data from Coxcatlán Viejo and Tlacuchcalco and by what we know of contemporary burials in adjacent areas, none of these excavated burials was an elite burial. All of the variation probably reflects differences in age, sex, and cause of death within the commoner class. The one exception is a burial in a stucco-lined tomb atop a pyramid in Group D Plaza at Coxcatlán Viejo. Unfortunately, this burial had been looted, and only badly scattered and fragmented bones and a single jade bead were recovered. Elite burials may have been placed in tombs beneath floors of temples atop pyramids. The presence of subfloor tombs may explain the systematic destruction of temples at Coxcatlán Viejo. In the four excavated plaza-pyramid complexes not a single temple was standing even to its foundation walls.

"Cacicazogo" Political Organization

The boundaries of Coxcatlán in 1580 are given on the map accompanying the 1580 "Relación Geográfica" (Paso y Troncoso, 1905-1906, vol. 5, pp. 46-54). The distribution of subject towns as summarized above is quite different from that suggested by MacNeish (1972, p. 89), who divides the Tehuacán Valley into five Late Postclassic polities on the basis of sites clustering around five "cities." His boundaries exclude from Coxcatlán the important saline springs to the west, some of the rich agricultural land to the south, and the "sierra" and tropical lowland areas to the east. It is clear that the delimiting of political boundaries by drawing lines around clusters of sites is imprecise at best. For example, all of the towns politically subject to Coxcatlán in

1599 were not contiguous. Petlapa and Mazateopan were isolated in the Veracruz lowlands.

Providing a convincing alternative technique for delimiting political boundaries has proved difficult. At the beginning of the 1972 field season, it was hoped that an analysis of the distribution of fortified sites in time and space would provide an alternative. The original Tehuacán Valley survey had located a number of fortified sites which clustered along the contemporary boundary between Coxcatlán and Teotitlán del Camino to the south. At the Conquest, these "cacicazogos" had controlled the southern end of the Tehuacán Valley. It seemed reasonable that more precise dating of these fortified sites would allow us to describe shifts in the political boundary between Coxcatlán and its southern neighbor. Resurvey and excavation demonstrated, however, that the sites were not fortified. What had been interpreted as fortification walls were only terrace retaining walls.

Alternatives employing indirect means of recognizing political boundaries may eventually prove useful. Possibilities include an analysis of the distribution of god effigies as depicted on censers and figurines and an analysis of the products of different ceramic workshops. Neither method would be convincing by itself. If, however, one could demonstrate that spatial clusters of sites were contemporary and characterized by different sets of gods and different ceramic inventories, then one would be more confident that the clusters represented distinct polities. The obvious drawback to this approach is that it entails "a priori" assumptions about the correlation of political, economic, and religious variables.

The testing of other hypotheses about the social, economic, political, and religious organization of Coxcatlán will be possible with the data in hand. Some problems, however, can only be resolved by further excavation at Coxcatlán Viejo, Tehuacán Viejo, or other sites. The growing information on, and interest, in the Late Postclassic polities of the Central Mexican Highlands indicate that this will continue to be an active, fertile area of research to which the Coxcatlán project will contribute.

REFERENCES

ANDERSON, A.J.O., and DIBBLE, C. E.
   1952.   Florentine codex, Book 2. The origin of the gods. Monographs of the School of American Research, no. 14, pt. 4.   The School of American Research and the University of Utah, Santa Fe.
BYERS, D. S., ed.
   1967a.   The prehistory of the Tehuacán Valley, vol. 1, Environment and subsistence.   University of Texas Press, Austin.

BYERS, D. S., ed.—continued
  1967b. The prehistory of the Tehuacán Valley, vol. 2, The non-ceramic arti-
          facts. University of Texas Press, Austin.
CALLEN, ERIC
  1967.   Analysis of the Tehuacán coprolites. Pp. 261-289 *in* Byers, 1967a.
CARRASCO, PEDRO
  1971.   Social organization of ancient Mexico. Handbook of Middle American
          Indians, vol. 10, Archaeology of Northern Mesoamerica, pt. 1, G. F.
          Ekholm and I. Bernal, eds. University of Texas Press, Austin.
COBEAN, ROBERT
  1974.   The ceramics of Tula. Studies of ancient Tollan: A report of the Universi-
          ty of Missouri Tula Archaeological Project. University of Missouri
          Monographs in Anthropology, no. 1, R. A. Diehl, ed.
DOBBS, William
  1972.   Material culture of contemporary Coxcatlán, Puebla. Unpublished
          manuscript.
DOELLE, WILLIAM
  1972a. The postclassic trade in basic resources in the Tehuacán Valley. Un-
          published paper, University of Arizona.
  1972b. Post classic salt production: Preliminary report on excavations in the Te-
          huacán Valley. Unpublished manuscript.
DRENNAN, R. D.
  1974.   The Palo Blanco Project: A report on the 1975 and 1976 seasons in the
          Tehuacán Valley, R. D. Drennan, ed.   Robert S. Peabody Foundation
          for Archaeology and University Museum of Anthropology, Andover and
          Ann Arbor.
  1978.   Excavations at Quachilco, a report on the 1977 season of the Palo Blanco
          Project in the Tehuacán Valley. Technical Reports, no. 7, Museum of
          Anthropology, University of Michigan, Ann Arbor.
  1979.   Prehistoric social, political, and economic development in the area of the
          Tehuacán Valley, some results of the Palo Blanco Project. Technical Re-
          ports, no 11, Museum of Anthropology, University of Michigan, Ann
          Arbor.
FLANNERY, KENT
  1967.   The vertebrate fauna and hunting problems. Pp. 132-177 *in* Byers,
          1967a.
GANNON, B. L.
  1973.   Preliminary excavations at structure N5E2-2. Unpublished manu-
          script.
JOHNSON, FREDERICK, ed.
  1972.   The prehistory of the Tehuacán Valley, vol. 4, Chronology and irriga-
          tion. University of Texas Press, Austin.
MACNEISH, RICHARD S.
  1967.   Summary of the subsistence. Pp. 290-309 *in* Byers 1967a.
  1970.   The prehistory of the Tehuacán Valley, vol. 3, Ceramics, R. S. Mac-
          Neish, ed.   University of Texas Press, Austin.

MacNeish, Richard S.—continued
  1972.   The prehistory of the Tehuacán Valley, vol. 5, Excavations and recon-
           naissance. R. S. MacNeish, ed.   University of Texas Press, Austin.
  1974.   Reflections on my search for the beginnings of agriculture in Mexico.
           Pp. 207-234 *in* "Archaeological Researches in Retrospect," G. R. Wil-
           ley, ed.   Winthrop Publishers, Inc., Cambridge.
Motolinia, Fray Toribio
  1950.   Motolinia's history of the Indians of New Spain, E. A. Foster, ed.   The
           Cortes Society, Bancroft Library, Berkeley.
Paso y Troncoso, Francisco del
  1905-1906.   Papeles de lo Nuevo España. Segundo serie. Madrid.
Péron, René
  1974.   Sierra survey 1974: Preliminary report.   Unpublished paper, Universi-
           ty of the Americas.
Scheraga, Deborah
  1973.   Pottery making: An example from the Tehuacán Valley, Mexico.   Un-
           published Master's Thesis, Brandeis University.
Sisson, E. B.
  1971.   An archaeological investigation of the City State of Coxcatlán, Puebla,
           Mexico, 1971.   Unpublished preliminary report to the National Geo-
           graphic Society, December 1971.
  1972a.   A report on the second season of the "Proyecto Coxcatlán," salt produc-
           tion.   71st Annual Meeting of the American Anthropological Associ-
           ation, Toronto.
  1972b.   An archaeological investigation of the City State of Coxcatlán, Puebla,
           Mexico, 1972.   Unpublished preliminary report to the National Geo-
           graphic Society, December 1972.
  1973a.   First annual report of the Coxcatlán Project.   Robert S. Peabody Foun-
           dation for Archaeology, Andover, Massachusetts.
  1973b.   The archaeology of Coxcatlán, Puebla, Mexico.   72nd Annual Meeting
           of the American Anthropological Association, 1973.
  1973c.   The Coxcatlán Project.   Paper read before the Haverhill chapter of the
           Massachusetts Archaeological Society, January 1973.
  1974.   Second annual report of the Coxcatlán Project.   Robert S. Peabody
           Foundation for Archaeology, Andover, Massachusetts.
  1975.   Of shoe-form vessels and ethnographic analogy.   American Antiquity,
           vol. 40, no. 4, pp. 475-476.
  1979.   A Central Mexican view of life after death.   43rd International Con-
           gress of Americanists, Vancouver, B.C.
Sisson, E. B., and Doelle, William
  1971.   Postclassic architecture of the Tehuacán Valley, Puebla, Mexico: A pre-
           liminary assessment.   37th Annual Meeting of the Society for Ameri-
           can Archaeology, Miami.
  1974.   Un pueblo Posclasico en el Valle de Tehuacán, Puebla, Mexico.
           Boletin, Instituto Nacional de Antropologia e Historia, Mexico, Epoca
           II, no. 10, July-September, 1974.

Spores, R. M.
1967.   The Mixtec kings and their people.   University of Oklahoma Press,
Norman.

Edward B. Sisson

Sedimentological Study of the Volta Delta, West Africa

Principal Investigator: John K. Adams, Temple University, Philadelphia, Pennsylvania[1]

Grant No. 1042: In support of a study of sedimentation patterns associated with pericratonic basins on the trailing edges of continental blocks.

The purpose of this paper is to discuss the Volta Delta of West Africa in terms of the concept of the new global tectonics. Deltas such as the Volta are not located randomly or by chance; rather, their positions are determined by certain geological and climatic conditions. In the case of the Volta, some of the more important conditions appear to have been (a) the locations of tectonic basins now marginal to the continent, (b) fluctuations in sea level, (c) stream piracy and other topographic modifications, and (d) variations in river discharge resulting from the variability of precipitation, evapotranspiration, and infiltration.

The environmental conditions displayed in the vicinity of the Volta Delta today may provide a modern analogue for older deltaic deposits that are known to underlie more mature coastal-plain provinces such as the Atlantic and Gulf Coastal Plains. Therefore, an understanding of the origin and evolution of modern deltaic deposits could provide clues to the understanding of continental accretion by the growth of coastal-plain provinces.

Geographic and Geologic Setting

The Volta Delta of West Africa is located at approximately 1° east by 6° north in southeastern Ghana and southwestern Togo. It is formed at the

---
[1] I wish to thank the many individuals and institutions who have assisted in this work. Financial support was provided by the National Geographic Society and the Research Corporation. A study leave for fieldwork was made available by Temple University. Professor A.F.J. Smit of the University of Ghana provided invaluable assistance, interest, and encouragement during my stay in Ghana. Dr. M. H. Khan of the Ghana Geological Survey and K. Krishnamurthy of the Ghana Public Works Department were generous in providing data and assistance. Dr. Alice M. Weeks of Temple University kindly reviewed the manuscript.

terminus of the Volta River, which with its tributaries drains an area of approximately 400,000 square kilometers. The maximum length of the river with its longest tributary is approximately 1,800 kilometers. The river system drains part of six West African states: Ghana, Togo, Dahomey, Upper Volta, Ivory Coast, and Mali. Climatic conditions within the drainage basin are variable, ranging from semiarid savanna grasslands to tropical rain forests. The river drains over a variety of rock types ranging from Precambrian crystallines to Quaternary unconsolidated sediments.

The modern Volta Delta is relatively small, occupying approximately 3,500 square kilometers. At the northwestern apex of the delta the river breaks through the folded crystallines of the Akwapim-Togo mountain range. From this point an alluvial valley widens to accommodate the meandering tributaries and shifting channels. The average gradient of the river between the scarp and the sea is less than 2 feet per mile. However, the longitudinal stream profile is parabolic, and the calculated theoretical shear stress on the channel bed can be large in the upper portion of the delta. As the upper deltaic plain gives way to tidal influence, a 100-kilometer-long band of lakes, lagoons, and marshlands of the lower deltaic plain is formed behind the protection of the fringing sands of the delta front. This deltaic depositional system is bounded on the west and northwest by a Precambrian crystalline pediment called the Accra Plains. It is bounded on the north and northeast by Tertiary lateratized sands and gravels. To the east the deltaic depositional system grades into the strand plain system of Togo and the barrier bar system of Dahomey. East of the bar system the Niger Delta coalesces with its western neighbors, and together these systems form a coastal-plain province more than 1,000 kilometers in length (fig. 1).

The deltaic and interdeltaic sediments of the eastern portion of the Gulf of Guinea overlie pericratonic basins of Mesozoic age or lie directly upon the Precambrian crystalline basement complex. This relationship of deltaic and interdeltaic sediments lying directly upon an older crystalline basement is reminiscent of the Cretaceous sediments that underlie the Atlantic Coastal Plain. The pericratonic basins of West Africa are also reminiscent of the structural basins that are presently being discovered along the Atlantic Coast of North America such as those southeast of Newfoundland (Ayrton et al., 1974). It is my contention that sedimentary processes which are active along the eastern margins of the Gulf of Guinea today are at least partly analogous to the processes that were operative during the Late Cretaceous and Tertiary, when sedimentation along the North American Continent led to the development of the Atlantic Coastal Plain.

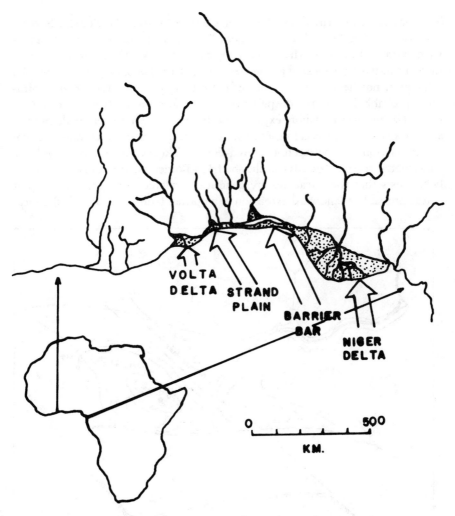

FIG. 1.   Index map showing deltaic and interdeltaic depositional systems.

Tectonic Control of Depocenter

The contact between the Precambrian basement complex and the unconsolidated Cretaceous and Tertiary sediments underlying much of the lower
deltaic plain of the Volta Delta appears to be steep and abrupt. Gravimetric
surveys begun by a Rumanian team in 1962 and expanded by the Ghana Geological Survey show a striking northeast-southwest trending gradient belt.

This has been identified by the Ghana Survey (Ghana Geological Survey, 1967) as the Ada-Fenyi Yakoe Gradient Belt. This gradient separates a gravity maximum lineament that strikes approximately N. 45° E. from a gravity minimum, which is located at the west end of Keta Lagoon approximately 20 kilometers northeast of the mouth of the estuary (fig. 2). The gravity minimum probably locates the deepest part of the basin presently above mean sea level. The results of offshore exploratory drilling have not been made public, and the shape of the basin in the seaward direction remains uncertain. The colinear relationship between the Ada-Fenyi Yakoe Gradient Belt and the bathymetric scarp at the edge of the shelf 35 kilometers south of Accra strongly suggests that these features are genetically related. The gravity gradient belt is probably a landward extension of a normal fault that controls the loca-

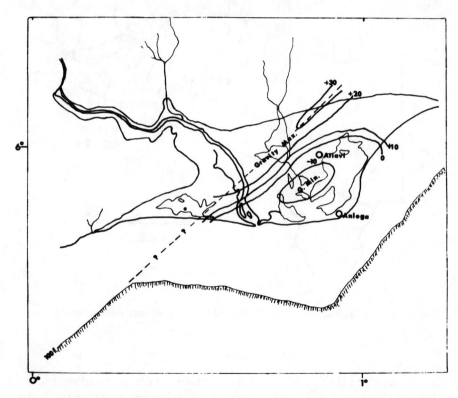

FIG. 2.   Abbreviated gravity (Bouguer) anomaly map of Volta Delta. Contours are in milligals. Notice apparent alignment of gravity maximum axis with continental slope. Note: This map is based on original data, and is not correlated with other geophysical surveys.

tion of the continental slope south of Accra. Burke (1969a) considered the fault to be an extension of the Chain Fracture Zone; recently Burke and others (1971) suggested that this submarine scarp may be as old as Cretaceous but bathymetrically still apparent because it is swept clean by geostrophic currents (the Guinea Counter Current). The Ghana Geological Survey (1967) states that "the Keta Basin has, on the whole, a tectonic block structure bounded by a fault system which trends N.E.-S.W. on the northern flank and a rise of the basement on the southern flank."

Two deep wells that have been drilled in the delta add stratigraphic evidence to support the claim that the Keta Pericratonic basin is fault controlled. The Atiavi No. 1 well penetrated 866 meters of Cretaceous and Cenozoic sediments before encountering 70 meters of dolerite, which is tentatively dated as Jurassic (Khan, 1972, pers. comm.). The well then penetrated 603 meters of Devonian shale and sandstone before encountering the basement at 1,539 meters. In the Anloga No. 2 well, 19 kilometers to the south, 2,131 meters of Cretaceous through Cenozoic sediments were penetrated without hitting basement. Also, 204 meters of Miocene were encountered in the Anloga well, but no Miocene was found in the Atiavi section, which is 19 kilometers to the north (fig. 3). The total absence of any Miocene only 19 kilometers away from a 204-meter section suggests that faulting was active as late as the Miocene and that the Anloga well site is located on the downthrown side of a fault and was dropped below sea level during the Miocene. The location of isoseismals associated with the 1906 earthquake plus reports of the 1862 and 1939 earthquakes suggest that the continental slope south of Accra is still mildly active (Burke, 1969a).

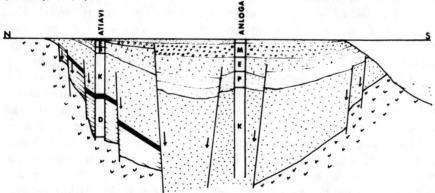

FIG. 3.   Generalized north-south cross section through the Keta Basin showing Atiavi and Anloga wells. D, Devonian; K, Cretaceous; P, Paleocene; E, Eocene; M, Miocene.

The orientation of the implied Ada-Fenyi Yakoe Fault, and the shore-line fluctuations associated with Pleistocene sea-level changes, have controlled the depositional sites of the Volta Delta throughout the Pleistocene and Recent Epochs. The most active deltaic sedimentation appears to be found on the downthrown side of the fault within the pericratonic basin. This is simply because renewed faulting or compaction of the thicker Cretaceous and Tertiary section of both results in greater subsidence within the basin. The implied Ada-Fenyi Yakoe Fault strikes N. 45° E. diagonally across a coastline and continental shelf, which trend approximately N. 70° E. The most active depocenters will remain on the southeast side of the fault, and so as fluctuations in sea level change the position of the shoreline the depocenter will migrate parallel to the fault. During times of transgression the depocenter migrates to the northeast; during regression the depocenter migrates to the southwest.

The fact that the Pleistocene and Recent depositional site for the Volta Delta is at least partly controlled by the orientation of a pericratonic fault basin is not at all unique for this part of West Africa. For example, the mouth of the Congo River is located at the approximate center of the Cretaceous Congo Salt Basin and less than 700 kilometers to the north; the Ogoouē River empties at the seaward edge of the Gabon Salt Basin (Belmonte et al., 1965). The Niger Delta, of course, is built across a huge pericratonic basin, which Weber (1971) describes as having formed by rift faulting. Dewey and Burke (1974) have proposed the interesting hypothesis that the Benue Trough, which underlies the Niger Delta, may be an aulacogen, the failed arm of a triple rift system. A little more than 600 kilometers west of the Niger, the Volta has built its delta on the western margin of the Keta pericratonic basin. Still farther west on the Ghana-Ivory Coast border, two small rivers (the Tano and the Komoe) have formed a marine-dominated, estuarine delta over the Ivory Coast Basin. A similar relationship may exist between the estuarine delta at the mouth of the St. Paul River and a sedimentary basin in northern Liberia.

Clearly, the Mesozoic Pericratonic basins of equatorial West Africa play significant roles in determining the sites of deltaic deposition. In light of this it is tempting to speculate as to what tectonic events might have preceded the formation of the more mature coastal plains throughout the world. To be sure, there are pericratonic basins on the western margin of the Atlantic. Belmont and others (1965) have pointed to the apparent fit, the similar stratigraphic sequences, and the similarity of faunas between the Gabon Basin and the Bahia and Tucano Basins of Brazil, and have suggested that African pericratonic basins on the east may be matched by South American basins on the western side of the Atlantic. Tanner (1966) has pointed to grabens or basins along the Gulf of Mexico, such as the South Georgia graben, which was active during the Tertiary. Spoljaric (1973) has described a graben in the basement complex of northern Delaware that may have been active in the Late Cretaceous. Higgins and others (1974) have proposed that a structural basin underlies the upper part of Chesapeake Bay. Ayrton and others (1974) described several structural basins in the Grand Banks southeast of Newfoundland, and Sheridan (1974) believes several basins may exist along the continental margin of eastern North America.

Climatic Control of Depocenters

An examination of shallow well logs and structural borings in the Volta Delta show that there is a great deal of facies variation through the Quaternary section. Facies trends are not vertically persistent; the strand line has naturally been migratory during the past million years as the result of glacioeustatic changes in sea level. River discharge has also been variable throughout the Pleistocene, as evidenced by such features as buried stream valleys, large potholes at various elevations, and coarse river gravels not associated with the present streams.

The classical concept that African pluvial events should be correlative with European glacial events due to a compression of the climatic belts during times of maximum glaciation may not completely satisfy all the available data. However, neither are the data satisfied by the converse concept that equatorial African pluvial episodes should be correlative with European interglacial stages. Rather, European glacial stages and African pluvial stages are probably somewhat out of phase. Data from the Ivory Coast (Martin, 1971) suggest that the sea-level minimum in the Ivory Coast during Pleistocene was greater than minus 100 meters. Also, pollen recovered from a peat dated at 23,000 B.P. and found 65 meters below present sea level indicates a savanna-type climate (probably not formed during a pluvial stage). This terrestrial peat overlies marine gravels and thus indicates a regressive stage before the last glacial maximum. However, a younger peat dated at 11,900 B.P. recovered from a similar depth (minus 62 meters) gave evidence of a moist climate. This peat was overlain by shallow marine sediments indicating the transgressive phase that followed the last glacial maximum (Martin, 1971). The suggestion from these data is that at 23,000 B.P. the West African coast was experiencing a regression associated with the increasing Würm glaciation. The climate was a savanna type, so river discharge was probably not much different from that of today. However, following maximum glaciation a more humid climate developed as indicated by 11,900 B.P. peat (fig. 4). The more humid climate doubtlessly resulted in increased river discharge. Wheth-

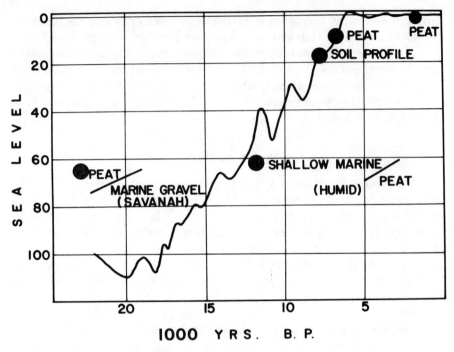

FIG. 4.   Inferred climatic and sea-level changes with dated peats.

er the enlarged Volta followed its present course is problematic. Evidence such as unconsolidated sands and gravels to a depth 65 meters below present sea level at the extreme western side of the Accra Plains may be interpreted as buried Pleistocene channels. Also, many of the coastal lagoons along the shoreline west of the Volta Delta show an increase in sediment thickness, which may imply buried channels. Burke (1969b) interpreted some of these features as evidence for recent faulting, but acknowledged the possibility that they may have resulted from Pleistocene drainage when sea level was lowered.

It is certainly most likely that oscillations in the strand line associated with glacioeustatic fluctuations in sea level coupled with the vicissitudes in river discharge resulting from climatic variations have resulted in the migration of the depocenters of the Volta Delta. When sea level is raised and river discharge is low, the delta would migrate to the northeast and probably become more cuspate. When sea level is low and river discharge is high, the delta would migrate to the southwest and become more lobate.

Geometry of the Volta Delta

The Volta Delta is an arcuate- to cuspate-shaped delta (terminology of Bernard, 1965) asymmetrical in plan view. It has a smooth coastline of continuous sandy beaches. Only one distributary connects the river and several lagoons with the open ocean. This river mouth is somewhat constricted, and the degree of constriction is a function of river discharge; when discharge is low, the river mouth becomes greatly constricted; when discharge is high the river mouth is less constricted. There are numerous beach ridges locally, but eolian dunes are not well developed. According to the twofold classification system of Fisher (Scott and Fisher, 1969), the delta is a wave-dominated high destructive delta system. The regional trend of the coastline (depositional strike) is approximately N. 70° E., but the protrusion of the delta is sufficient to distort this trend for approximately 75 kilometers, which is the width, w, of the modern delta. The maximum protrusion axis, L, is approximately 27 kilometers; therefore, the ratio of maximum protrusion to width (L/w), which was proposed by Wright and Coleman (1973) as an index to describe quantitatively the protrusion of deltas, is 0.36. The crenulation index, also proposed by Wright and Coleman (1973), is 1.14. This is the ratio of the length of the shoreline (L_S) to delta width (w). An increase in the value of the maximum protrusion index signifies a greater protrusion of the delta in the seaward direction. The higher the value of the crenulation index, the greater the irregularity of the coastline. The crenulation index of the Volta Delta being only 1.14 clearly indicates a smooth coastline, which is dominated by the energy of wave action and long shore drift. If one fabricates a crenulation index for the 40-foot isobath rather than the shoreline, one finds a slight increase in value to 1.26. This somewhat higher value is probably a reflection of a more complex energy regime along the submerged portion of the delta front. The more cuspate shape of the submerged portion of the delta may reflect countercurrents operating on the shelf.

The prevailing direction of long shore drift along the delta front is easterly. Beaches to the west of the Volta Delta are sediment starved, often rocky, and experiencing severe erosional problems. The sediment eroded from these beaches moves in the drift to the east until the long-shore current is interrupted by the effluent of the Volta River. The river acts as a natural groin, causing the sediment to be trapped on the upcurrent side. Thus the progradation of the western quarter of the delta is largely the result of the interruption of the long-shore drift by the river effluent. Discharge at the river mouth causes the submerged portion of the delta front to prograde from the river mouth to a position slightly downcurrent from the axis of maximum protrusion (fig. 5). Be-

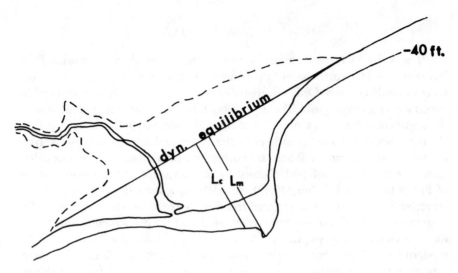

FIG. 5.   Geometry of Volta Delta showing maximum protrusion axis (Lm) and
central protrusion axis (Lc).

yond this point both the shoreline and the 40-foot isobath show a pronounced
erosional recess, which is in response to two factors. The first is that some sand
is probably lost to a deeper water sink offshore; the second is that the eastern
portion of the shore zone steepens to such a degree that there is much less power dissipation through wave attenuation in the shore zone. Consequently, the
portion of the delta front that trends north and northeast is experiencing severe erosion. Not only does erosion strike the fringing barrier beach from the
ocean side, but also during periods of high flood such as were experienced in
1931, 1947, and 1963, the barrier is breached from the lagoon side; the lower
Angaw River, which connects Keta Lagoon with the estuary, erodes the landward side of the barrier on the convex side of the river's meanders. Therefore,
although the fringing barrier sand that has formed between the lower deltaic
plain and the 40-foot isobath shows pronounced lateral continuity, the width
of the sand body varies from over 10 kilometers in the vicinity of the maximum protrusion axis to less than 60 meters at one location near the village of
Kedzi.

The thickness of the fringing sand body is in part structurally controlled.
Along the western beaches where the basement complex has behaved in a rigid
manner, the sand is sometimes no more than a meter thick. However, the barrier sands overlying the pericratonic basin at the Anloga No. 2 well site reach

70 meters in thickness (Khan, 1970, pers. comm.). Much of this 70-meter section, however, includes paralic sediments such as peats and muds. The very clean, well-sorted beach sand at this locality is 7 to 10 meters thick. The volumetric distribution of sediment within the delta is strongly skewed downdrift from the central axis of the delta protrusion. The skewness index of Wright and Coleman (1973) is $S_k = V_r/V_l$, where V_r and V_l equal the cumulative volumes of the right and left side of the delta. The skewness value for the Volta Delta is 1.23, which shows a skewness to the right or in the downdrift direction. The maximum protrusion axis is also to the right or downdrift from the central axis; however, if one computes the skewness about the maximum protrusion axis one obtains the value of 0.58, indicating that most of the volume of sediment within the delta lies to the left or updrift from the maximum protrusion axis. This results from the fact that much of the eastern portion of the delta is currently undergoing severe erosion, and sediment, which had accumulated during an earlier time when river discharge was higher, is now being lost through marine erosion.

Another factor affecting the geometry of the delta is the interaction between river discharge and long-shore drift at the mouth of the river. As mentioned earlier, the river acts as a natural groin, which interrupts the longshore drift at the river mouth and consequently traps sediment. Komar (1973) noted this effect in deltas, and in his computer model using a 10° breaker angle showed that the updrift side of a delta may build out more rapidly than the downdrift side. This effect is recognizable in the Volta Delta, but only in the proximity of the river mouth.

Conclusions

The modern delta of the Volta River is fairly typical of a wave-dominated, high-destructive type delta system. The subaerial deltaic environments, which are well developed, include the alluvial valley, the upper deltaic plain, the lower deltaic plain, and the delta front. The approximate boundary between the upper and lower deltaic plain environments is structurally controlled by a high-angle normal fault zone with the downthrown side toward the coast. This fault zone is an integral part of the pericratonic basin underlying the Volta Delta. Similar basins occur at several locations along the coast of Africa, and in many cases the rivers that drain the continent have adjusted their courses so that they now discharge over pericratonic basins.

The structural basin underlying the Volta Delta is at least 2,131 meters in depth and may be much deeper. The block faulting that led to the formation of the basin began during the mid-Cretaceous in association with the opening of the equatorial Atlantic Ocean. The faulting continued into the Miocene and may even be mildly active in the Holocene.

The pre-Maestrichtian sediments are chiefly continental and may be entirely so. Marine sediments range in age from Maestrichtian through Miocene with several unconformities or diastems. The modern delta is composed of Pleistocene and Holocene sediments.

The geometry of the delta front is controlled by wave energy with its associated long shore current and river discharge. Wave energy remains relatively constant from year to year, but river discharge is highly variable. This results in a very dynamic shoreline with rates of erosion and accretion varying with time and location. Variations of longer periodicity result from the climatic changes and sea level fluctuations concomitant with repeated glaciation.

Some relationship appears to exist between the formation of pericratonic basins, such as the one which underlies the Volta Delta, and the location and behavior of mid-Atlantic transform fracture zones. The exact nature of this relationship remains uncertain, but that the basins provide sites for deltaic sedimentation is certain. The deltas provide sediment to the continental shelf and thereby lead to the development of incipient coastal plains.

REFERENCES

AYRTON, W. G.; BIRNIE, D. E.; and SWIFT, J. H.
    1974. Grand Banks—future marine theater? Oil and Gas Journ., vol. 72, no. 2, pp. 78-80.

BELMONTE, Y.; HIRTZ, P.; and WANGER, R.
    1965. The salt basins of the Gabon and the Congo (Brazzaville). Pp. 55-74 *in* "Salt Basins around Africa," Institute Petroleum, London. Elsevier Publishing Co., Amsterdam.

BERNARD, M. A.
    1965. A résumé of river delta types. Abstr. Amer. Assoc. Petrol. Geol., vol. 49, no. 3, pt. 1, pp. 334-335.

BURKE, KEVIN
    1969a. Seismic areas of the Guinea coast where Atlantic fracture zones reach Africa. Nature, vol. 222, no. 5194, pp. 655-657.
    1969b. The Akwapim fault, a recent fault in Ghana and related faults of the Guinea coast. Journ. Mining and Geol., vol. 4, nos. 1, 2, pp. 29-38. Nigerian Mining, Geology and Metallurgical Society.

BURKE, KEVIN; DESSAUVAGIE, T.F.J.; and WHITEMAN, A. J.
    1971. Opening of the Gulf of Guinea and geological history of the Benue Depression and Niger Delta. Nature, Phys. Sci., vol. 233, no. 38, pp. 51-55.

DEWEY, J. F., and BURKE, KEVIN
    1974. Hot spots and continental breakup; implications for collisional orogeny. Geology, vol. 2, no. 2, pp. 57-60.

GHANA GEOLOGICAL SURVEY
1967.   Exploration for petroleum and gas in Ghana, 47 pp.   Ministry of Lands and Mineral Resources, Accra, Ghana.
HIGGINS, M. W.; ZIETZ, I.; and FISHER, G. W.
1974.   Interpretation of aeromagnetic anomalies bearing on the origin of Upper Chesapeake Bay and river course changes in the central Atlantic Seaboard region: Speculations.   Geology, vol. 2, no. 2, pp. 73-76.
KOMAR, PAUL D.
1973.   Computer models of delta growth due to sediment input from rivers and long shore transport.   Bull. Geol. Soc. Amer., vol. 87, no. 7, pp. 2217-2226.
MARTIN, L.
1971.   The continental margin from Cape Palmas to Lagos: Bottom sediments and submarine morphology. Pp. 79-95 *in* "The Geology of the East Atlantic Continental Margin."   Rpt. 70/16, Institute of Geological Sciences, London.
SCOTT, ALAN J., and FISHER, WILLIAM L.
1969.   Delta systems and deltaic deposition. Pp. 3-29 *in* "Delta Systems in the Exploration of Oil and Gas."   Bureau of Economic Geology, University of Texas, Austin, Texas.
SHERIDAN, ROBERT E.
1974.   Conceptual model for the black fault origin of the North American Atlantic continental margin geosyncline.   Geology, vol. 2, no. 9, pp. 465-468.
SPOLJARIC, N.
1973.   Normal faults in basement rocks of the northern Coastal Plain, Delaware.   Bull. Geol. Soc. Amer., vol. 84, no. 8, pp. 2781-2784.
TANNER, WILLIAM F.
1966.   Late Cenozoic history and coastal morphology of the Apalachicola River region, western Florida. Pp. 83-97 *in* "Deltas," M. L. Shirley, ed. Houston Geological Society, Houston, Texas.
WEBER, K. J.
1971.   Sedimentological aspects of oil fields in the Niger Delta.   Geol. Mijnboww, vol. 5, no. 3, pp. 559-576.
WRIGHT, L. D., and COLEMAN, J. M.
1973.   Variations in morphology of major river deltas as functions of ocean wave and river discharge regimes.   Bull. Amer. Assoc. Petrol. Geol., vol. 57, no. 2, pp. 370-398.

JOHN K. ADAMS

The Río Bec Ecological Project

Principal Investigator: Richard E. W. Adams, University of Texas at San Antonio.

Grant No. 1120:   In support of a study of ecological change and cultural history of the Río Bec region, Yucatán Peninsula.

Background and Research Design

This project was organized as a joint research endeavor of the University of Texas at San Antonio and the University of Wisconsin, Madison. R.E.W. Adams (University of Texas at San Antonio) acted as project director, J. D. Eaton (Tulane University) as field director for most of the season, and J. B. Stoltman (University of Wisconsin, Madison) as field director for the first month. Project personnel for all or part of the field season (February 15 to June 1, 1973) consisted of the following from the University of Wisconsin at Madison: John D. Shepherd (botany), R. B. Waide (ornithology), B. L. Turner (cultural geography), J. W. Ball (archeology), and J. Tascheck (archeology). All were advanced graduate students at the time and most met the stressful conditions of fieldwork with aplomb and truly professional responses. As field director, Eaton took on an extraordinarily difficult job and is largely responsible for the success of the fieldwork. From time to time we had consultants in camp working with their graduate students and lending their expertise to the project in other ways. Drs. William Reeder, Frank Iwen, William Denevan, and David Mikelson of the University of Wisconsin, Madison, all performed these services for the project.

Research in this part of Mexico was carried on under a permit from Monumentos Prehistoricos (Arq. Ignacio Marquina) of the Instituto Nacional de Antropología e Historia (Arq. Guillermo Bonfil Batalla). Both were very helpful to us. In addition, the subdirector of INAH for administration, Dr. Fernando Camara, and the assistant director of Monumentos Prehispanicos, Dr. Eduardo Matos, were extraordinarily kind and aided us in many ways. The head of the INAH Southeastern Regional Office, Arq. Miguel Messmacher, supervised our work. The then governor of the state of Campeche, Lic. Sansores Pérez, extended numerous courtesies to the project and smoothed our way. We thank all these gentlemen.

The Río Bec ecological project was conceived of as a multidisciplinary endeavor. It was oriented toward producing information on the Río Bec region

43

that would aid us in understanding the ecological as well as the culture-historical context of the failure of Maya Classic period civilization. Our proposal was formulated in this manner, submitted to the National Geographic Society as a pilot project, and funded by the Society in 1972.

The 1970 Santa Fe conference on the Classic Maya Collapse (Culbert, 1973) set up several hypotheses that were integrated into a model. Briefly, the model states that Maya culture seems to have undergone several changes and come under several stresses during the period A.D. 650 to 850. One stress was defined as being from a large growth in population accompanied by a disproportionate increase of the elite sector of society. It is thought that one reason for this growth is that Maya leadership sought to institute more formal political structures than they had possessed before. Specifically, it is postulated that the Maya elite tried to establish states modeled on urban states in central Mexico. A corollary is that large masses of manpower to exploit and manipulate were necessary to make such state organizations work. Whether or not this is exactly correct processually, our data show that population growth took place during the last 200 years of Classic Maya culture. Increasing competition among Maya states developed and took a military form. Militarism was not new to the Maya lowlands, as evidenced by the late pre-Classic fortress of Becan (ca. A.D. 250-300; Webster, 1972, 1976). The level and intensity of lowland Maya warfare, however, seem to have reached a new high during the period A.D. 650-850. Competition was at least partly over land and other subsistence resources. The feeling at the 1970 conference was that the systemic logic of the model called for much more population than was indicated by current data. O. G. Ricketson (Ricketson and Ricketson, 1937, p. 18) had suggested a high Classic period population based on intensive agriculture. Puleston (1968) had made the same suggestion from his work, which indicated that considerably more food was available to the ancient Maya than just the amounts to be produced by slash-and-burn agriculture. However, since these arguments implied some kind of intensive agriculture, and since positive evidence for that sort of activity was lacking, these conclusions were resisted. Ecological change was also indicated as a stress factor in the Maya collapse, but as brought about largely by man rather than exclusively by nature. Disease and associated increases in annual mortality were indicated as being important in studies by physical anthropologists (Saul, 1972).

By the end of the 1970 conference it was clear that ecological and population density information was lacking in the degrees needed to test these ideas. We set up the Río Bec project to deal partially with these problems, using the collapse model as a research guide. We hoped to outline the changing ecology and its use by man during the past 2,500 years. We focused our efforts on the period of the Maya collapse but hoped to gain data on periods before and after that event. We also used the regional rather than the individual archeological site approach, hoping thereby to gain greater reliability of data by larger and more diverse sampling. Specific activities involved were to be the following: inventories of vegetation, animal, bird, and insect life; studies of the interrelationships, systems, and zonation of these biological units; definition of the changing uses to which they had been put by man through time. Soil sampling was an emphasized technique, owing to the fact that we thought we could find a great deal of bones, seeds, and plant material in ancient refuse middens. This material in turn would indicate shifts in human diet through time. Small-structure excavation in rural areas by the archeologists was intended to produce such midden samples and to indicate any differences among social classes in diet. Examination of what was apparently agricultural terracing and associated features was designed to outline ancient land use and degrees of intensity of exploitation.

Finally, all the above activities took off from a baseline of substantial data produced by the previous projects in the region (R.E.W. Adams, 1974, 1977b; J. W. Ball, 1977), work also sponsored by the National Geographic Society.

Project Results

The information produced by the project falls into several categories, all of which overlap:

Ecological Inventory and Systems Studies. It is clear that there is an enormous diversity of vegetation within the concession area of 30-kilometer radius around Xpujil (fig. 1). Shepherd found that the undisturbed Yucatecan monsoon forest is largely a thing of the past. Thirty years of logging and chicle bleeding (for chewing gum) have reduced the climax forest to a few isolated relic stands, usually located in gullies. Most of the forest today, although it seems formidably undisturbed to the botanically naive, is in reality highly disturbed secondary forest. Shepherd and Waide agree that the climatic axis between the northern and southern Maya lowland forests probably lies about 65 kilometers to the south of present-day Xpujil.

It is hinted in the botanical data that significant and major changes can be made in tropical vegetation communities that, in turn, influence climatic changes. The late E. Wyllys Andrews IV thought that the low thorn forests of northern Yucatán were a result of intensive human use over thousands of years. If he was right, then the Río Bec zone may eventually turn into a Yucatecan-style forest through long-term human use. The first stages of such a conversion may be what is being observed at the moment. However, it should be pointed out also that the Maya lowland forests today, even in their undisturbed climax states, are quite likely different from those encountered by the first human pioneers about 2,500 B.C. Although abandoned in many areas for over 1,100 years, the forests were exploited and plant communities probably severely modified by the 3,000 or more years of human usage before the collapse of Maya civilization ca. A.D. 900.

Waide's work with birds produced a significant inventory of many species. As one example of information of cross-disciplinary utility, Waide noted a high net-catch count of ferruginous pygmy owls (*Glaucidium brasilianum*), which correlates, as he remarks, with a relatively high occurrence of these birds as offerings in Maya burials and as effigies on offertory vessels.

It became clear that bird species were quite sensitive to minor plant succession changes. This is especially apparent in land that had previously been planted to maize and is now in various stages of recovery. Since the end of the project, Waide has continued his work in the Río Bec zone with field time spent there in 1974 and 1975. His doctoral thesis will deal with the results of his Río Bec research.

Waide and Shepherd also collected snails and insects with a vacuum sampler. These specimens are being identified in the Madison laboratories.

Iwen and Reeder made a trip to the Río Bec zone in March, during which they collected 75 specimens of mammals, which are being identified in Madison. Bone material from these specimens will aid in identification of the archeologically derived bones.

Soil Sampling and Plant and Animal Remains. Trash middens and soil behind the ancient agricultural terraces were sampled and the material processed by dry screening. The material was examined also by Stoltman, who waterscreened it with a 30-micron screen. The results have been somewhat disappointing so far. Little bone is preserved and shell is scarce, except for that of an ubiquitous species of snail. Seeds seem to be rare. However, microscopic analysis may yet produce useful data. It seems clear that in the Maya lowlands, the optimum conditions for recovery of ancient plant and animal remains are deposition in ashy trash deposits.

Excavations of Small Structures. These were very fruitful, yielding data on household compounds, or "farmsteads," which look astonishingly modern in layout and size. These are groups of residential houses with storage buildings and enclosure walls, all of stone. Eaton has analyzed these data in his 1975 paper. These farmsteads are systemically related to the agricultural terraces and other evidences of intensive farming. Netting (1976) has pointed out the striking similarities between this Late Classic Maya settlement pattern and

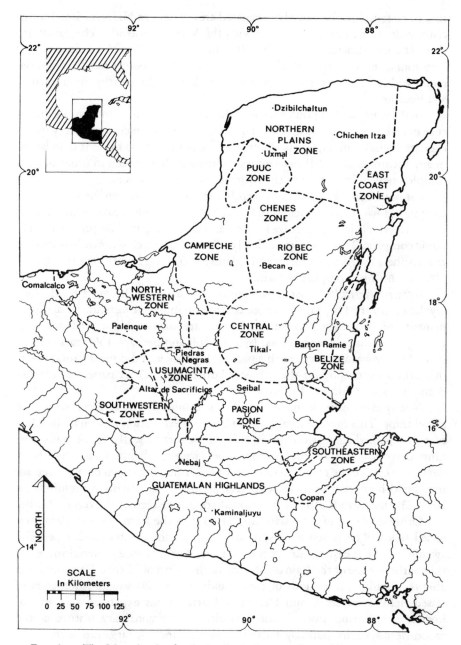

FIG. 1.   The Maya lowlands: Archeological zones (from Adams, 1977a, p. 8).

that to be found in the densely populated area of eastern Nigeria. Small water cisterns are to be found associated with the Maya farmsteads. The dating on them is approximately A.D. 600-830. They are related to the contemporary ceremonial centers in standard measurements. Eaton points out that average room width (2.4 meters) is the same as that in the nearby monumental architecture.

Ball's work with ceramics showed that there is a significant sample difference between pottery in use in the farmsteads and that in contemporary use in the ceremonial centers. These differences are so great as to make it mandatory in any future project that both zones be intensively sampled in order to gain completeness of inventory in the regional ceramic sequences.

Ceramic Analysis.   Dating controls were refined through further ceramic analysis. However, we unexpectedly added another 300 years to the earliest end of the ceramic sequence by finding and defining a middle pre-Classic ceramic complex. This complex is clearly related to the well-known Mamom ceramic sphere (Willey, Culbert, and Adams, 1967) and is dated approximately 600-300 B.C. by comparative studies.

Intensive Agriculture and High-Density Population.   The most revolutionary data from the project were those bearing on intensive agriculture and permanent, high-density population. In this area of the Maya lowlands such developments are present at least by A.D. 500 and perhaps 150 years earlier. B. L. Turner was in charge of this part of the work and did his doctoral thesis in cultural geography on the subject (Turner, 1974a). A paper has already been published (Turner, 1974b).

Nearly every hillside in the Xpujil zone is modified by terraces, which act as soil traps. This function was clearly shown by excavation in which black humus was banked against the uphill sides of the terrace walls. Stone walls running perpendicular to the contour lines were probably water-dispersion devices to ensure the even distribution of water flowing down over the terracing. Field boundary walls are also very common, indicating a premium on land. The farmsteads already mentioned are on the tops of the terraced hills.

Other evidence of intensive cultivation is in the form of check dams and raised fields. The raised-field systems are in a zone of present-day periodic swamp off to the east of our concession zone. Turner made an aerial survey of the southern edge of the Bajo de Morcoy to the north of Nicolas Bravo and was able to photograph sections of these fields. Over 120 square kilometers of raised fields were seen, and Dr. Peter Harrison has expanded this area of known distribution since Turner's work. An extraordinary feature of the raised-field systems found by Turner is that they include large canals that give access to groups of fields in much the same manner as similar canals gave access to the well-known *chinampas* of the Basin of Mexico.

All the above evidence—and there is much more—leads Turner and us to conclude that there were as many as 168 persons per square kilometer and possibly more. The already mentioned ecologically similar Nigerian areas are densely populated, with populations not uncommonly exceeding 400 persons per square kilometer (Netting, 1977). This would indicate that Turner's figure is probably very conservative.

Miscellaneous Studies. Carried on during the field season and still in progress, these miscellaneous studies are not trivial, but rather were supplementary to the original research design. Analysis of the stone artifacts and *débitage* produced by controlled excavation is being done by J. B. Stoltman and J. Rovner. These studies indicate that the commonly found flint celt was probably used as a hoe in intensive agricultural activities associated with the stone terraces. This was only one of the uses of this all-purpose tool, but clearly it is suited to the task.

Mickelson (geology), on a brief visit, examined problems of access to water in both ancient and modern times and concluded that water would have been a scarce commodity in ancient times at the end of the dry season. Previous experience in the zone had indicated that this is the case even today. Eaton's excavations in the bottom of the reservoir inside the fortified zone at Becan showed that the depression was likely artificial. The depression is deep and cut into the soft limy marl (sascab) typical of subbedrock strata in this zone. Further, Eaton found that the depression had been lined with cut masonry and clay and mud had been packed into the crevices between the stones. Clays were on top of the stone layer, increasing the impermeability of the lining. Water-laid silts lay over the clay cap, indicating that the depression had held water for a considerable time. It seems likely that nearly every modern surface water catchment in the Río Bec area had either been improved in ancient times or is entirely artificial.

An Interpretation of the Data

A preliminary interpretation of the season's data indicates the presence of high-density permanent population based on intensive agriculture from A.D. 500 to 830. This is in striking contrast to the picture of low-density, slash-and-burn population usually conjured up as a subsistence support for Maya civilization. Ester Boserup's theory of the conditions of agricultural growth (1965) seems especially appropriate here. She argues that intensity of agriculture is in response to population growth rather than the other way around.

Rather than population expanding to the limit of the food supplies, she argues that food supplies can be expanded to fit population growth, up to a certain point. Intensification of agriculture means more man-hours per unit of product in this case. Population growth, says Boserup, is a product of such factors as ideology, politics, biology, climate, etc. The Maya collapse model argues that population growth was probably in response to political and social changes. Boserup's theory would explain the situation we have around Xpujil.

Another theoretical scheme of great interest in dealing with our data is that advanced by Kent Flannery (1972). In this paper Flannery follows Rappaport in arguing that *over*-integration of social and political systems may be lethal to a culture, because the system becomes very vulnerable at all points. In other words, an effect akin to that of shorting a string of Christmas tree lights may occur in a too highly centralized society. Failure spreads rapidly to all other parts. Such hyperintegration is reflected archeologically in a very evenly patterned hexagonal arrangement of various sized communities. A trial map by Flannery of an area impinging on the Río Bec region shows an amazingly uniform lattice structure of Late Classic Maya settlements (Flannery, 1972, fig. 5). Work in the Río Bec zone by the preceding projects and our own indicate that such a lattice arrangement of tightly packed sites existed in the Late Classic.

Intensive farming with its major constructions, an artificially enlarged water impoundment system, and a hierarchically organized and specialized community system are all highly vulnerable to disruptions from within and without. Intensive farming also tends to be much more intricately scheduled. This overorganized system would contrast with the more segmented and less centralized Maya social, political, and demographic patterns of earlier times (i.e., prior to A.D. 500).

At this point it is appropriate to return to the collapse model and indicate very specifically and quantitatively the nature of some of the most important internal stresses which helped bring down Maya civilization. We are doing just that.

In 1974, partly motivated by the implications of the Río Bec data, a conference was organized on the subject of the Origins of Maya Civilization. Eleven scholars participated, and the results are being published in book form (Adams, 1977a).

REFERENCES

ADAMS, RICHARD E. W.
    1974.   Preliminary reports on archaeological investigations in the Río Bec area,
             Campeche, Mexico.   Middle Amer. Res. Inst. Tulane Univ. Publ. 31,
             pp. 103-146, R.E.W. Adams, ed.

1977a. The origins of Maya civilization, 465 pp., R. E. Adams, ed. University of New Mexico Press, Albuquerque.

1977b. Río Bec archaeology and the rise of Maya civilization. Pp. 77-79 *in* Adams, 1977a.

BALL, JOSEPH W.
1977. The rise of the northern Maya chiefdoms: A sociopolitical analysis. *In* Adams, 1977a.

BOSERUP, ESTER
1965. The conditions of agricultural growth, 124 pp. Aldine Publishing Co., Chicago.

CULBERT, T. PATRICK, ed.
1973. The Classic Maya collapse, 549 pp. University of New Mexico Press, Albuquerque.

EATON, JACK D.
1975. Ancient agricultural farmsteads in the Río Bec region of Yucatán. Contr. Univ. California Archaeol. Res. Fac., no. 27, pp. 56-82.

FLANNERY, KENT V.
1972. The cultural evolution of civilizations. Ann. Rev. Ecol. and Syst., vol. 3, pp. 399-426. Palo Alto.

NETTING, ROBERT McC.
1977. Maya subsistence: Mythologies, analogies, possibilities. Pp. 299-333 *in* Adams, 1977a.

PULESTON, DENNIS E.
1968. *Brosimum alicastrum* as a subsistence alternative for the Classic Maya of the central southern lowlands. Unpublished thesis in anthropology, University of Pennsylvania.

RICKETSON, OLIVER G., and RICKETSON, EDITH B.
1937. Uaxactún, Guatemala: Group E-1926-1931. Carnegie Inst. Washington Publ. 477.

SAUL, FRANK P.
1972. The human skeletal remains from Altar de Sacrificios. Pap. Peabody Mus. Amer. Archaeol. and Ethnol., Harvard Univ., vol. 63, no. 2.

TURNER, B. L., II
1974a. Prehistoric intensive agriculture in the Maya lowlands: New evidence from the Río Bec region. Unpublished Ph.D. thesis in geography, University of Wisconsin, Madison.

1974b. Prehistoric intensive agriculture in the Maya lowlands. Science, vol. 185, pp. 118-124, illus.

WEBSTER, DAVID L.
1972. The fortifications of Becan, Campeche, Mexico. Unpublished Ph.D. thesis, Department of Anthropology, University of Minnesota, Minneapolis.

1976. Warfare and the evolution of Maya civilization. *In* Adams, 1977a.

WILLEY, GORDON R.; CULBERT, T. PATRICK; and ADAMS, RICHARD E. W.
1967. Maya lowland ceramics: A report from the 1965 Guatemala City conference. Amer. Antiq., vol. 32, no. 3, pp. 289-315.

RICHARD E. W. ADAMS

Prehistoric and Historic Settlement Patterns in Western Cyprus

Principal Investigator: J. M. Adovasio, University of Pittsburgh, Pittsburgh, Pennsylvania.

Grant Nos. 1128, 1232.   For an archeological reconnaissance of the Khrysokhou drainage in western Cyprus.[1]

Cyprus, with an area of 6,093 square kilometers, is the third largest island in the Mediterranean. It is situated in the eastern portion of that sea, south of Turkey and west of Syria. As Catling (1966) noted, the north coast of the island lies under the eye of Anatolia. The nearest point on the Anatolian coast is some 69.2 kilometers north of Cape Kormatiki, while Latakia in north Syria lies but 122.3 kilometers east of Cape Andreas, the tip of the Cypriot "panhandle." From Larnaca on the south coast to Port Said in the Nile delta it is some 434.8 kilometers. The nearest Greek islands are 400-odd kilometers to the west.

Geologically, the island is of relatively recent origin and clearly constitutes a landmass formerly connected to the Anatolian Peninsula (Pantazis, 1971). Paleontological investigations have revealed a fauna that is appropriate to a region once an integral part of Asia.

The principal geographic features of Cyprus are two mountain ranges in the north and southwest, separated by the broad Mesaoria Plain. These ranges represent extensions of the Amanus and Casius ranges in nearby Anatolia and north Syria.

---

[1] Major assistance on Cyprus was provided by Dr. Vassos Karageorghis, director of the Department of Antiquities; Mr. Loulloupis, research archeologist, Cyprus Museum; George Maliotis, geologist, Hellenistic Mining Co.; and Th. M. Pantazis, Cyprus Geological Survey.

A special word of thanks is extended to the members of the Australian Civilian Police Detachment stationed in the town of Polis (U.N.), who assisted us in every possible way and whose hospitality rendered our stay in western Cyprus most pleasant. The 1972 contingent: P. Toy, O.I.C.; G. Hodgson, G. Galloway, W. Magnusson, T. Page, L. Senior, and C. Woolford. The 1973 contingent: T. Davies, O.I.C.; D. Hibbard, J. Power, B. Tite, K. Tucknott, R. Wile, and C. Zadow.

We note also with appreciation the cooperation extended to us by countless Greek and Turkish Cypriots, including government officials, museum staff, local businessmen, farmers, and shepherds. Without their help we would have accomplished little.

The Northern or Kyrenia range forms a narrow belt running practically the whole length of the north coast. The average elevation of this chain is about 600 meters, with a maximum elevation of 1,007 meters near the extreme western edge of the range. In the east these mountains gradually diminish in elevation as they extend out along the narrow Karpass Peninsula.

The mountains in the southwest are known as the Southern or Troodos range, a massif substantially larger in area as well as higher in elevation than the Kyrenia chain and occupying nearly one-half of the island. The highest point in the Troodos is Mount Olympus, or Chionistra, 1,920 meters above sea level.

The research reported herein was initiated in the Khrysokhou River drainage of the Paphos District in far-western Cyprus (fig. 1). This area lies west of the Troodos Massif and is the major drainage running to the north coast in the extreme western portion of the island.

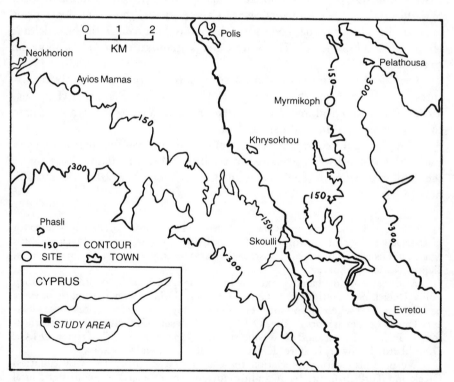

FIG. 1.   The Khrysokhou River drainage of western Cyprus.

Geology and Topography

The geology of the Khrysokhou drainage is relatively uncomplicated. (The summary presented below is drawn largely from a map prepared by Lapierre, 1971.) Directly adjacent to Khrysokhou Bay is a narrow strip of marine terrace deposits of Pleistocene age. This strip, which is, in effect, the delta of the Khrysokhou, extends inland some 1 to 2 kilometers and consists primarily of calcarenites. To the east this strip gradually feathers out along the coast, while 8 kilometers west of Polis it abuts the lower reaches (ca. 100 meters in elevation) of the Pakhna Formation and the Lefkara Group. These geological units are of Upper Cretaceous to Miocene age and will be discussed further below.

Directly south of Polis along the entire course of, and on both sides of, the Khrysokhou River are encountered the Myrtou marls, sandy marls and calcarenites of the Nicosia Formation. These low-lying (less than 100 meters in elevation), heavily dissected units are of Pliocene age.

Flanking terraces are pronounced on both sides of the Khrysokhou and rise in a series of steps to a maximum elevation of some 600 meters. These terraces consist of gypsum, marl, marly limestones, calcarenites, and chalks assignable to the Pakhna Formation and the Lefkara Group. These geological formations account for most of the exposures encountered in the uplands of the Khrysokhou drainage and include in certain areas large concentrations of chert contained within the chalk deposits.

Climate and Hydrology

The Khrysokhou drainage shares in the Mediterranean climate that prevails over the rest of the island. Mean maximum monthly temperatures range from 27° C. in July and August to 10° C. in January and February, while mean maximum daily temperatures range from 32°-35° C. to 7°-10° C. during the aforementioned months. Mean annual temperature is ca. 19° C.

The Khrysokhou drainage presently lies within the 450-600 millimeters per year rainfall cline with precipitation normally falling during the winter months (Tullstrom, 1970). However, the period encompassed by our survey was practically devoid of rainfall. In fact, December 1973 was the last month in one of the longest and most severe droughts in recent history.

The Khrysokhou is a "dry" river and contains water only after heavy rains, which are relatively infrequent. Contained ground water is restricted in the Khrysokhou area to a series of reef and detrital limestone aquifers within the Pakhna and Lefkara geological units. The aquifers are present on both the eastern and western flanks of the Khrysokhou River. The Pakhna Formation also contains confined ground water in highly retentive chalks interbedded with marls. The aquifers are confined to the higher elevations (i.e., above 100 meters) of the Khrysokhou drainage. Ground water in the lower elevation is generally unconfined and encountered in deltaic sand-gravel deposits, terrestrial fanglomerate, and terrace formations.

Flora and Fauna

The present flora of the Khrysokhou drainage may be accurately called depauperate. Overgrazing by sheep and goats coupled with the effects of cyclical erosion and drought has rendered much of the area a semidesert. Vegetation, where present, consists entirely of xeric flora with an occasional incidence in irrigated or otherwise well-watered localities of cultivated olive, carob, orange, lemon, and grapefruit trees. The most common domesticate found in this area is grapes. Aleppo pine is occasionally encountered in the higher elevations of the drainage.

Modern fauna, both terrestrial and avian, is likewise impoverished, owing chiefly to excessive hunting pressures. Sundays and Wednesdays are "shooting" days in the Khrysokhou area, with the unfortunate result that during two seasons of survey we observed but six wild animals (birds excluded)—one fox and five hares.

In prehistoric times this area may have been moderately to heavily forested, with a wide range of mammalian fauna present. However, controlled data on prehistoric flora and fauna in the Khrysokhou region are generally lacking.

History of Research and Methodology

In December 1972 an archeological reconnaissance of the Khrysokhou drainage was initiated. It was expressly designed to investigate this relatively remote and almost archeologically unknown portion of the island. As originally conceived, the survey had two principal objectives: (1) the delineation and elucidation of the nature, extent, and fluctuation of prehistoric and historic settlement patterns and (2) the collection and identification of Neolithic and possibly pre-Neolithic stone artifacts.

Survey headquarters were established in the town of Polis in the delta of the Khrysokhou River directly adjacent to Khrysokhou Bay. During the survey the west bank of the river was examined as far south as the village of Skoulli, a distance of some 5.6 kilometers. The east bank of the river was surveyed to the hamlet of Evretou, about 9.7 kilometers southeast of Polis. In addition to the river flood plain, the graded terraces, tributary gullies, washes, and canyons were surveyed to a distance of up to 4.8 kilometers east of the river at Phasli village. Other forays were made outside of the Khrysokhou drainage proper, to the uplands of the Akamas Peninsula to the west. All areas were examined on foot, and considerable effort was expended to insure that every potential site locus was investigated and recorded. This survey was terminated in January 1974.

We processed all ceramic artifacts recovered during the survey in the field and subsequently identified and assigned them chronological periods, using comparative collections in the Cyprus Museum. Lithic artifacts were analyzed in the Department of Anthropology of the University of Pittsburgh.

All pertinent data recovered during the 1972-73 reconnaissance were programmed for computer analysis. In all, 223 sites were recorded within the survey area delimited above. On the basis of extensive surface collections of ceramics and/or lithics, the great majority of sites appear to represent multi-component occupations. Individual components were identified on ceramic criteria by Mr. Loulloupis of the Cyprus Museum. For the purpose of this analysis, the presence of diagnostic rim sherds and/or bases of a known chronological period was sufficient to identify a component at any given site. In the case of Neolithic components, assignations occasionally were made on the presence of ground-stone tools of established Neolithic configurations. On these bases alone, a total of 706 components were recognized at the 223 sites identified during the survey. The mean number of components identified per site is 3.16.

The computer analysis, including mapping, treated all components of all sites as discrete representatives of temporal settlement patterns. For this reason the term "site" is frequently used interchangeably with "component" in this study. All components were analyzed relative to horizontal distribution, elevation, and proximity to aquifers or other potential sources of water. The patterns that emerged were contour mapped by SYMAP (Synagraphic Mapping), a program developed at Harvard University and maintained on the University of Pittsburgh Computer System.

Three occupational zones were utilized in this analysis: Zone I—0 to 150 meters; Zone II—150 to 300 meters; Zone III—300 meters and above. These zones were selected because they generally correspond to the three major topographic discontinuities that exist in the Khrysokhou drainage. Zone I includes the flood plain of the Khrysokhou and the lower flanking terraces on both sides of the river. Zone II includes gently sloping to relatively steep hillsides, while Zone III is the flat plateau country high above the valley of Khrysokhou.

The distribution of components within these zones was plotted through time. The sequent settlement patterns that emerged from this analysis are herein termed settlement systems and are described and discussed below by standard chronological periods. If patterns were constant for a number of periods, these periods were lumped in the analysis. The periods used below and their temporal limits are adapted from Karageorghis (1969) and Buchholz and Karageorghis (1973).

Settlement Systems in the Khrysokhou Drainage

PRE-NEOLITHIC: ?-5800 B.C.

Despite intensive scrutiny, no sites that could positively be identified as pre-Neolithic were recorded within the Khrysokhou drainage. However, several individual artifact discoveries were made that strongly suggest the distinct possibility of pre-Neolithic occupation of this area. All these discoveries were made in Zones II and III and include a bifacially worked chopper made on a partially decorticated cobble of pebble chert, a remarkably Levallois-like chalcedony uniface with a faceted platform, a unifacial side-scraper of Middle Paleolithic appearance, and a large nucleus, again with a faceted platform. All these specimens were found eroding out of gravel deposits and were not associated with any other artifactual materials. (For a fuller discussion of these items, see Adovasio et al., 1975.)

NEOLITHIC: 5800-3000 B.C.

Twelve Neolithic components were located in the Khrysokhou drainage. All, with one exception, appear to represent substantial settlements ranging from a minimum of 0.5 to a maximum of 5 hectares in extent. The exception is a very small settlement that may be a single homestead or hamlet. As indicated, there is a definite preference during this period for higher elevation sites on both the east and west flanks of the Khrysokhou. The majority (8) of the Neolithic sites are situated in elevational Zone II, that is, between 150 and 300 meters above sea level. Two sites are located in upper Zone I very nearly at the interface of Zones I/II, while three sites are located well up in Zone III. Topographically, Zones II and III include gently sloping to relatively steep hillsides, the tops of the steep hillocks, and high saddles as well as high plateaus. All these localities are directly adjacent to permanent water in the form of seeps and springs, and the distribution of Neolithic sites corresponds almost perfectly with the plotted extent of the limestone aquifers contained within the Pakhna and Lefkara geological units.

Of secondary, but by no means minimal, importance in the location of Neolithic sites is the immediate availability of a variety of high-grade cherts, flints, and other cryptocrystalline rocks within the limits of Zones II and III. Similarly, these zones are rich in andesite, which was heavily utilized in the manufacture of ground-stone tools during the Neolithic.

Arable land in the direct vicinity of Neolithic sites is, with the exception of the settlement at Myrmikoph, quite marginal and must have been so in prehistoric times. The locations of these sites does, however, provide ready access to the upland biota, which was apparently rich, as well as to resources of the Khrysokhou valley bottom. Defensibility, per se, does not appear to have been a major factor in the disposition of Neolithic sites within the Khrysokhou drainage, though their high elevation provides them with no little advantage in that regard. Significantly, the Neolithic settlement pattern represented in the survey area has also been repeated from elsewhere on the island and now appears to be the standard type for the Neolithic period (Catling, 1966; Karageorghis, 1969).

CHALCOLITHIC: 3000-2300 B.C.

Only two sites ascribable to this period were recorded in the survey area. Both are settlements located in Zone II. The low frequency of Chalcolithic sites may reflect a diminution of population during this period, or the more likely possibility that Chalcolithic sites are totally masked by later occupations. Since the location of the two Chalcolithic sites represents no change from the preceding period, they were mapped along with the Neolithic sites.

Presumably, the preference for higher elevations during the Chalcolithic reflects the continuing operation of the same selection processes as were operative during the Neolithic. The Chalcolithic preference for high-altitude settlements near permanent water has been documented for other parts of the island (Catling, 1966).

BRONZE AGE (EARLY TO LATE CYPRIOT): 2300-1050 B.C.

Twenty-four components ascribable to the early Bronze Age (Early Cypriot), 2300-2000 B.C., and 10 components of the Late Bronze Age (Late Cypriot), 1600-1050 B.C., were identified in the survey area. No Middle Bronze Age sites (Middle Cypriot), 2000-1600 B.C., were encountered anywhere in the Khrysokhou drainage or the adjacent Akamas highlands. The 34 Bronze Age components include: 20 small to medium sized settlements, 5 large settlements (surface scatters greater than 200 square meters), 4 settlements with adjacent cemeteries, and 5 cemeteries.

All Bronze Age components have been grouped together in this analysis because the basic settlement pattern is, with the notable hiatus during Middle Bronze Age, relatively homogeneous throughout this period. Bronze Age settlements tend to be located at lower elevations than their Neolithic predecessors. While a large number of sites continue to occur in Zone II, there is a dramatic increase in sites from Zone I. It should be stressed that the Bronze Age sites from Zone II are located, as a rule, proportionally lower than the earlier Neolithic sites within the same zone. Likewise, despite the fact that Bronze Age sites continue to be erected on eminences, perhaps for defensive reasons, rarely are these features as steep or precipitous as those utilized during the Neolithic. The above underscores the basic fact that Bronze Age sites tend to occur in closer proximity to the narrow Khrysokhou flood plain. This trend toward lower elevations as preferred site loci is probably related to the significantly greater amount of arable land available at these elevations. Conversely, proximity to lithic sources and aquifers appears to be a much less important settlement variable during the Bronze Age.

The absence of Middle Bronze age sites in the Khrysokhou area is somewhat enigmatic. According to Buchholz and Karageorghis (1973), Cyprus became wealthy during this period as a result of trade with its Near Eastern neighbors. Apparently, however, this wealth is not reflected in settlement density which Catling (1966) notes is generally low at this time, particularly in western Cyprus. It may well be that Middle Bronze Age sites within the Khrysokhou have been obliterated by later occupations. In this regard it may be noted that Late Bronze Age sites in the survey area are somewhat scarcer than Early Bronze Age sites and occasionally reverse the trend noted above to lower elevations. Several Late Bronze Age sites, including a substantial fortified settlement, occur in Zone III. These sites are anomalies of a sort, as they occur where arable land is scarce though permanent water is abundant. All the upland Late Bronze Age sites do have enormous defensive potential, however, which could account for their location. It should be added that the upland as well as lowland Late Bronze sites in the Khrysokhou drainage represent divergences from the Late Bronze pattern on the rest of the island. Sites of this period tend to be clustered on the coasts (Catling, 1966) rather than in the interior.

CYPRO-GEOMETRIC TO HELLENISTIC: 1050-50 B.C.

Included here are 1 Cypro-Geometric cemetery (1050-700 B.C.); 9 cemeteries, 1 household (hamlet), 14 small to medium sized settlements, and 1 large settlement of Cypro-Archaic Age (600-400 B.C.); 10 cemeteries, 2 households, 21 small to medium sized settlements, and 2 settlements with associated cemeteries of Cypro-Classical Age (400-325 B.C.); and 3 cemeteries, 18 small to medium sized settlements, 1 large settlement, and 4 settlements with adjacent cemeteries of the Hellenistic period (325-50 B.C.). All the foregoing components are restricted to Zones I and II and for this reason are treated as a unit.

The settlement pattern represented by the 87 sites ascribed to this settlement system reflects the culmination of the trend toward progressively lower site locus preference initiated in the Bronze Age. The prime locational variable in the distribution of all sites of this time appears to be access to arable lands. Virtually all the 87 sites are located on low-lying terraces or knolls directly adjacent to the flood plain, or on the slightly higher, gently sloping flanks on either side of the river. Few of the lowland sites appear to have been selected for their natural defensive potential.

A notable exception to the lowland preference pattern is a single very large Hellenistic town with associated cemetery located near the upper limits of Zone II. This town dominates a natural pass in the flanking hills adjacent to the Khrysokhou drainage and literally controls access to the valley bottom from this direction. If terracing is practiced, arable land is moderately plentiful in the vicinity of this settlement, and the defensive, or more accurately, strategic advantages of the site are great. This town probably represented the major upland habitation in the entire Khrysokhou drainage during Hellenistic times.

It should be added that with the exception of the Cypro-Geometric period, apparently represented by a solitary cemetery, the density of settlement appears to be more or less constant during this entire time span. The scarcity of Cypro-Geometric settlements is not readily explainable as the single cemetery located during the survey is exceptionally large and suggests a reasonably substantial population. Finally, if the sheer number of components ascribable to any settlement system considered in this study is any direct sign of population density, the system discussed here represents the highest population density yet encountered in the Khrysokhou archeological sequence.

ROMAN: 50 B.C. TO A.D. 400

The Roman settlement system in the Khrysokhou drainage subsumes 266 components assignable either to Early Roman (50 B.C.-A.D. 150) or Late Roman (A.D. 150-400) times. The 266 Roman components include 196 small to medium sized settlements, 16 large settlements, 20 settlements with adjacent cemeteries, 14 households, 16 cemeteries, and 4 nonsettlement sites that yielded one or more square-cut stone blocks in association with Roman ceramics. The Early and Late Roman components are virtually always present on the same site locus, indicating more or less continuous occupation throughout the Roman period.

There is a significant reoccupation of the Zone III highlands that had been abandoned throughout the preceding settlement system. Despite the reappearance of sites in Zone III, the bulk of Roman sites are clearly confined to Zones I and II, respectively. The lower elevations of the Khrysokhou, including every available terrace and hill, are filled with sites in greater density than in any other preceding or, for that matter, succeeding settlement system. On the basis of sheer numbers of components or sites proper, the densest occupation of the Khrysokhou at any point in its history would appear to have been during Roman times. This correlates well with data from elsewhere on Cyprus, which suggest very high population density during the relatively tranquil and prosperous period (Purcell, 1969) of Roman rule.

Primary settlement variables appear to be access to arable land and to the flood plain proper. The concentration of sites in the vicinity of modern Polis also suggests that access to the delta area and access to Khrysokhou Bay were likewise important settlement factors.

The reoccupation of the highlands is represented by a variety of sites, including small solitary farmsteads and an occasional small to medium sized settlement. While many of these upland sites are located on relatively flat, well-watered plateau land and were probably associated with viticulture, a number of them clearly represent loci of specialized industrial activities. These include four Zone III settlements with slag heaps of various sizes, which accumulated from the processing of copper ore. All these sites and an additional Zone I site with cuprous slag are concentrated in the vicinity of modern Pelathousa, in a copper-rich area currently being exploited by Limni mines of the Cyprus Sulphur and Copper Co., Ltd. Though the lowland slag heap gives an indication of pre-Roman copper processing by the presence of a Cypro-Archaic component, all the other slag heaps apparently accumulated from Roman times on.

Also included in the uplands is a single fortress or fortified camp, which was, like the Hellenistic site noted previously, located in a strategic pass that controls access to the valley.

BYZANTINE AND MEDIEVAL: A.D. 400-1489

The end of Roman rule and the onset of Byzantine domination mark the appearance in the Khrysokhou drainage of a settlement system which, with slight modifications, persists to the present. Byzantine components and Medieval (Luisignan) components are herein lumped because the dates for indigenous Late Byzantine ceramics are synchronous with those for the period of Luisignan domination of the island in Medieval times (A.D. 1192-1489). Medieval ceramics are different, however, from local Late Byzantine wares; thus, the two ceramic traditions, while synchronous, are not synonymous.

Included in this settlement system are 88 components of Early Byzantine age (A.D. 400-700), 15 components of Middle Byzantine age (A.D. 700-1192), 36 components of Late Byzantine age, and 20 Medieval (Luisignan) components (A.D. 1192-1489). The 159 Byzantine/Medieval components include 108 small to medium sized settlements, 10 large settlements, 14 households, 12 settlements with adjacent cemeteries, 8 cemeteries, and 7 nonsettlement/cemetery sites with evidence of Byzantine or Medieval utilization.

With the exception of a slight decrease in the proportion of sites in Zone I and a marked decrease in the total number of sites represented, there is little change from the preceding Roman settlement system.

The dramatic diminution of sites during Byzantine times is ascribable to a number of factors (Purcell, 1969). Of primary importance is a series of earthquakes that struck Cyprus from A.D. 332 to the end of Roman rule on the island. These quakes caused severe damage to settlements and disrupted water supplies either by destroying aqueducts (Karageorghis, 1969) and/or altering the prevailing water table. The effects of the latter would be felt most profoundly in lowland areas, heavily dependent on unconfined ground water, such as Zone I in the Khrysokhou drainage.

To compound matters further, the isostatic cataclysms noted above were often accompanied by droughts, famines, plagues, and other disastrous "acts of God," with the result that the first half of the fourth century saw a catastrophic decline in Cypriot population (Purcell, 1969).

While Cypriot population density increased somewhat after the effects of the natural calamities had dissipated, a series of Arab raids from ca. 648-965 caused further settlement destruction and attendant loss of life.

It is presumed that the decrease in frequency of sites in the Khrysokhou drainage is but a reflection of the more general population decline and settlement attrition evidenced throughout Cyprus during earlier Byzantine times. An eloquent testimonial to local conditions within the Khrysokhou drainage is available from the industrial sites isolated in the preceding period. While all show signs of continuing occupation in Early Byzantine times, the smelting of copper ceases abruptly thereafter and was never resumed until the present.

Finally, it should be noted that the distribution of Medieval and Late Byzantine sites in the Khrysokhou drainage is not identical. While Late Byzantine sites occur on both sides of the river, Medieval (Luisignan) components are markedly clustered on the east flank of the Khrysokhou. This clustering is not readily explainable in terms of water availability, arable land, etc., and may well be the result of political factors operative in this area during the time period in question.

MODERN: A.D. 1489 TO PRESENT

Under the term "Modern" are grouped 19 components of the Venetian period (A.D. 1489-1571), 9 components of the Turkish period (A.D. 1571-1878), and 119 components ranging in age from A.D. 1878 to the present. The 146 components so grouped include 108 small to medium sized settlements, 7 households, 11 large settlements, 13 settlements with adjacent cemeteries, and 7 cemeteries.

The post-A.D. 1878 settlement pattern data are incomplete and do not include all the contemporary villages in the survey area. Their distribution does not differ, however, from the pattern described here.

The Modern settlement system in the Khrysokhou area is essentially an extension of the preceding Byzantine/Medieval pattern. The distribution of sites within Zones I, II, and III is quite similar and differs only in a slight increase in Modern times of Zone I sites with a concomitant decrease in Zone III occupations. The decrease in Zone III sites is, in some cases, directly related to the recent political turmoil which has resulted in the abandonment of some upland villages, notably Phasli.

Summary and Conclusions

SETTLEMENT SYSTEM

The 1972-73 reconnaissance of the Khrysokhou River valley drainage identified 706 discrete components on 223 site loci. These components have been ascribed to six sequent systems. Despite certain gaps in the record (e.g., the Middle Bronze Age), the available data clearly suggest a number of basic trends in the evolution of settlement systems within the Khrysokhou drainage.

During the Neolithic/Chalcolithic settlement system there is a definite preference for high-altitude habitations with a corresponding avoidance of the Zone I lowlands. Primary locational considerations appear to have been access to permanent, contained ground water in the Zone II aquifers and the availability of various cryptocrystalline rocks and andesite within the same zone and adjacent Zone III. Of marginal concern, at least during this settlement system, is access to arable land, which is generally scarce in the vicinity of all but one Neolithic/Chalcolithic site. The lack of arable land is perhaps indicative of a low reliance on agricultural products with a corresponding dependence on wild-food resources. If this is the case, the location of the Neolithic/Chalcolithic sites provides ready access to the potentially rich highland biome. While Neolithic/Chalcolithic sites tend to occur in naturally defensible localities, this does not appear to have been a primary locational concern.

The Bronze Age settlement system is marked by the initiation of a trend toward lower elevations as preferred site loci. Access to arable land and access to the Khrysokhou flood plain appear to be the primary settlement variables. Proximity to lithic sources would seem to be of much less importance than in the preceding settlement system; while access to aquifers of Zone II is likewise a reduced, though by no means inconsequential, settlement factor. Defensive potential may well be a consideration during this time, particularly in the location of certain Zone III loci toward the end of this settlement system.

During the Cypro-Geometric to Hellenistic settlement system, the trend toward lower site loci reaches its zenith. Most sites are concentrated in the lower portions of Zone II and in the lowlands of Zone I, while the uplands of Zone III are deserted. Again, access to arable land and access to the flood plain are primary settlement considerations. Continued selection for defensive potential is reflected in the upper Zone II Hellenistic fortress/town.

The Roman settlement system witnesses the reoccupation of the Zone III highlands as well as the continued proliferation of sites in lower Zones II and I, respectively. The reoccupation of the uplands is apparently related both to agricultural, or more properly viticultural, concerns and to a new variable— access to copper deposits. The concentration of sites in the vicinity of modern Polis suggests that access to the delta as well as to Khrysokhou Bay was likewise an important Roman settlement variable.

The settlement system initiated in Byzantine/Medieval times is, with minor fluctuations, continued to the present. Sites are encountered in all three zones, though the concentration is in the lower elevations. Arable land is the primary locational consideration. The operation of various political factors is apparent at several junctures during all the post-Roman settlement systems and is manifested today by the desertion of certain Zone III sites.

With the signal exception of the trend toward lower site loci as preferred habitations, perhaps the most notable factor in the six settlement systems summarized above is the relatively constant proportion of sites in Zone II. Though the number of sites in Zones I and III changes considerably through time, Zone II is never seriously depopulated, much less abandoned totally (cf. Bronze Age Zone III). This settlement continuity is probably directly tied to the reef and detrital limestone aquifers of Zone II which may well have provided a constant supply of water even during the disastrous earthquakes of the late fourth century A.D.

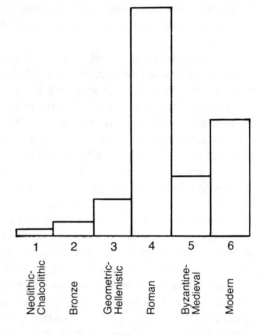

FIG. 2.   Histogram of reconstructed population curve for the Khrysokhou River drainage.

POPULATION TRENDS

Certain trends in the population of the Khrysokhou drainage through time may, with caution, be abstracted from the settlement data presented above. Using the sheer number of components of all types per settlement system as general indicators of population density, we can reconstruct a population histogram for the Khrysokhou drainage. Such a histogram is presented in figure 2. This histogram represents the number of components per settlement system, corrected for time by dividing the number of components by the number of years per system. As is apparent, population increases steadily from the Neolithic/Chalcolithic period to Roman times, at which point the number of people inhabiting the Khrysokhou drainage is at an all-time high. Population falls disastrously during Byzantine/Medieval times and thereafter increases steadily until the present. It should be noted that the current population of the Khrysokhou area is apparently less than that of Roman times.

While it is recognized that the histogram presented here is to be used with caution, it does correspond to known historical facts. The Roman population of Cyprus was great, and there was, as noted previously, a drastic depopulation during Byzantine times. The only major variance of the Khrysokhou histogram with documented Cypriot population trends is the relatively low number of persons apparently living in the survey area during Luisignan (Medieval) times. While Medieval Cyprus allegedly supported a population of some 500,000 (Purcell, 1969), this does not seem to be the case for the survey area. Given the available data, we can only presume that the depopulation of the Khrysokhou area during earlier Byzantine times was of sufficient severity to offset any modest increases in the Medieval period.

It is hoped that an extended program of excavation will test the validity not only of the population model above but also of the general settlement sequence postulated in this study.

REFERENCES

ADOVASIO, J. M.; FRY, G. F.; GUNN, J. O.; and MASLOWSKI, R. F.
  1975.   Prehistoric and historic settlement patterns in western Cyprus (with a discussion of Cypriot Neolithic stone tool technology). World Archaeol., vol. 6, no. 3, pp. 339-364.
BUCHHOLZ, HANS-GÜNTER, and KARAGEORGHIS, VASSOS
  1973.   Prehistoric Greece and Cyprus: An archaeological handbook, 514 pp., illus. Phaidon Press, London.
CATLING, H. W.
  1966.   Cyprus in the Neolithic and Bronze Age periods. Cambridge Ancient Hist. Fasc., no. 43, pp. 3-78.
KARAGEORGHIS, VASSOS
  1969.   The ancient civilization of Cyprus, 260 pp. Nagel Publishers, Geneva; Cowles Educational Corporation, New York.
LAPIERRE, H.
  1971.   Geologic map of the Polis-Paphos area. Drawn and prepared for lithographic printing by the Geological Survey Department, Cyprus. Copies available from Director of the Lands and Surveys Department, Nicosia, Cyprus.
PANTAZIS, TH. M.
  1971.   An outline of the geology and geomorphology of Cyprus. Bull. Cyprus Geogr. Assoc., March. Nicosia.
PURCELL, HUGH D.
  1969.   Cyprus, 416 pp., illus. Frederick A. Praeger, New York.
TULLSTROM, N.H.O.
  1970.   Hydrogeological map of Cyprus. Drawn and prepared for lithographic printing by the Geological Survey Department, Cyprus. Copies obtainable from Director of Lands and Surveys Department, Nicosia, Cyprus.

J. M. ADOVASIO
G. F. FRY
J. D. GUNN
R. F. MASLOWSKI

Accumulated Bones in a Pliocene Cave in Cerro Pelado, Spain

Principal Investigator: Emiliano Aguirre, Instituto Lucas Mallada, Madrid, Spain.

Grant No. 1071:   In support of a study of vertebrate remains found in a Villa-franchian cave in association with the bones of scavengers.

Cerro Pelado is a part of the Spanish highland known as "Parameras de Molina," in the Castillian branch of the Cordillera Iberica. Some 3,500 feet above sea level, it constitutes the watershed between the Tajo (Atlantic) and the Ebro (Mediterranean) basins. Cerro Pelado, composed of "suprakeuper" or early Jurassic magnesiferous limestones, is an almost unproductive stony surface with very poor soil, abandoned by its former cultivators, and limited by confluent shallow depressions—shrunken dolines refilled with colluvia—which constitute the only currently cultivated areas other than the "vegas" or valley bottoms.

There are iron-oxide mines on Triassic levels in the area near the hamlet Layna (fig. 1), and in 1966 the two brothers Maestro thought they had discovered a new iron mine in an outcropping of red sediments on one of the slopes of Cerro Pelado. The red material found on the site, since known as "La Mina," was in fact a portion of a karst deposit full of bones, jaws, and teeth of small vertebrates and containing some bones of larger mammals and stalagmites as well.

One of us (Aguirre) pointed out the site to Dr. M. Crusafont of Sabadell, Spain, and he, during my absence in Peru in 1967, obtained a number of fossils by enlarging the hole (5 by 4 by 4 meters) originally opened by the Maestro brothers. A preliminary note by Crusafont, Aguirre, and Michaux (1969) was the first notice of the site and of its importance to science. Subsequently, Crusafont and Aguirre (1971) studied the fossil Hyaenidae; and mentions of Lagomorpha, Canidae, and various rodents are to be found in several revision papers by European paleontologists. A guidebook for the First International Symposium on the boundary between the Neógene and Quaternary introduces a few corrections in the faunal list, establishes a preliminary stratigraphy of the karst deposit, defines the stratigraphic age more precisely, and shows a map of the excavations carried out in 1972 under the present grant (Hoyos et al., 1974).

A recent study by Soria and Aguirre (1976) and a note by Soria and Morales (1976) enlarge again the faunal list for this site, one of major interest for west-European Pliocene stratigraphy and paleogeography, and unique in western Europe for its abundance of remains of small mammals of this age. Other published works by Alberdi (1974), Cordy (1976), N. López (1977), Sanchiz (1977), Sanz (1977), Van de Weerd et al. (1977), Guérin and Santafé (1978) also include study and discussion on fossils recovered in the excavation here reported. Layna has, moreover, a relevant place among the most significant sites in the detailed stratigraphic subdivision of the Neogene system in international programs (Mein, 1975; Alberdi and Aguirre, 1977), and also has been taken in consideration for a discussion on the problem of implemental activity on bones by early Hominids (Rincón and Aguirre, 1974).

Aims

Apart from taxonomic and phylogenetic determinations of the Layna fauna in comparison with the geographic and faunal evolution during the Pliocene in western Europe—with the opportunities for correlations provided by the richness of the deposit in both small and large mammals—and detailed study of the evolution of dolines in that area and geologic stage, our primary intention was to contribute an approach to faunal studies that would provide answers (even from fragmentary fossils) to such paleoethological questions as implemental activity on bones by very early hominids.

In fact, one of the alternative interpretations most favored by authors critical of Dart's theories on implemental activity on bones by australopithecines is that the hyaena is responsible for both the accumulation and fragmentation of skeletal remains. More recently, Read-Martin and Read (1975) have attempted a method of faunal analysis to test the hypothesis of scavenging practices in australopithecines through comparison with Bronze Age hunters' remains. We started, similarly, with the study of assemblages of broken bones which could be attributed mainly to scavengers, with similar climatic, taphonomic, and chronostratigraphic circumstances.

Methods

One of us (Aguirre, 1973) proposed the methodological grounds for an approach to the question of the bones in very early prehistory, having earlier developed experimental evidence in a study of broken elephant bones (Biberson and Aguirre, 1965).

Briefly, we needed more comparative and correlative morphological and statistical studies, using broken bones assembled under different, well-

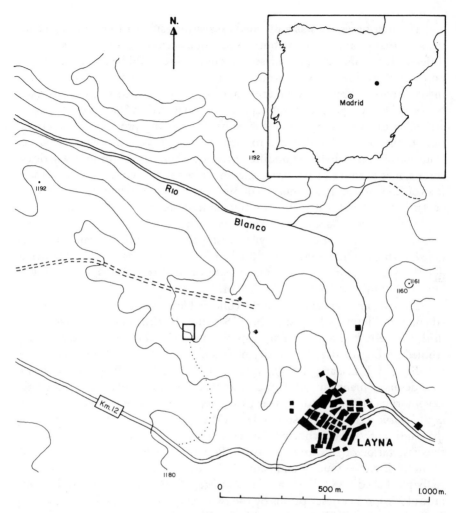

FIG. 1. Cerro Pelado site, Layna, Soria Province, Spain. (The Cerro Pelada site is
represented on this map by the open rectangle northwest of Layna.)

defined, and experiment-tested conditions by controlled "natural" and human agents of different kinds. One of the analytical approaches is similar to
that utilized by Read-Martin and Read (1975). It is also our intention to develop the analyses on dimensions and proportions of samples of fragments of
herbivore bones established by Rincón and Aguirre (1974).

The first necessity was a planned excavation, similar to that of archeologists, so that patterns of distributions and/or association, frequencies, etc., at different levels and topographic sections of the site could be analyzed. Where portions of red breccia were exposed in the soil, the area was divided into 2-meter squares. First, all vegetation and soil were cleaned from the surface, bones and breccia pebbles being separated and labeled "S" (surface). The usual archeological tools and methods were used as the dig proceeded. Good portions of the matrix, identified as to square and level, as well as the overburden from the old pit, labeled as undifferentiated, when passed through a series of three sieves produced such objects as small bones of medium-sized animals, jaws of Rodentia and Lagomorpha of different sizes, insectivores, and portions of reptiles, isolated teeth, and postcranian fragments of small mammals.

A few blocks containing mixed bones of a skeleton of *Hipparion* were extracted in their actual position with plaster casts. For others, gauze impregnated with celoidine acetate was used to fix more-or-less complete bones in delicate states of preservation; other features were consolidated in situ with "Primal," a mixture of glue and alcohol.

The paleontological study of the collected fossil vertebrates was distributed among different scholars: F. Borja Sanchiz, Instituto Lucas Mallada, Madrid, has described a piece of an amphibian (1977); the Chelonians are being studied by E. Jiménez, University of Salamanca, yet unpublished, and other reptilians by J. L. Sanz (1977), Instituto Lucas Mallada: the presence of *Varanus* deserves mention. N. López, Instituto Lucas Mallada, has studied the Lagomorpha (1977), finding a very early representative of the rabbits, *Oryctolagus laynensis;* the initial list of rodents (Michaux, 1969) has been increased by the studies of various scholars. The description of a rhinoceros is included in the dissertation of J. Santafé, Instituto Provincial de Paleontología, Sabadell, Spain (in litt.; see Guérin and Santafé, 1978). The carnivores have been partially published by D. Soria and E. Aguirre (1976) and D. Soria and J. Morales (1976), other descriptions by the two last authors on the Felidae, and by Soria on the Hyaenidae, being still unpublished. The study of ruminants is not yet finished.

The fossil specimens were freed from the matrix in the laboratory of restoration of the Sección de Paleontología de Vertebrados y Humana, Instituto Lucas Mallada, Madrid, Spain, either by mechanical techniques, when possible, or with acetic acid (10 percent) when the matrix was cemented by carbonate. The paleontologists cooperating in the project were in many cases able to examine the materials existing in other collections, namely Instituto de Paleontología, Sabadell, University of Utrecht, University of Montpellier, University of Lyon.

Alfredo Pérez González, Manuel Hoyos, and Felix Míguez conducted a regional stratigraphical survey in which field observations and aerial photography were used to detect possible relationships between the development, deposition, and fauna of the Layna karst with respect to its position in the sequence of geodynamic events from late Miocene to early Pleistocene (in Hoyos et al., 1974; Aguirre et al., 1976).

In the excavation, successively appearing horizons were labelled differently in each of the various sections to avoid confusion, since the horizons change horizontally and are locally dislocated. After discussion between the undersigned and the above-mentioned geologists, a guide-level was developed to aid in correlating the diverse sections, and a stratigraphic interpretation of the main area was proposed by M. Hoyos (op. cit.).

J. Ontañón and M. C. Cid visited the site and identified soil structures in definite clayish fossil-bearing levels (verbal communication).

Results and Preliminary Conclusions

The vertebrate fossil taxa so far identified are:

Amphibia:	cf. *Bufo* sp.
Reptilia:	*Varanus* sp.; Serpentes; Chelonia
Mammalia:	
Insectivora:	*Episoriculus gibberodon; Erinaceus* sp.
Primates:	*Dolichopithecus ruscinensis*
Rodentia:	*Stephanomys donnezani; Castillomys crusafonti; Occitanomys brailloni; Anthracomys meini; Apodemus* sp. cf. *dominans; Apodemus jeanteti; Rhagapodemus frequens; Blancomys neglectus; Ruscinomys europaeus; Trilophomys pirenaicus; Mimomys stehlini; Sciurus* sp.; *Hypnomys* sp. *Eliomys intermedius; Hystrix* sp.
Lagomorpha:	*Prolagus* aff. *michauxi; Prolagus ibericus; Oryctolagus laynensis; Lepus* sp.
Carnivora:	*Nyctereutes donnezani; Ursus ruscinensis; Euryboas lunensis; Hyaena pyrenaica; Lynx* aff. *issiodorensis; Machairodontini* gen.; *Felini* gen.
Artiodactyla:	*Gazella borbonica; Leptobos* sp.
Perissodacytla:	*Hipparion fissurae; Dicerorhinus miquelcrusafonti.*

Several of these taxa are new, as the mentioned species of rabbit (the most primitive one in present knowledge; N. López, 1977), the three-toed horse (Crusafont and Sondaar, 1971, revalidated by Alberdi, 1974), the rhinoceros (Guérin and Santafé, o.c.), and the genus *Blancomys,* which has also been recognized in other sites of eastern and southern Spain and Sète, France—all corresponding to the younger levels of the Ruscinian mammal age (Van de Weerd et al., 1977). Other species are new for Spain, among which *Ursus ruscinensis.* The studies of some of the collected fossil vertebrates have allowed revision of materials from Perpignan and other European Pliocene localities, as in the case of the canid (Soria and Aguirre, 1976), the bear (Soria and Morales, 1976), and the hyaenas (Soria, thesis unpublished), resulting in new taxonomic arrangements and relevant phylogenetic conclusions.

Most of the above-mentioned medium- to large-size mammals are known from Serrat d' en Vacquer, the type-site of the Ruscinian faunas, which characterize the early Pliocene in continental environments (Pliocene starts with the Zanclean transgression, while the regressive stages characterized by the early *Hipparion* fauna pertain to the former cycle, or system, i.e., Miocene). Nevertheless, the new—and here dominant—hyaena *Euryboas lunensis* will characterize a younger (i.e., Villafranchian) fauna; Cerro Pelado stays as its earliest appearance in the present record, notwithstanding being an immigrant.

The association of the two Hyaenidae listed above is unique and should validate the assumption that the Layna fauna is intermediate between those of Perpignan and Les Étouaires. These two well-known faunas of the French Pliocene are separated in terms of absolute age by no more than one million years (my); since the accepted K/A age for Les Étouaires is 3.4 my, and the base of the Pliocene (Zanclean) is dated as 5.1 my; above 1,000 feet of early Pliocene marls we must consider the Montpellier bay tilting, and the marine Pliocene sands with a mammalian fauna older than that of Perpignan, so that Perpignan could be inferentially dated approximately between 4.5 and 4.0 my. On the other hand, the faunal succession Hautimagne—Montpellier sands—Montpellier Palais de Justice and Celleneuve constitutes the Neogene mammal unit MN14, using the nomenclature introduced in Madrid 1974 and Bratislava 1975 (Alberdi and Aguirre, 1977); while Perpignan, and the later Sète, constitute the French types of unit MN15. Les Étouaires, with Vialette, Tuluçesti, Villarroya, and many other sites in central and eastern Europe are clearly correlated and grouped into unit MN16. Mein (1975) includes the karst deposit faunas of Balaruc II and Seynes in this MN16.

The advantage of La Mina site is the coincident concentrations of small and large mammals. Several species of carnivores, like the *Nyctereutes* and the

Ursus, are represented by markedly progressive populations related to those of Perpignan. Consequently, the position of La Mina between MN15 and MN16 may be a matter of discussion and compromise. What is clear is that toward the end of the early Pliocene some major changes in small mammal faunas precede those changes in the large mammal associations which characterize the late Pliocene or "early Villafranchian" fauna.

The karst deposit of La Mina in Cerro Pelado has not yet been excavated in its totality. Only in the old pit did the Maestro brothers reach a depth of some 4 meters. The maximum depth reached by us in the 1972 excavation may be hardly more than 2.5 meters. We have no record of faunal change along the sequence of horizons, but there is evidence of at least two or three different cycles in karst construction with at least an intercalated episode of roof collapse. The cycles presently discovered cannot represent a total time interval of more than 250,000 years. The opening of this karst follows a major phase of tectonic activity, which deforms a surface established late in early Pliocene (Aguirre et al., 1976), and may correspond to the sea-level decrease or basin sinking recorded in the Mediterranean by Selli and Fabri (1971), to which an age of approximately 4 my is attributed. This is the age suggested by the analysis of the Layna fauna in the above paragraphs. At best, our knowledge of the record and development of the Cerro Pelado Pliocene karst is only partial. The actual exposure of the bone-bearing breccia is caused not by a collapse of the cave ceiling but by differential erosion of the dolomitic limestones into which the doline was opened and subsequently filled.

PALEOGEOGRAPHY

A comparison with 12 European mammal faunas ranging from late late Miocene (Messinian, probably less than 6.5 or 6 my) to Early Pleistocene (no less than 1.5 my) reveals that the composition of European Pliocene faunas is constant enough, exceptions probably being due to depositional or taphonomic conditions. Perhaps a more profound analysis could detect, in several cases, particular conditions of climate either deteriorating or improving— cases with more than one (exceptionally three) species of Cercopithecoidea (Aguirre and Soto, 1978) in a single fauna, or rich in diversified Cervidae and Bovidae, or abundant in proboscidians. In the case of Cerro Pelado, the lack of proboscidians in the fauna can be explained by the nature of the site, but the absence of Cervidae and Suidae can only be attributed to particular climatic or geographic conditions. The evidence of Mediterranean red soil and of the abundance of gazelles and hipparions with scavengers living on these, as well as the variety of rodents and lagomorpha, speaks in favor of a low grassland or savanna spotted with bushes. In a high temperate climate with seasonal rains, conditions may have permitted a soil to develop on high rock plateaus, favoring the formation of dolines and local water springs in an inland plateau. This interpretation is consistent with the warmer climatic conditions and high carbonate content of Mediterranean sea sediments recorded by Cita and Ryan (1972) around 4 my before the present (B.P.). We emphasize that near this date there are several changes of terrestrial polarity, with repeated normal periods during the Gilbert paleomagnetic epoch of reversed polarity. This, hypothetically, may have affected the high rate of evolution and faunal changes recorded between Perpignan (indirectly estimated at 4.5 my) and Vialette (recorded as K/A 3.8 my B.P.); but successive migrations from Asia must be responsible for the relay of continental faunas in the Pliocene of Europe.

PALEOECOLOGY, PALEOETHOLOGY

Most of the work planned to obtain conclusions from this study has only just been initiated. It will be necessary to excavate squares in the site almost untouched at this point, and to expand the excavation. The test "walls" separating excavated squares must be carefully sampled for more detailed sedimentological analysis, and comparative investigation must be undertaken into possible differences in the content of small vertebrates according to variances in level and/or in sedimentary material. At present we can state that:

1. The mixed samples from surface and from overburden are not sufficient for reliable statistical analysis.

2. The fossils recovered in controlled levels of excavation are also insufficient; only level C_2 has yielded abundant material for mammal macrofauna. We may assume that most of the fossils recovered in former uncontrolled excavations came from this same level.

3. The composition of the Layna fauna has been compared, separately, for mid- to large-size Carnivora (Ursidae, Canidae, Hyaenidae, Felidae) and for mid- to large-size predated vegetarians (Proboscidea, Ceratomorpha, Hippomorpha, Suiformes, Cervidae, Bovidae, Primates), with five Pliocene faunas of Europe, plus one of latest Miocene and one of earliest Pleistocene.

The four families of Carnivora are the same represented in the circum-Mediterranean region in that time, and the number of species (6) equals the average and is near the mode (7) for those 14 representative and rich faunas. The Layna fossil assemblage can be considered as very likely corresponding to the original biocenosis.

4. On the other hand, the proboscidians are absent: this can be satisfactorily explained by a selection in the taphocenosis due to the karstic (fissure filling) nature of the site. The Suiformes are also missing, as they are in the 50 percent of those faunas even richer in diversity of species; this may be due to

ecological conditions such as aridity rather than to any particular bias in the fossil assemblage. Primates are present, as in the other 7 assemblages represented in figure 2.

But Layna is unique in the total absence of Cervidae; this fact can only be satisfactorily explained by an actual lack of those ruminants in the biocenosis represented due to ecological conditions, namely, a high-temperate steppe with seasonal rain enough for the soil and karst development, and for a vegetation able to sustain the recorded variety of animal species.

5. A late Miocene phase of aridity is succeeded in the early Pliocene by a forestation reflected in the Montpellier faunal composition. The Perpignan fauna again indicates drier conditions; and the aridity reaches a climax in the Layna steppe. New forest expansion from Kvabebi in Transcaucasia to Les Étouaires in central France characterizes the early Villafranchian that is the beginning of late Pliocene (ca. 3.5 my B.P.), while Villarroya in Spain reflects a comparatively higher aridity; later, in late Pliocene or early Pleistocene, La Puebla de Valverde reflects drier conditions than Saint-Vallier and Le Coupet, almost contemporary, where forest and grassland species are well balanced. In Middle to Upper Pliocene sites of the same age, the rate of individuals of cervids in relation to bovids is 5/1 in France and 1/4 in Spain (Heintz, 1970). To explain this disproportion, consideration must be given to differences in latitude and also in altitude above sea level and in other geographical conditions such as climate, either continental (as in Layna) or with marine influence.

6. The percentage of estimated number of individuals of carnivores over the total of medium- to large-size mammals is very high in Layna, much larger than commonly in surface sites. Such disproportion can be influenced by the particular taphocenotic conditions of the site, but may also reflect the utilization of the site as a living place by one or more species of carnivores, particularly by *Euryboas lunensis*. This hyaenid, usually rare in the Villafranchian sites elsewhere, is uniquely abundant in Cerro Pelado; it shows peculiar felid-like adaptations, as if it occupied, at least occasionally, the ecological niche of a large predator. The taphonomic condition of the extremely abundant rodents in this site has not yet been clarified: it may be diverse in nature.

7. The largest population representation is that of small bovids. The relative frequencies (percentages) of occurrence of the different parts of the skeleton differ, in a preliminary approach, from that of Makapansgat (according to the figures published by Read-Martin and Read (1975).

8. With the above-mentioned doubts in mind, we note that the frequency figures for hind limbs of herbivores are similar to those for forelimbs, while Read-Martin and Read (1975) record remarkably higher frequencies of forelimb remains in all categories of prey animals. We should emphasize the al-

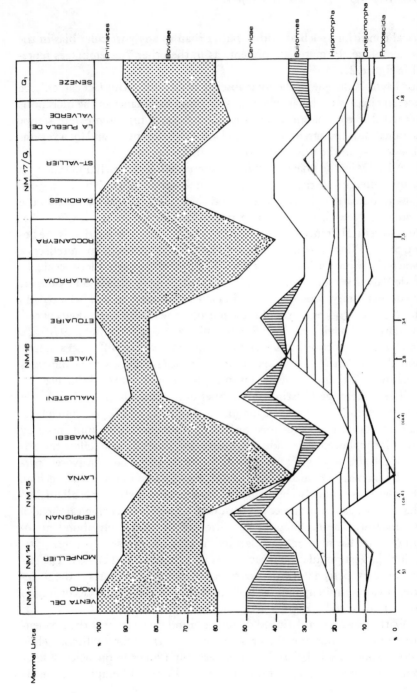

FIG. 2. Distribution of percentages of vegetarian predable species, according to different orders in 14 rich mammalian faunae from Europe in stratigraphical sequence. Figures above refer to "Mammal Units" (Mein, 1975), and figures below to K-Ar dates.

most total absence of skull material, and the abundnce of *calcanei* and *tali,* considered both absolutely and comparatively with the site of Makapansgat.

9. Teeth marks are evident on many bone fragments. Rincón and Aguirre (1974) have statistically tested the proportions of a sample of fragments; these differ significantly from a sample from Olduvai I, where human activity on bone, strictly implemental, is beyond question in the opinion of one of us (Aguirre).

Remarks

There is material not yet processed, mostly from screening both overburden and sediments controlled by squares in surface and subsurface levels. And since 1972 we have had no material means of pursuing the excavations in Cerro Pelado. Let us hope to obtain some financial support for this purpose in the near future. Only after more complete and intensive excavations can we expect to have samples of sufficient size for the statistical analyses necessary to provide answers to the proposed problems of paleoethology and taphonomy.

REFERENCES

AGUIRRE, EMILIANO
1973.   Industries ostéïques anciennes: méthode et un essai de typologie.   Actes VIII Congr. Internat. Sci. Préhist. et Protohist. (Beograd), vol. 2, pp. 57-68.
1974.   Correlación continental-marino en el Neógeno mediterráneo.   Estudios Geológicos, vol. 30, pp. 655-660.
AGUIRRE, E.; DIAZ MOLINA, M.; and PEREZ GONZALEZ, A.
1976.   Datos paleomastológicos y fases tectónicas en el Neógeno de España. Trabajos sobre Neógeno-Cuaternario (Secc. Paleont. Vert. y Hum., Instituto Lucas Mallada, Madrid), vol 5, pp. 7-30.
AGUIRRE, E., and SOTO, E.
1978.   *Paradolichopithecus* in La Puebla de Valverde, Spain: Cercopithecoidea in European Neogene stratigraphy.   Journal of Human Evolution, vol. 7, pp. 559-565.
ALBERDI, M. T.
1974.   El genero *Hipparion* en España.   Trabajos sobre Neógeno-Cuaternario (Secc. Paleont. Vert. y Hum., Instituto Lucas Mallada, Madrid), vol. 1, pp. 7-139.
ALBERDI, M. T., and AGUIRRE, E.
1977.   Round-Table on mastostratigraphy of the W. Mediterranean Neogene. Trabajos sobre Neogeno-Cuaternario (Madrid), vol. 7, pp. 1-48.
BIBERSON, P., and AGUIRRE, E.
1965.   Expérience de taille d'outils préhistoriques dans des os d'élephant. Quaternaria, vol. 7, pp. 165-183.

CITA, M. B., and RYAN, W. B. F.
1972.   The Pliocene record in deep-sea Mediterranean sediments. 5, Time scale and general synthesis. *In* "Initial Reports of the Deep Sea Drilling Project," Ryan, W. B. F., et al., eds.   U. S. Government Printing Office, Washington, D. C.

CORDY, J. M.
1976.   *Essai sur la microévolution du genre "Stephanomys" (Rodentia, Muridae).* Thèse. Université de Liège, 351 pp.

CRUSAFONT, M., and AGUIRRE, E.
1971.   *Euryboas lunensis* et *Hyaena donnezani* associées en Espagne, dans le gisement . . . de Layna (Soria).   Compt. Rend. Acad. Sci. Paris, vol. 273, pp. 2476-2478.

CRUSAFONT, M.; AGUIRRE, E.; and MICHAUX, J.
1969.   Un nouveau gisement de Mammifères d'âge Villafranchien inférieur . . . découvert à Layna (Soria, Espange).   Compt. Rend. Acad. Sci. Paris, vol. 268, no. 17, pp. 2174-2176.

CRUSAFONT, M., and SONDAAR, P.
1971.   Une nouvelle espèce d'*Hipparion* du Pliocène terminal d'Espagne. *Paleovertebrata,* vol. 4, pp. 59-66.

GUÉRIN, C., and SANTAFÉ-LLOPIS, J.
1978.   *Dicerorhinus miquelcrusafonti* nov. sp., une nouvelle espèce de Rhinocéros (Mammalia, Perissodactyla) du gisement pliocène supérieur de Layna (Soria, Espagne) et de la formation pliocène de Perpignan (Pyrénées-Orientales, France),   Geobios, vol. 11, pp. 457-491.

HEINTZ, E.
1970.   Les Cervidés villafranchiens de France et d'Espagne.   Mémoires Muséum nat. d'Hist. naturelle, vol. 22, pp. 5-303.
1975.   La gazelle (Artiodactyla, Mammalia) et l'âge de la faune de la Puebla de Almoradier (Toledo, Espagne). *In* Actas I Coloq. Internac. Biostratigrafía Neógeno Sup. y Cuatern. Inf., M. T. Alberdi and E. Aguirre, eds.   Trabajos sobre Neógeno-Cuaternario (Secc. Paleont. Vert. y Hum., Instituto Lucas Mallada, Madrid), vol. 4, pp. 83-90.

HOYOS, M.; AGUIRRE, E.; MORALES, J.; PEREZ GONZALEZ, A.; and SORIA D.
1974.   Yacimiento de Layna. *In* "Libro-Guía," Aguirre, E., and Morales, J., eds.   Coloq. Internac. sobre Biostratigrafía Contin. del Neógeno Sup. y Cuaternario Inf. (Secc. Paleont. Vert. y Hum., Instituto Lucas Mallada, Madrid), pp. 137-48.

LÓPEZ MARTÍNEZ, N.
1977.   Nuevos Lagomorfos (Mammalia) del Neógeno y Cuaternario español. Trabajos sobre Neógeno-Cuaternario (Instituto Lucas Mallada, Madrid), vol. 8, pp. 7-46.

MEIN, P.
1975.   Proposition de biozonation du Neogène méditerranéen à partir des mammifères. *In* Actas I Coloq. Internac. Biostratigrafía Neógeno Sup. y Cuatern. Inf., M. T. Alberdi and E. Aguirre, eds.   Trabajos sobre Neógeno-Cuaternario (Secc. Paleont. Vert. y Hum., Instituto Lucas Mallada, Madrid), vol. 4, p. 112.

MICHAUX, J.
1969.   Muridae (Rodentia) du Pliocène supérieur d'Espagne et du Midi de France. Palaeovertebrata, vol. 3, pp. 1-25.
READ-MARTIN, C. E., and READ, D. W.
1975.   Australopithecine scavenging and human evolution: An approach from faunal analysis. Current Anthrop., vol. 16, pp. 359-368.
RINCÓN, A., and AGUIRRE, E.
1974.   Analyse comparative et discriminante des assemblages de fragments osseux pour vérification d'hypothèse d'action culturelle. 1er. Colloque International sur l'industrie de l'os dans la Préhistoire, Abbaye de Sénanque, pp. 111-118. Editions de l'Université de Provence.
SANCHIZ, F. B.
1977.   La familia Bufonidae (Amphibia, Anura) en el Terciario europeo. Trabajos sobre Neógeno-Cuaternario (Madrid), vol. 8, pp.75-112.
SANZ, J. L.
1977.   Presencia de *Varanus* (Sauria, Reptilia) en el Plioceno de Layna (Soria). Trabajos sobre Neógeno-Cuaternario (Madrid), vol. 8, pp. 113-126.
SELLI, R., and FABRI, A.
1971.   Tyrrhenian: A Pliocene deep-sea. Accad. Naz. Lincei, Cl. Sci., vol. 50, pp. 104-116.
SORIA, D., and AGUIRRE, E.
1976.   El Cánido de Layna. Revisión de los *Nyctereutes* fósiles. Trabajos sobre Neógeno-Cuaternario (Secc. Paleont. Vert. y Hum., Instituto Lucas Mallada, Madrid), vol. 5, pp. 83-116.
SORIA, D., and MORALES, J.
1976.   Hallazgo de un úrsido en el yacimiento de Layna (Soria). Trabajos sobre Neógeno-Cuaternario (Secc. Paleont. Vert. y Hum., Instituto Lucas Mallada, Madrid), vol. 5, pp. 129-140.
VAN DE WEERD. A.; ADROVER, R.; MEIN, P.; and SORIA, D.
1977.   A new genus and species of the Cricetidae (Mammalia, Rodentia) from the Pliocene of South-Western Europe. Proceedings of the Koninklijke Nederlandse Akademie van Wetenschappen, Amsterdam, series B, vol. 80, pp. 429-440.

EMILIANO AGUIRRE
DOLORES SORIA
JORGE MORALES

A Survey of Pastoral Nomadism in Northeastern Afghanistan

Principal Investigator: Asen Balikci, University of Montreal, Montreal, Quebec, Canada.

Grant No. 1085A: For a cultural-ecological study of Pashtoon pastoral nomadism in Afghanistan.

In February 1973 I undertook anthropological field research among a semisedentary lineage of Pashtoon pastoralists in northeastern Afghanistan. From the beginning I pursued two parallel aims: (1) a purely research objective concerning the processes of ecological adaptation and forms of economic integration of the social unit under investigation; (2) selection of actors and settings for the production of an anthropological film describing lineage social activities. During five field trips in 1973, 1974, and 1975 I was continuously assisted by my counterpart Bayazid Atsak, lecturer in Pashtoon linguistics at Kabul University. Thanks to the friendly cooperation of the pastoral nomads, their sedentary relatives, and various Afghan officials, we were able to gather substantial data on settlement and migratory patterns, kinship organization and family styles, exchange practices inside and outside bazaars, "tribal" leadership and rivalries between chiefs, and other aspects.

The research method adopted combined participant observation and much interviewing of single informants with the use of cassette tape recorders. The systematic use of tape recorders allowed for continuity in the flow of information together with maximal accuracy in transcription. As unit of observation and analyses we selected the family of the lineage chief characterized by great diversity in economic endeavors with family members distinctly specializing in pastoralism, trading, or agriculture. We were able thus to relate dynamically these three main segments of Afghan economy within the framework of a single social unit.

During May and June 1975 the filming phase of our integrated project took place, sponsored by the National Anthropological Film Center of the Smithsonian Institution, with funds from the National Endowment for the Humanities and technical help from the National Film Board of Canada. We exposed 80,000 feet of film mainly on the social life of the pastoral nomads along the migration trek. An educational film has been edited by the National Film Board of Canada.

Summary of Field Observations

The lineage studied is named Lakernkhel and belongs to the Andir tribe with origins in Ghazni Province. At the end of the last century the Lakernkhel together with other Ghilzai tribes revolted against the authority of Amir Abdur Rahman and suffered greatly. They lost their sheepflocks and were relocated on the southern slope of the Hindu Kush as landless laborers. Gradually they reconstituted their flocks and started caravaneering with their camels between Peshawar and the Oxus Valley, across the Khawak Pass where they had traditional grazing rights. At first they acted simply as transporters and later they became traders. Their route crossed the sparsely populated Nahrin Valley on the northern side of the Hindu Kush Range. About 50 years ago the Lakernkhel started acquiring agricultural land in Nahrin and thus was initiated their gradual sedenterization.

The Lakernkhel actually form a maximal lineage, and today no elder is capable of establishing a genealogical link with the apical ancestor. This maximal lineage comprises four distinct named lineages, and each lineage is divided into several minimal sublineages each including a number of extended families. At present practically all the Lakernkhel reside in three neighboring villages. Lineages tend to behave as residential clusters and so do minimal sublineages. Pastoral activities are concentrated nowadays in only one lineage, the others remaining completely sedentary following loss or sale of sheep at different times of recent history. The settlement pattern reveals typically a cluster of mud houses for the poor or fortified, walled compounds for the rich, grouped together in a nucleated village with terraced paddy fields all around.

There are two types of agriculture in the area: The first involves irrigated fields located at the bottom of the valley and crisscrossed by an elaborate network of canals and secondary ditches. Two crops are obtained here with manure as fertilizer crucially important to the success of the second crop. The principal cultigens are wheat, maize, and green plants for animal feed with rice, onions, and potatoes of lesser importance. There are irrigated timber plantations but practically no orchards. Vegetable gardens are few and small. The second involves dry fields with no irrigation, located on hill slopes at far distance from the village. Here wheat and barley are cultivated and occasionally some watermelons. Naturally there is only one crop, in spring, and productivity varies enormously from year to year according to precipitation.

The traditional pastoral nomadic pattern has been replaced by the practice of transhumance. The following arrangement is typical. A fraternal joint family consists of two married brothers and their descendants. The first brother is

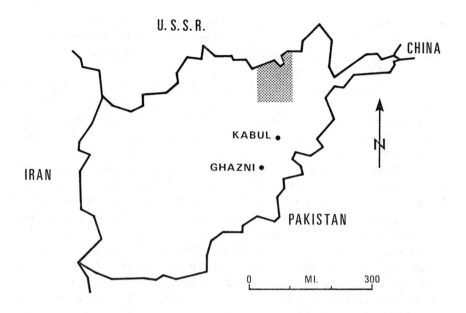

FIG. 1. Map of Afghanistan showing field research area.

fully sedentary and will spend all his time with agricultural activities. The second brother is devoted to the care of the sheep. Early in March a lambing camp is established in the lowlands where the lambs are born. His wife and daughters will milk the ewes, make yogurt in a skin bag, and shake it into butter. The flock remains under the constant control of the shepherd and his assistant with the owner exercising only a right of supervision. The family lives under a large black tent made of goat hair. Early in June the lambs are strong enough and the long migration to Khawak Pass begins. Caravans and flocks have to cross large rivers, rapids, deserts, narrow gorges, and snowy mountain passes until they reach their traditional camping site at an elevation of nearly 3,000 meters, where they remain until the middle of August after the sale of the male lambs. Once back home in the lowlands these families be-have as sedentary villagers completely separated from the flocks which remain under the care of the shepherds.

Trading is another activity that keeps many Lakernkhel men extraordi-narily busy. In a sense practically any villager or pastoralist, rich or poor, is primarily a trader. The long pastoral migration is first a trading expedition. The propensity to trading is so strong that practically anything can be bought or sold provided that the price is right. Hoarding of wheat or onions, sale of camels to distant lands, speculation on sheep, and even accumulation of antique carpets and guns are common practices. The Lakernkhel are distinguished by their bazaar mentality.

There is a clearly visible class structure among the Lakernkhel. The people distinguish five classes defined exclusively in terms of wealth: *der mur* and *mur* are the very rich flock owners, with rich land; *guzarani* are self-sufficient without debts; *kampagala* are dependent upon the rich and have debts; while the *miskin* are hopelessly poor and stand no chance to better their position.

The Pashtoons conceive relations as dyadic alignments between one superordinate and one subordinate person (Barth, 1959, p. 41). This strongly determines the form of economic integration (above the household level), which is performed by a multiplicity of dyadic contracts some of which involve service prestations like sharecropping and others, capital transactions such as joint commercial ventures. Thus in the practice of *mazaribat* the capital owner gives a fixed sum to a trader for a determined period and for a precise commercial transaction. At the end of the contract the trader returns the capital and half of the benefit to the moneylender. At the regional level the bazaar functions as economic integrator.

The propensity for spending is extremely limited for all classes and is in harmony with attitudes of organized acquisitiveness. The very nature of the dyadic economic contracts places the capital holder in a strongly privileged position with the capacity to translate wealth into political influence and vice versa.

In the field of kinship the Lakernkhel are strongly patrilineal and patrilocal, polygyny being limited to the rich and very rich. The extended family has a developmental cycle of its own with the centrally important father-son relationship gradually replaced by an alignment of brothers. In time the relations between brothers frequently become ambivalent and a process of fission is initiated. This ambivalence grows dramatically among first cousins *(tirbur)*, with the derivative term *tirbgana* defining a general pattern of competitiveness, rivalry, and hatred. On the other hand, relations with affines are generally amiable and frequently exploited for political reasons.

Some persons among the very rich act as chiefs. They advise people on a variety of situations, solve directly complicated cases, and manipulate the assembly of elders to their own benefit. Further, they can order their subordinates to beat a recalcitrant, and in dealings with government officials they act as brokers in power. Social atmosphere is permeated with the spirit of rivalry: "a woman is the rival of a woman, a shepherd is the rival of a shepherd, a chief is the rival of a chief." Rivalry among chiefs is incessant, their political fortunes rapidly changing, and this creates a highly unstable balance of power at the regional level.

At the end of our research among the Lakernkhel, I decided to check some of my conclusions with observations among a purely nomadic unit, the Wuluki Shinwari, used as control group. The Wuluki migrate between the Indus Valley and the Kohi Baba Range in central Afghanistan and own no land whatsoever. In their case the poor nomads after loss of sheep become agricultural laborers, while the rich sheepowners remain nomads and distribute sections of their flock among poorer lineage members under the *mazaribat* system. If we conceive of pastoral society as a pyramid with the rich at the top and the poor at the large base we can assert that in the case of the Wuluki the apex is closed; the rich remain within the pastoral group while the poor filter through the bottom of the pyramid. In the case of the Basseri studied by Barth (1961) the pyramid is open at both ends with the very rich showing the tendency to sedenterize as landowners and the poor becoming laborers, while the bulk of the tribe (the central segment of the pyramid) continues on the migration trek. As for the Lakernkhel, the whole lineage has sedenterized while a fraction of the rich at the apex of the pyramid practices transhumance, retaining thus the benefits of a dynamic pastoral economy and continuously reaffirming its superordinate position within the lineage class structure.

REFERENCES

BARTH, FREDRIK
  1959.   Political leadership among Swat Pathans.   London School Econ. Monogr. Social Anthrop., no. 19, 144 pp.   University of London: Athlone Press.
  1961.   Nomads of South Persia: The Basseri tribe of the Khamseh Confederacy, 159 pp., illus.   Little, Brown & Co., Boston; Oslo University Press; Humanities Press, New York.
BALIKCI, ASEN
  1978.   Buzkashi.   Natural History, February, pp. 54-63.
NATIONAL FILM BOARD OF CANADA
  1979.   Sons of Haji Omar. 56-minute film in color with English commentary. Co-produced by the Smithsonian Institution and the National Film Board of Canada.

ASEN BALIKCI

Biological Colonization of a Newly Created Volcanic Island and Limnological Studies on New Guinea Lakes, 1972-1978

Principal Investigators: Eldon E. Ball, Australian National University, Canberra City, Australia, and Joe Glucksman, Department of Agriculture, Stock and Fisheries, Konedobu, Papua New Guinea.

Grant Nos. 1117, 1386, 1649, and 1898.   To study the biogeography of New Guinea lakes and biological colonization of a recently formed volcanic island.

Biological Colonization of Motmot

Newly created islands such as Surtsey, or islands devastated by volcanic eruptions such as Krakataua, provide rare opportunities for studying biological colonization and succession. In 1969, during an Alpha Helix Expedition to Papua New Guinea, we had the good fortune to discover an island created by a volcanic eruption the previous year (Bassot and Ball, 1972). This island, Motmot, which has a circumference of about 800 meters, lies about 3 kilometers from the nearest shore of Lake Wisdom, a large fresh-water lake filling the central caldera of Long Island, Papua New Guinea (fig. 1 a, b). Since 1969 we have returned to Lake Wisdom in 1971, 1972, 1973, 1974, 1976, and 1978, with support from the National Geographic Society in 1972, 1974, 1976, and 1978.

FINDINGS, 1969-1974

From 1969 to 1972 Motmot contained a small crater lake (fig. 2) around which plants grew in steadily increasing numbers. The number of species of higher plants on Motmot rose from 1 in 1969 to 14 in 1972. Sedges of the genus *Cyperus* were the most successful colonists by any measure. From the distribution and composition of the flora it appears likely that most of the plants originated from seeds carried to the island by black ducks (*Anas superciliosa* Gmelin).

The invertebrates that had succeeded in colonizing Motmot by 1972 can be grouped as follows: (1) A strand fauna of small beetles, ants, and bugs de-

89

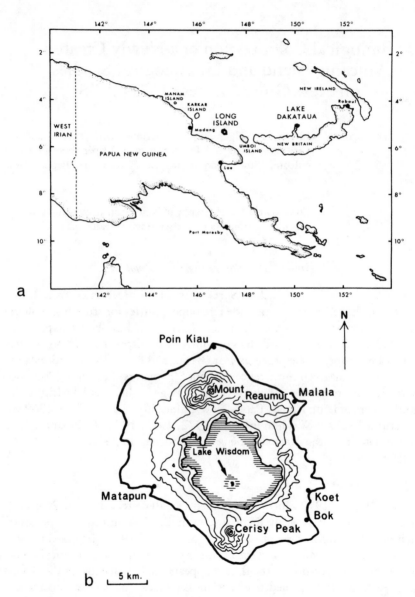

FIG. 1.   a, Map of Papua New Guinea showing the locations of Long Island and
Lake Dakataua; b, map of Long Island showing mountain peaks, villages, and the
location of Motmot in Lake Wisdom.

FIG. 2.   Motmot in 1972 (a) from Lake Wisdom and (b) from the air.

pendent, either directly or indirectly, on the input of organic material from off-island; (2) ants, which were established in fair-sized colonies among vegetation around the crater pond; (3) earwigs and lycosid spiders which by 1972 were found in almost all parts of the island; and (4) staphylinids and collembolans found beneath a hardened algal crust on the margins of the crater pond.

The lycosids were present in 1969 while the other organisms appeared in later years. Black ducks have been nesting on the island since 1969, while swallows (*Hirundo tahitica* Gmelin) were first noted nesting there in 1971.

In 1973 the north end of Motmot erupted repeatedly creating a volcanic cone where the crater lake had been and there were several lava flows, which considerably enlarged the island. By November, only three mature plants were left on the island, all of a single species of sedge. In spite of the death of large numbers of individuals, however, the fauna that survived at the south end of the island was more diverse than in preceding years.

By November 1974 the number of sedges had increased and there were immature plants of various species scattered about the island, although many of these appeared unlikely to survive. The south end of the island had heated up considerably and faunal diversity was reduced from that of 1973.

The diversity of life on Motmot in 1974 was considerably reduced from its 1972 peak. However, Motmot has been periodically appearing and disappearing since the 1940's, with periods of activity alternating with longer quiescent periods, and so it seems likely that the present activity will eventually die down, and when this does occur the lava flows of 1973 will prevent the rapid erosion of the island that has occurred in the past. Also, we have now accumulated enough information about the biology of the species involved, or potentially involved, in colonization to ask more quantitative questions.

FINDINGS, 1976

The major physical change in Motmot since 1974 was the creation of a new group of collapsed craters on the east side of the island (fig. 3). Water temperatures all around the island have increased, especially at the north end where further eruptive activity appears likely. The circumference of the island, measured at the water line, has decreased approximately 100 meters owing to wave erosion.

Plants have increased on Motmot in terms of both number of species and number of individuals. On the basis of two nights spent on Motmot, it appears that the black duck was again the means by which seeds were carried there since the plants were found in the areas where the ducks spend the night. One unusual feature of the plant distribution this year was the almost total absence of seedlings on the beaches of Motmot, where they are normally common.

Although the number of invertebrate species on Motmot remained essentially the same, the number of individuals was considerably reduced from 1974 owing to the increased temperature of the substratum. Some parts of the island were covered by a hard pavement of sulphur which cements stones to the ground and on which nothing can grow, while in other areas the surface material was loose but simply too hot for organisms to live. Lycosid spiders and earwigs, formerly found over much of the island, occupied greatly reduced areas and the same was true of the strand fauna.

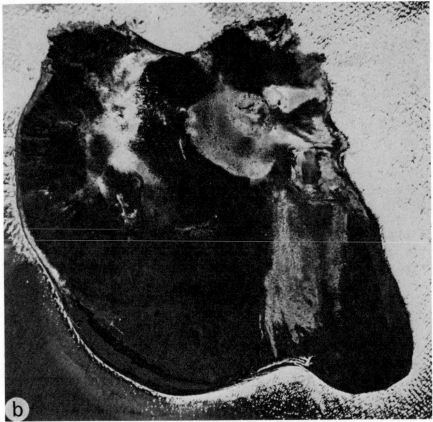

FIG. 3.   Motmot in 1976, to show the changes since 1972.

Black ducks, swifts, and waders were all abundant on Motmot in 1976. There were nine active black duck nests and the nesting behavior of the ducks was particularly interesting in that it seemed so nonadaptive. The lava flows of 1973-1974 created many small caves on Motmot and the ducks were using these for nesting sites. However, many of the nests are separated from the water by a considerable distance of very rough terrain and even if the ducklings manage to cross this they are then faced with a belt of water so hot that they cannot cross it (the bodies of four ducklings that apparently died trying to do so were found during our stay). Therefore, in spite of the large number of eggs present on Motmot it appears that very few ducklings survive much beyond hatching.

FINDINGS, 1978

Preparation for this Long Island expedition was more difficult than in the past because of the departure from New Guinea of my former collaborator, Joe Glucksman. The study was carried out as planned except for the aerial photography; no photographs could be taken on the way to Long Island because of the lack of an adequate aircraft and none on the return because of the lack of pilots.

The survey of Motmot was carried out in conjunction with Chris McKee of the Volcanological Observatory, Rabaul, who spent the first week on Long Island with me. We managed to make all the measurements desired although we were hampered by high winds for most of this period. Chris then left the island and for the next four days I walked around Long Island along the seashore collecting further information. By the time I had completed this circuit of the island, the wind had died so I returned to Motmot for an additional two days of observation.

Physically, Motmot has not changed a great deal during the past 2 years. There has been some further wave erosion and the island has generally cooled a bit. Plant diversity and numbers have increased considerably over 1976. Six trees that were small in 1976 have now reached a height of ca. 2 meters, the main sedge bed has expanded considerably, the north crater now contains abundant ferns, and there are new clumps of grass in several areas at the north end of the island.

In contrast to the flora, the fauna appears to have reached a plateau. Two species of spiders, earwigs, midges, and ants are still present in considerable numbers. However, the formerly rather diverse strand fauna has now been greatly reduced probably mainly owing to the heating of the beaches.

Limnological Studies of New Guinea Lakes

Associated with our studies on Motmot, a volcanic island in Lake Wisdom, we have studied the physical properties and biota of the lake on each of our visits to Long Island, Papua New Guinea. Our interest was initially attracted by the apparent simplicity of the fauna of the lake (Bassot and Ball, 1972), and this eventually led to a more detailed and wider ranging study.

Lake Wisdom is a large almost circular caldera lake with a maximum width of about 12.9 kilometers and an area of about 86 square kilometers. We have constructed an approximate bathymetric map of the lake to depths of 300 meters from fathometer transects. Repeated sounding in the deeper parts of the lake gave depths in the vicinity of 360 meters. The surface of the lake is approximately 190 meters above sea level, and inasmuch as water samples from near the bottom of the deepest part of the lake are fresh, the basin is apparently sealed. The level of the lake shows annual fluctuations of 1-1.5 meters.

We selected six stations in different parts of the lake for comparison with one another and for monitoring changes in the physical and chemical properties of the lake over time. The surface temperature of Lake Wisdom has been a very constant 28°C. on all our visits, and the temperature falls gradually to about 27°C. at 60 meters. One of the most unusual features of the lake is the relatively high O_2-saturation clear to the bottom, as shown by Winkler titrations, the presence of mollusks and midge larvae in the deepest part of the lake, and the total absence of any smell of H_2S from bottom samples. Light penetration in the lake varies greatly depending on the amount of rainfall and the volcanic activity of Motmot.

There is a relatively low standing crop of phytoplankton in the lake, but a fair diversity and abundance of benthic algae exist. The zooplankton consists of two species of cladoceran and one species of notonectid. There are one species of sponge, four species of mollusks, and a relatively small number of aquatic insects including chironomids, dragonfly and damselfly larvae, and the larvae of a pyrallid moth. Water birds, such as ducks and waders, are relatively abundant. The lake also contains one or more crocodiles, but how they arrived there is a mystery.

It seems likely that the caldera that now contains Lake Wisdom was formed between 1700 and 1750 (Ball and Johnson, 1976) and the depauperate fauna of the lake can probably be accounted for mainly by the short period of time since the creation of the lake and by the distance from sources of colonists.

In 1974 we investigated Lake Dakataua, West New Britain (see fig. 1), in order to try to evaluate our theory that the simple flora and fauna of Lake Wisdom could be accounted for mainly by the recency of the lake's creation. Lake Dakataua is a caldera lake about 285 kilometers away from Lake Wisdom in an area with a basically similar flora and fauna. The principal difference between the lakes is Lake Dakataua's greater age of at least 1,000 years.

A peninsula produced by volcanic activity subsequent to caldera collapse divides Lake Dakataua into two basins connected by a narrow channel. The surface of the lake is ca. 76 meters above sea level, the surface area 48 square kilometers and the maximum depth ca. 120 meters. On arrival, we made a bathymetric survey and on the basis of this six stations were chosen for further measurements and collecting. The bathymetric data have since been converted into an approximate bathymetric map.

The lake was alkaline throughout, with surface pH 7.6-8.2; acidity increased with depth to pH 7.1-7.5. Surface temperatures were ca. 31°C. There were thermoclines at 22 and 40-45 meters, with a minimum temperature of 26.8°C. at 80 meters. Oxygen saturation curves paralleled the temperature curves with sharp gradients at 22 and 40-45 meters, but there was no measurable O_2 from 80 meters downwards. Living organisms were common in dredge hauls to 20 meters but were not found in those from greater depths. Carbon dioxide concentration rose steadily from 1.4 mg/l at the surface to 19.6 mg/l at 80 meters.

In contrast to Lake Wisdom, shallow water areas supported dense beds of mixed aquatic plants. Invertebrates collected included 2 species of sponge, a rotifer, an ostracod, 6 species of mollusks, 7 species of cladoceran, a copepod, 8 species of bugs, 2 species of caddis-flies, 10 species of dragonflies and damselflies, 2 species of beetles, and 7 species of chironomids. In addition there were frogs (2 species) and crocodiles. Water birds, including grebes, ducks, and waders, were abundant.

As can be seen from the above descriptions, the two lakes differ in several important ways. The greatest physical differences are in size and depth, with Lake Wisdom being approximately twice as large and three times as deep as Lake Dakataua. A second major difference is in oxygenation, with Wisdom having high O_2 levels to the bottom and life on the bottom, while Dakataua is anoxic below 80 meters and apparently lacks a bottom fauna. One of the most striking biological differences between the two lakes is the presence of extensive beds of rooted aquatic plants—these are entirely absent from Lake Wisdom—in Lake Dakataua. As we had predicted, diversity in almost all categories of organisms was higher in Lake Dakataua. We attribute this to two factors: greater age and greater proximity to sources of colonists. Most of the species found in Lake Wisdom are also found in Lake Dakataua, so their absence from the former could be due either to chance or to poor colonizing ability.

REFERENCES

BALL, ELDON E.
   1977.   Life among the ashes.   Australian Natural History, vol. 19, no. 1, pp. 12-17.
BALL, ELDON E., and GLUCKSMAN, JOE
   1975.   Biological colonization of Motmot, a recently created tropical island. Proc. Roy. Soc. London, ser. B, vol. 190, pp. 421-442.
   1978.   Limnological studies of Lake Wisdom, a large New Guinea caldera lake with a simple fauna.   Freshwater Biol., vol. 8, pp. 455-468.
   1979.   A limnological survey of Lake Dakataua, a large caldera lake on West New Britain, Papua New Guinea, with comparisons to Lake Wisdom, a younger nearby caldera lake.   Freshwater Biol., vol. 9 (in press).
BALL, ELDON E., and JOHNSON, R. W.
   1976.   Volcanic history of Long Island, Papua New Guinea.   Pp. 133-147 *in* "Volcanism in Australia," R. W. Johnson, ed.   Elsevier, Amsterdam.
BASSOT, J. M., and BALL, ELDON E.
   1972.   Biological colonization of recently created islands in Lake Wisdom, Long Island, Papua New Guinea, with observations on the fauna of the lake.   Proc. Papua New Guinea Sci. Soc., vol. 23, pp. 26-35.
DIAMOND, J. M.
   1977.   Colonisation of a volcano inside a volcano.   Nature, vol. 270, no. 5632, pp. 13-14.

ELDON E. BALL
JOE GLUCKSMAN

Swaziland-Fennoscandia Trondhjemite Collecting Expedition, 1972

Principal Investigator: Fred Barker, U. S. Geological Survey, Denver, Colorado.

Co-investigators: Hugh T. Millard, Jr., and Zell E. Peterman, U. S. Geological Survey, Denver, Colorado.

Grant No. 1054:   For a study of trondhjemites: their development and the earth's early sialic crust.

The major objectives of this project were to collect both trondhjemitic gneisses and relatively pristine intrusive trondhjemites and the associated mafic rocks from the very old (3.6 billion years or older) gneiss terrane of southern Africa and from the Proterozoic part of the Baltic Shield and the adjacent Paleozoic Caledonides. In all, 48 samples were collected; 14 powders already analyzed for major elements by the Institute of Geological Sciences for the Geological Survey of Swaziland were retrieved from storage; and an additional 14 samples of gabbro, anorthosite, syenite, and potassic granite were collected for a satellitic investigation. Localities and rock units include the following: Swaziland—the Ancient Gneiss Complex and Granodiorite Suite (the latter actually is a gabbro-diorite-tonalite-trondhjemite suite); Transvaal, Barberton Mountain Land—tonalite diapir, Bosmanskop syenite, and siliceous tuff of the Sandspruit Formation; Rhodesia—Rhodesdale Gneiss, and gneiss and amphibolite of Gwenoro Dam; Finland—the hornblendite-gabbro-diorite-tonalite-trondhjemite suite of the Uusikaupunki-Kalanti area, and gabbro, anorthosite, syenite, and potassic granite of the Ahvenisto and Suomenniemi massifs; Norway—diorite, trondhjemite, leucogranodiorite, and pillow greenstone of the Støren, Innset, and Meldal areas; and Sweden—gabbro, anorthosite, and potassic granite of the Nordingrå area. Local geologists were very cooperative and extremely helpful in the collecting. Three of these have joined us as co-investigators and will share authorship of papers to be published: Professor D. R. Hunter, former director of the Geological Survey of Swaziland and now at the University of Natal, Pietermaritzburg; Dr. Atso Vorma, Geological Survey of Finland; and Dr. Thomas Lundqvist, Geological Survey of Sweden.

Analyses of the samples are nearly completed. U. S. Geological Survey chemists have performed major-element analyses of 58 whole-rock samples and 2 mineral separates. Dr. Millard has finished minor-element analysis by instrumental neutron activation of 51 samples, and 14 remaining ones are now (November 1975) going through their last computer run. Dr. Peterman has determined Rb, Sr, and Ba abundances in 62 samples and has dated the trondhjemitic intrusives of Norway and southwestern Finland by Rb-Sr isotopes. Sixty samples have been analyzed for their $^{18}O/^{16}O$ ratios by Dr. Irving Friedman (Barker, Friedman, et al., 1976). Dr. Joseph G. Arth joined us as a postdoctoral associate early in 1973 and assumed major responsibility for the Uusikaupunki-Kalanti suite. He has analyzed 20 samples for rare-earth elements by the isotope-dilution technique. Dr. M. Tatsumoto soon will attempt to date the Ancient Gneiss Complex of Swaziland by analysis of U and Pb isotopes of single grains of zircon. A new two-stage mass spectrometer has been installed and brought into operation (October 1975) in the Denver laboratories of the U. S. Geological Survey for this sort of work. The oldest "date" obtained so far on this complex is 3,390 million years, but this figure almost certainly represents resetting of an older age, for the initial $^{87}Sr/^{86}Sr$ ratio of this isochron (R. Davies, 1971, unpubl. Ph. D. thesis, Univ. of the Witwatersrand) is a high value of 0.7048. Ages recently obtained by several laboratories on nearby, geologically simpler (and perhaps younger?) rocks of 3.5 to 3.6 billion years suggest that the Ancient Gneiss Complex *may* be the oldest rock exposed at the earth's surface. Samarium-neodymium dating also will be tried in mid-1976 in Dr. Tatsumoto's laboratory, following developmental work on lunar samples.

The general problem of trondhjemites is a significant one. Trondhjemites, or oligoclase/albite granites of low color index, were treated by geologists as an unusual but unimportant type of granite for many years after V. M. Goldschmidt named them in 1916. In the late 1960's, however, several independent lines of evidence began to suggest that trondhjemites are not genetically related to granitic rocks but that they are generated in much different environments and from different parental materials. From plate tectonics we knew that Phanerozoic trondhjemites typically form at continental margins above Benioff zones and that their volcanic equivalents form in island arcs. Second, published descriptions of Archean gneiss terranes indicated that foliated and compositionally banded trondhjemitic gneisses are one of the most important petrographic types in these samples of the earth's early crust. Third, geochemical studies of Sr isotopes and minor elements began to suggest that trondhjemites are derived from the mantle and that they differ from many granites in containing little or no earlier crustal material. These results led us in an early paper (Barker et al., 1969) to compare the 1.8-billion-year-old trondhjemitic and originally volcanic Twilight Gneiss of Colorado to the

40-million-year-old trondhjemitic dacite of Saipan. By early 1972 we had suggested (Barker and Peterman, 1974) that generation of trondhjemite from mantle sources in the early Precambrian may have been the key process in the formation of earth's protocontinents. We realized then that solutions to early continental evolution required much more geochemical data on three different types of trondhjemitic rocks. These are the Archean gneiss complexes, such as that in Swaziland; the well-developed and well-preserved intrusive suites, such as those in Finland and Norway; and the compositionally equivalent volcanic rocks, as found in Saipan, Tonga, Shasta volcano, and elsewhere in oceanic and continental-marginal environments. Thus, this grant from the National Geographic Society was used to obtain important samples of the first two types.

Preliminary results on the Ancient Gneiss Complex, Swaziland, show marked heterogeneity of minor elements in both the siliceous gneisses and metabasalts. The older part of this complex, termed the bimodal suite by Hunter (1974), consists largely of light-gray trondhjemitic gneiss and metabasalt. In view of very similar major-element compositions, these gray gneisses surprisingly show two distinct types of rare-earth patterns. Three samples show the common pattern of depletion of heavy rare earths and no Eu anomaly; two show marked negative Eu anomalies and *flat* (or nondepleted) heavy rare-earth patterns; all five show moderate enrichment of the light rare earths. The first type of pattern may arise from generation of this magma by partial melting of quartz eclogite at minimum depths of 60 kilometers (Arth and Hanson, 1972, 1975). The second type, however, has not previously been found in the Archean and could result either from differentiation (by settling of plagioclase, pyroxenes, and hornblende) of low-K andesitic liquid at shallow levels (less than 40 kilometers) or by shallow partial melting of gabbro or diorite. The only other known occurrences of this type of pattern in the Precambrian are of two Proterozoic bodies in Colorado and New Mexico—the Twilight Gneiss and trondhjemite of Rio Brazos (Barker, Arth, et al., 1976). It is significant that such patterns are common in young island-arc dacites, as at Saipan and Tonga. The metabasalts of the Ancient Gneiss Complex give flat rare-earth patterns, like those of other Archean basalts. But they are enriched in Rb, which probably was introduced during one of the several metamorphic events that affected the bimodal suite.

The younger part of the Ancient Gneiss Complex, as determined by field relations and termed the metamorphite suite by Hunter (1974), consists largely of quartz monzonitic gneiss and metabasalt, and of only minor trondhjemite gneiss. The quartz monzonitic gneiss probably formed by the partial melting of earlier siliceous bimodal gneisses; their rare-earth patterns show negative Eu anomalies and similar slopes but greater abundances than the patterns of the depleted type of bimodal gneiss. The metabasalt is similar to modern low-K oceanic type. Thus the origin of the Ancient Gneiss Complex is not simple; it probably formed by partial melting and differentiation of mafic or intermediate sources in the mantle, when heat flow through a thin crust was high. Our results on the geochemistry of these gray gneisses and amphibolites of the Kaapvaal craton demonstrate that these rocks definitely are not laterally equivalent to, and were not derived from, the rocks of the Barberton greenstone belt—as a number of workers have speculated.

Rare-earth patterns of the two Archean gneisses from Rhodesia are highly depleted in the heavy rare earths. These rocks, probably about 3.6 billion years old (as inferred from their similarity to a dated trondhjemite from near Shabani), thus formed either by partial melting of an eclogite parent or by settling of hornblende and biotite from a gabbro-diorite-tonalite liquid series. (See the following discussion on Finland.)

The gabbro-diorite-tonalite-trondhjemite suite of the Uusikaupunki-Kalanti area, southwestern Finland, is the most compositionally complete one known. Rb-Sr dating of these rocks by Drs. Peterman and Arth gives an age of 1,930 million years, which places them early in the Sveco-Karelian orogeny. Our 18 major-element analyses and the 13 published by Hietanen (1943) show a range of SiO_2 content of 42 to 73 percent. The parental liquid was a mildly alkaline, wet but not saturated, tholeiitic partial melt of mantle origin that contined about 50 percent SiO_2. Dr. Arth's computer modeling program indicates that hornblende was the predominant early liquidus phase; its settling produced hornblendite cumulates and dioritic liquid. As the SiO_2 percentage of the liquid increased to the high 50's, biotite also started to settle out, producing hornblende-biotite diorite. Continued settling of hornblende and biotite caused the liquid to become tonalitic, and plagioclase and quartz became liquidus phases. As the SiO_2 percentage of the liquid approached the middle 60's, and as hornblende continued to settle out, there is a strong possibility that plagioclase and quartz floated upward in the magma chamber and produced trondhjemite of 69 to 73 percent SiO_2. The details are presented by Arth et al. (1978). In this differentiation process the abundances of K, Rb, and rare earths in the liquid go through a unique series of maxima when SiO_2

FIG. 1.   Rare-earth contents (normalized to abundances in chondrites) of hornblende gabbro, hornblende-biotite diorite, biotite tonalite, and trondhjemite of the Uusikaupunki-Kalanti area, southwestern Finland. A: patterns for rocks having SiO_2 contents from 54.5 to 59.5 percent. B: patterns from rocks having SiO_2 contents from 59.- to 70.4 percent.

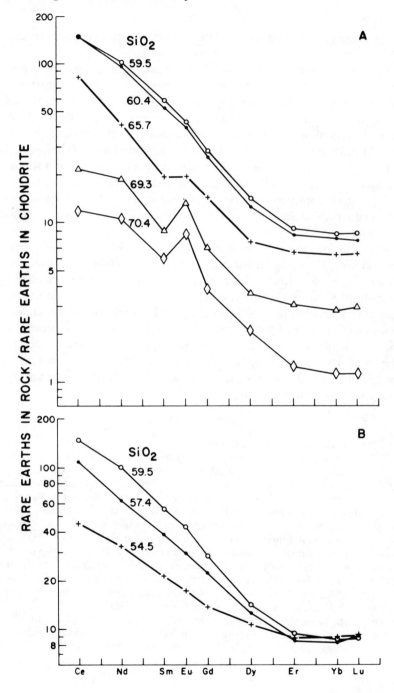

is in the range of 58 to 60 percent. The series of rare-earth patterns from 54.5 to 70.4 percent SiO_2 is shown in figures 1a and 1b.

Trondhjemite of the type area (Goldschmidt, 1916) and the cogenetic hornblende-biotite diorite show major- and minor-element compositions very similar to those of the more complete suite of Uusikaupunki-Kalanti, and we (Barker and Millard, 1979) infer a similar mode of genesis. Rb-Sr dating of these rocks (Peterman and Barker, 1976) gave the unexpectedly old figure of 560 ± 35 million years—or Middle Cambrian. Earlier workers had suggested that these rocks were intruded in the Early Ordovician—or about 450 million years ago. The stratigraphy and fossil control of the strata enclosing the trondhjemites are imperfectly known, but work in progress by several groups of Norwegian and British geologists should resolve the problem in the next several years.

In conclusion, the samples of trondhjemitic rocks and related types collected on this 1972 expedition are providing a welcome addition to our knowledge of these suites. Work of this same nature is continuing on our domestic samples, which include the Archean of Wyoming and Minnesota, the Proterozoic of Colorado and New Mexico, the Devonian of California, and the Mesozoic of California, Oregon, and Idaho. But we face several more years of work, at least, in determining the geochemical parameters that are diagnostic of the parentage and mechanisms of generation of the various types of trondhjemite and dacite. These investigations, we hope, will shed light on generation of the early crust of the earth.

REFERENCES

ARTH, JOSEPH G., and HANSON, GILBERT N.
 1972.   Quartz diorites derived by partial melting of eclogite or amphibolite at mantle depths.   Contr. Min. and Petr., vol. 37, pp. 161-174.
 1975.   Geochemistry and origin of the early Precambrian crust of northeastern Minnesota.   Geochim. et Cosmochim. Acta, vol. 39, pp. 325-362.
ARTH, JOSEPH G.; BARKER, FRED; PETERMAN, ZELL E.; and FRIEDMAN, IRVING
 1978.   Geochemistry of the gabbro-diorite-tonalite-trondhjemite suite of southwest Finland and its implications for the origin of tonalitic and trondhjemitic magmas.   Journ. Petrol., vol. 19, pp. 289-316.
BARKER, FRED; ARTH, JOSEPH G.; PETERMAN, ZELL E.; and FRIEDMAN, IRVING
 1976.   The 1.7- to 1.8-b.y.-old trondhjemites of southwestern Colorado and northern New Mexico: Geochemistry and depths of genesis. Bull. Geol. Soc. Amer., vol. 87, pp. 189-198.
BARKER, FRED; FRIEDMAN, IRVING; HUNTER, D. R.; and GLEASON, J. D.
 1976.   Oxygen isotopes of some trondhjemites, siliceous gneisses, and associated mafic rocks.   Precambrian Res., vol. 3, pp. 547-557.

BARKER, FRED, and MILLARD, HUGH T., JR.
1979.   Geochemistry of the type trondhjemite and three associated rocks, Nor-
         way.   Pp. 517-529 *in* "Trondhjemites, Dactites, and Related Rocks,"
         649 pp., F. Barker, ed. Elsevier Scientific Publishing Co.,
         Amsterdam.
BARKER, FRED; PETERMAN, ZELL E., and HILDRETH, ROBERT A.
1969.   A rubidium-strontium study of the Twilight Gneiss, West Needle
         Mountains, Colorado.   Contr. Min. and Petr., vol. 23, pp. 271-282.
BARKER, FRED, and PETERMAN, ZELL E.
1974.   Bimodal tholeiitic-dacitic magmatism and the early Precambrian crust.
         Precambrian Res., vol. 1, pp. 1-12.
GOLDSCHMIDT, VICTOR M.
1916.   Geologisch-petrographische Studien im Hochgebirge des südlichen
         Norwegens, IV: Übersicht der Eruptivgesteine im kalendonischen Ge-
         birge zwischen Stavanger und Trondhjem.   Vid.-Selsk. Skr., I. Math.-
         Nat. Klasse, no. 2, pp. 75-112.
HIETANEN, ANNA
1943.   Über das Grundgebirge des Kalantigebietes im südwestlichen Finnland.
         Finlands Comm. Géol. Bull., vol. 130, pp. 1-105.
HUNTER, DONALD R.
1974.   Crustal development in the Kaapvaal craton, I: The Archean.   Precam-
         brian Res., vol. 1, pp. 259-294.
PETERMAN, ZELL E., and BARKER, FRED
1976.   Rb-Sr whole-rock age of trondhjemites and related rocks of the south-
         western Trondheim region, Norway.   U. S. Geol. Survey Open File
         Report 76-670, 17 pp.

FRED BARKER

The Thermal Significance of the Nest
of the Sociable Weaver

Principal Investigator: George A. Bartholomew, University of California, Los Angeles, California.

Grant Nos. 1060, 1085B, 1247. In support of studies on the ecological role of the nest of the sociable weaver in the Kalahari Desert.[1]

The following report is adapted in part from papers we published in 1975 and 1976, in *Ibis,* where references to other related publications may be found.

The sociable weaver *(Philetairus socius)* of the arid parts of southern Africa builds the largest and most spectacular of all bird nests. Unlike most other members of the family Ploceidae, which build large colonies of separate nests, many pairs of sociable weavers occupy a single compound nest, each bird contributing not only to the building of the individual chambers but also to the maintenance of the structure as a whole. A single nest may be 5 to 6 meters long, 3 to 4 meters wide, and 1 to 2 meters thick, weigh more than a metric ton, and be occupied by 100 or more pairs of birds. A large nest is the work of many generations of weavers and may be used at least for decades and sometimes for a century or more (Collias and Collias, 1964).

Friedmann (1930) and Collias and Collias (1964) provide general descriptions of the nest of the sociable weaver, but the most detailed account of the nest and the natural history of the species is included in an unpublished doctoral dissertation by Maclean (1967). In our account we refer to the total structure as "the nest" and the individual units within it as "nest chambers"; the components of the nest apart from the chambers we call the "matrix." The nest is a nonwoven, thatchlike structure composed of grass stems and twigs

[1] This study was supported by a grant from the National Geographic Society and carried out with the cooperation of the National Parks Board of South Africa and the Percy FitzPatrick Institute of African Ornithology. We are grateful to Dr. G. de Graaf, Dr. W. Roy Siegfried, Dr. A. S. Brink, Mr. Christoffer LeRiche, and Mr. and Mrs. I. J. P. Mayer for advice and assistance, and for help and hospitality during our stay at the Kalahari Gemsbok National Park. Dr. Gordon L. Maclean facilitated our fieldwork by introducing us to the avifauna of the Kalahari and the biology of the sociable weaver. Maxine White and Elizabeth Bartholomew aided in the collection of data.

and is situated in a tree or on a man-made structure such as a utility pole. The chambers formed within the nest are more or less spherical and communicate with the exterior by a short, vertically directed, tubular passageway. All the chambers have individual entrances and are completely separate from one another, although they are usually packed closely together. All chambers open to the underside and form a single, more or less horizontal layer that follows the contours of the nest. The top of the nest is thatched with a coarse layer of larger grass stems and twigs. Adults of both sexes and even juvenile weavers continuously insert more grass stems into the nest and add sticks to the top. Old chambers are filled in, and the nest gradually expands both vertically and horizontally; it may ultimately enlarge to the limits that the tree in which it is located can support. Sociable weavers are abundant in the Kalahari Desert of southern Africa, an area characterized by intense summer heat, sparse and erratic rainfall, and cold dry winters during which air temperatures may fall to $-10°C$ at night. Breeding may occur at any season, including the winter months of July and August (Maclean, 1970), and is associated with the effects of rainfall rather than photoperiod.

Winter Observations, 1972

Previous investigators have dealt primarily with the natural history and behavior of this remarkable species. Our study examines the role of the nest in ameliorating the effects of the physical environment on the birds occupying it. We made our winter measurements and observations in the vicinity of Twee Rivieren in the Kalahari Gemsbok National Park of South Africa during July and August 1972, when many sociable weavers were breeding.

Air temperatures within nest chambers were measured by implanted thermistors with long leads. Temperatures at different levels within the matrix were measured with thermocouples implanted at intervals in fiberglass fishing-pole stock that was thrust through the nest. External air temperatures in the shade and daily minimum and maximum temperatures were monitored by instruments attached to the nest tree.

Our study coincided with a rainless winter season in the Kalahari, with warm days and cold nights. The nest chambers and matrix were dry, with no sign of trapped moisture or fermentation. Air temperatures ranged from $-2.5°$ to $24.5°C$, with a typical 24-hour cycle spanning $20°$ to $25°C$.

We concentrated on a typical large nest containing 70 chambers and an estimated population of 150 weaverbirds. (One nest chamber was taken over for roosting by a pair of pigmy falcons, *Polihierax semitorquatus,* that apparently fed on insects and did not prey on the birds.) In this large nest some chambers were unused, some were occupied by weaverbirds with eggs or young, and others were used only for roosting, with as many as 4 or 5 adults in a single chamber.

Our measurements (fig. 1) show that the nest buffers the effects of external environmental temperature. External air temperature fell greatly at night, and air temperature in unoccupied nest chambers paralleled this fall but remained 4° to 6°C higher. Evidently some heat was transferred from nearby

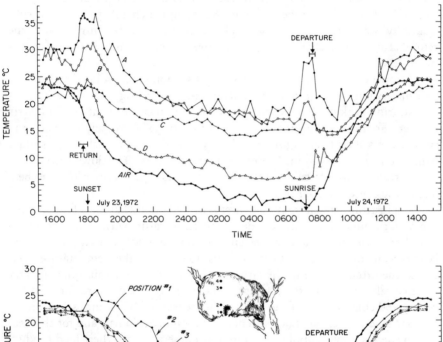

FIG. 1. Graph of 24-hour record of temperatures associated with large sociable-weaver nest. *Upper:* Air temperature in chambers (*A, B,* and *C* occupied by roosting birds; *D,* unoccupied chamber). *Lower:* Temperature through the nest matrix; numbers represent the relative positions of the thermocouples in the structure.

occupied nests as activity in these was reflected in higher temperatures in the empty chambers; this phenomenon was especially conspicuous during activity at sunrise and sunset.

Active nest chambers may be continuously occupied by at least one adult · or may be frequently visited by them. Activity was marked by sharp rises in chamber temperature, and when adults returned en masse to roost at sunset the temperature within occupied chambers rose appreciably, despite falling external temperature—in one such case we recorded a nest chamber temperature of 37°C, 23° above the ambient. All occupied chambers remained substantially warmer than the external air throughout the night, and the temperature in each chamber depended directly on the number of birds occupying it.

Temperatures taken through a vertical section of the solid thatch of the nest matrix followed the daily cycle of air temperature (fig. 1). At night, however, during peak occupancy, the birds' heat production maintained a matrix temperature higher than that of the external air. The coarsely thatched top surface cools sharply at night, but the layer of air trapped below the surface helps retard heat loss from the denser internal matrix. The downward-facing orientation of entrance tubes of the nest chambers (fig. 2) also minimizes heat loss to the colder exterior below.

We instrumented a small new nest with only four chambers for comparison with the much larger mature nest. The temperature within an unoccupied chamber of the small nest was essentially the same as external temperature both day and night (fig. 3). Occupied chambers had higher temperatures, but not to the extent shown in the large nest. The larger nest thus offers greater thermal advantages to its occupants, and recruitment of more birds to the colony and enlargement of the nest should be favored by natural selection.

Sociable weavers are both sedentary and highly colonial, and for this reason an adequate food supply is required in a desert region where food production (seeds, insects) is erratic because of scant and seasonal rainfall. In this situation, a strategy that reduces the over-all energy requirements of a population should be favored by natural selection. Many other birds achieve such energy conservation by using natural cavities or man-made structures for their nesting and roosting (Kendeigh, 1961). Our observations suggest that the extraordinarily large, cumulative nest of the sociable weavers ameliorates the effects of environmental temperature on the birds' metabolism and thus diminishes their impact on the local food supply. This could result in (1) increased environmental carrying capacity, (2) increased population density, (3) reduction in time spent foraging, and (4) independence from seasonality of reproduction.

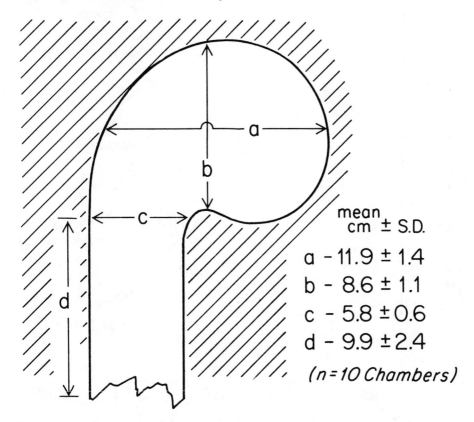

mean
cm ± S.D.

a - 11.9 ± 1.4
b - 8.6 ± 1.1
c - 5.8 ± 0.6
d - 9.9 ± 2.4

(n = 10 Chambers)

FIG. 2.   Confirmation and dimensions of sociable-weaver nest chamber. The nest
matrix is represented by cross-hatching.

All adults in a colony participate in the construction and maintenance of
the nest throughout the year. The insulative effectiveness of the nest increases
with size, and the metabolic heat input increases with the number of occupants. Hence, the larger the population and the larger the nest, the greater
the amount of heat conserved within the nest during the cold winter months.
As a result, such populations in large nests find it possible to breed during the
colder months provided that insect food for the young is available (as it is during the warm days). Opportunistic breeding during the winter should diminish competition with those "small nest" species that depend on similar food
resources but that can breed only during the warmer months. The development of larger and larger colonies and nests is thus self-reinforcing, and many
nests increase in size until the branches supporting them finally collapse. We

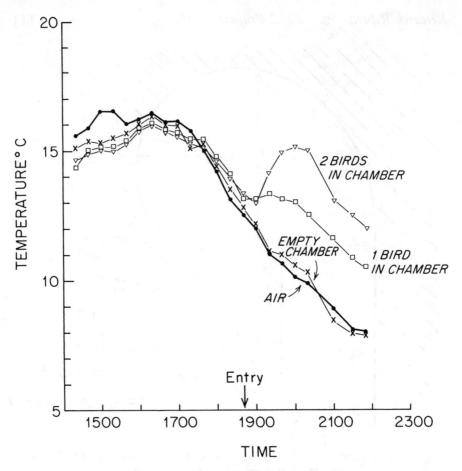

FIG. 3. Relationship of chamber occupancy to external air and chamber temperatures in a small sociable-weaver nest (total, 4 chambers) that was under construction.

have not yet had an opportunity to investigate the advantages of the large nest during the hot season but hypothesize that the insulation it provides is as advantageous in protecting against heat stress as it is in diminishing heat loss.

We have calculated the energy savings provided by the nest to the birds by estimating their standard metabolic rates from their body size (mean = 27.5 grams) and assuming their thermal neutral zone (range of ambient temperatures at which normal body temperature is maintained at rest without changing metabolic heat production) to be the same as that of other ploceids of similar size. From all-night temperature recordings of occupied nest chambers, we can approximate the number of hours spent resting at a given air temperature and the number of hours during which the birds aroused and were

active, and from these data we can estimate their nocturnal metabolic expenditure. By huddling together in nest chambers, the weaverbirds consumed 43
percent less oxygen than if they had roosted individually in the open air. Extrapolating from the data on individual chambers, we estimate that the entire
population in this colony thus saved 618 kcal per night as a result of roosting
in the large insulative nest. This figure gains ecological impact if converted
into the energetic equivalent in seeds or insects. Using standard caloric and
physiological data, we calculate that the daily savings to the weaverbird colony would be 177 grams of seeds or 239 grams of insects. If the average weight
of insects used as food were 50 milligrams, the members of the colony would
have to capture 4,500 insects per day (50/bird) to supply the energy needed to
roost in the open instead of roosting in the nest. These figures omit the energy
cost of foraging and thus are conservative estimates of energy savings.

Apart from any possible social influences and predator protection, the
large nest is energetically and ecologically advantageous. This species' nest is
also extraordinary in that it is cumulative, with each generation contributing
to its increased size and thus conferring increasing advantages to subsequent
generations over many decades—a situation that is unique within the class
Aves.

Summer Obervations, 1973

Continuing the previous study of the thermal significance of the nest of
the sociable weaver, carried out during the winter, we measured temperature
and humidity in the matrix and chambers of a large nest of this species in the
Kalahari Gemsbok National Park, South Africa, during the austral summer
in December 1973.

Air temperatures outside the nest ranged from 16° to 33.5°C but temperatures in occupied chambers varied over a range of only 7° or 8°C and remained well within the zone of thermal neutrality for a passerine bird of this
size. Compared to outside air temperatures, those within the nest matrix were
lower during the day and higher at night. Thus, the nest ameliorates the effects of external temperatures and allows maintenance inside the chambers of a
range of temperature favorable to the birds. In winter we had found up to 4 or
5 roosting adults per chamber, with some chambers left empty. In the same
nest in summer we found no more than two adults per chamber but virtually
all chambers were occupied. The principal mechanism for maintaining chambers within the zone of minimal energetic cost is changes in the number of
birds in the nest chambers at night. Humidity inside the occupied and unoccupied chambers was somewhat higher in the former but always less than that

of outside air in both situations. Air movement through the desiccated nest materials causes uptake by these materials of most of the water vapor introduced by the birds, and this moisture is dissipated to the outside during the day so that the nest remains dry.

The highly social and colonial habits of the birds and their year-round occupancy and maintenance of the nest favor a system of opportunistic breeding that may be initiated by rainfall at any season. Larger nests provide the most favorable environment for energy conservation and successful reproduction (fig. 4). Even the largest nests, however, do not prevent predation during the warm season by snakes such as the Cape cobra, which may consume all the eggs and young in all the chambers of a large nest. The effects of such heavy predation may be offset by the birds' capability for breeding during times too cold for reptile activity. It seems likely that in smaller nests such as those on telephone poles, lack of predation would favor summer breeding but thermal problems would limit breeding success in winter. In larger nests, breeding success may be lower in summer because of predation and higher in winter when reptile predation is lacking and thermal problems are minimized by the

FIG. 4.   Nest of sociable weaver.

nest structure. The large nest not only makes possible the success of the sociable weaver in desert areas, but the nest can only exist in such areas, and the species' range is thereby restricted. Higher humidity and heavier rainfall would cause fermentation within the nest mass, loss of its thermoregulatory advantages, and ultimately its decomposition and destruction. Therefore, the unique nesting system of the sociable weaver appears to be initially self-reinforcing and ultimately self-limiting.

REFERENCES

BARTHOLOMEW, GEORGE A.; WHITE, FRED N.; and HOWELL, THOMAS R.
  1976.   The thermal significance of the nest of the sociable weaver, *Philetairus socius:* Summer observations.   Ibis, vol. 118, pp. 402-410.
COLLIAS, NICHOLAS E., and COLLIAS, ELSIE C.
  1964.   Evolution of nest-building in the weaverbirds (Ploceidae).   Univ. California Publ. Zool., vol. 43, pp. 1-239.
FRIEDMANN, HERBERT
  1930.   The sociable weaverbird of South Africa.   Nat. Hist., vol. 30, pp. 205-212.
KENDEIGH, S. CHARLES
  1961.   Energy of birds conserved by roosting in cavities.   Wilson Bull., vol. 73, pp. 140-147.
MACLEAN, G. L.
  1967.   A contribution to the biology of the sociable weaver, *Philetairus socius* (Latham).   Ph.D. thesis, Rhodes University, Grahamstown, South Africa.
  1970.   The breeding seasons of birds in the southwestern Kalahari.   Ostrich, suppl. 8, pp. 179-192.
WHITE, FRED N.; BARTHOLOMEW, GEORGE A.; and HOWELL, THOMAS R.
  1975.   The thermal significance of the nest of the sociable weaver, *Philetairus socius:* Winter observations.   Ibis, vol. 117, pp. 171-179.

FRED N. WHITE
GEORGE A. BARTHOLOMEW
THOMAS R. HOWELL

A Quantitative Analysis of Middle Carboniferous Scottish Delta Deposits

Principal Investigator: Edward S. Belt, Amherst College, Amherst, Massachusetts.

Grant No. 1078:   For a statistical analysis of 320-million-year-old Carboniferous delta deposits, County Fife, Scotland.

How does one assess the possible changes that might take place from the base to the top of a stratigraphic section that consists of hundreds of repetitions of lithologies through thousands of meters of strata? This was the problem I faced in my study of a 320-million-year-old (middle Carboniferous) Scottish delta deposit. The section of strata occurs in southeast Scotland, County Fife, along the coast overlooking the city of Edinburgh across the Firth of Forth and but a dozen or so miles south of the famous golfing center of St. Andrews. There is an almost completely exposed succession of strata all around the shore of Fife. The section between Anstruther and St. Monance was selected because of its general absence of structural complexity. It was soon discovered that a repetition of lithologies (termed a cyclothem) occurred throughout the succession, such as is shown in figure 1, and after a careful analysis that determined the origin of those lithologies they were grouped into a basal shelly limestone transgressive phase (phase T of fig. 1), a shale and shale-and-sandstone (coarsening-up) progradational phase (phase P of fig. 1), and at the top an aggradational phase of various lithologies (mudrock, shaly sandstone) containing fossilized plant roots and pure plant remains (coal). Such a regular repetition of phases was combined into cyclothems (E_1, E_2, etc.) according to the "European School" method where the base of the cycle was placed at the aggradational phase contact with the overlying transgressive phase. The more traditional "American School" method (see fig. 1), was clear-

---

[1] The author acknowledges with thanks the financial support of the National Geographic Society and the American Philosophical Society for fieldwork in Scotland during 1972-73. He also thanks all those individuals mentioned in his earlier (1975) report, who were so generous with their time, laboratory facilities, and encouragement. In particular, thanks are due W. A. Read who first suggested trying the cumulative thickness plots while Schwarzacher's book was still in the proof stage and not available for general perusal. W. A. Read, W. Schwarzacher, I. H. Forsyth, and J. D. Collinson reviewed the manuscript and made helpful suggestions.

117

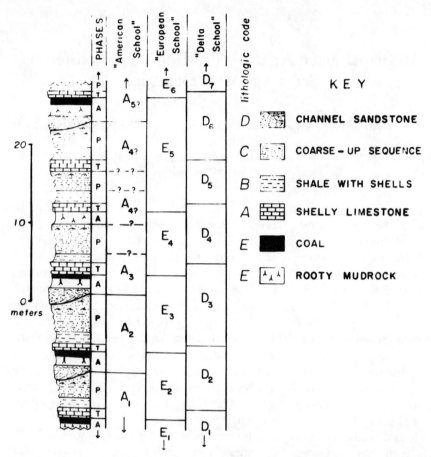

FIG. 1. Comparison of cyclothem boundaries according to different schools of thought. The smaller letters, T, P, A, refer to transgressive, progradational, and aggradational phases of cycles. The lithologic code *A, B, C, D,* and *E* is used for the purpose of comparing one cyclothem with another (e.g. *ABCDE* vs. *ACE*). The thickness scale is approximate, as the cycles shown here are generalizations of the actual cycles.

ly inadequate and the method shown as the "Delta School" will be discussed later, as it offers some possible advantages for our particular delta.

Once the lithologies were identified as to their depositional environment, they were analyzed according to the changes in the sequence of lithologies from one cycle to the next up the 1,700-meter section. This method, termed successional analysis, clearly showed (Belt, 1975, tables 2 and 3) that the most common (modal) cycle pattern in the early (lower part of the section) part of the delta was that of *ABCDE,* where the codes for the lithologies are as shown in the key on figure 1, and where the *D* unit is interpreted as a distributary sandstone. The *E* unit is interpreted as delta top levees, marshes, and/or swamps, depending on what rock type the roots occur in and on the presence of coal. In the intermediate period of delta development (the middle of the composite section), the modal cycle is *ABCE;* that is, there is no distributary sandstone between the progradational and aggradational phases. This was interpreted to signify a less active building out of the delta into the basin of deposition: *D* units or distributary sandstones became less abundant. In the later period of delta development (the upper part of the composite section), multiple transgressive and progradational phases (e.g., *ABCABCE)* are found, some showing bioturbated cross-bedded sandstone (*X* units; e.g., *ABCX-ABCE*). These multiple transgressive and progradational phases signified that multiple delta lobes developed in the basin but did not go to completion as a delta top with rooty beds. Here again was evidence of the waning effect of the delta, and the increased influence of the submarine portions of the delta. All the above I reported in a recent publication (1975).

Work in Progress (1975)

Obviously the next type of analysis that ought to be used would take into account the *thickness* of each lithology, especially the variation in thickness sequentially from oldest to youngest up the composite section. After comparing the thicknesses of each lithology *(A, B, C, D, X,* and *E),* a method that yielded no systematic results, I soon discovered that a systematic variation of thickness occurred when the various phases (A, T, and P, fig. 1) of each cyclothem were compared. Specifically, when the aggradational phase of each cycle was plotted (see fig. 2) against the total cumulative thickness in the manner of Schwarzacher (1975, pp. 245, 286), an exponential curve results, the significance of which will be explained shortly. Similarly, when the transgressive and progradational phases of each cycle are lumped and plotted (see fig. 3) against total cumulative thickness, two straight line trends become obvious (see also Schwarzacher, 1975, fig. 9.16, p. 248).

The rationale behind these types of plots is as follows: Thickness of each lithologic unit represents time, but at an unknown rate because the absolute rate of deposition of each lithology is unknown. The plots of figures 2 and 3 represent cumulative thickness of each cycle (ordinate) versus each cycle or portion of a cycle in sequence (abscissa). As each cycle is plotted at equal spaces (and simultaneously total cumulative thickness), a perfect straight line

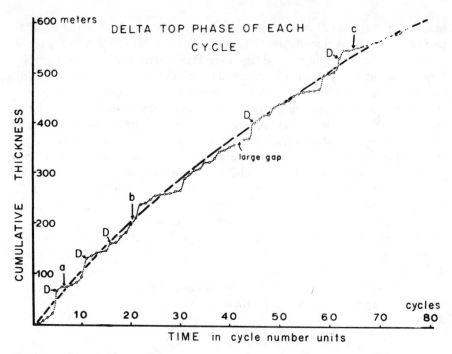

Fig. 2.   Cumulative thickness versus time for each successive aggradational phase
   throughout the composite section. Small gaps in the composite section occur at a,
   b, and c (less than 5 cycles missing). A large gap of some thirty cycles is indicated.
   Cycles containing unusually large, distributary sandstones are indicated by D.

or curve generated by the data points would indicate a *constant rate* or gradual
change in the rate of sedimentation. The "best fit" line of the data points suggests the best hypothesis for the data. A change in constant sedimentation rate
becomes immediately apparent when one "best fit" straight line passes into
another straight line with a different slope.

   The figure 2 data are interpreted as follows: Apart from a few "jumps" in
the thickness data of the aggradational phase, the majority of which are attributable to extra thick (D on fig. 2) distributary sandstones, the data fit an exponential curve. This suggests that regardless of the behavior of the transgressive
and progradational ("basin") phases of each cycle the delta top (aggradational)
phase was gradually decreasing in thickness throughout the time represented
by the composite section. This fact is quite compatible with the successional
data mentioned above (see Belt, 1975, table 3). Note there is no obvious
"break" in the data points, such as is found in figure 3. From figure 2 it is con-

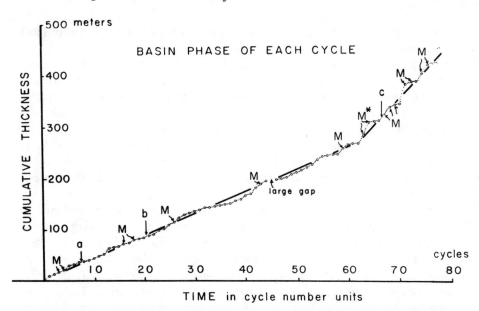

Fig. 3. Cumulative thickness versus time for each successive transgressive plus progradational phase throughout the composite section. Small gaps at a, b, and c, and
large gap in the section are as in figure 2. Cycles containing marine shells are indicated by M. The two cycles with M* are the Lower and Upper Ardross Limestones,
respectively.

cluded that the amount of sediment included in the aggradational phase of
each cycle gradually diminished with time. It will be seen that this has important ramifications when figure 4 is discussed.

Figure 3, on the other hand, shows a constant rate of sedimentation for
nearly three-fourths of the lower part of the plot, and a constant but higher
rate of sedimentation for the upper (younger) one-fourth of the plot. The
break conveniently occurs at the Lower Ardross Limestone (M*, fig. 3), a fully
marine limestone of more widespread occurrence than earlier limestones.
Shelly limestones and shales (*A* units or *B* units, by the code, fig. 1) that lie
stratigraphically below the Lower Ardross Limestone have little geographic
distribution; many shelly limestones and shales above (and including) the
Lower Ardross Limestone have much wider geographic distribution, although
some are clearly restricted. Obviously, the Lower Ardross Limestone marks a
change in style of deposition, a fact known for years by previous workers, but
only *quantitatively* demonstrated for the first time by fig. 3. Perhaps this con-

clusion can be of some use in searching for Ardross Limestone equivalents where they have not yet been reported.

Figure 4, the final plot considered here, shows the thickness of "basin" phases of each cycle plotted in its true stratigraphic position. Note that the log transform of thickness is given (because bed thicknesses are log-normally distributed; Schwarzacher, 1975, pp. 137-141), and that a large segment (between 700 and 1,200 meters on the abscissa) of the graph is not represented by data points (other than one marine point). This unmeasured segment is indicated by "large gap" in figures 2 and 3; when cumulative thickness is plotted against cycle number in figures 2 and 3, gaps make very little difference in the over-all plot when cumulating thicknesses. It is important to note that in both figures 2 and 3 the trends on each side of the "gap" remain unchanged. This is especially important in interpreting the straight-line trend of figure 3: sedimentation remained at a constant rate from the base of the composite section (0 meters on fig. 4) to the position of the Lower Ardross Limestone (approximately point 1,450 meters from the base in fig. 4). Note in figure 4 that some of the "basin" phases are nonmarine and some are marine. The distinction between these two types is based on table 1 of Belt (1975, p. 439). In brief, shelly limestones and/or shales with the marine brachiopod *Lingula* or with other marine organisms were considered "marine phases" for the purpose of figure 4. Any shelly limestones and/or shales not marine enough to contain *Lingula* were classed as "nonmarine," even though they were most likely estuarine and had some connection with the marine sea in the basin of deposition. Thus the marine "basin" phases lie along a straight line until the position of the Ardross Limestones (AL, fig. 4); above that point the thickness of marine "basin" phases is very scattered. Although the straight line is fairly flat, note that it has a slope, the right side being at about 1,500 centimeters (15 meters) and the left side being at 400 centimeters (4 meters). Note that the nonmarine basin phases (crosses on fig. 4) lie intermixed with the marine basin phases (open circles, fig. 4) in the lower 600 meters of the section, but they lie entirely below the marine basin phases in the upper 500 meters (1,200 to 1,700 meters position) of the composite section. This clearly shows the decline in the importance of the nonmarine basin phase and the increase in importance in the marine basin phase within the upper 500 meters of the section, a result predicted by an increase in depositional rate.

The next problem to assess is whether the data can be used to sort out the *relative* importance of continuous or discontinuous (a) uplift in the source area, (b) tectonic subsidence in the basin, and (c) eustatic (absolute) sea level rise. If we start at the base of the composite section with a certain rate of subsidence, a certain water depth in the basin, and a particular relief in the source area, were

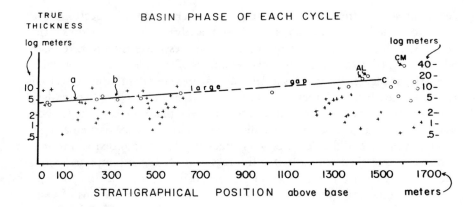

FIG. 4.   Log-thickness of each transgressive plus progradational phase of each cycle plotted against the stratigraphical position of each cycle. The open circles represent the marine cycles, the crosses represent the nonmarine (estuarine to fresh water) cycles. Small gaps in the section located at a, b, and c. This figure shows the true thickness of the large gap (data for all gaps from I. H. Forsyth, personal communication, 1973). AL represents the position of the Ardross Limestones. CM represents the position of the Charleston Main Limestone and overlying Nielson shell bed.

there any changes in these parameters that can be deduced from figures 2, 3, and 4? Starting with figure 2, we see that the amount of sediment available for the delta top phase decreased with time, and yet the amount of sediment available for the basin phase (fig. 3) was relatively constant throughout the lower 62 cycles (approximately 1,400 meters of total composite thickness as adjusted for fig. 4). We thus conclude that *at least* there was no marked uplift in the uplands supplying the sediment from the source area, and most likely we are dealing with a gradually eroding source area (little or no uplift) but yet with a constantly sinking basin. If we subscribe to the hypothesis of Klein (1974), a gradual increase in water depth in the basin of deposition would be indicated by the figure 4 data on marine cycles for the lower 1,500 meters of section. At about 1,500 meters from the base of the section, a threshold was passed such that marine basin phases varied greatly in thickness (fig. 4, to the right of AL) and a greater rate of subsidence in the basin occurred (fig. 3, from M^* to the right). Meanwhile the sediment contribution to the delta top in the upper 300 meters of section continues to decrease with time (fig. 2). Thicker marine basin phases can easily be explained by strike-fed sediment coming from elsewhere in the basin, and thus the independent nature of the two graphs, figures 2 and 3, becomes apparent. We therefore conclude that the sediment supply from the source area was either constant or declined with time from the base to the top of the section analyzed. There was thus either constant uplift or no uplift at all, allowing progressive erosion to take place. The next aspect to analyze is the relative effects of subsidence and/or absolute (eustatic) sea-level change. A sudden increase in water depth due to tectonic causes in the Midland Valley would have the same effect as a sudden sea-level rise all over the world or at least for the European plate. During the Carboniferous in general, the Southern Hemisphere was known to be participating in glacial events. Worldwide eustatic changes would be recorded as instantaneous jumps in thickness on either figure 3 or 4. No such jumps are seen in the lower 1,500 meters (62 cycles) of the composite section; the time for deposition of those 1,500 meters would surely be rated in the millions of years. However, four jumps are recorded in figure 3, starting with M^* and progressing to the right. The largest of these are the Ardross Limestones and shales (AL, fig. 4) and the Charleston Main Limestone and overlying shale (CM, fig. 4). Whether or not all these represent local tectonic effects or regional sea-level effects can be resolved only by constructing similar graphs for other sections of *precisely the same age* across the Midland Valley of Scotland, and then into England and the Continent. The precise age correlation of limestones and changes in sedimentation rate, when plotted on a map to show regional versus local effects, ought to resolve the problem of whether it is eustasy or local tectonism that has caused the effects seen. The Midland Valley of Scotland was a complex rift with abundant volcanism and ample evidence of differential tectonism throughout middle Carboniferous time (Goodlet, 1959; Francis, 1965). I suspect that local tectonism played a major role in the effects on the cycles herein described. On the other hand, the Charleston Main Limestone and overlying shale just might be the consequence of an eustatic sea-level rise. This problem can be rephrased as a question: Does one emphasize the wiggly line produced by the connecting of data points on figure 3, or does one emphasize the "best fit" line drawn through all the points? Only other data from other sections can resolve this matter.

One other aspect of figures 3 and 4 needs to be discussed. Why is it that, in spite of a constant rate of sedimentation (and therefore rate of subsidence) in the basin for the lower 62 cycles, there is an apparent independence of behavior when comparing a plot of the thickness of wholly marine basin phases with a plot of the thickness of nonmarine basin phases (fig. 4)? The former increases, whereas the latter stays the same or decreases. If each cycle truly represented a delta cycle in the sense of Coleman and Gagliano (1964), then *each cycle* ought to have a marine transgressive phase (fig. 1). Furthermore, when considering fig. 4, one concludes that water depth for the nonmarine phases of cycles remained the same for the lower 1,500 meters of section while the marine phases of cycles indicate a progressive increase in water depth. Several hypotheses can be constructed to explain these conclusions, the most commonly accepted, perhaps, being that the sea entered the Midland Valley of Scotland only periodically, and when it did so it lingered a bit longer each time. Support for this concept is seen in the thickness data for the lower 62 cycles. Marine cycles are no thicker than nonmarine cycles above and below them. This implies that the marine events are no different than the nonmarine events with regard to the delta lobes; nonmarine cycles are not merely crevasse lobes within the delta top environment. A more radical hypothesis is that each true delta cycle begins with a fully marine phase (including multiple phase of two marine cycles in successive cyclothems) and ends just prior to the next fully marine phase. Thus, in figure 4, if multiple marine phases are counted as the base of one cycle, there would have been only eight true delta cycles in the lower 1,500 meters of the section. Nonmarine phases would be developed on the delta platform in interdistributary bays, isolated or semi-isolated ponds surrounded by marsh vegetation, much like the present map of the Mississippi delta birdsfoot. A variety of salinities would be present in these nonmarine cycles, including the possibility of salt-marsh peat forming from the *Stigmaria* rootlet beds and coal. The large, primitive rootlets of the arborescent lycopods could certainly have been euryhaline; there is simply no evidence from the plants themselves as to what salinity they could tolerate. On the other hand, I have seven cases in Fife of *Stigmaria* rootlets *interbedded* with marine burrow structures (an authochthonous feature) as well as marine bivalves (possible transportation of the shells, but not likely). In each case the rootlets penetrated the marine sand, eroded at the top, and this was succeeded by another marine sand (often after a brief interval of shale with shells and rootlets). Clearly the plants and the sea were so close in elevation that it becomes extremely difficult to accept the entirely fresh-water origin of the *Stigmaria* rootlets. Perhaps the large lycopods behaved like modern mangroves in a marginal marine environment, and like cypress when in an entirely fresh-water environment.

Completion of the Project (1979)

Since the above was written, further work has resulted in the publication of: (1) an abstract given at a Geological Society, National Meeting (Belt, 1976), and (2) the final resolution of many of the questions raised in 1975 (Belt, in prep.). This resolution came about by considering the frequency distribution of thickness for: (a) D-units, (b) basin phases of each cycle, (c) delta top units (excluding the D-units that exceeded 2 meters), and (d) total thickness of each cycle. This method of analysis clearly pinpointed 19 cycles that contained units of extraordinary thickness (were responsible for more time elapsed than could be accounted for by a model of simple delta-lobe switching). When these thick cycles were removed from the cumulative thickness (Schwarzacher) plots, both the basin phase plot (fig. 3) and the delta top plot (fig. 2) developed compatible straight lines. I suggest, therefore, that these extraordinary cycles were a consequence of effects to the succession that are not related to the normal switching of delta-lobe distributaries, but are a consequence of tectonism and/or eustasy. When the 19 thick cycles were isolated from the larger set of 80 cycles and put into context of the section (stratigraphic order), 13 of them were explained by rational geologic evidence to be either tectonism or eustasy. That is, 11 clustered into four groups and ought to have resulted from tectonism that acted more slowly than the rate of delta lobe switching. The other two are extremely widespread as isolated marine units, and are best explained as eustatic events (St. Monance Brecciated Limestone; Charlestown Main/Neilson Shell Bed), although "proof" would only come when they are correlated onto other continents.

REFERENCES

BELT, EDWARD S.
  1975.   Scottish Carboniferous cyclothem patterns and their paleoenvironmental significance.   Pp. 427-449 *in* "Deltas, Models for Exploration," M. L. Broussard, ed.   Houston Geological Society.
  1976.   Cumulative plots of successive delta cycles as subsidence/eustatic indicators.   Geol. Soc. America, Abstracts with Programs, vol. 8, no. 6, pp. 771-772.
  _____.   Quantitative analysis of Late Dinantian cyclothems, East Fife, Scotland. Presented at a symposium of the Neuvième Congrès International de Stratigraphie et de Géologie du Carbonifère, Urbana, Illinois, U.S.A., May, 1979. (In preparation.)
COLEMAN, JAMES M., and GAGLIANO, SHERWOOD M.
  1964.   Cyclic sedimentation in the Mississippi River deltaic plain.   Trans., Gulf Coast Assoc. Geol. Soc., vol. 14, pp. 67-80.
FRANCIS, E. H.
  1965.   Carboniferous, Midland Valley.   Pp. 309-339 *in* "The Geology of Scotland," G. Y. Craig, ed.   Oliver & Boyd, Edinburgh.
GOODLET, G. A.
  1959.   Mid-Carboniferous sedimentation in the Midland Valley of Scotland. Trans. Edinburgh Geol. Soc., vol. 17, pt. 3, pp. 217-240.
KLEIN, GEORGE DEVRIES
  1974.   Estimating water depths from analysis of barrier island and deltaic sedimentary sequences.   Geology, vol. 2, pp. 409-412.

SCHWARZACHER, WALTER
   1975.   Sedimentation models and quantitative stratigraphy.   *In* "Developments in Sedimentology, 19." 382 pp.   Elsevier Publishing Co.

EDWARD S. BELT

Biology of the Franciscana Dolphin
(*Pontoporia blainvillei*) in Uruguayan Waters

Principal Investigator: Robert L. Brownell, Jr., National Museum of Natural History, Smithsonian Institution, Washington, D. C.[1]

Grant Nos. 1097, 1197: To study the life history and behavior of the Franciscana dolphin.

The Franciscana, *Pontoporia blainvillei,* is a small dolphin restricted to the coastal central Atlantic waters of South America. The recorded range of this species is from Valdes Peninsula (ca. 42° S.), in northern Chubut, Argentina, north to the Tropic of Capricorn around Ubatuba (23° 30′ S.), Brazil (Praderi in Ximénez et al., 1972). I know of no records from the Uruguay and Paraná Rivers, which empty into the La Plata Estuary.

Pontoporia is currently placed in the river-dolphin family Platanistidae with three other genera. All four genera are long snouted and similar in appearance; the Franciscana is the smallest. The other members of the family are: the Baiji dolphin, *Lipotes vexillifer,* known only from the T'ungt'ing Lake, People's Republic of China; the Ganges susu, *Platanista gangetica,* widely dis-

---

[1] The following individuals helped in this study: Charles O. Handley, Jr., Thomas J. McIntyre, James G. Mead, Clayton E. Ray, Henry W. Setzer, George E. Watson, and Francis S. L. Williamson (all Smithsonian Institution); and Miguel A. Klappenbach, Beba Filippi, Alvaro Mones, Ricardo Praderi, and Alfredo Ximénez (all Museo Nacional de Historia Natural, Montevideo, Uruguay). Others in Uruguay who helped were the Olivera family of Punta del Diablo, the Toscano and Redin families in Montevideo, and especially all the fishermen of Punta del Diablo who made my work in the village possible. Sol Toscano also helped in many ways during this study. Major financial support came from the National Geographic Society, the Office of Naval Research, and the Smithsonian Institution. Additional support came from Herman Adair Fehlmann (Smithsonian Oceanographic Sorting Center); I. Eugene Wallen and William I. Aron (both formerly of the Smithsonian's Office of Environmental Sciences); Masaharu Nishiwaki (University of Tokyo, Ocean Research Institute) and his staff; the National Science Foundation, Office of Polar Programs (R/V *Hero* cruise); Museo Nacional de Historia Natural de Montevideo; and the Ocean Research Institute, University of Tokyo. John E. Fitch, Murray D. Dailey, and Thomas E. Bowman provided assistance with the identifications of stomach contents and parasites. I extend my sincere thanks to all these individuals and institutions for their aid and cooperation.

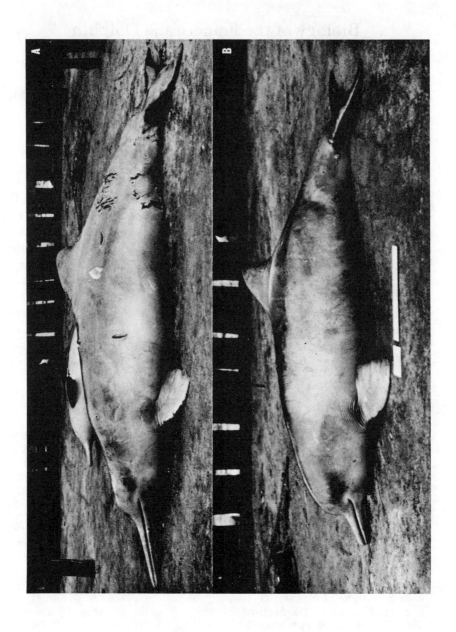

tributed in the Ganges and Brahmaputra of India and Bangladesh; the Indus susu, *P. minor,* in the Indus River system of Pakistan; and the bouto, *Inia geoffrensis,* found in the Amazon and Orinoco River basins. *Pontoporia* is the only member of the family that inhabits salt water.

At Punta del Diablo, Uruguay, Franciscanas and two species of sea lions, *Arctocephalus australis* and *Otaria flavescens,* are caught in gill nets by local fishermen in shark-fishing operations. The gill nets *(trasmallos)* are approximately 60 meters in length and 3 meters in depth. Two nets are joined together to form what is called a *vaga.* Each boat *(chalana* or *lancha)* has between 8 and 14 *vagas.* The mesh size is either 10 or 15 centimeters depending upon the size of the sharks being taken. Additional details on the fishing methods used at Punta del Diablo are given by Van Erp (1969), Brownell and Ness (1970), and Pilleri (1971a). Similar fishing operations occur at four other localities along the Uruguayan coast.

Some of the more important older references that deal with *Pontoporia* are Burmeister (1869), Lahille (1899), and Cabrera and Yepes (1940), but these reports give little information on the biology and ecology of this species. Recent authors deal with biology and ecology, but their findings are based on small numbers of dolphins (Carvalho, 1961; Brownell and Ness, 1970; Fitch and Brownell, 1971; Harrison and Brownell, 1971; Pilleri, 1971a, b; and Pilleri and Gihr, 1971).

A research project on the life history and ecology of *Pontoporia* was initiated in December 1970, and data were collected almost continuously until the end of 1973 in Uruguay. This paper is a preliminary summary of these findings on the Franciscana's biology (also see Brownell, 1975).

Materials and Methods

Two reconnaissance trips in February and August 1969 were conducted to determine the feasibility of a study on *Pontoporia* at Punta del Diablo. These proved successful, and a research program was started in December 1970. Biological data and specimens were collected from more than 400 dolphins during the baseline study, which ended in December 1973. Samples from

FIG. 1. Franciscanas *(Pontoporia blainvillei)* taken incidentally in gill-net fishery for sharks off Punta del Diablo, Uruguay: A, Lateral view of lactating female, specimen RLB 837, 160 centimeters long, weight 45.5 kilograms, taken offshore of Punta del Diablo on December 28, 1972. B, Lateral view of juvenile taken in same net close to above female and possibly its calf, specimen RLB 838, 84.5. centimeters long, weight 10.9 kilograms.

eight animals were collected in November and December 1974 for organo-chlorine analyses.

Nomenclature

The generic name *Stenodelphis* d'Orbigny, 1847, was used throughout most of this century. Hershkovitz (1961) stated that *Pontoporia* Gray, 1846, is the earliest valid generic name for the Franciscana dolphin. According to him the "widely circulated name *Pontoporia* is not a homonym of *Pontoporeia* Kroyer, 1842, a crustacean, nor has it been proven that the name is antedated by *Pontoporia* Agassiz, 1846 (Nomencl. Zool., p. 305), an invalid emendation of *Pontoporeia* Kroyer." *Stenodelphis* is then a junior objective synonym for *Pontoporia*.

Delphinus blainvillei was described by Gervais and d'Orbigny (1844). The type specimen, a skull, was collected near Montevideo, Uruguay. It was deposited in the Museum National d'Histoire Naturelle, Paris.

The only other nominal species described in this genus is *P. tenuirostris* Malm, 1871. The holotype, a mounted skin and skull, was collected at Montevideo, Uruguay, and is deposited in the Göteborg Naturhistoriska Museum, Sweden.

Age and Reproductive Cycles

Deposition of dentinal and cemental layers is annual, with the formation of an unstainable layer between August and November. Cementum deposition continues after the probable cessation of dentine deposition at four to seven layers (Kasuya and Brownell, 1979).

Harrison and Brownell (1971) and Harrison et al. (1972) summarized available data on the reproductive cycles of male and female *P. blainvillei*. They reported that females become sexually mature between total lengths of 134 and 137 centimeters; males at lengths greater than 140 centimeters.

During the study a total of 220 females and 213 males were examined to determine their reproductive state. The length frequencies of females and males examined are given in table 1 (all total-length measurements were taken in a straight line from the tip of the rostrum to the notch in the flukes).

The smallest mature and largest immature females were 137 and 146 centimeters, respectively. Sexual maturity is attained in both sexes at an age between two and three years, which corresponds to a length of 131 centimeters and weight of 25 to 29 kilograms in males, and to 140 centimeters and

33 to 34 kilograms in females (Kasuya and Brownell, 1979). The maximum recorded size of male and female *Pontoporia* is 158 and 174 centimeters, respectively (Lahille, 1899). The largest male and female that I have examined were 152 and 173 centimeters, respectively.

Females usually have a two-year reproductive cycle. Calves are probably born at a length of 70 to 75 centimeters, after a gestation period of about 10.5 months. They are weaned before one year of age (Kasuya and Brownell, 1979).

TABLE 1.   Body Length, Frequency, and Maturity of Male and Female Franciscana Dolphins, *Pontoporia blainvillei,* examined at Punta del Diablo, Uruguay. (These data include animals from Brownell and Ness, 1970, table 1.)

Size Range (cm.)	Male		Female	
	Number	Percent of total	Number	Number and percent sexually mature
81-85	3	.014	1	
86-90	1	.005	0	
91-95	4	.019	1	
96-100	9	.042	6	
101-105	10	.047	12	
106-110	12	.056	8	
111-115	22	.103	14	
116-120	24	.113	19	
121-125	30	.140	17	
126-130	28	.131	19	
131-135	21	.098	11	
136-140	25	.117	16 + (11)	7— 48
141-145	12	.056	14 + (6)	12— 86
146-150	9	.042	9 + (3)	8— 89
151-155	3	.014	15 + (5)	15—100
156-160			11 + (6)	11—100
161-165			5 + (4)	5—100
166-170			3 + (2)	3—100
171-175			1 + (1)	1—100
81-155	213	.997		
81-175			220	

Food Habits

Fitch and Brownell (1971) summarized available data on the food habits of *P. blainvillei*. Fish, squid, octopus, and shrimp are reported to be eaten. During the current project food habits of the Franciscanas, sea lions, and sharks were studied to obtain information on feeding strategies and seasonal variation in the feeding habits of these top trophic feeders.

The predominant food organisms taken by *P. blainvillei* during the austral summer were *Cynoscion striatus*, *Porichthys porosissimus*, and *Trichiurus lepturus*. These prey species were probably taken at, or near, the bottom.

During the austral winter *P. blainvillei* feeds mainly upon *Cynoscion striatus*, *Trachurus lathami*, and *Engraulis anchoita*, which are all very common in the relatively shallow coastal Uruguayan waters. *Cynoscion striatus* are also important food items for sea lions and sharks in these waters, but Franciscanas feed on smaller-sized individuals.

Other fish found in the stomachs of these dolphins are: cf. *Anchoa* sp., *Ariosoma* sp., *Conger multidens*, *Cupiceps* sp., cusk eel, goby, *Macrodon ancylodon*, *Micropogon furnieri*, *Peprilus* sp., *Polyclemus brasiliensis*, *Stromateus brasiliensis*, *Symphurus* sp., *Umbrina canosai*, and *Urophycis* cf. *brasiliensis*.

Squid beaks of at least one species, *Lolliguncula brevis*, and three species of shrimps, *Artemesia longinaris*, *Hymenopenaeus mulleri*, and *Penaeus (Melicertus) paulensis*, have been found in the stomach contents of Franciscanas.

Acoustic Signals

Franciscanas are not gregarious and usually avoid boats. It is, therefore, difficult to observe them and to record their acoustic emissions. However, three kinds of echolocation clicks of low, high and ultra-high frequency were recorded off Punta del Diablo in December 1972 (Busnel et al., 1974). The characteristics of these signals resembled those of the harbor porpoise, *Phocoena phocoena*, but they differed in the absence of synchronization between clicks.

Endoparasites

Two types of parasites have been reported from *P. blainvillei* (Dailey and Brownell, 1972; Schmidt and Dailey, 1971). One is an acanthocephalan, *Polymorphus (Polymorphus) cetaceum* (Johnston and Best, 1942), and the other is a nematode, *Contracaecum* sp. Both of these parasites have been found only in the stomach. I observed four species of endoparasites associated with the digestive system, including one trematode, one cestode, one nematode, and one acanthocephalan. No parasites were found in the lungs, intestine, heart, brain, kidneys, body cavity, blubber, or air sinus system. The number of parasites observed was recorded in the field as light (1-25), medium (25-100), and heavy (100+) infestations.

Trematodes. An unidentified fluke was found in only one Franciscana. This specimen may have come from the liver.

Cestodes. Several unidentified cestode larvae were found attached to the outer surface of the lower intestine of one dolphin. A specific search was not made for cestodes in the 193 Franciscanas examined for nematodes and acanthocephalans, but because of their external attachment and location, it would be difficult to overlook them. I consider them to be uncommon. It is noteworthy to report the absence of larval cestodes, *Phyllobothrium* spp., in the blubber and *Monorygma* spp. in the lower abdominal cavity of this dolphin. Both of these parasites have been reported from almost all the genera of marine odontocetes (Daily and Brownell, 1972).

Nematodes. Nematodes were found in 97 (51.0 percent) of 190 Franciscanas examined. *Contracecum* sp. and representatives of at least one other genus were collected. These nematodes were found in the main stomach compartment and were either free or firmly attached to the mucosa. In only two cases were nematodes found in the stomach without acanthocephalans. The infestation rate observed and recorded in the field for nematodes was: 94 light, 3 medium, and 0 heavy.

Acanthocephalans. *Polymorphus (Polymorphus) cetaceum* occurred in 175 (91.6 percent) of the 191 dolphins examined. The site of attachment of this acanthocephalan was the stomach, mainly in the passageway connecting the first two compartments. The infestation rate of *P. cetaceum,* recorded in 175 animals, was: 118 (67.4 percent) light, 47 (26.9 percent) medium, and 10 (5.7 percent) heavy.

The site of occurrence of *P. cetaceum* in the stomach of *Pontoporia* is unique among vertebrates higher than fishes. In all other higher vertebrates acanthocephalans are known only from the intestines. All acanthocephalans were firmly attached to the mucous membrane of the stomach. No lesions were produced aside from local irritation at the site of attachment.

In addition to the above endoparasites, I found isopods, *Cirolana* sp., on several occasions in the blowholes and stomachs of *P. blainvillei.* Only two previous reports noted the occurrence of isopods associated with cetaceans. Hale (1926) listed *Cirolana woodjonesi* from a porpoise (no scientific name given), and Bowman (1971) reported a new species *(Cirolana narica)* from the blowhole of Hector's dolphin *Cephalorhynchus hectori.* The association between

Cirolana and dolphins is not well understood, but these isopods probably enter the dolphin's blowhole after death. They are commonly observed in the gills of dead sharks taken from gill nets in Uruguayan waters.

Ectoparasites

Before these studies no ectoparasites had been reported from the Franciscana. I found two species of ectoparasites, both of which were crustaceans. One was a barnacle and the other an isopod.

Barnacles. *Xenobalanus* is a genus of pseudo-stalked, sessile cirripeds commonly found on cetaceans. Two dolphins each had one specimen of this barnacle attached on the flukes, one at the tip and the other in the notch. The same species, *Xenobalanus* cf. *X. globicipitis,* has been reported from various other species of cetaceans.

Cyamids. No cyamids were observed on Franciscanas.

Isopods. A parasitic isopod, *Nerocila* sp., previously known only from sharks and fishes was found attached to the skin in the neck region of one dolphin. The isopod may have transferred from a shark or fish to the dolphin while it was in the gill net.

In addition to the above, diatom films were observed on the dorsal and lateral surfaces of most fresh Franciscanas examined. Samples were collected from ten *Pontoporia.* Specimens of *Cocconeis ceticola* were present in all samples. Naviculoid diatoms were found on two dolphins taken during the austral winter (Nemoto et al., 1977).

Predators

The seven-gill shark, *Notorynchus ocellatus,* is a predator on the dolphins caught in shark gill nets, but it is not known if this shark preys on free-ranging dolphins. Remains of sea lions have also been found in the stomachs of seven-gill sharks, but marine mammal remains have not been found in the stomachs of the larger sharks in these waters.

Killer whales, *Orcinus orca,* are commonly sighted around the various offshore Uruguayan islands that support large sea-lion populations (*Arctocephalus australis* and *Otaria flavescens;* Brownell et al., 1973). I assume that *Orcinus orca* preys on *Pontoporia,* but I do not know of any definite cases.

Naturally Occurring Diseases

Normal tissue samples and those with possible pathology were collected from all major organ systems. Gross pathologic conditions were observed in the following localities: lungs, aorta, adrenals, uterus, and stomach. An adult male, 147 centimeters in length, had small punctate atherosclerotic lesions on the thoracic segment of the aorta, but less than 5 percent of the intimal surface was involved. A number of dolphins had ulcerated sores present in the main compartment of their stomachs, probably the result of parasitic nematode activity.

Environmental Pollution

A small number of samples were collected for organochlorine analyses. Dieldrin, PCB's, and DOT and its metabolites were present in blubber of all individuals examined. PCB's were the only residues detected in muscle and brain (O'Shea et al., in press).

Past Exploitation

Brownell and Ness (1970) reported that fishermen at Punta del Diablo in 1969 estimated the annual catch of Franciscanas at 2,000. Pilleri (1971a),

TABLE 2.   Catch Statistics of the Franciscana Dolphin, *Pontoporia blainvillei*, Between 1969 and 1973 at Punta del Diablo, Uruguay.[1]

Month	1969	1970	1971	1972	1973	Total
January			98		51	149
February	10		11			21
March			25			25
April			11			11
May			7			7
June			10		10	20
July			20	4	6	30
August	1		24	20		45
September			5	26	4	35
October			5	20	15	40
November			7		21	28
December		28	8	45	44	125
Total	11	28	231	115	151	536

[1] Includes seven listed by Pilleri (1971a).

based on his contact with the same fishermen in 1970, estimated that about 1,500 are caught annually. Past exploitation by these fishermen "must have been" on Franciscanas as the fishing grounds were closer to shore (Pilleri, 1971a). Over the years the fishing grounds have moved farther offshore because the shark populations are moving offshore. Boats fishing 30 to 40 kilometers offshore do not get P. *blainvillei* in their gill nets, but fishing with smaller gill nets for teleost fishes in inshore waters has increased during the past few years.

This shark fishery at Punta del Diablo started in 1942 (Van Erp, 1969). Some catch statistics for P. *blainvillei* between 1969 and 1973 at Punta del Diablo are presented in table 2.

REFERENCES

BOWMAN, THOMAS E.
1971.   *Cirolana narica* n. sp., a New Zealand isopod (Crustacea) found in the nasal tract of the dolphin *Cephalorhynchus hectori*.   Beaufortia, vol. 19, no. 252, pp. 107-112.
BROWNELL, ROBERT L., JR.
1975.   Progress report on the biology of the Fransicsana dolphin, *Pontoporia blainvillei,* in Uruguayan waters.   Journ. Fish. Res. Board Can., vol. 32, pp. 1073-1078.
BROWNELL, ROBERT L., JR., and NESS, RACHEL
1970.   Preliminary notes on the biology of the Franciscana, *Pontoporia blainvillei* (Cetacea: Platanistidae).   Pp. 23-28 *in* "Proceedings of the Sixth Annual Conference on Biological Sonar and Diving Mammals," Stanford Research Institute, Palo Alto, California.
BROWNELL, ROBERT L., JR.; OLAZARRI, J.; and ACHAVAL, F.
1973.   Marine mammal and bird observations and trawling off Uruguay: R/V *Hero* Cruise 72-3a.   Antarctic Journ. United States, vol. 8, no. 1, pp. 9-10.
BURMEISTER, R.
1869.   *Pontoporia blainvillii* Gray.   Pp. 389-445 *in* "Descripción de Cuatro Especies de Delfinides de la Costa Argentina en el Oceano Atlántico," An. Mus. Público Buenos Aires I.
BUSNEL, R.-G.; DZIEDZIC, A.; and ALCURI, G.
1974.   Études préliminaires de signaux acoustiques du *Pontoporia blainvillei* Gervais et D'Orbigny (Cetacea, Platanistidae).   Mammalia, vol. 38. pp. 449-459.
CABRERA, ÁNGEL, and YEPES, JOSÉ
1940.   Mamíferos sud-americanos (vida, costumbres y descripción), 370 pp., illus.   Buenos Aires.
CARVALHO, CORY T. DE
1961.   *"Stenodelphis blainvillei"* na costa meridional do Brasil, com notas osteologicas (Cetacea, Platanistidae).   Rev. Brasil Biol., vol. 21, pp. 443-454.

DAILEY, MURRAY D., and BROWNELL, ROBERT L., JR.
   1972.   A checklist of marine mammal parasites.   Pp. 528-589 *in* "Mammals of the Sea: Biology and Medicine," Sam H. Ridgway, ed.   Charles C Thomas, Springfield, Illinois.
FITCH, JOHN E., and BROWNELL, ROBERT L., JR.
   1971.   Food habits of the Franciscana *Pontoporia blainvillei* (Cetacea: Plantanistidae) from South America.   Bull. Marine Sci., vol. 21, pp. 626-636.
GERVAIS, PAUL, and D'ORBIGNY, ALCIDE
   1844.   M. Paul Gervais, nom de M. Alcide D'Orbigny et au sien, met sous les yeux de la Société trois planches representent des dauphins observés par ce dernier pendent son voyage dans l'Amérique meridionale.   Bull. Soc. Philom. Paris, 1944, pp. 38-40.
HALE, HERBERT M.
   1926.   Review of Australian isopods of cymothoid group, pt. 1.   Trans. Roy. Soc. South Australia, vol. 49, pp. 128-185.
HARRISON, RICHARD J., and BROWNELL, ROBERT L., JR.
   1971.   The gonads of the South American dolphins *Inia geoffrensis, Pontoporia blainvillei,* and *Sotalia fluviatilis.*   Journ. Mamm., vol. 52, pp. 413-419.
HARRISON, RICHARD J.; BROWNELL, ROBERT L., JR.; and BOICE, R. C.
   1972.   Reproduction and gonadal appearances in some odontocetes.   Pp. 361-429 *in* "Functional Anatomy of Marine Mammals," vol. 1, R. J. Harrison, ed.   Academic Press, London.
HERSHKOVITZ, PHILIP
   1961.   On the nomenclature of certain whales.   Fieldiana, Zool., vol. 39, no. 49, pp. 547-565.
KASUYA, TOSHIO, and BROWNELL, ROBERT L., JR.
   1979.   Age determination, reproduction, growth of the Franciscana dolphin, *Pontoporia blainvillei.*   Sci. Rep. Whales Res. Inst., no. 31, pp. 45-67.
LAHILLE, F.
   1899.   Notes sur dimensions du *Stenodelphis blainvillei.*   Rev. Mus. La Plata, vol. 9, p. 389.
MALM, AUGUST WILHELM
   1871.   Hvaldjur i Sveriges Museer, aar 1869.   Kongl. Svenska Vet.-Akad. Handl., vol. 9, no. 2, pp. 1-104, illus.
NEMOTO, TAKAHISA; BROWNELL, ROBERT L., JR.; and ISHIMARU, TAKASHI
   1977.   *Cocconeis* diatom on the skin of Franciscana.   Sci. Rep. Whales Res. Inst., no. 29, pp. 101-105.
O'SHEA, THOMAS J.; BROWNELL, ROBERT L., JR.; CLARK, DONALD R., JR.; WALKER, WILLIAM A.; GAY, MARTHA L.; and LAMONT, THAIR, G.
   ———.   Organochlorine pollutants in small cetaceans from the Pacific and South Atlantic oceans.   Pestic. Monit. Journ. (In press.)
PILLERI, G.
   1971a.   On the La Plata dolphin *Pontoporia blainvillei* off the Uruguayan coasts.   Pp. 59-67 *in* "Investigations on Cetacea," vol. 3, G. Pilleri, ed. Berne.
   1971b.   Epimeletic (nurturant) behavior by La Plata dolphin *Pontoporia blainvillei.*   Ibid., pp. 74-76.

PILLERI, G., and GIHR, M.
    1971.   Brain-body weight ratio in *Pontoporia blainvillei*.   Ibid., pp. 69-73.
SCHMIDT, GERALD D., and DAILEY, MURRAY D.
    1971.   Zoogeography and the generic status of *Polymorphus (Polymorphus) ceta-
             ceum* (Johnston and Best, 1942) comb. n. (Acanthocephala).   Proc.
             Helm. Soc. Washington, vol. 38, p. 137.
VAN ERP, INGEBORG
    1969.   In quest of the La Plata dolphin.   Pacific Discovery, vol. 22, no. 2, pp.
             18-24.
XIMÉNEZ, ALFREDO; LANGGUTH, A.; and PRADERI, RICARDO
    1972.   Lista sistemática de los mamíferos del Uruguay.   An. Mus. Nac. Hist.
             Nat. Montevideo, ser. 2, vol. 7, no. 5, pp. 1-49.

                                                           ROBERT L. BROWNELL, JR.

Ethnoecological Studies among the Tarahumara of Chihuahua, Mexico

Principal Investigator: Robert A. Bye, Jr., Botanical Museum, Harvard University, Cambridge, Massachusetts.

Grant No. 1088:   For a study of the ethnoecology of the Tarahumara.

The botanical approach to ethnoecological studies is a relatively new field. Ethnoecology is defined here as the study of the biological and ecological bases of man's relationship to and interaction with plants.

The Tarahumara people number over 50,000 and live in the Sierra Madre Occidental of southwestern Chihuahua. Wild and cultivated plants of the cool pine-oak forests of the sierras and of the arid subtropical forests of the barrancas or deep canyons are important to the Tarahumara way of life. The Tarahumara influence on the total flora and individual species has expanded since the first contact with Spanish missionaries in the early 1600's. Their mark as well as the mark of the Mexican and foreign cultures can be seen in the altered vegetation and in the evolution of certain plants.

Our knowledge of Tarahumara relationships with plants began with the Franciscans' "Relaciones Geográficas." The first ethnobotanical data (specimens and notes) were obtained by Dr. Edward Palmer in 1885. Dr. Carl Lumholtz's expedition in the 1890's added more information and specimens. Bennett and Zingg (1935) formally recognized ethnobotany in two chapters of their ethnographic treatise on the Tarahumara. Recently, Pennington (1963) gathered more ethnobotanical data while studying the relationship of the Tarahumara material culture to the environment.

I completed about two years of field observations and collections during the period 1972–1975. General plant collecting and ethnobotanical research at various localities in the sierras and barrancas were carried out in order to:

1. Obtain botanical specimens to define the vegetation and flora of the northern Sierra Madre Occidental and determine the potential vegetal resources available.
2. Record information on the Tarahumara's knowledge, uses, and folk taxonomy of plants, and on the human activities associated with them. The uses of plants by the Tarahumara and their associated activities provide data on the biological and ecological relationships between the plants and the Tarahumara.

141

Over 4,000 botanical and market specimens were collected. Although there is no published flora available for comparison, the specimens have increased our herbarium record of the plants of the northern Sierra Madre Occidental and will provide a wide base for a proposed flora of the region. The collections include specimens of poorly known species as well as a number of new species. Data were gathered on the reaction of plants to various human related activities such as fires, browsing, agriculture, and wild-food gathering. Transects of assumed wild vegetation revealed the strong influence of man on the environment.

Results

A few examples from the studies conducted on the inter-relationship of the vegetation of the Sierra Madre Occidental and the Tarahumara demonstrate the preliminary results of this ethnoecological research.

1. Incipient domestication of *Brassica campestris,* a mustard, is an example of the importance of the human factor in plant evolution on an adventive member of the Sierra Madrean flora. The Tarahumara have been conscientiously sowing seeds of this mustard, introduced as a weed from Europe, in fertilized fields since the late 1700's. The leaves are highly valued as a "quelite" or potherb and are a rich source of vitamin C in the Tarahumara diet. The seeds are planted in the fall to increase the yield of leaves. This demonstrates the Tarahumara's recognition of the long-day photoperiod flowering requirement of *Brassica.* Fields planted with mustard often contain fewer weeds during the following year and indicate the Tarahumara utilization of the allelopathic properties of *Brassica.*

2. The disturbance of the fields in the sierra has increased the size and the duration of hybrid populations of *Bidens* species. The Tarahumara are an important factor in encouraging the expanded potential of the evolution of these herbs.

3. Anthropogenic plant communities (vegetation initiated and maintained by man) are an important source of Tarahumara food and medicinal plants. The so-called "wild" plants are easily available and more abundant to the Tarahumara by their unconscious encouragement through disturbance of the environment. Among the prominent herbs are members of the genera *Amaranthus, Bidens, Chenopodium, Cosmos,* and *Lepidium.*

4. The collection of wild onions (*Allium scaposum*) in the moist upland meadows increases the abundance of this prized food resource. Breaking up the densely rooted soil and selecting the large bulbs with small bulblets, which fall back into the ground, encourage the development of large wild-

onion populations. Disturbance of the land coupled with vegetative reproduction by the bulblets of the large onions has increased the Tarahumara's ability to live off the land.

5. Medicinal plants are an important necessity in the Tarahumara way of life and are articles of outside commerce with the Mexicans. The bark of "copalquin" (*Hintonia latiflora*) is a popular febrifuge and traditional "remedio" for malaria and wounds. The Tarahumara use of copalquin is well founded, as it contains quinine and quinidine, which have proved antipyretic, antimalarial, and antiseptic properties.

Expanding the botanical foundation and testing the biological and ecological bases of plant-man relationships are the tasks of the botanist working in cooperation with anthropologists and geographers. Ethnoecological and ethnobotanical information can offer new interpretations and directions in all related fields and can be applied toward meeting future demands on our limited vegetal environment. The human factor has become the most important element in much of the ecology and evolution of the world's vegetation. Understanding the principles and variations of plant-man relationships and interactions is the key to encouraging a REALISTIC ecological balance with nature.

REFERENCES

BENNETT, WENDELL C., and ZINGG, ROBERT M.
 1935. The Tarahumara, an Indian tribe of northern Mexico, 412 pp., illus. University of Chicago Press.
BYE, ROBERT A., JR.
 1976. Plantas psicotrópicos de los Tarahuamaras. Pp. 49-72 *in* "Drogas Latino-americanas de Origen Vegetal," J. L. Díaz, ed. México, D. F.
 1979a. Incipient domestication of mustards in northwest Mexico. Kiva, vol. 44, nos. 2-3, pp. 237-256.
 1979b. Hallucinogenic plants of the Tarahumara. Journ. Ethnopharmacology, vol. 1, no. 1, pp. 23-48.
 1980. Quelites—ethnoecology of edible greens—past, present and future. *In* "Ethnobiology Today: A collection of papers honoring Lyndon L. Hargrave and Alfred F. Whiting." Flagstaff, Arizona, Museum of Northern Arizona. (In press.)
BYE, ROBERT A., JR.,; BURGESS, D.; and MARES TRIAS, A.
 1975. Ethnobotany of the western Tarahumara, I: Notes on *Agave*. Bot. Mus. Leafl. Harvard Univ., vol. 24, no. 5, pp. 85-112.
BYE, ROBERT A., JR., and CONSTANCE, LINCOLN
 1979. A new species of *Tauschia* (Umbelliferae), from Chihuahua, Mexico. Madroño, vol. 26, no. 1, pp. 44-47.
BYE, ROBERT A., JR., and SOLTIS, DOUGLAS E.
 1979. *Parnassia townsendii* (Saxifragaceae), a Mexican endemic. Southwestern Naturalist, vol. 24, no. 2, pp. 209-222.

CONSTANCE, LINCOLN, and BYE, ROBERT A., JR.
1976.   New Chihuahuan Umbelliferae.   Bot. Mus. Leafl. Harvard Univ., vol. 24, no. 8, pp. 225-240.
CONSTANCE, LINCOLN; CHUANG, T. I.; and BYE, ROBERT A., JR.
1976.   Chromosome numbers in Chihuahuan Umbelliferae.   Bot. Mus. Leafl. Harvard Univ., vol. 24, no. 8, pp. 241-247.
HERRERA, T.; TOBOADA, J.; and ULLOA, M.
1972.   Fijación de nitrógeno en el tesgüino y el pulque.   An. Inst. Biol. Univ. Autón. México, ser. biol. exp., vol. 43.
HERRERA, T., and ULLOA, M.
1973.   Una levadura fermentadora del tesgüino de los indios tarahumares. Bol. Soc. Mex. Micologia, vol. 7, pp. 33-38.
PENNINGTON, CAMPBELL W.
1963.   The Tarahumar of Mexico: Their environment and material culture, 267 pp., illus.   University of Utah Press, Salt Lake City.
ULLOA, M.; SALINAS, C.; and HERRERA, T.
1974.   Estudio de *Bacillus megaterium* aislado del tesgüino de Chihuahua, México.   Rev. Lat.-Amer. Microbiol., vol. 16, pp. 209-211.

ROBERT A. BYE, JR.

Heat Exchange of Nesting Hummingbirds in the Rocky Mountains

Principal Investigator: William A. Calder III, University of Arizona, Tucson, Arizona, and Rocky Mountain Biological Laboratory, Crested Butte, Colorado.

Grant No. 1130: To support the study of heat exchanges of nesting hummingbirds in the Rocky Mountains.

Life is maintained with energy extracted from the environment. Physiological energy requirements must be balanced by food energy intake. Mild climates are energetically less demanding, but when easy habitats were populated to capacity, colonization of, and adaptation to less hospitable climates was the only evolutionary "option" for the excess. There, energy needs may be greater, making more difficult the energy balance, a prerequisite for success. This objective could be attained by increasing intake and/or by energy-conserving behavior such as careful microhabitat selection.

Body size, more than any other factor, determines an animal's physiological requirements (Adolph, 1949). The smaller the animal, the more intense its metabolism per gram of tissue because of higher surface/volume ratio and less total insulation. Thus small body size has been regarded as posing a challenge to the achievement of energy balance. On the other hand, the smaller animal requires less energy than the larger one.

The smallest homeothermic animals are hummingbirds and shrews. Of these, the hummingbirds are more directly exposed to the environmental extremes and are more easily observed under natural conditions. Hummingbirds in stressful climates should therefore provide important insight into animal-environmental coupling (see King, 1974).

The abundant flowers of a short montane summer provide an attractive energy resource for hummingbirds, but the cold mountain nights are a liability in a bird's energy budget. Adiabatic cooling, clear dry air, and the heat sink of the cold sky result in chilling conditions for the incubation of eggs by a tiny hummingbird.

A diurnal hummingbird must invest its daytime effectively to meet the physiological energy requirement. Nightfall marks the onset of fasting. The energy reserves for this fasting are proportional to body mass (m^1; Tucker, 1971; Hainsworth and Wolf, 1972; Calder, 1974a). The metabolic rate at

which these reserves are depleted is proportional to $m^{3/4}$ (Kleiber, 1961; Lasiewski and Dawson, 1967; Aschoff and Pohl, 1970a, b) so the fasting endurance would be:

$$\text{time} = (\text{amount} \div \text{rate}) \propto (m^1 \div m^{3/4}) = m^{1/4}$$

The smaller the bird, the shorter its fasting endurance. When the climate is cold and metabolic rates are high, refueling of small birds may be critical. The energy budget is jeopardized not only by the intense metabolism but by short supply or insufficient opportunity for feeding during the day. Nest attentiveness (percent of daytime spent on the nest) is increased during rainstorms (review: Drent, 1972). The longer the hen must remain on the nest, the less time she has to feed. If inclement weather persists, her energy reserves may not be filled by nightfall. As the flowers fade at the end of the season, energy shortage can also occur.

I became interested in the energy problems of hummingbirds by observing the nesting of the very small calliope hummingbird *(Stellula calliope)* in Jackson Hole, Wyoming, where freezing temperatures are often recorded at night. The physical factors seemed to have been seriously neglected in the study of bird behavior, so further investigation of the heat exchanges of hummingbirds promised to be worthwhile. The population of broad-tailed hummingbirds *(Selasphorus platycercus)* near the former silver-mining townsite of Gothic, Colorado (now the Rocky Mountain Biological Laboratory, fig. 1), has been ideal for this. They are breeding in a marginal energetic situation, as evidenced by (1) the necessity for torpor when storms reduce feeding time and by (2) the abandonment of live nestlings when flower availability declined in mid-summer of 1971 and 1972 (see Calder and Booser, 1973; Calder, 1973c). A grant from the National Geographic Society supported continuation of this research in 1973. An opportunity was thus provided to detail the chronology of the breeding season, to document the correlation between hypothermic torpor and reduced feeding opportunity, and to obtain data necessary for estimating the rate of heat loss from nesting hummingbirds in the cold pre-dawn hours.

The Rocky Mountain Biological Laboratory is located at 2,900-meter elevation in the glacier-carved East River Valley of the Elk Mountains. Nights there are usually clear in the nesting season, and the valley bottom accumulates cold air draining from the surrounding mountains (fig. 1). Temperatures frequently descend to freezing or below. Only 50 meters up the hillsides, minimum air temperatures may be 2.8 to 8.5° warmer.

FIG. 1.   The Rocky Mountain Biological Laboratory, Gothic Townsite, as seen from Avery Peak, elevation 3,856 meters, NNE of Rocky Mountain Biological Laboratory. Gothic Mountain (upper right) rises to a height of 3,848 meters.

The night sky is a very cold heat-sink, with effective black-body temperature colder than −20°C. Mountains block a portion of the celestial hemisphere so that in an open meadow the hemispherical long-wave influx on a clear night may be 23.3 mW cm^{-2}, equivalent to radiation from a −19.6° black-body.

The broad-tailed hummingbirds nest in seral aspen stands (*Populus tremuloides*) on the slopes and in spruce (*Picea engelmannii*) and fir (*Abies concolor*) along the East River and Copper Creek and scattered in the dense aspen stands (fig. 2). Branches or stubs suitable for nesting are from 3 to 12 meters above ground in the aspens. The conifers border the streams, and also occur singly as pre-fire relicts in the aspen stands. Boughs suitable for nesting are usually 2 meters or less off the ground. Seventy-three nest-sites have been observed in three summers, twenty-seven in 1973. The hummingbirds seem to select nest-sites where branches overhead provide shelter from rain, sleet, hail, and the heat-sink of the cold sky (Calder, 1973a).

The Annual Cycle

If the energetic situation of montane hummingbirds is as tight as I have viewed it, seasonal timing should be critical. This can be studied by correlating the chronology of hummingbird breeding seasons with environmental factors. Central American hummingbirds nest mostly at the onset of the dry season when sunny skies follow recent moisture to produce a profusion of flowers. This may occur from November to February in different locations. The nectar drinkers "provide one of the most remarkable instances . . . of the dependence of a bird's season of reproduction on the food supply . . . in defiance of apparently inimical features of the climate" (Skutch, 1950). The testicular cycle of the Anna's hummingbird (*Archilochus anna*) suggests that an inherent rhythm was modifiable by rainfall and factors such as the presence of females. The ensuing breeding season occurs in the period when food plants are most numerous (Williamson, 1956). In the Santa Monica Mountains, breeding territories are occupied when *Ribes malvaceum* blooms, immediately after the first winter rains. The Anna's hummingbird is the only breeding bird in the cold winter months in the chaparral (Stiles, 1973). Ruby-throated hummingbirds (*Archilochus colubris*) arrive near the northern limit of their range in Saskatchewan in late May, nearly a month before flowers are available, feeding on sap from sapsucker holes and small arthropods (Miller and Miller, 1971).

The broad-tailed hummingbird is essentially a mountain bird (Bent, 1940). It encounters and breeds in chilling climates where the energy supply might be crucial. Its advance to the breeding grounds, establishment of territory, and nesting in relation to environmental factors are, therefore, of special

Fig. 2. Rocky Mountain Biological Laboratory as viewed from Gothic Mountain. A = Aspen stand with scattered spruce and fir (darker); S = riparian spruce corridor.

interest. The broad-tail returns to the mountains of southern Arizona in late February or early March when there may still be snow on the ground. The only flowers are some manzanitas *(Arctostaphylos pringlei)* beginning to bloom on warmer slopes (Phillips et al., 1964; Calder, 1974a). In early April they arrive in northern Arizona, and from late April to mid-May in Colorado (Phillips et al., 1964; Bailey and Niedrach, 1965).

Male broad-tailed hummingbirds were heard in Gunnison, Colorado (elevation 2,350 meters) on May 12, 1973 (Mrs. R. E. Richards) and at the Crested Butte Ski Area (2,900 meters) on May 13 (Manager, Matterhorn Lodge). We arrived in Gothic (2,900 meters) on May 16 to hear and see males flying there. They had not been noted before May 14 when the only year-round residents, George and Barbara Sibley, departed for supplies. The chronology of male broad-tailed hummingbird activity is correlated with some qualitative environmental observations in figure 2. Spring 1973 was late compared with the 1972 season, in terms of initial melt and snowstorms in late May and early June (figs. 3 and 4). A daily time-base for the 1973 study was provided by 1971 and 1972 data. Males were first active 19.8 ± 4.7 (s.d.) minutes before sunrise in 1971, 21.7 ± 2.5 (s.d.) minutes before sunrise in 1972 (ca. 0522) when territories had been established (Calder, 1975). In 1973 this did not occur naturally until June 8, when enough low larkspurs *(Delphinium nelsoni)* were blooming for feeding. Artificial feeders put up May 31-June 1 resulted in 0530-0532 onset of activity and territorial display, but this ceased immediately upon removal of the feeders the next day. The birds probably derived their energy elsewhere, making scouting trips to Gothic until conditions were favorable for energy balance on the breeding grounds. Opportunism thus appears to be the rule, as noted in daily hummingbird feeding at high elevations in Mexico (Swan, 1952), in the territoriality of migrating rufous hummingbirds *(Selasphorus rufus)* at nectar sources (Armitage, 1955) and in the tie between flowers and breeding (Skutch, 1950). When larkspurs were available, territorial claims and then courtship and nest-building followed. Nest-building in the aspens was also correlated with the reduction in radiative heat loss when the aspen stands leafed out. The hemispherical radiometer was suspended 1/2 meter beneath a nest branch of previous seasons and readings were compared with those from an open hill nearby. Before leaf-out, the aspen trunks and bare limbs provided 13 percent more long-wave influx than the open sky. Leaf expansion increased shielding from the sky, resulting in a 23 percent (at onset of nest-building) to 26 percent greater influx of long-wave radiation. The radiative heat loss by a bird is the difference between the radiation from the bird (at its surface temperature) and the lesser influx from colder surroundings. The sky temperature at the zenith on clear nights was

FIG. 3.   Not a hummingbird in sight as the snow falls on our weather station.

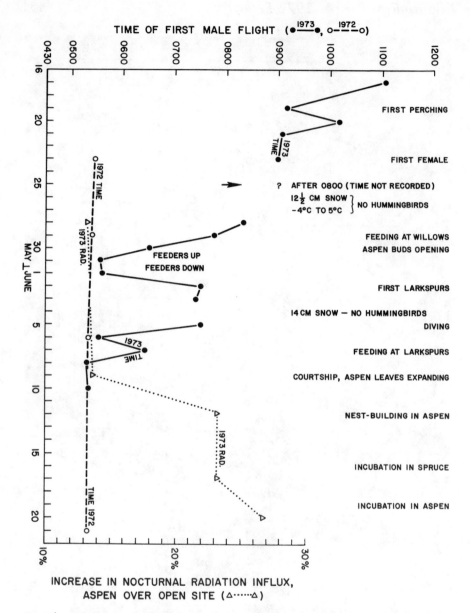

FIG. 4. The chronology of the nesting season, correlated with environmental factors. Solid dots and line show daily arrivals of male broad-tailed hummingbirds, compared to the regular 0520-0525 first daily flights of 1972 (open circles, dashed line). Nocturnal hemispherical radiant influx (triangles, dotted line) increased as the aspen leaves expanded, reducing net loss by radiation when nest construction was begun.

FIG. 5.   A view of the aspen canopy. Bill Calder IV, on lineman's spurs is installing temperature-sensor and suspension for hemispherical radiometer at Nest 1-73.

below $-20°C$. Any portion of the sky blocked by branches, leaves, and topography would be closer to air temperature (-5 to $+5°C$) and thus would emit more heat to reduce the net loss from a bird (fig. 5).

Once the two eggs were laid, a total of 34 to 39 days to fledging were needed for incubation (15-19 days), brooding (9-12 days) and postbrooding (8-10 days). Incubation was 13 days later in spruce and 14 days later in aspen compared to 1972, but similar to 1971 (fig. 6). Renesting or late nesting may be attempted if a nest fails, but the likelihood of success diminishes with time. The breeding season ended with successful fledging or late failure (which may result from an energy crisis). In 1971 and 1972 the apparently

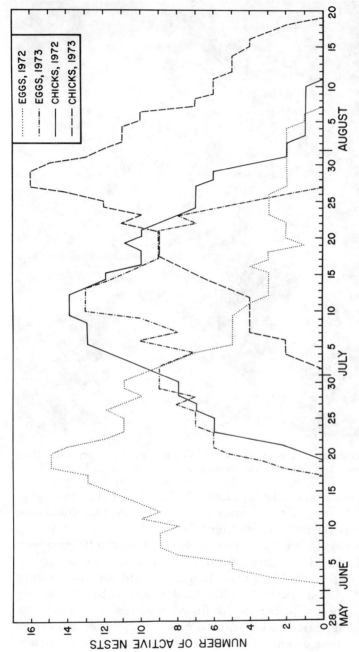

Fig. 6.   The late nesting season of 1973 compared with the early season of 1972.   The early start of 1972 left time for a long tapering-off of egg-dates (dotted line) probably reflecting renesting by unsuccessful females.   The egg dates in 1973 extended from 17 dates later onset to 4 days later termination.   Abundant rain of the 1973 nesting season maintained the flowers long enough for successful but late fledging.

negative energy balance was contemporaneous with the demise of the nectar-providing flowers. It was complicated by the arrival of aggressive migratory rufous hummingbirds which compete for the remaining nectar in scarlet gilia (*Ipomoxis aggregata*), tall larkspur (*Delphinium barberi*), and paintbrush (*Castilleja* spp.). If energy intake were reduced to the point that hen and chicks could not balance losses, nests with live chicks may have to be abandoned (Calder, 1973c). The frequent rains of 1973 maintained the major nectar flowers longer, and absence of artificial feeders perhaps made Gothic less attractive to the rufous hummingbirds. The transient rufous population had obviously declined drastically by August 11, as Nick Waser's actual counts (pers. comm.) confirmed. We observed no abandonment of broad-tail chicks in 1973, as in 1971 and 1972.

Thus, as for other hummingbird species, the breeding season is closely tied to flower supply (Waser, 1976). Snow melt sets the limit for onset, while seed-set of flowers and invasion by migrants marks the end of nesting for the broad-tailed hummingbird. Both ends of the season must act as cutting edges for natural selection, to channel breeding into an opportunistic exploitation of the earliest possibility for energy balance during the high demands of nesting.

The Daily Time Budget

In nature, the bird must convert its time to energy. Inefficient conversion may prevent energy balance and the bird will die. The hummingbird's utilization of time, therefore, is very important. A positive energy budget must be attained by day to provide a reserve for the nocturnal fast. During the nocturnal fast, energy must be expended at rates that will spare some fuel for resumption of feeding in the morning. This nocturnal energetic cost will be a function of the nesting or roosting microclimate, the body temperature level being maintained, and the length of night.

Within a stage (incubation or brooding) the broad-tailed hummingbird hen's total time away from the nest appeared similar to the average constancy (percent of time on nest) of five hummingbird spp. in Central America, which was 70 percent (Skutch, 1962). The broad-tailed hummingbird females were on the nest for 78 percent of the available day-length during incubation, but with the demands of the nestlings, this decreased to 62 percent; the difference presumably reflects the more intense foraging of the mother. The onset of the feeding phase is correlated with light intensity. If the day is shorter, a smaller percentage of it can be spent on the nest. The number of feeding trips may be a function of distance to and quality of the food supply. Information from higher and lower latitudes is needed.

Telemetry transmitters suitable for hummingbirds have not yet been developed so we communicated via two-way radios while observing a leg-tagged male hummingbird. The time spent in flight, perching, feeding, etc., was logged on a series of switch-controlled electric clocks by Susan R. Calder, at our "Mission Control" station. The male spent an average of 76 percent of the time perching in his territory, similar to the time spent incubating by the female. The sexual specialization may seem chauvinistic, but thus far the energetic load of the two sexes appears equal (Waser and Calder, unpubl.).

Hypothermic Torpor

Man first responds to the threat of shortage by seeking to extract more. In nature, animals must conserve. Hummingbirds could conserve energy reserves by careful choice of microhabitats and by reducing the metabolic rate through hypothermic torpor. When the body temperature is reduced, the gradient for heat loss from body to environment is less "steep," reducing heat flow and the metabolic requirements for heat production. As the tissues cool, the metabolic rate is decreased (the "Q_{10} effect"). In hummingbirds, a decrease of 10°C may reduce the metabolism to one-fourth the previous value (Lasiewski, 1963; Lasiewski and Lasiewski, 1967).

Nest temperatures of the Anna's and calliope hummingbirds indicated that incubating females did not become torpid, but were able to maintain homeothermy all night (Howell and Dawson, 1954; Calder, 1971). However, extensive recording from broad-tailed hummingbird nests has yielded evidence of torpor during incubation (Calder and Booser, 1973, and the present study).

The hypothermic or torpor state in hummingbirds is regulated, not the reversion to poikilothermy as thought previously. Three species increased their oxygen consumption in proportion to the temperature difference (T_b-T_a) when exposed to air temperatures below the lower, regulated body temperature of torpor. (Hainsworth and Wolf, 1970; Wolf and Hainsworth, 1972). In hypothermia the nest temperature of the broad-tail reached a low of 6.7 to 7°C; further cooling was apparently prevented by regulation (Calder and Booser, 1973, and the present study).

FIELD OBSERVATION OF TORPOR OR HYPOTHERMIA

Most information on hummingbird torpor has come from captive birds in the aviary and laboratory. Hummingbirds can maintain nocturnal homeothermy if the energy intake is adequate; conversely, torpor results from depletion of energy reserves (Lasiewski, 1963, 1964; Dawson and Hudson, 1970).

TABLE 1. Hypothermia of the Nesting Broad-tailed Hummingbird at Gothic, Colorado (2,900 Meters)

Date	Nest	Stage	Min. air temperature (°C.)	Min. nest temperature (°C.)	Fraction of recorded nests showing hypothermia that night	Weather, conditions preceding day
1972:						
June 9[a]	1-Spruce	incubation	2	6.5	2/3	Rain 0830-0945,
	5-Spruce	incubation	−1	6.5		1520-1710 (1.6 cm., 5½ km. distant)
July 5[a]	14-Spruce	hatching	3		1/5	Interrupted recess pattern, presence of observer?
July 29[b]	28-Spruce	chicks, 9 da. age	5.5	7-7.5	1/4	Preceded abandon- ment of nest and
July 30[b]	28-Spruce	chicks, 10 da. age	5.5	—	1/4	chicks. Flower supply fading.
1973:						
June 29	5-Spruce	incubation	1	*	2/3	1.3 cm. rain, 1625-
	9-Spruce	incubation	1	7.5-8		1700, 1730-1900
July 13	1-Aspen	chicks, 6 da. age	4.5	12.5	1/2	1.0 cm. rain, 1330-
	5-Spruce	chicks, 6 da. age	2	11.0		1800, heaviest 1425-1510
July 19	1-Aspen	chicks, 12 da. age	1	13.7	2/3	0.8 cm. rain
	11-Spruce	incubating	8.5			
July 20	1-Aspen	chicks, 13 da. age	6	11.0	1/5	1.1 cm. rain (0.4 cm. to 0700, 0.2 cm. to 0930, 0.5 cm. to 2140)

[a]Calder and Booser, 1973.
[b]Calder, 1973c.
*Thermistor placement poor, qualitative indication only.

This makes rare observations of torpor in nature of special interest with respect to questions of cause (climatic and feeding conditions), depth of hypothermia, and the timing of onset and arousal.

Frequent rainstorms in 1973 (June 29 and July 13, 19, 20) provided a convincing correlation between missed feeding opportunity and recourse to

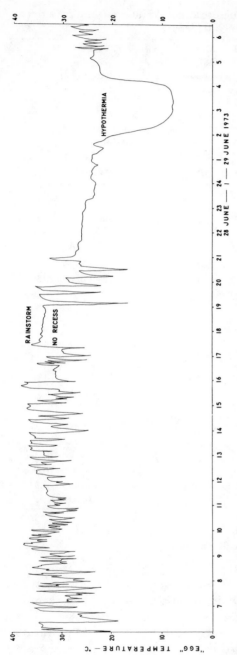

FIG. 7. Nest temperature/activity record of a hummingbird nest. Each downward pen movement (cooling) indicates one trip off the nest during the day. Note absence of feeding during rainstorm, which led to energy crisis at night, necessitating hypothermia, in order to conserve enough energy to resume feeding in the morning (Calder, 1974b).

hypothermia (Calder, 1974b). The continuous recordings of nest temperatures for the broad-tailed hummingbird indicated, by the lack of cooling intervals, that the females did not take feeding recesses during rainshowers in
the day preceding episodes of nocturnal hypothermia (see fig. 7). In all, seven
torpor cycles occurred among four nests, including both aspen and spruce sites
and all stages in the nesting cycle. Neither rain during the nonfeeding night-
time nor colder air temperatures on clear nights resulted in hypothermia.
Thus it is as if there were a physiological fuel gauge telling how much energy
remained and a biological clock telling how much time remained until morning light would permit refueling.

TABLE 2.   Revised Estimate of Heat Loss Rate from a Nest of the
Broad-tailed Hummingbird in Riparian Spruce, Gothic, Colorado
$(T_a = 1.8°C \qquad V = 17.6 \text{ cm.s}^{-1})$

Convection[*]	60.1 mW
Radiation[*]	48.4 mW
Conduction[+]	145.0 mW
Evaporation[**]	10.1 mW
Total	263.6 mW
Resp. Chamber[**]:	320 mW
Nest/Chamber:	82%

[*]Calder (1973b, 1975).
[**]Calculated from Lasiewski (1963).
[+]$\dot{H} = k(T_{in}-T_{out})$; k from lab, $\triangle T$ mean of field measurements.

Radiative Heat Exchange

The dorsal surface temperature of the incubating female is needed to calculate the upward-radiated heat loss. Placed within 28 centimeters of her
back, the PRT-5 (figs. 8, 9) reads the temperature of a spot 1 centimeter in
diameter (field of view 2°). In the period well after she settled on the nest and
before her first takeoff for feeding in the morning (2335-0555 hours), the
mean surface temperature was 15.3 ± 1.9°C when the air temperature averaged 4.4 ± 1.4°C (see fig. 10). There was an amazing gradient of over 20°C
across her skin and feathers (body to surface temperature difference).

The wider field of the PRT-10 might have included adjacent materials.
The surfaces of the folded wing and tail would probably be cooler than the

FIG. 8.   Radiation equipment at the hummingbird nest. Precision Radiation Thermometer (PRT) reads the surface temperature of the hen when she returns to the nest. Hemispherical radiometer (RAD) measures the hemispherical infrared influx from branches and sky, which is subtracted from the radiant loss calculated from PRT readings, to determine the net loss by radiation.

FIG. 9.   The female hummingbird incubates her two eggs, flanked by the radiation
sensors.

feathers of the back (Veghte and Herreid, 1965), which might also explain the
cooler dorsal temperatures in my earlier papers (Calder, 1973a, b). The sensor
is difficult to aim, but was apparently squarely pointed at the center of nest 10
since it read 39°C just after the hen departed to feed.

There seems to be a warming trend in dorsal surface temperature in an-
ticipation of the first feeding trip. Excluding those temperatures to get a representative value for pre-dawn incubation and brooding, the mean value was
14.1°C. Assuming an emissivity of 1.0, the radiation efflux would be 38.5
mWcm^{-2}, slightly higher than my estimates of 36.6 to 38.4 mWcm^{-2}
(Calder, 1973b).

HEMISPHERICAL LONG-WAVE INFLUX AT THE NEST AT NIGHT

Nest-site selection can increase the hemispherical radiant influx by about 35 percent in either aspen (31.7 ± 1.1 mWcm^{-2}) or spruce (31.4 ± 0.7 mWcm^{-2}) sites in the coldest, pre-dawn hours before the sun hits the nest. The difference in total heat loss between an aspen and a spruce nest (Calder, 1973b) can only be due to greater air velocity.

The difference between the estimated radiation from the hen's dorsal surface of 15.3°C and the hemispherical influx is the net radiative heat loss of 7.8 mWcm^{-2}. This is about 55 percent higher than the mean of my previous estimates. With one-quarter of the hen's surface (an estimated 6.2 cm^2; Calder, 1973b) exposed above the nest-cup, the rate of radiative heat loss would be 48.3 mW. The significance of this value is conveyed by comparison to total heat loss under laboratory conditions. In air of 5°C, the standard metabolism of hummingbirds of this size is equivalent to a power output of 320 mW (Lasiewski, 1963). Thus at the coldest part of the cycle, the broad-tailed hummingbird loses by radiation about 15 percent of the total heat loss of an unsheltered hummingbird exposed to a similar air temperature in the laboratory. If she (foolishly) nested on a treetop or in an open meadow, her radiation loss could be 98.7 mW, twice that when she nests under branches (ignoring the possibility that her dorsal surface might be somewhat cooler). If the energy reserves were only barely adequate for the nocturnal fast, as the occasional hypothermia suggests, the hummingbirds probably could not nest successfully in the open. Thus, in addition to protection from predators and precipitation, the "roof" is apparently significant in the energetic economy of hummingbirds, reducing the power requirement for thermoregulation 50.4 mW (Calder, 1974b).

Estimates of Heat Output from Hummingbirds Nesting in Nature

Additional data and better instrumentation permit revision of previous estimates (Calder, 1973b) for heat output during the coldest hour before sunrise. Drent (1972) pointed out that the eggs should be considered an extension of the body core. The hen increases heat flow from her brooding patch to keep the eggs warm, so the fact that the nest temperatures are in her thermoneutral zone does not mean that a proportion of her metabolic output is at the thermoneutrality rate observed in the laboratory. However, having no better information, I assumed, as a conservative lower limit, the three-fourths of the body is at thermoneutrality in arriving at the value for conducted heat loss.

Estimates of 167.5 mW in a low, streamside spruce nest and 180.5 mW in a higher nest on an aspen hillside suggest that microclimate selection and

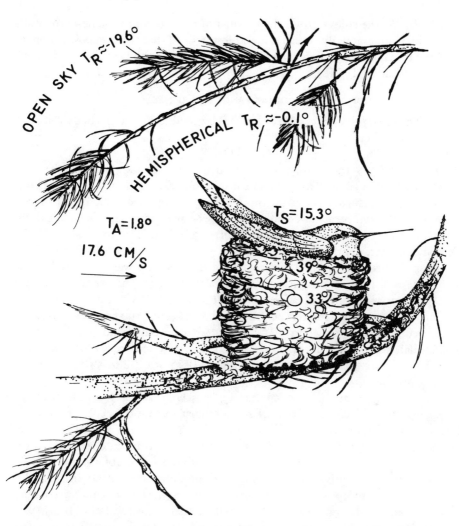

FIG. 10. The thermal environment of the Broad-tailed hummingbird's nest. T_s = surface temperature; T_a = air temp.; T_r = effective blackbody temperature derived from hemispherical radiometer, showing effect of branch in shielding from excessive heat loss by radiation. Wind velocity, 17.6 cm/s, an average used in estimating convective heat loss. From Calder (1974b).

nesting insulation cut the necessary heat output to about one-half that sustained at a similar air temperature in a metabolic chamber (320 mW for hummingbirds of similar body size, data from Lasiewski, 1963; see Calder,

1974b). As the chicks grow, the female must sit higher in the nest, the walls of which are gradually spread out and lowered, so that she is exposed more to the external climate. This may be counterbalanced with heat liberated by the chicks (Calder, 1974b).

MEASUREMENT OF THERMAL CONDUCTANCE OF THE NEST

The steady-state rate of heat loss ($\dot{H}$) by conduction from a body across an insulation layer is:

$$\dot{H} = k(T_{in}-T_{out})$$

where T_{in}, T_{out} = the temperature at the inside and outside surfaces of the nest, and k = conductance (reciprocal of insulation). The conductance was determined by measuring electrical input to a spherical heated body within the nest, in a temperature-chamber. Copper-constantan thermocouples (36 grams) were used to monitor temperatures on both sides of the nest wall. The nest diameter, depth, and wall thickness were measured with a vernier caliper and millimeter ruler. The surface area of the nest-cup was calculated as the surface of a hemisphere plus a cylindrical section for the excess of interior depth over hemispherical radius. The heat flux (mW) divided by the nest interior surface area and the temperature difference across the nest wall gives the nest conductance (mW/cm² · °C). The nest had been abandoned before the eggs hatched and was in perfect condition. The conductance was 8.78 mW/°C ± 0.38 for n = 5 determinations, which is 0.55 ± 0.02 mW/°C per cm² of interior surface.

Of energetic significance to the female is the total heat loss of the nest resulting from the temperature differential in nature (Table 1, col. 2). Previous estimates of heat-losses from broad-tail nests (Calder, 1973b, 1975) rest on the assumption that the three-fourths of the hen within the nest-cup (a proportion since confirmed as realistic from infrared scope observations) could suffice with the equivalent of the standard thermoneutral metabolism of 48.9 mW. That assumption is invalidated by the product of laboratory conductance value and temperature differentials measured in the field (145 mW). This indicates a higher total heat loss rate of 260.6 to 263.6 mW from a nest of the broad-tailed hummingbird in a valley bottom spruce site. This is 56 percent above my previous calculation (Calder, 1973b), but 18 percent less than the metabolic rate necessary for temperature regulation outside of the nest in a 1.8°C environment. This is the same proportionate saving that has been calculated for the incubation of three different passerines (flycatcher, blackbird, sparrow; see Walsberg and King, in press).

Smith et al. (1974) studied the nocturnal energetic cost of incubation by the Anna's hummingbird *Archilochus (Calypte) anna* and estimated a nocturnal

thermoregulatory cost of 3.62 kcal for 10.65 hr; $T_a = 8°C$, a power requirement averaging 395 mW. This is 52 percent higher than what I estimate for
the incubating broad-tailed hummingbird in an even cooler environment.
However, errors in his calculation "give overestimates of metabolic output by
a factor of almost three." (Smith, pers. comm.) This would then be considerably less than what I have estimated.

Thus, the probable heat output of the nesting broad-tailed hummingbird
is between the laboratory (no nest insulation) value and four-fifths of that value. This is a long way from being precise, so a challenge still remains in finding out how much energy it costs to be a hummingbird on a cold night, high
in the Rocky Mountains.

Success

The "proof of the pudding" in adaptation of small homeotherms to a rig-
orous environment can be measured by the survival of individuals and by the
reproductive success of the population. The influence of funding by the National Geographic Society does not end with the grant period. Natural history
research leads to questions as well as answers and the fascination is addictive.
Thus we return to the scene because of new problems, but can also profit from
past associations with the population by recapturing banded birds and revisiting nest sites. Waser and Inouye (1977) made an interim report on nesting
success and longevity observations. To this we can add the following update
on what is now the most extensively studied hummingbird population.

The apparently crucial importance of locating a nest for favorable shelter-
ing would favor reuse of the best sites. The energy cost of hovering to gather
spider-webbing and fine bark flakes for the well-insulated hummingbird nests
would seem to make it desirable to use old material for the nest base. It is thus
interesting to examine the records for reuse of nest sites.

There have been frequent reports of female hummingbirds of various species that returned to the same nest "year after year" (Bent, 1940; D. S. Farner,
pers. comm.; O. Barnwell, pers. comm.; Brunton et al., 1979). Frequently
nests are located which have been built upon the matted remains of old nests
from past years. However, in no case has it been established by banding that
the same female returned to the site, until follow-up studies of Gothic broad-
tails included a banded female which returned to the same nest in 1978 and
1979. The 1978 nest had older, weathered material at its base, suggesting
that it had been used in 1977 or earlier.

Of 118 nestings observed in nine seasons, 32 (27%) have been in the same
position as nests observed in previous seasons. Of these reuses of the same

branches, 56 percent have been in successive years, the other 44 percent having been vacant for one year or more between reuses. Of those used two or more years in succession, 55 percent were successful in the previous nesting. (The mean success ratio was 46% of all nests. Success is defined here as producing one or two chicks developed sufficiently to fledge or take flight from the nest if threatened. Actual fledging could not be observed at all nests).

If the use of a nest site had been unsuccessful, we might expect the female to go elsewhere, learning to avoid the scene of predation, intrusion, or inadequate shelter. When nest sites are reused with almost equal likelihood of following tragedy as success, this suggests that other females are involved. In other words, the hens' search image for a favorable site is behaviorally standardized. Lacking a record of the previous outcome a new hen would then be likely to accept an apparently good site even though her predecessor met with grief.

Over one-fourth of the observed nestings were at previously used sites, a fact that seems to confirm the favorable-site-image hypothesis. The slight edge of 56 to 44 percent for successive reuses compared to alternatively vacant sitings may well reflect the addition of a component of experience.

The study could not be pursued throughout the summer of 1977, so it is difficult to fully utilize 1978 observations, except in the case of one nest obviously built up on a previous-year nest and one that was observed in use during the brief inspection of 1977 as well as in 1975, 1976, and 1978. Limiting the data to the 1971-1976 and 1978-1979 periods, the success rates can be compared between sites used only one time (44% successful, n = 81), reused but not successively (63% successful, n = 8), and used again in successive seasons (85% successful, n = 13). These figures seem indicative of a synergistic effect of favorable site and experience.

With a success rate of 46 percent that includes nests where only one chick was produced, and a short season (mean date for start of incubation June 12; declining probability of success late in the season), renesting may have to wait until the next year. That there is further opportunity for replacement was dramatically emphasized in 1979 when we recaptured two females banded as adults by Waser in 1972, a record longevity of eight years for wild hummingbirds!

Fortunately an NSF grant for studies of fluid and electrolyte balance in hummingbirds will necessitate being at the Rocky Mountain Biological Laboratory for continued observation of nest-site use and success!

Acknowledgments

Professor R. E. Richards of Western State College, Gunnison, made the full season coverage possible by keeping us advised of snow conditions, loaning snowshoes, and opening up laboratory facilities early. I am indebted to William A. Calder IV and Susan R. Calder for field assistance and to Lorene L. Calder for help in many stages of the work. I have benefited greatly from sharing observations, ideas, banding and tracking efforts with Drs. Nicholas Waser and David Inouye. The cooperation and aesthetic sacrifice of the Rocky Mountain Biological Laboratory in refraining from use of artificial feeders made possible observations of a natural summer, and was deeply appreciated. The study was supported by grants from the National Geographic Society (1130) and the National Science Foundation (GB 38291). Follow-up studies have been made possible by NSF grants PCM-76-09411 and DEB-79-03689, and by the conscientious assistance of Sara Hiebert and Cecilia Richards.

REFERENCES

ADOLPH, E. F.
  1949.   Quantitative relations in the physiological constitutions of mammals.   Science, vol. 109, pp. 579-585.
ARMITAGE, K. B.
  1975.   Territorial behavior in fall migrant Rufous Hummingbirds.   Condor, vol. 57, pp. 239-240.
ASCHOFF, J., and POHL, H.
  1970a.   Rhythmic variations in energy metabolism.   Fed. Proc., vol. 29, pp. 1541-1552.
  1970b.   Der ruheumsatz von vogeln als funktion der tageszeit und der korpergrosse.   Journ. Ornithol., vol. 111, pp. 38-47.
BAILEY, A. M., and NIEDRACH, R. J.
  1965.   Birds of Colorado, 895 pp.   Museum of Natural History, Denver.
BENT, A. C.
  1940.   Life histories of North American cuckoos, goatsuckers, hummingbirds, and their allies, 506 pp.   U. S. Nat. Mus. Bull. 176. Washington, D. C.
BRUNTON, D. F.; ANDREWS, S.; and PATON, D. G.
  1979.   Nesting of the calliope hummingbird in Kananskis Provincial Park, Alberta.   Can. Field-Nat., vol. 93, pp. 449-451.
CALDER, W. A.
  1971.   Temperature relationships and nesting of the Calliope Hummingbird. Condor, vol. 73, pp. 314-321.
  1973a.   Microhabitat selection during nesting of hummingbirds in the Rocky Mountains.   Ecol., vol. 54, no. 1, pp. 127-134.
  1973b.   An estimate of the heat balance of a nesting hummingbird in a chilling climate.   Comp. Biochem. Physiol., vol. 46A, pp. 291-300.

CALDER, W. A.—continued

1973c. The timing of maternal behavior of the Broad-tailed Hummingbird preceding nest failure.   Wilson Bull., vol. 85, pp. 283-290.

1974a. The consequences of body size for avian energetics. Pp. 86-151 *in* "Avian Energetics," R. A. Paynter and W. R. Dawson, eds.   The Nuttall Ornithological Club, Cambridge, Mass.

1974b. Factors in the energy budget of mountain hummingbirds. Pp. 431-442 *in* "Perspectives in Biophysical Ecology," D. M. Gates, ed., "Ecological Studies: Analysis and Synthesis."   Springer-Verlag, New York.

1975.   Day length and the hummingbird's use of time.   Auk, vol. 92, pp. 81-97.

CALDER, W. A., and BOOSER, J.

1973.   Hypothermia of Broad-tailed Hummingbirds during incubation in nature with ecological correlations.   Science, vol. 180, pp. 751-753.

DAWSON, W. R., and HUDSON, J. W.

1970.   Birds. Pp. 223-310 *in* "Comparative Physiology of Thermoregulation," G. C. Whittow, ed.   Academic Press, New York.

DRENT, R.

1972.   Adaptive aspects of the physiology of incubation.   Proc. XV Intern. Ornith. Congr., pp. 255-280.

GREENEWALT, C. H.

1960.   The hummingbirds.   Nat. Geogr. Mag., vol. 118, pp. 658-679.

HAINSWORTH, F. R., and WOLF, L. L.

1970.   Regulation of oxygen consumption and body temperature during torpor in a hummingbird, *Eulampis jugularis*.   Science, vol. 168, pp. 368-369.

1972.   Crop volume, nectar concentration, and hummingbird energetics.   Comp. Biochem. Physiol., vol. 42, p. 359.

HOWELL, T. R., and DAWSON, W. R.

1954.   Nest temperatures and attentiveness in the Anna Hummingbird.   Condor, vol. 56, pp. 93-97.

KING, J. R.

1974.   Seasonal allocation of energy resources in birds. Pp. 4-85 *in* "Avian Energetics," W. R. Dawson, ed.   The Nuttall Ornithological Club, Cambridge, Mass.

KLEIBER, M.

1961.   The fire of life, 454 pp.   Wiley, New York.

LASIEWSKI, R. C.

1963.   Oxygen consumption of torpid, resting, active and flying hummingbirds.   Physiol. Zool., vol. 36, pp. 122-140.

1964.   Body temperatures, heart and breathing rate, and evaporative water loss in hummingbirds.   Physiol. Zool., vol. 37, pp. 212-223.

LASIEWSKI, R. C., and DAWSON, W. R.

1967.   A re-examination of the relation between standard metabolic rate and body weight in birds.   Condor, vol. 69, pp. 13-23.

LASIEWSKI, R. C., and LASIEWSKI, R. J.
  1967. Physiological responses of the Blue-throated and Rivolis Humming-
         birds.   Auk, vol. 84, pp. 34-48.
MILLER, R. S., and MILLER, R. E.
  1971. Feeding activity and color preference of Ruby-throated Hummingbirds.
         Condor, vol. 73, pp. 309-313.
PHILLIPS, A. R.; MARSHALL, J.; and MONSON, G.
  1964. The Birds of Arizona, 212 pp.   University of Arizona Press, Tucson.
SKUTCH, A. F.
  1950. The nesting seasons of Central American birds in relation to climate and
         food supply.   Ibis, vol. 92, pp. 185-222.
  1962. The constancy of incubation.   Wilson Bull., vol. 74, pp. 115-152.
SMITH, W. K.; ROBERTS, S. W.; and MILLER, P. C.
  1974. Calculating the nocturnal energy expenditure of an incubating Anna's
         hummingbird.   Condor, vol. 76, pp. 176-183.
STILES, F. G.
  1973. Food supply and the annual cycle of the Anna Hummingbird.   Univ.
         Calif. Publ. in Zool., vol. 97, pp. 1-109.
SWAN, L. W.
  1952. Some environmental conditions influencing life at high altitudes.
         Ecology, vol. 33, pp. 109-111.
TUCKER, V. A.
  1971. Flight energetics in birds.   Amer. Zool., vol. 11, pp. 115-124.
VEGHTE, J. H., and HERREID, C. F.
  1965. Radiometric determination of feather insulation and metabolism of
         Arctic birds.   Physiol. Zool., vol. 38, pp. 267-275.
WALSBERG, G. E., and KING, J. R.
  _____. The energetic consequences of incubation for two passerine species.   (In
         press).
WASER, N. M.
  1976. Food supply and nest-timing of broad-tailed hummingbirds in the
         Rocky Mountains.   Condor, vol. 78, pp. 133-135.
WASER, N. M. and INOUYE, D. W.
  1977. Implications of recaptures of broad-tailed hummingbirds banded in
         Colorado.   Auk, vol. 94, pp. 393-395.
WILLIAMSON, F.S.L.
  1956. The molt and testis cycles of Anna Hummingbird.   Condor, vol. 58,
         pp. 342-366.
WOLF, L. L., and HAINSWORTH, F. R.
  1972. Environmental influence on regulated body temperature in torpid
         hummingbirds.   Comp. Biochem. Physiol., vol. 41, pp. 167-173.

WILLIAM A. CALDER III

Long-term Changes in Dry Tortugas Coral Reef Environments

Principal Investigator: Richard H. Chesher, Marine Research Foundation, Key West, Florida.

Grant No. 1073:   For an evaluation of long-term ecological changes at the Dry Tortugas, Florida.

From July 1972 to September 1973 the National Geographic Society supported a Marine Research Foundation evaluation of long-term ecological changes at Dry Tortugas, Florida. The principal objective of the program was to determine whether work done by researchers during the early part of this century could be utilized to establish extended trends in tropical marine environments.

Recent concern over the impact of man on coral reefs has made it essential that we establish long-term, natural, and artificial trends in these environments. Unfortunately, there are few places in the world where baseline information exists on the condition of tropical marine communities in past years. Indeed, the extensive work carried out by marine scientists at the Dry Tortugas appears to be the only reservoir of such information that is more than a few years old.

Between 1904 and 1940 the Carnegie Institution of Washington maintained a tropical marine biological station at Dry Tortugas, a small group of islands located 70 miles west of Key West, Florida. The islands, accessible only by boat, harbored a lush terrestrial and marine fauna and flora. Coral reefs surrounded the numerous shoals and islands, often in shallow, protected environments, which enabled researchers to investigate the subsea world with little difficulty.

Scientists from various universities and museums came to the Dry Tortugas in early summer and remained for 8 to 10 weeks of undisturbed research. Most of the work was in an island-based laboratory complex, but the scientists conducted a great deal of underwater study in situ using Miller-Dunn diving helmets and glass-bottomed buckets. More than 30 volumes of scientific research reports appeared in the Carnegie Institution's "Papers from the Dry Tortugas Laboratory." Additional reports were issued annually in the Institution's Yearbooks and other scientific journals. In addition, many scientists

kept accurate, detailed field notes and collections of specimens, which are today preserved in major museums.

The accumulated mass of scientific data concerning the marine and terrestrial biota of the Tortugas is both voluminous and of high caliber. It represents one of the most complete long-term records of environmental conditions
in a coral-reef realm.

The Marine Research Foundation reviewed the available data and the existing conditions at the Dry Tortugas to see if it was possible to establish long-
term trends in coral-reef development. Initially, records at the Carnegie Institution of Washington were examined to find out who had studied at the laboratory and where their field notes, specimens, or maps might be located.
Published volumes of research reports were gone over, and the most promis-
ing material for baseline information was noted. Many of the earlier workers
were associated with the Smithsonian Institution, and an examination of the
files at the U. S. Museum of Natural History disclosed field notes, specimens,
and records left by the geologist and coral specialist, Dr. T. Wayland Vaughan.

After review of the available information, the Marine Research Foundation conducted a series of four field trips to the Dry Tortugas, revisiting the
earlier field stations and accumulating research data that could provide insight into long-term changes.

Vaughan, Carey, and Wells conducted qualitative and quantitative studies on coral populations and coral physiology. Vaughan (from 1907 to 1917)
and Wells (in 1932) drew maps showing the distribution of scleractinian corals. When these were combined with written reports of these and other workers, aerial photographs of 1960 and 1973, and surveys made during this
study, an interesting picture of coral distribution emerged.

Acropora cervicornis, a large, branching coral, was once the dominant coral
in the Dry Tortugas. In 1873 almost all of the *A. cervicornis* died, leaving massive beds of rubble that were later found and described by Vaughan and Carey.
Observers of the coral death blamed the kill on "black water." The "black water" was probably a symptom of massive tissue putrefaction rather than the
cause of death, but the real cause was never discovered. From 1904 to 1917,
A. cervicornis was found only in two areas on each side of Loggerhead Key. By
1932, when Wells studied the corals of the Dry Tortugas, *A. cervicornis* thickets had spread to other shoals and had increased considerably in extent. By
1973 it was again the dominant coral in the Dry Tortugas but had not completely recolonized parts of the northeast reefs.

Examination of color aerial photographs taken in 1960 and 1973 showed
that, although the coral has obviously been spreading rapidly over the past few
decades, the growth has not been uniform. Some beds were noted that have

markedly decreased in size since 1960. Others have increased in size.

Numerous studies have been conducted on the growth rate of *A. cervicornis* branches. This is normally done by tagging individual branches and measuring changes in branch length with time. We determined, for example, that branch growth in a thicket near Garden Key varied from 6 to 9 inches per year. This growth rate would not account for the widespread redistribution of the *Acropora* evident from the earlier records.

Surveys at the leading edges of the recolonizing areas showed how the coral was advancing. Initially, new colonies appeared through settlement of favorable areas by *A. cervicornis* planulae. The young colonies were not randomly distributed in advance areas but grouped in localized pockets. Rapid growth of the clustered, individual colonies then produced the large thickets that characterize most of the reefs.

As the thickets matured, they literally overgrew other species of corals. Skeletal remains of a wide variety of corals typical to Dry Tortugas patch reefs were found within several *A. cervicornis* thickets. The process of overgrowth was clearly seen in various stages of completion along the advancing areas of the *A. cervicornis* growth.

Few other species of corals can survive in a mature *A. cervicornis* thicket. Some small, encrusting scleractinians such as *Favia fragum* or *Siderastrea siderea,* were occasionally found growing on the lower portions of the *A. cervicornis* branches, but these seldom grew more than an inch in diameter and were short-lived.

In contrast to the rapid changes associated with the *A. cervicornis* thickets, comparison of earlier data with the 1973 surveys revealed a startling stability in some shallow-water, patch-reef environments.

During his studies on growth rates of corals, Vaughan attached young coral specimens to cement discs and mounted the discs on iron stakes driven into the coral reefs. We were able to find many cement discs still standing as he had left them. Most were solidly encrusted with massive overgrowths of fire coral, gorgonians, or zooanthids. Interestingly, however, some of the discs were not fouled at all, looking much as they must have when first placed on the reef. The barren discs were part of a series that stretched across one of the patch reefs. Discs located in lush coral areas were overgrown, whereas those located in barren areas of the patch reef were not fouled.

Zones of little, or no, macroinvertebrate sessile growth are common on patch reefs. The origin of these zones is unknown. They were generally thought to be transient conditions as bare, hard surfaces are normally rapidly fouled in marine waters. The evidence provided by the bare discs placed on the reef 50 years ago indicates that the barren zones may be much more stable than previously thought. Whatever kept the natural rock from becoming overgrown with living organisms obviously acted upon the artificial substrate placed in that zone. Initially, we hypothesized that the zones might be caused by periodic overgrowth by an organism (such as a zooanthid or an algae) which prevented settlement of other animals yet died off leaving no skeleton, perhaps on a seasonal basis. The area has since been examined over a 3-year period, during each season, and no such overgrowth has been noted. A second hypothesis, that grazing animals, such as echinoids, were keeping the area clean, was not substantiated by population studies or day and night surveillance.

Whatever the cause, the condition has existed with little change for almost 50 years, indicating a high degree of community stability on these patch reefs.

The preliminary Dry Tortugas survey also disclosed three long-term ecological studies set up during the Carnegie days, which could provide valuable information if they were completed.

In 1938, 4,000 mangrove seedlings were planted on Long Key, a coral rubble shoal, submerged at high tide. Mangroves were reportedly absent from the Dry Tortugas prior to the planting. The experiment was initiated to discover if the natural process of island evolution could be artificially accelerated. Today, 34 years later, Long Key has significantly enlarged in size and has a well-developed stand of mangroves. Numerous plants and animals normally associated with mangrove habitats have also appeared. The experiment was checked two years after the planting but then ignored. Although this is the oldest experiment on artificial mangrove planting in the United States, no one has taken advantage of the wealth of information available by completing the study.

In the later years of the Carnegie endeavor, Australian pine trees were planted on Loggerhead Key. Today they cover the entire island and have forced out most of the native flora. Their growth has been so rapid and complete that the ruins of the Carnegie buildings are almost completely obscured, and the U. S. Coast Guard base personnel on Loggerhead Key have undertaken a program of thinning the forest. Terrestrial floral studies were conducted in the 1930's, and it would prove worthwhile to document succession changes by resurveying the island and comparing the data with original conditions.

In 1908, Dr. Paul Bartsch began a series of evolutionary experiments on land snails of the genus *Cerion*. Numerous species of the genus appear on different Bahamian Islands. Bartsch considered their natural diversity a result of rapid evolutionary changes. By importing selected species to the Dry Tortu-

gas he hoped to determine how rapidly land snails would evolve new morphological characters. He measured thousands of snails of each species and studied
their natural history over an 18-year period and then abandoned the populations on Loggerhead and Garden Keys. *Cerion* populations are still common in
the Dry Tortugas today. Preliminary studies show some hybridization has occurred on both islands. A detailed, statistical analysis of the existing populations may provide substantial information on natural genetic processes.

This preliminary survey, supported by the National Geographic Society,
demonstrated the wealth of information available in the scientific history of
the Dry Tortugas. It also demonstrated some of the problems in obtaining and
planning baseline data for long-term studies. Much of the earlier research did
not permit specific evaluation of environmental changes, primarily because of
nonspecific data on field-station location and general community structures.
Over-all community structure studies are a fairly recent field of investigation.
Since temporal changes in the environment are more evident in community
studies, it is imperative that such information be the prime objective of baseline data accumulation.

Ongoing research is continuing with programs of the National Park Service and the Harbor Branch Foundation. It is hoped that the numerous discussions held with various scientists during the course of this study will promote
further research into the use of the Dry Tortugas data for establishing long-
term trends in tropical environments.

RICHARD H. CHESHER

Shark Repellent Effect of the Red Sea Moses Sole, *Pardachirus marmoratus*

Principal Investigator: Eugenie Clark, Department of Zoology, University of Maryland, College Park, Maryland.

Grant No. 1119:   In support of studies on the shark repellent and other toxic effects of the Red Sea sole, *Pardachirus marmoratus*.

Soles of the genus *Pardachirus* (family Soleidae) can be distinguished from all other flatfish (Order Pleuronectiformes) by the presence of a series of pores at the bases of the dorsal and anal fins. Clark and Chao (1973) demonstrated that the milky fluid from these pores in the Red Sea species *Pardachirus marmoratus* (Lacépède), the "Moses sole," was toxic and lethal to teleost fishes. This led to studies on the shark repellent effects of this toxin (Clark, 1974), to comparisons of *P. marmoratus* with other species in the genus (Clark and George, 1976, 1979), and a series of chemical and pharmacological studies on the toxin of *P. marmoratus* by Primor and other investigators (see reviews in Primor et al., 1978; and Clark and George, 1979).

This report is on shark repellent tests made at the Heinz Steinitz Marine Biology Laboratory in Elat, Israel, and field tests made at the southern tip of the Sinai Peninsula at Ras Muhammed. Three types of tests were conducted: (1) specimens of *Pardachirus marmoratus* were presented to captive sharks, (2) nontoxic teleost fish bathed in dilutions of the secretion from *P. marmoratus* were presented to captive sharks, and (3) a line of 10 teleost fish, including *P. marmoratus,* was presented to sharks in the open sea.

Materials and Methods

Tests on captive sharks were made at the Heinz Steinitz Marine Biology Laboratory of Hebrew University at Elat, Israel, in 1972-73. Two female reef white-tip sharks, *Triaenodon obesus,* caught locally in 1970, were kept in an outdoor, shaded, cement holding tank (3 x 3 m, water depth 96 cm) with continuously running seawater. The seawater was turned off when observations on sharks were being recorded. The sharks measured approximately 110 and 125 centimeters total length. Also present in the tank were a discfish or remora, *Echeneis naucratus,* ca. 40 centimeters long and a hawksbill turtle, carapace length ca. 35 centimeters. The turtle was removed during tests after

177

1972. These animals were fed small or cut fish regularly several times a week. For test periods feeding was discontinued several days in advance and during tests except for "control fish." Control fish consisted of small whole or cut pieces (10-18 cm) of teleost fish (fresh or defrosted) of the following genera: *Siganus, Upeneus, Lethrinus, Lutianus, Gerres, Sparus,* and *Bothus.* A control fish was presented before or at the start of each test and if not eaten by the sharks within 3 minutes, the test was postponed. Fish offered to the sharks were tossed in or suspended near the center of the tank, on a thread, within 30 centimeters of the water surface. Male and female specimens of *Pardachirus marmoratus* (12.3 to 20.5 cm standard length) caught near Elat (fig. 1) were always presented to the shark suspended on a string that had been threaded through the gill opening and out the mouth with a blunt needle. This string in turn was looped onto the center of a second string across the top of the tank. Control fish were strung the same way except by only one long string held by the experimenter. Underwater photographs were taken by means of an under-water camera and strobe on tripods with a remote control cable release.

P. *marmoratus* was offered to the sharks in several ways: alive and therefore wriggling, at least intermittently, setting up the low-frequency vibrations of a struggling fish; freshly dead, intact or sometimes after the toxic secretion had been partly "milked" from the pores; frozen then freshly defrosted with-out removing any toxic secretion.

The amount of toxic solution that can be pressed out of a large P. *marmor-atus* is about 2 milliliters. "Milking" the sole was done by blotting the skin dry with a paper towel, pressing on the glands, and drawing the secretion into a pipette (Clark, 1974; Clark and George, 1979). The secretion was diluted with seawater.

In the shark repellent experiments where nontoxic fish (bait) were bathed in dilutions of the toxic secretion of P. *marmoratus* we followed a method simi-lar to that of Gilbert and Springer (1963, p. 482) who tested chemicals on sharks in enclosures in the Bahamas. We placed a 1.2-centimeter-diameter Teflon tube, carrying a continuous supply of seawater directly over the bait. When an attack on the bait was imminent (head of shark within 20 cm) a known dilution of the toxic secretion was injected with a hypodermic syringe into the upper end of the Teflon tube. The secretion was then carried along by the seawater, flowing continuously in the tube, onto the bait with no change in turbulence. Each experiment was terminated (after several attacks were aborted by toxic injections) by allowing a shark to take the bait without bath-ing it in toxic secretion.

The activity patterns of sharks in the cement tank were noted before and after bait was presented. This was facilitated by dividing the water surface

FIG. 1. The Moses sole is a relatively slow swimmer. Its more than 200 poison glands occupy some of the space of swimming muscles that operate the movements of the dorsal and anal fins. Here a specimen caught by hand is released before being grabbed again.

into 9 square meters (using 4 strings tied across the top, tic-tac-toe fashion) and recording the number of square meters a shark passed through in a unit of time.

Field tests at Ras Muhammed were made by hanging a main line near the surface between coral projections in water over 50 meters deep. The main line had 10 side lines, each 20 centimeters long, spaced 80 centimeters apart. A baitfish was tied to the end of each side line. Baitfish were usually defrosted *Caesio* sp. but also other nontoxic teleost fishes of the families Mugilidae, Mullidae, Scaridae, and Labridae.

Results

1. Figure 2 summarizes the results of 11 tests on the shark repellent effect of live *Pardachirus marmoratus* presented to 2 captive sharks. Tests 1 to 5 were terminated to examine the condition of the sole. In each case the sole did not appear harmed by the sharks; not one scratch was evident, even at the end of test 5 in which the sole was dead at least 7 of the last 22 hours of exposure to

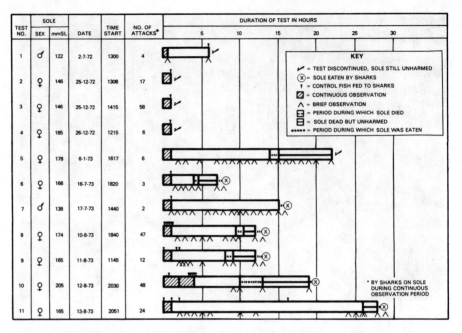

FIG. 2. Shark repellent effect of live Moses sole, *Pardachirus marmoratus*, on two captive sharks, *Triaenodon obesus*. (*Attack = fast swim toward sole with head of shark approaching within 10 cm of sole.)

the sharks. In tests 6 to 11 the sole was left in the tank until one of the sharks ate it. In test 6 the sole was removed briefly from this tank when it was found dead; some milky secretion could still be squeezed out showing no depletion of toxic secretion during 4 hours of exposure to attacking sharks.

During the first 1/2 to 4 hours of each test we continuously recorded the sequence and duration of behavior patterns of the fish. "Hunting turns" (Gilbert and Springer, 1963), the increased swimming speed and tight turns of sharks near the bait (fig. 3) usually started within a few seconds after we introduced the bait. Sharks attacked the bait (approached within 10 cm of the baitfish or mouthed it) on the average of 17.7 times per hour. Of 116 attacks recorded on the soles within the first hour, a shark approached the sole 85 times with its mouth closed (fig. 4); 21 times with its mouth open but not with the sole between its jaws (fig. 5); and 10 times it mouthed the sole by taking the sole in its open jaws (fig. 6). In 31 of the 216 attacks, the shark showed a strong repellent reaction involving one or a combination of the following: violent shaking of the head from side to side; jerking away and dashing around

Fig. 3. Two female reef white-tip sharks, *Triaenodon obesus* approach a live Moses sole, struggling and tied on a line in test No. 10 (see fig. 1). Larger shark (on right) has a remora, *Echeneis naucratus,* attached to its belly.

the tank, sometimes banging into the side walls; holding its mouth open for several seconds to over a minute; swimming or curling on the bottom of the tank, belly-up, sometimes with its mouth held open, in one case for over 3 minutes. In only two instances did we see the milky secretion released into the water by *P. marmoratus,* both times after a series of attacks by the sharks.

Control fish were usually eaten by the sharks in less than 1 minute (0'2" minimum, 2'25" maximum, 0'50"$\bar{x}$, N=33). *P. marmoratus,* presented alive, were not eaten for at least 7 to 28 hours ($\bar{x}$ 14 hours, N=6) and in most cases were eaten only after they had been dead for hours.

In 8 tests similar to the above we presented dead, or nearly dead, specimens of *P. marmoratus* to the sharks. These specimens had much of their toxic secretion squeezed out (for other experiments not reported here) before the test started and were eaten by the sharks usually in less than 2 hours (0'40" to 360', $\bar{x}$ 92', N=8). In the 2 shortest tests (0'40" and 9') the toxic secretion

FIG. 4.   Reef white-tip shark turns directly toward a struggling Moses sole, before turning aside.

FIG. 5.   A reef white-tip shark approaches a Moses sole with its mouth open.

Fig. 6.   A reef white-tip shark with its mouth around a Moses sole. The shark's thick, white nictitating membrane has closed over its eye. The shark is making an abrupt stop from a fast swim, rotating its pectoral fins nearly 90°. The remora hanging onto its belly has been swung around 180°. The shark did not complete this bite but jerked away violently, hitting itself against the walls of the cement tank with its mouth still open. The sole was not harmed or scratched by the shark's teeth.

was coagulated in the glands and was not fluid and milky when pressed out as it was in the *P. marmoratus* used in the other 6 tests, which ran 25 minutes to 3 hours.

In 2 tests we presented the sharks with a freshly dead *P. marmoratus* that had not been milked of its toxic secretion but had the mucus on its body removed with ethyl alcohol. In each case the sole was eaten by a shark within 1 minute.

In a series of tests using dead goatfish *(Upeneus)* tied progressively closer to a live *P. marmoratus* we obtained the following results: a goatfish tied 100 centimeters from the sole, a shark ate in 0′14″; at 30 centimeters from sole, shark ate in 1′26″; at 10 centimeters (2x) sharks ate in 3′40″ and 4′35″; less than 10 centimeters (4x), sharks did not eat during the 1 hour tested.

Two goatfish soaked in 50 percent and 4 percent solutions of toxic secretion, then immediately put into the tank with sharks, were eaten in 0′26″ and 1′20″ respectively.

2. Captive sharks were presented with nontoxic baitfish bathed in a stream of running seawater (control tests) from a Teflon tube. In repellent tests, a 1-percent solution of *P. marmoratus* secretion was injected into the Teflon tube and therefore further diluted in the running seawater and in the tank water surrounding the baitfish hanging under the lower opening of the tube. In 11 control tests (before and after tests with toxic solutions) sharks ate the baitfish in about 1 minute (0'3" to 2'40", x̄ 1'06"; N=11). In 5 tests with diluted *P. marmoratus* secretion running over the baitfish, sharks attacked the baitfish 60 times during 38'10" and the baitfish were never eaten.

3. Field tests at Ras Muhammed, with a line of 10 baitfish set overnight, attracted 4 species of sharks *(Carcharhinus albimarginatus, C. amblyrhynchus, C. limbatus,* and *Triaenodon obesus).* Preliminary tests run during the day attracted too many small teleost fishes (e.g., surgeon fish) that nibbled away most of the nontoxic baitfish before the sharks came around. The main test lines of 10 fish each were therefore set in the late afternoon (between 1500 and 1800 hours). Eleven of these were set (4 during winter 1972 and 7 during summer 1973). The 4 sets during winter were made under difficult field conditions (e.g., with only three observers and with weather and army security problems) when the lines could not be checked at regular intervals. Lines checked after 24, 15, 17, and 16 hours had all the fish removed (both nontoxic fish and *Pardachirus marmoratus*). In summer 1973, six of us camped near the lines and took turns checking the lines frequently. In one test the entire line disappeared shortly after it was set, probably taken by a shark. In 6 tests we monitored the set lines for periods of 12 to 19 hours (x̄ 15)) and used 25 *P. marmoratus* (20 dead and 5 alive) and 35 nontoxic dead baitfish. Sharks and one large moray eel usually started eating the baitfish off the lines within the first few hours after the line was set. The nontoxic fish were eaten off the lines first. The 25 *P. marmoratus* were taken by the predators as follows: 16 never; 2 after 10 hours; 5 after 5 hours; 2 after 3 hours; none in less than 3 hours. In 2 tests a grouper was tied on a side line with a *P. marmoratus.* In both tests neither the grouper nor the attached sole were taken and the tests were terminated after 15 and 16½ hours.

Conclusions

Live *Pardachirus marmoratus* presented to sharks in captivity can repel sharks 7 to 28 hours even though they die during the last few hours. Dead *P. marmoratus* with part of their toxic secretion squeezed out repel sharks for only about 2 hours.

Baitfish bathed in a dilute running solution of toxic secretion from *Pardachirus marmoratus* are 100 percent effective in repelling sharks.

Fig. 7.   A shark line, set near the surface at Ras Muhammed, is baited with one
Moses sole and nine nontoxic teleost fish.

Live and dead specimens of *Pardachirus marmoratus* tied to a set line with
nontoxic baitfish repelled at least 4 species of sharks in the open sea for periods
of 3 to 16½ hours, usually more than 10 hours.

The repellent effect of *Pardachirus marmoratus,* which works on other
predators and is toxic to fishes and invertebrates, is due to a toxic secretion in
small amounts retained in the mucous covering of the sole. When this mucus
is removed, the sole no longer can repel predators.

An area approximately 10 centimeters around *Pardachirus marmoratus* re-
pels sharks; nontoxic baitfish within this area are not taken by sharks. Sharks
are deterred from entering an area up to 30 centimeters around *P. marmoratus.*

Acknowledgments

This study was supported by the National Geographic Society and the
United States Office of Naval Research. I am grateful to many who aided this
work. Professor F. D. Por and the staff of the Heinz Steinitz Marine Biology
Laboratory of Hebrew University in Elat, Israel, extended laboratory facilities
and cooperation. David Fridman was most helpful in collecting specimens
and Abshalom, Avi Barnes, Willard Cook, Nikolas Konstantinou, and Gail

Weinmann helped in laboratory and field experiments. The photographs taken by David Doubilet documented these studies and allowed more detailed analyses of shark reactions. Taz Rufty prepared figure 1.

REFERENCES

BALRIDGE, H. DAVID
    1976.   A reminder of the impracticability of chemical shark repellents.   P. 18
             in "Sharks and Man: A Perspective," W. Seaman, ed.   Florida Sea
             Grant Program Conf. Proc. Report No. 10.
CLARK, EUGENIE
    1974.   The Red Sea's sharkproof fish.   National Geographic, vol. 145, no. 5,
             pp. 718-727.
CLARK, EUGENIE, and CHAO, STELLA
    1973.   A toxic secretion from the Red Sea flatfish, *Pardachirus marmoratus* (Lacé-
             pède).   Bull. Sea Fish. Res. Station. (Haifa), vol. 60, pp. 53-56.
CLARK, EUGENIE, and GEORGE, ANITA
    1976.   A comparison of the toxic soles *Pardachirus marmoratus* of the Red Sea and
             P. pavoninus from southern Japan.   Rev. Trav. Inst. Marit., vol. 40,
             pp. 545-546 (abstract).
    1979.   Toxic soles, *Pardachirus marmoratus* from the Red Sea and *P. pavoninus*
             from Japan, with notes on other species. Env. Biol. Fish., vol. 4, no. 2,
             pp. 103-123.
GILBERT, PERRY. W., and SPRINGER, STEWART
    1963.   Testing shark repellents.   Pp. 477-494 *in* "Sharks and Survival,"
             P. W. Gilbert, ed.   D. C. Heath Co., Boston.
PRIMOR, NAFTALI; PARNESS, JEROME; and ZLOTKIN, ELIAHU
    1978.   Pardaxin: the toxic factor from the skin secretion of the flatfish *Parda-
             chirus armoratus* (Soleidae).   Pp. 539-547 *in* "Toxins: Animal, Plants
             and Microbial," P. Rosenberg, ed.   Permagon Press, Oxford.

EUGENIE CLARK

Phytogeographical Survey of the Burica Peninsula of Panama and Costa Rica

Principal Investigator: Thomas B. Croat, P. A. Schulze Curator of Botany, Missouri Botanical Garden, Saint Louis, Missouri.

Grant No. 1104:   In support of a phytogeographical survey of the Burica Peninsula of Panama and Costa Rica.

The Burica Peninsula, a narrow tongue of land jutting into the Pacific Ocean southwest of Puerto Armuelles, Panama, belongs to both Panama and Costa Rica (see fig. 1). It is 30 kilometers long and 4 kilometers wide at its narrowest point near Puerto Limones. At the latitude of Puerto Armuelles, which served as our headquarters for the expedition, the peninsula is 20 kilometers broad. The region consists of a series of hills mostly less than 250 meters elevation but reaching 600 meters elevation in the northern part near San Bartolo Limite. The frontier between Panama and Costa Rica follows an irregular course relatively near the shore along the west coast near the mouth of the Golfo Dulce, which separates the Burica Peninsula from the Osa Peninsula in Costa Rica. The Costa Rican side of the peninsula rises rather uniformly to the divide which forms the frontier, but in general the Panamanian side has a series of low hills lying between the divide and the ocean.

Although no roads exist throughout most of the peninsula, it is sparsely populated throughout. Local traffic is by horse or boat. Most of the population live along the coast on the Panamanian side of the peninsula owing to the fact that landing a boat on the opposite coast is hazardous.

The vegetation of much of the peninsula is now secondary, but much of it was cut off a very long time ago and is now quite advanced. Slash and burn agriculture is still practiced throughout the region. Most of the eastern side of the peninsula and all of the lower 2/3 of the peninsula consists of tropical moist forest (Holdridge life zone system) but to the west it becomes premontane wet forest and finally tropical wet forest.

Preliminary studies with the few existing collections suggested that the region was of interest phytogeographically because the species were found nowhere else in the province of Chiriquí.

Our expedition, which consisted of myself and two other botanists, Ron Liesner and Phillip Busey, visited the peninsula in February and March of 1973. Although part of the peninsula had been visited by R. E. Woodson and

COSTA RICA

PANAMA
Chiriqui´ Province

San Bartolo
Arriba

Puerto
Armuelles

BAHIA DE CHARCO AZUL

Golfo de
Chiriqui´

BAHIA
DE PAVON

Limones

Punta de Burica

PACIFIC OCEAN

FIG. 1.   The Burica Peninsula, on the Pacific Ocean side of Costa Rica.

R. W. Schery, the authors of the *Flora of Panama,* and somewhat later by K.
Chambers and W. Stern, and also by Roy Lent (approaching from the Costa
Rican side), no extensive collecting had been done in the region.

Because of the absence of roads, collecting excursions were made mostly
on foot from the beachhead on the west shore. It was possible to drive part way

down the beach with a four-wheel-drive vehicle during low tide, but most trips were made by boat to designated points along the shore where we set up camp. The routes of the survey are shown on the map.

Through the generosity of the Chiriquí Land Company, we were able to use a bungalow on the company grounds for processing and drying our collections. This insured the success of the expedition, since there was no other comparable place to stay in Puerto Armuelles where we could have processed and dried so many collections. In all, 1,289 collections were made totaling more than all the collections made previously from all areas of tropical moist forest in Chiriquí Province. More than 25 percent of the species collected had not previously been reported for Chiriquí Province or western Panama. The region of highest elevation to the west of Puerto Armuelles near San Bartolo Limite, where limited amounts of virgin tropical wet forest still exist, proved very interesting. This area was reached by means of a recently constructed logging road made by the Chiriquí Land Company. To my knowledge it had not previously been visited by any botanist. Most expeditions to western Panama have neglected the lowlands, which are now nearly devoid of native forest, and instead have concentrated on the more pleasant, cooler areas around Boquete and Volcán. Thus the region we visited, which consists of a series of high hills reaching about 600 meters, has been overlooked by botanists. This region turned up a number of new species and even a genus new to the flora of Panama. This vegetation proved to be most closely related to that of the Osa Peninsula of Costa Rica and finds its exact counterpart nowhere else in western Panama.

THOMAS B. CROAT

Reconstitution of Bird Community Structure on Long Island, New Guinea, After a Volcanic Explosion

Principal Investigator: Jared M. Diamond, School of Medicine, University of California, Los Angeles, California.[1]

Grant No . 1042:   For study of recolonization of exploded volcanic islands by New Guinea birds.

The expression "convergent evolution" was coined by anatomists to describe the independent evolution of similar body structure in distantly related species exposed to similar selective pressures. Famous examples are the resemblance of large marine carnivores of four different vertebrate classes (sharks, teleost fish, ichthyosaurs, and whales); and the resemblance of marsupial "moles," "mice," "cats," "wolves," and flying phalangers to their placental equivalents.

Once ecological communities are adequately understood, it should be possible to recognize properties constituting their "ecological structure," in analogy to the morphological structure of an animal's body. Examples of properties that might usefully define ecological structure include number of species (MacArthur and Wilson, 1963), distribution of population survival times (Mayr, 1965), distribution of species among trophic categories (Lein, 1972; Heatwole and Levins, 1972), and distribution of species over habitat gradients (Cody, 1975). In recent years ecologists have begun to compare these properties in communities of phylogenetically distant species living under similar climatic conditions at different localities or on different continents, in order to recognize convergent evolution in community structure (e.g., chapters 10-14 of Cody and Diamond, 1975).

The species composition of communities is subject to turnover because of local extinctions and immigrations. If community structural properties are nevertheless maintained in a steady-state, these extinctions and immigrations cannot be random as to species but must be biased by ecological constraints.

---

[1] It is a pleasure to acknowledge my debt to the National Geographic Society and to the Sanford Trust of the American Museum of Natural History for support; to E. E. Ball, R. W. Johnson, E. Lindgren, and F. Moeder for information about Long Island; to M. LeCroy and E. Mayr for discussions of Bismarck and New Guinea birds; and to many residents of Papua New Guinea for making the fieldwork possible.

191

Similar constraints must operate on immigrations alone when a community is created *de novo*. These constraints are well illustrated by two classic studies that helped crystallize thinking about community structure. In the first of these studies, based on the recolonization of Krakatau following its defaunation by a volcanic explosion in 1883, the number of resident bird species was found to have returned to a value expected for an undisturbed island of Krakatau's area by about 36 years after the explosion (Dammerman, 1948). In the second study, based on the recolonization of isolated mangrove trees following their experimental defaunation by fumigation, the number of arthropod species (Wilson and Simberloff, 1969), as well as the trophic structure of the arthropod community (Heatwole and Levins, 1972), were found to have returned to approximately the original condition within a few years.

The present project sought evidence for reconstitution of community structure on Long Island near New Guinea. This island appears to have been largely or completely defaunated by a volcanic explosion in the 18th century, which deposited a layer of ash up to 30 meters thick or more (Johnson, Taylor, and Davis, 1972; Ball and Johnson, 1975). Although no literate observer was present to witness Long's defaunation, the event is inferred from several independent lines of evidence: descriptions of Long by early European explorers before and after the presumed explosion, geological surveys, carbon-14 dating, present composition of the fauna and flora, and genealogies and traditional accounts of Melanesian peoples now resident on Long and neighboring islands. In 1933 the birds of Long were well surveyed by W. Coultas of the Whitney South Sea Expedition from the American Museum of Natural History. In June-August 1972, with the generous support of the National Geographic Society and also of the Sanford Trust of the American Museum of Natural History, I resurveyed the birds of Long (Diamond, 1973 and 1974). Additional observations of birds on Long were made by Dr. Eric Lindgren in November 1972, by Dr. Eldon Ball in 1969, 1971, 1972, 1973, and 1974, and by Mr. Franz Moeder during residence of many years. In this paper I shall summarize the extent to which the bird community of Long has regained its equilibrium species number, its distribution of species among colonist categories, and its trophic structure, and I shall describe the rapid evolution of a distinct new subspecies in one of the colonist populations.

Species Number

During my 1972 expedition I also surveyed the avifaunas of 14 other islands of various sizes near Long. Figure 1 plots the number of resident, nonmarine, lowland bird species (S) on each island, as a function of island area (A)

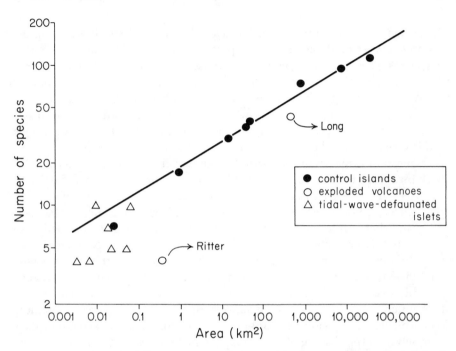

FIG. 1.   Number of resident, nonmarine, lowland bird species, S, on Long Island
and neighboring islands, plotted as a function of island area A (in square kilometers) on a double logarithmic scale. Closed circles, relatively undisturbed islands;
open circles, recently exploded volcanoes; triangles, coral islets defaunated by a tidal wave in 1888. The straight line $S = 18.9 \ A^{0.18}$ was fitted by least mean squares
through points for the seven larger undisturbed islands. (After Diamond, 1974.)

in square kilometers. On the large islands not recently defaunated by volcanic
explosions, species number increases regularly with island area according to
the empirical equation $S = 18.9 \ A^{0.18}$. As also noted for birds of the Solomon
Islands (Diamond and Mayr, 1976), S on the smallest islands varies more ir-
regularly, because of statistical fluctuations in their small number of species
and of individuals.

The lowland species number, 43, I found on Long is somewhat less than
the number 57 expected for an undisturbed island of the same area (i.e., predicted by substituting Long's area of 447 square kilometers into the equation
$S = 18.9 \ A^{0.18}$). Coultas did not reach Long's lake and mountains in 1933 and
therefore missed their bird species, but in lowland terrestrial habitats he recorded nearly as many species as I did in those same habitats 39 years later.
Thus, by 1933, about two centuries after the explosion, Long had recovered

75 percent of its "quota" of bird species, but made little if any progress towards recovering the remaining 25 percent in the next 39 years. Evidently, lowland species numbers on Long rose rapidly at first and then became "stuck" at a quasi-steady-state value below the eventual equilibrial value.

What is retarding the final approach to equilibrium? I think that two factors may be operating. First, the lowland forest of Long is still more open and savanna-like than the structured rain forest of older islands, because Long's soil is very porous and rainwater runs off rapidly. Even at equilibrium one expects fewer bird species in a less structured forest. Thus, equilibration of Long with birds may be partly rate-limited by regrowth of vegetation and not just by dispersal of birds themselves. This interpretation is supported by the fact that Ritter, a nearby island that was defaunated by a volcanic explosion in 1888 and that still has much scantier vegetation than Long, correspondingly has a much larger deficit of bird species (4 species present, compared to an equilibrial value of 16 predicted for Ritter's area). Second, the colonists now established on Long have occupied all habitats in great abundance and are presumably making it difficult for new colonists to become established. It may take much longer for several specialist species to outcompete one of these broad-niched early colonists than for the early colonists to have established themselves in the absence of any competition. In Wilson's (1969) terms, the initial quasi-steady-state value of species number may be significantly below the number at "assortative equilibrium," when colonists have slowly been sorted out into the most stable combinations of species.

In contrast to the extensive equilibration of the lowland avifauna on Long, equilibration of the montane avifauna is far less complete. Long supports only 2 montane bird populations, far below the predicted number of 7 at equilibrium on an island of Long's area and elevation. Since regrowth of forest has been more complete in Long's mountains than in the lowlands, slow colonization by montane birds themselves must be the explanation. Elsewhere, too, in the Southwest Pacific, montane bird species are underrepresented among superior colonists (Mayr and Diamond, 1976).

Distribution of Colonist Types

Bird species of the Bismarck Archipelago, the island group to which Long belongs, differ greatly in colonizing ability and in properties correlated with colonizing ability, such as dispersal rate, reproductive potential, harvesting strategy, and distributional strategy. These properties may be used to classify Bismarck bird species into arbitrary categories, ranging from "supertramps" (the most rapidly dispersing colonists) through "D-tramps and C-tramps" (the next-best colonists) and "B-tramps and A-tramps" (slower colonists) to "high-S species" (the most sedentary species: Diamond, 1975). Extinction rates of populations increase with decreasing population size and island size, so that an increasing fraction of the populations must be recent arrivals on islands of decreasing size. That is, in the steady-state, small islands have a high fraction of supertramps, while large islands have a high fraction of high-S species.

What distribution of colonist types should Long have at equilibrium? In the Bismarck Archipelago the closest model for Long at equilibrium is Umboi, a similar-sized island that is near Long but that has not been recently defaunated. Umboi proves to have only two supertramp populations, both very local, but 16 high-S species. In contrast, Long has 10 out of the 13 Bismarck supertramps and only 1 of the 52 Bismarck high-S species. That is, in comparison with an island at equilibrium, Long has close to the expected number of species, but this agreement conceals the fact that many of the particular species involved are not ones expected at equilibrium. Naturally, the rapidly dispersing supertramps were overrepresented among the early colonists of Long. They will presumably be gradually replaced by high-S species and tramps until Long attains a distribution of colonist types expected for its area at equilibrium.

Trophic Structure

Birds of the Bismarck Archipelago may be somewhat arbitrarily divided into 17 trophic groups or "guilds," based on diet and habitat preference. Table 1 lists the species in each guild on Long and also on Karkar Island, 120 kilometers west of Long. Karkar was chosen for comparison because its area (386 square kilometers), elevation (1,650 meters), and number of lowland bird species (44) are similar to those of Long (447 square kilometers, 1,310 meters, and 43 species, respectively), but colonization of Long and Karkar by birds has largely been independent. Karkar has derived most of its bird populations directly from New Guinea, whereas most birds of Long have been derived from New Britain and adjacent islands. Karkar has not been recently defaunated. Thus, comparison of Long and Karkar permits one to assess how closely a new bird community resembles in trophic structure an older bird community on a physically similar island. Table 1 suggests the following conclusions:

1. Both Long and Karkar support only small subsets of the species pools from which they are derived. While New Guinea has 513 species, Karkar has only 52 (44 in the lowlands plus 8 confined to the mountains). While New Britain and adjacent islands have 133 species (88 of them shared with New

TABLE 1. Trophic Comparison of the Avifaunas on Long and Karkar Islands

(The avifaunas of the Bismarck Archipelago and New Guinea region may be somewhat arbitrarily divided into 17 ecological "guilds," based on diet and habitat. The table names each bird species in each guild on Long and Karkar. The number following each species is the weight in grams on that island. If the weight on that island is not known, the weight of the same race of that species on other islands is instead given in parentheses. The more abundant species on each island are set in bold-face, while less abundant species are in italics. Species in square brackets are confined on that island to the mountains.)

Guild	Long Island		Karkar Island	
Littoral	*Halcyon saurophaga*	114		
	Egretta sacra	(530)	*Egretta sacra*	(530)
	Esacus magnirostris	(920)		
Fresh-water	*Tachybaptus ruficollis*	251		
	Anas superciliosa	670		
Open-country, terrestrial omnivore	*Amaurornis olivaceus*	(208)	*Amaurornis olivaceus*	(208)
	Rallus philippensis	260		
Open-country, insectivore	*Saxicola caprata*	18		
Grass finch or warbler	**Lonchura spectabilis**	10	*Rhipidura leucophrys*	(29)
	Acrocephalus stentoreus	18	*Lonchura tristissima*	10
Aerial, insectivore	**Collocalia esculenta**	6	**Collocalia esculenta**	8
			[*Collocalia hirundinacea*	9]
	Collocalia vanikorensis	10		
	Hirundo tahitica	16	*Hirundo tahitica*	(15)
	Merops philippinus	39		
			Eurystomus orientalis	(168)
Nocturnal, insectivore-carnivore	*Caprimulgus macrurus*	(67)	*Caprimulgus macrurus*	69
			Ninox connivens	405
	Tyto alba	(~1000)	*Tyto alba*	(~1000)

Category	Species		Species	
Forest, terrestrial frugivore	*Gallicolumba beccarii*	83	*Gallicolumba beccarii*	81
	Chalcophaps stephani	113	*Chalcophaps stephani*	110
			Gallicolumba jobiensis	147
Forest, terrestrial omnivore	*Megapodius freycinet*	556	*Megapodius freycinet*	677
Forest, terrestrial insectivore	*Pitta sordida*	63	[*Pitta sordida*	74]
	Nycticorax caledonicus	560		
Forest, arboreal frugivore, Treroninae (fruit pigeons)	*Ptilinopus solomonensis*	97	*Ptilinopus iozonus*	(112)
			Ptilinopus superbus	121
	[*Ptilinopus insolitus*	132]	[*Ptilinopus rivoli*	136]
			Ptilinopus magnifica	175
	Ducula pistrinaria	549	*Ducula spilorrhoa*	(560)
	Ducula spilorrhoa	(560)	*Ducula zoeae*	567
Forest, arboreal frugivore, other species	[*Erythrura tricbroa*	14]	[*Erythrura tricbroa*	15]
			Loriculus aurantiifrons	16
	Aplonis cantoroides	53	*Aplonis cantoroides*	55
	Aplonis metallicus	60	*Aplonis metallicus*	58
			[*Turdus poliocephalus*	74]
			Macropygia nigrirostris	82
	Macropygia mackinlayi	87	*Macropygia mackinlayi*	87
	Macropygia amboinensis	(147)		
	Eudynamis scolopacea	178	*Eudynamis scolopacea*	219
			Reinwardtoena reinwardtsi	264
Forest, arboreal omnivore			*Dicaeum pectorale*	8
			Micropsitta pusio	(14)
	Zosterops griseotincta	14		
	Coracina tenuirostris	68	*Coracina tenuirostris*	73

Table 1. Trophic Comparison of the Avifaunas on Long and Karkar Islands—continued

Guild	Long Island		Karkar Island	
Forest, arboreal insectivore			*Gerygone magnirostris*	9
			[*Phylloscopus trivirgatus*	9]
			Ceyx lepidus	17
			Myiagra alecto	26
	Monarcha cinerascens	25	*Monarcha cinerascens*	30
	Pachycephala melanura	26		
			Ceyx azureus	35
			Cacomantis variolosus	40
			Tanysiptera galatea	55
	Halcyon chloris	76		
Carnivore			*Aviceda subcristata*	333
	Falco berigora	460	*Falco berigora*	(460)
	Haliastur indus	(497)	*Haliastur indus*	517
			[*Accipiter meyerianus*	(815)]
	Falco peregrinus	(816)		
	Pandion haliaetus	(1154)		
	Haliaeetus leucogaster	(2000)	*Haliaeetus leucogaster*	(2000)
Arboreal, nectarivore, *Myzomela* (honeyeaters),	*Nectarinia jugularis*	(9)	*Nectarinia jugularis*	10
	Myzomela sclateri	10	*Nectarinia sericea*	10
			[*Myzomela sclateri*	11]
Nectariniidae (sunbirds)	*Myzomela pammelaena*	16		
Arboreal, nectarivore, Lorinae (lories)	*Vini placentis*	31	*Vini rubrigularis*	37
	Trichoglossus haematodus	98	*Trichoglossus haematodus*	102

Guinea, 45 absent on New Guinea), Long has only 45 (43 in the lowlands plus 2 confined to the mountains). Thus, if successful colonists of Long and Karkar had been drawn randomly from their respective source faunas, one would expect only $(52/513)(88/133)(45) = 3$ species to be shared between the islands. In fact, 20 species are shared (19 lowland species and 1 montane species). This unexpected degree of resemblance means that the successful colonists were not at all a random selection from their source faunas, but that source species differ greatly in colonizing ability, and that a subset of superior colonists is over-represented in the faunas of both Long and Karkar. For several of these shared species *(Megapodius freycinet, Eudynamis scolopacea, Coracina tenuirostris)*, sub-specific characters show that the Long and Karkar populations were derived from different immediate sources.

2. All 17 guilds are represented on Long. Most guilds are occupied by similar numbers of species on Long and Karkar. While there are differences which will be noted in the following paragraphs, it is still true to a first approximation that something close to an equilibrium trophic structure was rapidly reconstituted on Long. Part of the trophic resemblance between Long and Karkar is of course due to the 20 shared species, but much of the resemblance lies in the fact that different species or groups of species fill similar trophic roles on the two islands.

3. The only instances in which a guild is unrepresented on Long or Karkar are that Karkar lacks fresh water species and lowland forest terrestrial insectivores, of which Long has 2 each. The reason for the difference in freshwater species is simply that Long has a large lake while Karkar does not. It is not obvious, however, why Karkar lacks forest terrestrial insectivores in the lowlands (although there is 1 such species in the mountains, the same species as one of the 2 species in the Long lowlands). This niche on Karkar may be partly filled by the abundant forest arboreal insectivorous kingfisher *Tanysiptera galatea,* which often feeds on the ground, and by occasional insectivory in Karkar's 2 *Gallicolumba* ground-dove species, which I have categorized as frugivores but which sometimes take insects.

4. There are 2 guilds in which closely related, similar-sized, trophically identical species replace each other on Long and Karkar: the grass finches *Lonchura spectabilis* (Long) and *L. tristissima* (Karkar), and the arboreal nectarivorous lorikeets *Vini placentis* (Long) and *V. rubrigularis* (Karkar). In effect, the trophic structure has been reshuffled on a one-for-one basis.

5. In other guilds the trophic structure has been reshuffled on a more complex basis than one-for-one, although the two islands still support similar numbers of species. For example, the abundant small arboreal nectarivores *(Myzomela* and Nectariniidae) in lowland forest are *Myzomela sclateri* and

M. pammelaena on Long, *Nectarinia jugularis* and *N. sericea* on Karkar, with *N. jugularis* present on Long but uncommon and confined to the coast, and *M. sclateri* present on Karkar but confined to the mountains (cf. fig. 41 of Diamond, 1975, for further reshufflings of this guild). In the guild of forest arboreal frugivorous pigeons (Treroninae) each island has several species spanning a more than fivefold size range in the lowlands, plus an additional species of 132 or 136 grams confined to the mountains. Nevertheless, the reshuffling has been so complete that only 1 species *(Ducula spilorrhoa)*, the rarest one of the guild, is shared by the two islands.

6. In some cases the outcome of the reshuffling has been that a few supertramp species on Long replace several more sedentary species on Karkar. For instance, in the forest arboreal insectivorous guild, the single supertramp kingfisher of Long *(Halcyon chloris stresemanni)* replaces 3 kingfishers forming a graded-size series on Karkar *(Ceyx lepidus, C. azureus, Tanysiptera galatea)*, while 2 supertramp gleaning flycatchers of Long *(Monarcha cinerascens* and *Pachycephala melanura)* replace 1 supertramp flycatcher *(Monarcha cinerascens)*, 1 "normal" flycatcher *(Myiagra alecto)*, and 3 insectivores of other bird families on Karkar *(Gerygone magnirostris, Phylloscopus trivirgatus, Cacomantis variolosus)*. Among the *Ptilinopus-Ducula* pigeons in the lowlands, the 2 supertramps *P. solomonensis* and *D. pistrinaria* of Long replace 4 species on Karkar while spanning nearly as wide a size range (cf. fig. 45 of Diamond, 1975, for further reshufflings of this guild). These guilds illustrate in detail how, at assortive equilibrium, several more sedentary species may eventually come to oust an ecologically equivalent but more species-poor combination of supertramps on Long.

The overall conclusion is that the trophic structure of the bird community has been rapidly reconstituted on Long, as Heatwole and Levins (1972) also showed for arthropod communities on fumigated mangrove trees. Despite the

TABLE 2.   Wing Length of *Myzomela pammelaena*

(Numbers are the average value and standard deviation, in millimeters, of wing length in six individuals of each sex from each population.)

Subspecies	Island	Wing (male)	Wing (female)
M. p. pammelaena	Admiralties (Nauna, San Miguel)	74.0 ± 1.7	66.7 ± 1.4
M. p. ernstmayri	Admiralties (Hermit, Ninigo, Anchorite)	75.6 ± 1.8	68.5 ± 1.5
M. p. nigerrima	Long	77.3 ± 0.8	69.8 ± 0.8

substantially different species pools from which the Long and Karkar avifaunas were assembled, these two islands have achieved trophically similar species sets. This finding parallels Lein's (1972) demonstration that avifaunas of different continents are trophically similar. The intercontinental similarities had to be achieved by much more drastic convergences, namely, convergent morphological evolution of phylogenetically distant bird stocks, whereas the similarities of Long and Karkar required only selection of colonists from closely related and partly overlapping species pools.

Rapid Evolution

Biologists have often speculated about the length of time required for a new subspecies or species to evolve. Usually, one can do no better than guess, based on geological histories or the paleontological record. In a few cases, however, it has been shown that colonists introduced into an area formerly lacking the species in question may diverge rapidly in a few centuries or even decades. Notable examples are that 5 species of endemic moths dependent on bananas have evolved on Hawaii in the one or two millennia since man introduced bananas to Hawaii (Zimmerman, 1960); the house sparrow has differentiated locally in size and color in response to environmental temperature and humidity within the century since man introduced it to North America (Johnson and Selander, 1964); and a brown-bellied race of finch, *Lonchura spectabilis gajduseki,* evolved from a white-bellied ancestor in the humid Karimui Basin of New Guinea within one or two decades after man created grassland habitat for this finch at Karimui (Diamond, 1972).

In the two centuries since Long became available for recolonization by birds, recognizable morphological changes have taken place in at least three colonist species. The Long population of the white-eye *Zosterops griseotincta* has legs and perhaps plumage slightly more yellowish than those of the ancestral population in the Admiralty Islands (Mayr, 1955). The more interesting case involves 2 honey-eaters, *Myzomela pammelaena* and *M. sclateri.* The former is a large species (16 grams) that colonized Long from the Admiralty Islands to the north, while the latter is a small species (10 grams) that probably colonized from islets on the north coast of New Britain to the east. Long, and two neighboring islands (Crown and Tolokiwa) colonized from Long, are the sole localities where these 2 species coexist. The Long population of *M. pammelaena* is now recognized as an endemic subspecies, *M. p. nigerrima,* distinguished by being darker and larger than its Admiralty ancestors (Salomonsen, 1966). Table 2 illustrates the size difference as illustrated by wing length. Table 3 shows that the *Myzomela sclateri* population of Long, Crown, and Tolokiwa is

TABLE 3.   Weight of *Myzomela sclateri*

(Numbers are the average value and standard deviation, in grams, of weight; n, the number of individuals weighed.)

Island	Male	Female
Karkar	10.9 ± 0.7 (n = 17)	10.0 ± 1.0 (n = 11)
Long, Crown, Tolokiwa	10.0 ± 1.7 (n = 50)	9.6 ± 0.9 (n = 25)

smaller than that of Karkar as illustrated by weight. Tentatively, I interpret these shifts to mean that coexistence of these 2 honey-eaters is facilitated by size differences, as in so many pairs of congeners; and that they have therefore been diverging in size since achieving sympatry on Long, Crown, and Tolokiwa, so that the large *M. pammelaena* is now larger and the small *M. sclateri* smaller than ancestral populations living in the absence of the other species. A definitive assessment of this interpretation must await completion of more extensive measurements on these populations, and comparison of my 1972 specimens with Coultas's 1933 specimens to detect possible divergence with time.

Conclusion

The avifauna of Long is a young community that has been assembled by overwater colonization in the two centuries since Long was defaunated by a volcanic explosion. In its distribution of colonist types the Long avifauna is still far from achieving the equilibrium distribution expected for an older island of the same size, in that Long has a large excess of rapidly colonizing supertramps and an almost complete lack of slowly colonizing high-S species. Nevertheless, species number on Long has already reached 75 percent of the equilibrium value, and the remaining deficit is due at least partly to incomplete recovery of Long's vegetation rather than to any lag in equilibration by the birds themselves. The trophic structure of Long's avifauna has achieved a state like that of an island at equilibrium, by several means: some of the same superior colonist species that are widespread on older islands also recolonized Long; a few species on older islands have been replaced one-for-one by other colonists on Long; and other guilds have been reshuffled on a more complex basis, so that the local guild on Long is ecologically equivalent to local guilds elsewhere with which the Long guild shares only some or few species in common. For the most part, this rapid convergent evolution of community structure on Long has just involved sieving of potential colonists, rather than the dramatic morphological convergences that underlie intercontinental similarities in community structure. That sieving has actually occurred is shown by the fact that at least 11 other Bismarck or New Guinea species are known to have reached Long prior to my visit but were not successful in founding populations. In addition, there has apparently been at least one case involving significant morphological change on Long, resulting in a broadened size sequence of honey-eaters.

REFERENCES

BALL, E. E., and JOHNSON, R. W.
———.   Volcanic history of Long Island, Papua New Guinea.   Pp. ___ *in* "Volcanism in Australasia," R. W. Johnson, ed.   Elsevier, Amsterdam. (In press.)
CODY, M. L.
    1975.   Towards a theory of continental species diversities.   Pp. 214-257 *in* "Ecology and Evolution of Communities," M. L. Cody and J. M. Diamond, eds.   Harvard University Press.
CODY, M. L., and DIAMOND, JARED M., eds.
    1975.   Ecology and evolution of communities, 545 pp.   Harvard University Press.
DAMMERMAN, K. W.
    1948.   The fauna of Krakatau, 1883-1933.   Verh. Ned. Akad. Wet., Afd. Natuurk., ser. 2, vol. 44, pp. 1-594.
DIAMOND, JARED M.
    1972.   Avifauna of the Eastern Highlands of New Guinea, 438 pp.   Nuttall Ornithological Club, Cambridge, Massachusetts.
    1973.   Recolonization of exploded volcanic islands by New Guinea birds.   Explorers Journ., vol. 52, pp. 2-11.
    1974.   Colonization of exploded volcanic islands by birds: The supertramp strategy.   Science, vol. 184, pp. 803-806.
    1975.   Assembly of species communities.   Pp. 342-444 *in* "Ecology and Evolution of Communities," M. L Cody and J. M. Diamond, eds.   Harvard University Press.
DIAMOND, JARED M., and MAYR, ERNST
    1976.   Species-area relation for birds of the Solomon Archipelago.   Proc. Nat. Acad. Sci., vol. 73, pp. 262-266.
HEATWOLE, HAROLD, and LEVINS, RICHARD
    1972.   Trophic structure stability and faunal change during recolonization.   Ecology, vol. 53, pp. 531-534.
JOHNSON, R. W.; TAYLOR, G.A.M.; and DAVIES, R. A.
    [1972.]   Geology and petrology of Quaternary volcanic islands off the north coast of New Guinea.   Bur. Min. Resources Austr. Rec. (Unpublished.)
JOHNSTON, RICHARD F., and SELANDER, ROBERT K.
    1964.   House sparrows: Rapid evolution of races in North America.   Science, vol. 144, pp. 548-550.

LEIN, M. ROSS
 1972. A trophic comparison of avifaunas. Syst. Zool., vol. 21, pp. 135-150.
MACARTHUR, ROBERT H., and WILSON, EDWARD O.
 1963. An equilibrium theory of insular zoogeography. Evolution, vol. 17, pp. 373-387.
MAYR, ERNST
 1955. Notes on the birds of northern Melanesia. 3: Passeres. Amer. Mus. Novitates, no. 1707, 46 pp.
 1965. Avifauna: Turnover on islands. Science, vol. 150, pp. 1587-1588.
MAYR, ERNST, and DIAMOND, JARED M.
 1976. Birds on islands in the sky: Origin of the montane avifauna of northern Melanesia. Proc. Nat. Acad. Sci., vol. 73, pp. 1765-1769.
SALOMONSEN, F.
 1966. Preliminary descriptions of new honey-eaters (Aves, Meliphagidae). Breviora, no. 254, 12 pp.
WILSON, EDWARD O.
 1969. The species equilibrium. Brookhaven Symp. Biol., no. 22, pp. 38-47.
WILSON, EDWARD O., and SIMBERLOFF, DANIEL S.
 1969. Experimental zoogeography of islands: Defaunation and monitoring techniques. Ecology, vol. 50, pp. 267-278.
ZIMMERMAN, ELWOOD C.
 1960. Possible evidence of rapid evolution in Hawaiian moths. Evolution, vol. 14, pp. 137-138.

JARED M. DIAMOND

Botanical Exploration
of the Maya Mountains in Belize

Principal Investigator: Dr. John D. Dwyer, Missouri Botanical Garden and Saint Louis University, Saint Louis, Missouri.

Grant No. 1132:   In support of the botanical exploration of the Maya Mountains in Belize (formerly British Honduras).

The country of Belize, formerly British Honduras, which gained internal self-government in 1964, is located in the southeast portion of the Yucatán Peninsula about 800 miles south of New Orleans. The country is bounded on the north by the Mexican State of Quintana Roo, on the west and south by Guatemala, and on the east by the Caribbean Sea. In length, Belize extends from the Rio Hondo in the north to the Sarstoon River in the south, a distance of about 174 miles. At its widest point, the country is 68 miles from the largest city, Belize, to the village of Benque Viejo on the western border. In areal extent, Belize is approximately the size of the state of Massachusetts, about 8,750 square miles not including the approximately 116 square miles of offshore islands or cays.

The country is divided approximately in half by the Belize River. The northern half of the country is similar to other parts of the Yucatán Peninsula in that it is a fairly level plain with a maximum elevation of about 400 feet above sea level. The southern half of the country is dominated by the Maya Mountains, the object of our attention. Flanking these mountains on both north and south are subsidiary masses of limestone which reach an elevation of about 1,500 feet, or about half the height of the Maya Mountains. These limestone masses predominately form a karst topography of great variety. Much of the karstland is of the cone and tower varieties, with all intergradations between the two being found, from incipient cone to the more pronounced towers (Sweeting, 1968). Certain areas, particularly in the western part of the country, have a much more rolling and hummocky landscape with more surface drainage and only a weak development of conical hills and shallow dolines (Sweeting, 1968).

Altogether, hilly and mountainous land occupies about 60 percent of the land area of Belize. The Maya Mountains are formed chiefly from hard and very ancient rocks, predominately granite and porphyrite. According to Dixon (1955), the Maya Mountains were once an upland plateau approached by a climb up a steep rock wall on the northern and eastern face and with a very gentle fall away to the west and south. On top of the mountains, at an altitude of about 2,200–2,800 feet, there are less than 20 square miles of undulating to rolling upland which appear to be part of the original peneplain. During Cretaceous times, almost the whole of the plateau was beneath the sea and several hundred feet of limestone were laid down. Dixon further states that the northeast part of the plateau may have escaped this submergence, and thus would not have been inundated since the Permian—well before the origin of the angiosperms. Since the Cretaceous there has been a great deal of erosion and part of the limestone mantle has disappeared from the summit of the plateau. Streams have cut deeply to expose the Paleozoic granites. The north and east edges of the plateau have degenerated into a serrated ridge which curves in an arc from east to south to west. This arc has saddles as low as 1,800 feet, and high points which are mostly above 3,000 feet. The Coxcomb Range, with the highest measured peak in the country (Mount Victoria), is now an outlier of the main divide, lying about 10 miles to the east.

Climatically, Belize is described as subtropical, although under the Koeppen classification, it is classed as Am (tropical monsoon) north of the Maya Mountains, and af (tropical rain forest) along the southern coastal areas and in the southern parts of the Maya Mountains. In reality, the southern portion should most likely be classified as a tropical-wet forest because of the length of the dry season.

According to Lundell (1945, 1970) Belize has a floristic diversity which is perhaps unequaled, for the size of the country, among the other Latin American countries. In 1924 Sprague and Riley estimated that the total number of vascular plants would be about 4,000 species, an estimate in concurrence with Lundell. I estimate that the number will not exceed 3,500.

Fieldwork and Results

During the period March 21–28, 1973, I made a preliminary visit to Belize to make preparations for the field trip in May-June, 1973. During this period 144 numbers of vascular plants were collected and dried. On May 23, Dr. Thomas Croat; Paul A. Schulze, Curator of Botany; and Dr. Alwyn Gentry, Associate Curator at the Missouri Botanical Garden, flew with me to Belize. Mr. Bruce Vanderveen, a graduate student at Saint Louis University, joined the team in Belize. After having obtained collecting permits from the Acting Chief Forestry Officer, Mr. E. O. Bradley, the team checked out plant-collecting gear at Saint John's College, Belize, where the equipment is stored for qualified scientists to use. Due to the generosity of Mr. Robert Baumgartner, an American businessman residing in Belize, the team was able to utilize the facilities of one of his cottages on the Belize River, at Mile 11 1/2, Northern Highway, outside Belize City. As a boat with an outboard motor was furnished with the cottage, the group was able to do some botanizing on the Belize River. With these facilities serving as a base, several field trips were made in the direction of the Maya Mountains, utilizing a rented Land Rover. Once in the field, it became obvious that, in view of the field-work being confined to a few weeks and in view of the precipitous character of the terrain of the Maya Mountains, especially in the rainy season, the team would have to confine its efforts to botanizing at the base of the mountains. To collect at the summits would require an expedition of several months and would necessitate establishing camps at the summit. Most of the collecting was done along the Southern Highway, immediately south of Belmopan, the new capital of Belize, in the Cayo and Stann Creek Districts, as well as at Millionario and Cuevas, beyond Mountain Pine Ridge, Cayo District, and in the vicinity of the Mayan village of San Antonio, Toledo District. Native guides were hired for the Cuevas trip and for the botanizing in the vicinity of San Antonio. Dr. Alwyn Gentry, being acquainted with one of the Royal Air Force pilots stationed in Belize arranged with the Command to be flown by helicopter to the foot of Mount Victoria where he was able to collect for 2 days.

In approximately 33 man-hour days and 21 field days, from May 23 to June 19, 1973, the team collected almost 3,500 numbers of flowering plants and ferns with an estimated additional 3 samples (duplicates) for each number collected. This represents the largest number of vascular plants collected and dried for herbarium deposit from Belize in such a time span. Virtually all the plants have been identified and the vast majority of duplicates have been distributed to botanical institutions throughout the world. The number of Belize collections from the Maya Mountains expedition of 1973 established the Missouri Botanical Garden as having the largest number of Belize specimens of any institution. Such primacy has to be assessed in terms of the fact that the Garden had already acquired duplicates of many of the 10,000 numbers which a native Belizean collector, the late Percy Gentle, had collected between 1931 and 1958, first under the direction of Dr. H. H. Bartlett and later under Dr. C. L. Lundell, the foremost student of the flora of Belize. Other collections have been added to the herbarium of the Missouri Botanical Garden since the Maya Mountains expedition of 1973. A goodly number of these were collected by anthropologists and archeologists.

Principally as a result of the stimulus resulting from such an influx of collections from the Maya Mountains expedition, Dr. D. L. Spellman, Dr. Gerrit Davidse, and I (1975) published *A List of the Monocotyledoneae of Belize Including a Historical Introduction to Plant Collecting in Belize*. This included not only the team's collections but all available collections made by 17 collectors in Belize in the years 1959 to 1972. The assistance given by the grant of the National Geographic Society was acknowledged in this paper. Twenty-two species of grasses and sedges were recorded for the first time in Belize.

At the end of 1979, Dr. David Spellman and I completed the manuscript in which the Dicotyledoneae of Belize are listed, including all available collections made since 1957. This is the counterpart of the list of Monocotyledoneae published in 1975. About 2,300 taxa are found in the list and approximately 7,000 collections, virtually all of the latter being deposited in the herbarium of the Missouri Botanical Garden. The Maya Mountains collections represent almost two-thirds of all of the collections cited.

In conclusion, although the team did not collect the summits of the Maya Mountains, being forced to restrict their efforts to the lowlands at the base of the mountains, the numerous collections that were made represent a distinct contribution to the floristic studies of the country and provide a working base for subsequent botanizing in the Maya Mountains. As in the case of the Monocotyledoneae list, the Dicotyledoneae list provides workers with a tool to use when faced with the problem of identifying vascular plants from Belize.

REFERENCES

DIXON, C. G.
   1955.   Geology of Southern British Honduras with notes on adjacent areas, 85
            pp.   Government Printer, Belize.
DWYER, J. D., and SPELLMAN, D. L.
   _____.   A list of the Dicotyledoneae of Belize with all collections since 1957.
            Rhodora (in press).
LUNDELL, C. L.
   1942.   The vegetation and natural resources of British Honduras.   Vol. 7, pp.
            169-171), *in* "Plants and Plant Sciences in Latin America," F. Verdoorn,
            ed.   Chronica Botanica Co., Waltham, Mass.
   1970.   Studies of American plants . . . II.   Wrightia, vol. 4, p. 129.
SMITH, J. N.
   1945.   Forest associations of British Honduras II. and III.   Carib. Forester,
            vol. 6; pp. 45-61, 131-147.
SPRAGUE, T. A., and RILEY, L.A.M.
   1924.   Materials for a flora of British Honduras I.   Kew Bull., 1924; pp. 1-
            21.

SPELLMAN, D. L.; DWYER, J. D.; and DAVIDSE, G.
    1975.   A list of the Monocotyledoneae of Belize including a historical introduction to plant collecting in Belize.   Rhodora, vol. 77; pp. 105-140.
STANDLEY, P. C., and RECORD, S. J.
    1936.   The forests and flora of British Honduras.   Field Mus. Publ. Bot., vol. 12; pp. 1-432.
STEVENSON, N. S.
    1942.   Forest associations of British Honduras I.   Carib. Forester, vol. 3; pp. 164-171.
SWEETING, M. M.
    1968.   Karstic morphology of the Yucatán in University of Edinburgh Expedition to British Honduras. 1966.   Pp. 37-40 in "General Report," P. A. Furley, ed.   University of Edinburgh, Edinburgh, Scotland.

JOHN D. DWYER

The Survival Value of Synchronized Calving in the Wildebeest

Principal Investigator: Richard Despard Estes, Academy of Natural Sciences, Philadelphia, Pennsylvania.[1]

Grant No. 1112: To study the biological significance of the reproductive system of the wildebeest *(Connochaetes taurinus)*.

Unlike other African antelopes, whose offspring remain concealed for some time after birth, the young of most Alcelaphini accompany the mother from the very first hour (hartebeeste, however, still pursue the concealment strategy—Gosling, 1969; Ansell, 1971). Most other ungulates that have follower young (cattle, equids, muskox) have evolved a group defense, but in the Alcelaphini usually only the calf's own mother defends it, against predators up to the size of the spotted hyena, the primary predator on the young (Estes, 1964, 1966, 1976; Kruuk, 1972).

Births in *Connochaetes* and *Damaliscus* occur during a very short season: in a given locality over 80 percent of the calves are born within two to three weeks (Estes, 1976; Watson, 1969). Evidence gathered during three different wildebeest calving seasons in Ngorongoro Crater, Tanzania, indicated that mortality in small, dispersed herds was consistently higher than in large aggregations (Estes, 1976). It suggested that this antelope's unusual reproductive strategy is adapted to the mobile-aggregated distribution pattern characteristic of migratory populations, rather than to the dispersed-sedentary pattern seen in resident populations (Estes, 1976). Further study on this specific question was undertaken during the 1973 calving season from January 6 to February 26, with particular attention to calf survival in small herds.

A pregnancy rate close to 95 percent was found in adult females of aggregations and small herds alike, whereas the rate among primiparous 2-year-olds was probably under 10 percent, indicating poor nutrition in the months prior to the 1972 rut (in good years up to three-fourths of yearling females conceive).

Calf survival in small herds averaged just over half at the end of the birth peak, compared to 84 percent in aggregations. Daily sampling revealed that

[1] For permission to continue research in Ngorongoro and to live in Munge Cabin, we are indebted to the acting conservator, Anthony Mgina. R. K. Estes and K. Fuller participated in the research.

calving peaked at different times in different parts of the Crater, resulting in an extended season, although the peak in each population unit was of approximately equal duration. In some areas calving was virtually finished weeks before the peak began in the aggregations. Mortality ranged from very high among early calves to low in herds whose peak coincided with that of a nearby aggregation.

Low calf density combined with a lack of synchrony between small herds makes wildebeest living in the dispersed/sedentary pattern subject to high calf mortality from the spotted hyena; in effect, resident subpopulations that calved ahead of the main population were providing a steady protein windfall for the 420 Ngorongoro hyenas (Kruuk, 1972). In the large aggregations, there were enough older calves to provide "cover" for neonates during the crucial first day or two, making it much harder for hyenas to single out easily caught individuals. Therefore lack of synchrony between aggregations did not affect calf mortality to the same extent as it did in small herds. However, migratory wildebeest can further reduce calf vulnerability by moving beyond the ranges of territorial predators. Calf survival was appreciably higher in an aggregation that calved outside the Crater in an area with few hyenas; even inside Ngorongoro the thousands of wildebeest that calve on slopes peripheral to the floor when these pastures are short and green may thereby avoid many of the hyenas, leaving those that calve on the Crater floor to bear the full brunt of predation (Estes, 1964).

The wildebeest reproductive cycle is adapted to the climatic regime in such a way that both the rutting and birth peaks (8 months apart) occur during the rainy part of the year. Variations in rainfall distribution and amount are reflected by differences of up to 2 months in the timing of peak calving from year to year. Nutrition prior to the rut probably determines timing as well as fecundity (Fraser, 1968). The lack of synchrony between Ngorongoro subpopulations apparently reflects microclimatic differences, there being a pronounced rainfall and vegetation gradient within the caldera despite its small (265 square kilometers) floor (Herlocker and Dirschl, 1972).

The available evidence supports the hypothesis that the wildebeest's reproductive system evolved as part of its migratory foraging strategy (Talbot and Talbot, 1963). Given a feeding specialization for short, green grass and large, necessarily mobile aggregations, several synergistic selection pressures against concealment and in favor of a follower strategy can be readily imagined (Estes, 1976). Breeding synchrony and large aggregations are seen as the keys to the success of this strategy and an alternative to group defense, whereby the predator population is glutted without being sustained and the most vulnerable neonates are protected through the confusion effect created by many

calves. This strategy is much less adaptive in a dispersed/sedentary population—which is the distribution pattern common to most antelopes—suggesting that this organization has arisen in the wildebeest as a secondary
adaptation to stable environments. Yet reproduction even in resident populations is probably equal to that achieved by associated antelopes, and apparently adequate to the more limited resources available in such situations.

REFERENCES

ANSELL, P.D.H.
   1970.   More light on the problem of hartebeest calves.   Afr. Wildl., vol. 24,
            pp. 209-212.
ESTES, RICHARD D.
   1964.   Third progress report to National Geographic Society, 43 pp. (mimeo).
   1966.   Behavior and life history of the wildebeest.   Nature, vol. 212, pp. 999-
            1000.
   1969.   Behavioral study of East African ungulates, 1963-1965.   Nat. Geogr.
            Soc. Res. Rpts., 1964 Projects, pp. 45-57.
   1976.   The significance of breeding synchrony in the wildebeest.   East Afr.
            Wildl. Journ., vol. 14, pp. 135-152.
FRASER, A. F.
   1968.   Reproductive behavior in ungulates, 202 pp.   Academic Press, London
            and New York.
GOSLING, L. M.
   1969.   Parturition and related behavior in Coke's hartebeest, *Aleclaphus busela-
            phus cokei* Günther.   Journ. Reprod. Fert., Suppl., vol. 6, pp. 265-
            286.
HERLOCKER, D. J., and DIRSCHL, H. J.
   1972.   Vegetation of the Ngorongoro Conservation Area, Tanzania.   Can.
            Wildl. Serv. Rpt. Ser., no. 19, pp. 5-37.
KRUUK, HANS
   1972.   The spotted hyena, 335 pp., illus.   University of Chicago Press.
TALBOT, LEE M., and TALBOT, M. H.
   1963.   The wildebeest in western Masailand, East Africa.   Wildl. Monogr.,
            no. 12, pp. 8-88.
WATSON, R. M.
   1969.   Reproduction of wildebeest, *Connochaetes taurinus albojubatus* Thomas, in
            the Serengeti region, and its significance to conservation.   Journ. Re-
            prod. Fert., Suppl., vol. 6, pp. 287-310.

RICHARD D. ESTES

Studies on the Biology of Sea Lions in British Columbia

Principal Investigator: H. Dean Fisher, Department of Zoology, The University of British Columbia, Vancouver, British Columbia, Canada.

Grant No. 1061: In support of a study of the biology of Steller sea lions.

This grant enabled two studies on sea-lion biology to be completed, one involving breeding biology of Steller sea lions *(Eumetopias jubatus)* at Cape St. James at the southern tip of the Queen Charlotte Islands, and the other involving social behavior of Steller sea lions in a nonbreeding colony about 100 miles east of Cape St. James at McInnes Island. In addition, a survey and selection of a study site was made possible for a third study, on interactions between Steller sea lions and California sea lions *(Zalophus californianus)* at a winter haul-out site on Folger Island in Barkley Sound, southwest Vancouver Island.

Until 1972, the biology of sea-lion populations in British Columbia was largely unstudied. Pike and Maxwell (1958) reviewed known breeding and other haul-out sites of Steller sea lions and estimated population size. No studies had been made on breeding biology at either of the two major breeding colonies in British Columbia of the Steller sea lion (Cape St. James and Cape Scott Islands), even though these animals were under intensive control during the 1950's and 1960's by Canadian federal fisheries officers for depredations on fishing operations. Nothing was known about seasonal movements. However, intensive behavioral studies on breeding populations had been done at the north and south ends of the breeding range of Stellers on the west coast of North America; for example, Sandegren (1970) in Alaska and Gentry (1970) in California. Populations of sea lions in those areas can be considered as relatively stable, for they have been under protection for a long time. British Columbia populations on the other hand are in a state of recovery from the reduction program of the 1950's and early 1960's.

Because of this, and because the British Columbia population of Steller sea lions is in the middle of the two populations at the extreme ends of the continental range that have been studied, it was felt that British Columbia studies would provide a more complete picture of the biology of this species on the North American coast.

215

Distribution and Movements of Steller Sea-lion Cows on a Pupping Colony

A prefabricated hut, built at The University of British Columbia and shipped to Cape St. James by the Coast Guard, was lowered in sections onto the rookery by chartered helicopter. It was assembled and fastened to the rock by steel bolts, cables, and pitons. Studies were made from this hut over the ensuing three seasons, with an operational base at the Cape St. James Weather Station one mile north of the rookery islet.

This project, the major one of the three, was carried out by Allan Edie, a graduate student in zoology at the University of British Columbia, and student assistants Stacey Tessaro, Ken Arthur, and Dan Clark.

The initial objective was to study the territorial system among bull Steller sea lions. It soon became obvious that "harems" in the strict sense were not maintained, i.e., males did not restrict movements of females in the breeding colony although they maintained definite territories. It also became obvious that females copulated with the bull of whatever territory they happened to be in when they entered oestrus. Because of this, the emphasis shifted to an examination of the distribution and movements of breeding females and of the factors influencing the distribution of copulations among territorial bulls.

The major contribution of this study is in quantitative assessments of the effects of factors such as accessibility from the sea, protection from waves, and degree of crowding on the movements and distribution of pre-oestrous cows. These movements reflect trade-offs in advantages and disadvantages involved. The prevailing wind in this area is northwest. Unseasonable southeast gales during the breeding season from mid-May to mid-July were found to cause heavy pup mortality in those areas chosen because of protection from northwest gales.

Other significant influences in spatial preferences of cows are ruggedness of terrain, the tendency to "home," access routes on the colony, and availability of water pools for thermoregulation. Some cows using access routes to their pupping sites, that are on bull territories, are bred in transit to and from the sea by those bulls rather than by the ones in whose territory their pupping sites are located.

An evolutionary sequence is proposed in which the extreme concentration of breeding otariids in space can be accounted for by positive feedback mechanisms first proposed by R. A. Fisher in 1929 (Edie, 1977).

An interesting occurrence at the Cape St. James rookery during the breeding season in 1974 was the presence of a maturing California sea-lion bull (*Zalophus californianus*) in the rookery, far north of the northernmost breeding area in California. This reflects the gradually increasing extension of the northward winter migration of California male sea lions over the past few years, a trend that is particularly evident at the Folger Island study site in Barkley Sound (Guiguet, 1971; Bigg, 1973). In addition, a sea otter *(Enhydra lutris)* spent some time at the rookery in the summer of 1972. This is the first published record for the Queen Charlottes and possibly, though unlikely, a migrant from the transplant of them on Vancouver Island (Edie, 1973). (Three transplants of sea otters from Alaska to British Columbia were made in 1969, 1970, and 1972. A total of 89 otters were transplanted.)

During the summers of 1973, 1974, and 1975, 565 sea-lion pups were tagged at Cape St. James. Details of this tagging are on file with the Marine Mammal Tagging Office of the United States Fish and Wildlife Service, National Museum of Natural History, Washington, D. C. Tagged animals from this work have been sighted at Prince William Sound, Alaska, and near Tofino on the southwest coast of Vancouver Island, indicating migrations of immature Steller sea lions in both north and south directions from their pupping sites.

During the study season of 1973, Mr. Randy Hicks, National Exploration Award winner in the United States, was part of the field party, sponsored by The Explorer's Club.

Social Behavior in a Nonpupping Colony of Steller Sea Lions

Unlike the breeding rookeries, all ages and sexes intermingle at nonbreeding haul-out areas at the same times that breeding is in progress but located often at considerable distances from the breeding colonies. The site studied is at McInnes Island (lat. 52° 16' N. long. 128° 43' W.). The study was carried out by Alton Harestad, a graduate student in zoology at the University of British Columbia, and student assistant Peter Maser.

Three small observational huts were located around the haul-out rock just off McInnes Island Light Station, the operational base. These were fabricated at the University of British Columbia and shipped up by the Coast Guard. Studies concentrated on the behavioral interactions of various age and sex groups during the summer of 1972.

The major contribution of this study was to indicate the importance of nonbreeding gatherings as "training" grounds for building up those behavioral patterns which establish dominance relationships among these various groups. These achieve their main importance in efficiency of reproduction, through the social stability imposed by breeding bulls in whose territories breeding females can bear their young, suckle them, and mate in relative peace (Harestad and Fisher, 1975). Also studied were the diurnal activity of the sea lions as well as their seasonal abundance (Harestad, 1977b, 1978).

Comparisons of studies at nonpupping and pupping colonies will facilitate a better understanding of the social organization of sea lions and of polygyny generally.

Inter and Intraspecific Behavior of Steller and California Sea Lions on a Winter Haul-out Area

The study of Steller and California sea lions on a winter haul-out area was not financed by the National Geographic Society grant, but location of the haul-out area as a good study site, and the realization that both Steller and California sea lions come together there in winter, came during aircraft surveys, funded by the National Geographic Society, to locate sites for the other two studies. The result was the study by Brenton (1977), using a hut patterned after that placed at the Cape St. James breeding rookery.

REFERENCES

BIGG, M. A.
    1973.   Census of California sea lions on southern Vancouver Island, British Columbia.   Journ. Mammal., vol. 54, pp. 285-287.
BRENTON, C. M.
    1977.   Inter and intraspecific behaviour of *Eumetopias jubatus* and *Zalophus californianus* on a winter haulout area.   M.Sc. Thesis, Univ. British Columbia, 131 pp.
EDIE, ALLAN G.
    1973.   Sea otter sighting at Cape St. James, British Columbia.   Syesis, vol. 6, 1 p.
    1977.   Distribution and movements of Steller sea lion cows *(Eumetopias jubatus)* on a pupping colony.   M.Sc. Thesis, Univ. British Columbia, 81 pp.
FISHER, R. A.
    1958.   The genetical theory of natural selection, 291 pp.   Dover, New York. (Reprint).
GENTRY, R. L.
    1970.   Social behavior of the Steller sea lion.   Ph.D. Thesis, Univ. California Santa Cruz, 113 pp.
GUIGUET, C. J.
    1971.   An apparent increase in California sea lion, *Zalophus californianus* (Lesson), and elephant seal, *Mirounga angustirostris* (Gill), on the coast of British Columbia.   Syesis, vol. 4, pp. 263-264.
HARESTAD, A. S.
    1977a.   Social behaviour in a non-pupping colony of Steller sea lion *Eumetopias jubata*.   M.Sc. Thesis, Univ. British Columbia, 83 pp.
    1977b.   Seasonal abundance of northern sea lions, *Eumetopias jubatus* (Schreber) at McInnes Island, British Columbia.   Syesis, vol. 10, pp. 173-174.
    1978.   Diurnal activity of northern sea lions, *Eumetopias jubatus* (Schreber).   Syesis, vol. 11, pp. 279-280.

HARESTAD, A. S., and FISHER, H. DEAN
   1975.   Social behaviour in a non-pupping colony of Steller sea lions *(Eumetopias jubata)*.   Canadian Journ. Zool., vol. 53, pp. 1596-1613.
PIKE, G. C., and MAXWELL, B. E.
   1958.   The abundance and distribution of the northern sea lion *(Eumetopias jubata)* on the coast of British Columbia.   Journ. Fish. Res. Bd. Can., vol. 15, pp. 5-17.
SANDEGREN, F. E.
   1970.   Breeding and maternal behavior of the Steller sea lion *(Eumetopias jubata)* in Alaska.   M.Sc. Thesis, Univ. Alaska, 138 pp.

H. DEAN FISHER

The Reproductive Biology of *Osteoglossum bicirrhosum* Vandelli (Osteichthyes, Osteoglossidae) in Amazonas

Principal Investigators: Joan D. Fuller and David B. C. Scott, University of St. Andrews, Fife, Scotland.

Grant No. 1111:   To study the reproductive biology of osteoglossid fishes in South America.

It is now generally accepted that the "teleost" fish are not a single homogeneous group but a polyphyletic assemblage of four separate evolutionary lines descended from holostean ancestors. The four lines are: (1) the euteleosts, the "mainstream" of teleost evolution, comprising the Protoacanthopterygii, Paracanthopterygii, Acanthopterygii, Ostariophysi, and Atherinomorpha, 371 extant families in all; (2) the Elopomorpha, a marine group of 32 families; (3) the Clupeomorpha, 4 families; and (4), the Osteoglossomorpha, an aberrant fresh-water group comprising 7 families. The Osteoglossomorpha are divided into 2 suborders: (1) the Notopteroidei, which include the only nontropical genus of the order, the North American *Hiodon,* and the knife fishes and electric fishes of Asia and Africa; and (2) the Osteoglossoidei, or bonytongues *sensu strictu* (Greenwood, Rosen, Weitzman, and Myers, 1966; Greenwood, 1973). The extant osteoglossid species are circumtropically distributed, isolated in the various continents by considerable bodies of salt water. In tropical Australasia occur *Scleropages leichardti* and perhaps *S. guntheri. Scleropages formosus* occurs in Malaysia. In Africa occur *Pantodon buchholtzi* and *Heterotis niloticus.* In South America occur *Osteoglossum bicirrhosum, O. ferreirai,* and *Arapaima gigas.* Oddly, the most widely separated of these genera, *Osteoglossum* and *Scleropages,* are probably the most closely related (Nelson, 1969). The survival of these archaic fishes despite competition from more modern forms probably depends largely on their highly specialized reproductive biology.

In 1970 we investigated the reproductive biology of the Malaysian bonytongue, *Scleropages formosus* (Müller and Schlegel), the kelesa (fig. 1*a*) in Tasek Bera in Pahang, and studied some of its endocrine glands (Scott and Fuller, 1976). The present report is a comparative account of the reproductive biology of the South American bonytongue *Osteoglossum bicirrhosum* Vandelli, the arawana (fig. 1*b*) in the Amazon Basin, as studied in 1972.

Methods

This study was carried out from October to November 1972 at Leticia, Colombia. Arawana were collected in backwaters of the Río Xavari about 100 kilometers upstream from its confluence with the Amazon at Benjamin Constant. Fishing and the processing of the fish were carried out at an encampment in the jungle, which imposed practical limits on the techniques available. All specimens were caught by local fishermen hired for the purpose; most by harpooning from dugout canoes, but also one on hook and line, and one by shotgun. Numerous young fish (<6 centimeters) were taken by seining. The fish were weighed, measured, and dissected on the spot as soon as possible after catching—generally around dawn, a peak mosquito hour.

The brain with pituitary in situ, the gonads, and the headkidneys were fixed in Bouin's aqueous fixative for 24 hours and progressively dehydrated in 30, 50, and 70 percent ethanol, in which solution they were transported to Scotland. Two specimens were preserved whole in 10 percent formalin. Tissues were wax embedded in Fibrowax, by means of a 2-methylpropan-2-ol/paraffin dehydrating system (Scott, 1974), serially sectioned at 3 to 5 microns, and stained in a variety of stains.

The present report is a summary of the results; a detailed report including the histology of the endocrine glands is in preparation and will be published separately.

Results

GENERAL BIOLOGY

Osteoglossum bicirrhosum, the arawana, is a common species in the Amazon and its tributaries; fresh and dried specimens were regularly on sale in Leticia fishmarket, though in very much smaller quantity than the usual catfishes and characins. Arawana is less esteemed as food than the other, much bigger bony-tongue *Arapaima gigas,* the pirarucu or paiche (fig. 1c). In Malaya, *Scleropages formosus,* the kelesa, is likewise highly regarded both as a food fish and as a game fish, but it is rare and ranks as a "depleted species" in the Red Data Book of the International Union for the Conservation of Nature and Natural Resources (IUCN, 1969).

FIG. 1. *a, Scleropages formosus* adult ♀, 57 centimeters, 1740 grams; Tasek Bera, Malaya, 1970. *b, Osteoglossum bicirrhosum* adult ♀, 80 centimeters, 4 kilograms, with its ripe ovary; Río Xavari, Brazil/Peru border, 1972. *c, Arapaima gigas,* immature ♂, 76 centimeters; Río Amazonas, Leticia, Colombia, 1972.

The biggest arawana caught during this study weighed over 5 kilograms, with a total length of 94 centimeters; the biggest kelesa caught in Tasek Bera in 1970 weighed 1.8 kilograms, with a total length of 59 centimeters, but there are records of bigger specimens, one a 3-foot (91.4-centimeter) specimen weighing 16 pounds (7.3 kilograms), in other Malayan fresh waters (Alfred, 1964).

The habitats of arawana and kelesa are essentially similar: lakes and the slow-flowing backwaters of rivers in densely forested areas. Both species are territorial, and they spend the daylight hours hidden among vegetation. A wide range of animal food is taken, but mainly terrestrial insects and arachnids, which are caught at night when the fish move out of shelter into open water (so incidentally exposing themselves to the attentions of the fishermen). The sad depletion of the kelesa stocks is largely due to destruction of their habitat by deforestation, rather than to direct human predation (Alfred, 1969). Similar deforestation is now, of course, occurring also in the Amazon Basin.

REPRODUCTIVE BIOLOGY

Arawana spawn between October and December, when the single ovary of mature adult females 80-90 centimeters long contains between 250 and 300 ripe ova, each 1.2 centimeters in diameter (fig. 2*a*). The ripe ovary represents up to 9.9 percent of total body weight. Secondary (vitellogenic) oocytes grow to 3.4 millimeters in diameter; the oolemma and follicular granulosa penetrate deeply into the cytoplasm, as in kelesa. Primary (previtellogenic) oocytes grow to 1.3 millimeters in diameter. The testes are paired; even when fully ripe they are exceptionally small, less than 0.2 percent of total body weight, and contain relatively few spermatozoa. After spawning, the male (not the female, as local fishermen insist) incubates the fertilized eggs in his mouth for an undetermined period. He may also guard the free-swimming young for some time, as young are often found in the vicinity when a male is caught; however, they may have escaped from his mouth during capture. The yolk-sac is completely resorbed by the time the young arawana are 5 centimeters in length.

In their reproductive adaptations arawana and kelesa are very similar. The Malayan species seems the more highly specialized, though in certain other respects *Osteoglossum* is more advanced than *Scleropages* (Nelson, 1969). The ripe ovary of mature adult kelesa contains only from 20 to 25 ova, each with a diameter of 1.9 centimeters (fig. 2*b*); such an ovary comprises up to 11.5 percent of total weight. Female kelesa take up to 2 years to ripen one crop of ova; we do not know how arawana compares in this respect. Both species spawn at

a

b

FIG. 2. *a,* Ripe ovary (310 grams) of *Osteoglossum bicirrhosum* (80 centimeters, 4 kilograms), showing fully developed ova; October; scale line corresponds to 5 centimeters. *b,* Ripe ovary (82 grams) of *Scleropages formosus* (46 centimeters, 850 grams) showing fully developed ova. Scale line corresponds to 5 centimeters.

about the same time of year, though this is probably coincidental to the prevailing rainy seasons. The ripe testis of kelesa, like that of arawana, is small—at most 0.3 percent of total weight—and contains remarkably little sperm. Eggs and yolk-sac stage young are orally incubated by the male kelesa. The local aboriginal fishermen in Malaya, too, insist that it is the female that performs this function. The confusion is no doubt partly psychological but partly also because of the minute size of the ovary in spent females and of the absence of other sex distinctions. It is not at all easy, without histological examination, to distinguish the ovary of a spent female from a testis. There are marked differences in the testis histology in the two species, especially in brooding males; more detailed histological studies are now in progress.

Young kelesa do not completely resorb the yolk-sac until they have reached 8 centimeters in length.

PITUITARY MORPHOLOGY

The morphology of the pituitary gland of arawana is typical of bony fishes generally (Ball and Baker, 1969). The gland in mature adults (fig. 3*b*) is about 3 millimeters in length and is closely attached to the hypothalamus. There is no *saccus vasculosus*. The adenohypophysis (derived from the stomodaeum of the embryo) is clearly divided into 3 zones, a small rostral *pars distalis* anterodorsally; a bigger proximal *pars distalis;* and a large *pars intermedia* posteriorly. The neurohypophysis (derived from the brain of the embryo) ramifies very extensively in the *pars intermedia,* and the third ventricle of the brain penetrates deeply into this zone as a core to the main neurohypophyseal trunk. There is less extensive ramification into the anterior zones of the pituitary. In the hypothalamus dorsal to the anterior end of the pituitary lies a concentration of neurosecretory cells, the nucleus *lateralis tuberis,* from which fibers run to the highly vascularized connective tissue that forms the dorsal boundary of the *pars distalis* and also penetrates into the gland. The other main neurosecretory center, the supraoptic nucleus, lies dorsal to the optic chiasma. In all these respects the pituitaries of arawana (fig. 3*b*) and kelesa (fig. 3*a*) are essentially the same.

FIG. 3.   *a,* Sagittal section, 5 microns, of pituitary gland of mature ♂ *Scleropages formosus;* anterior to right. Dash-lines represent approximate boundaries of the rostral *pars distalis* (RPD), proximal *pars distalis* (PPD), and *pars intermedia* (PI). H = hypothalamus, N = neurohypophysis, O = optic nerve. Scale line corresponds to 1 millimeter.   Masson's trichrome stain.   *b,* Sagittal section, 5 microns, of pituitary gland of mature ♂ *Osteoglossum bicirrhosum* (94 centimeters, incubating ova); anterior to right; legend as in *a* above.   Scale line corresponds to 1 millimeter. Masson's trichrome stain.

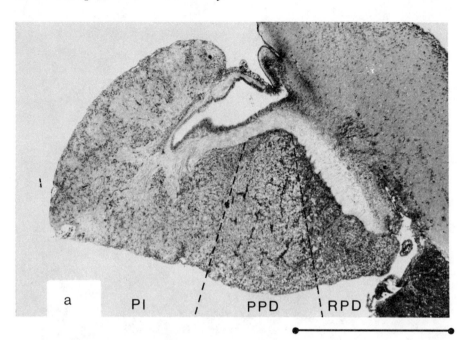

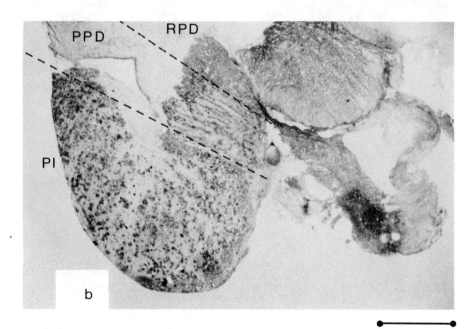

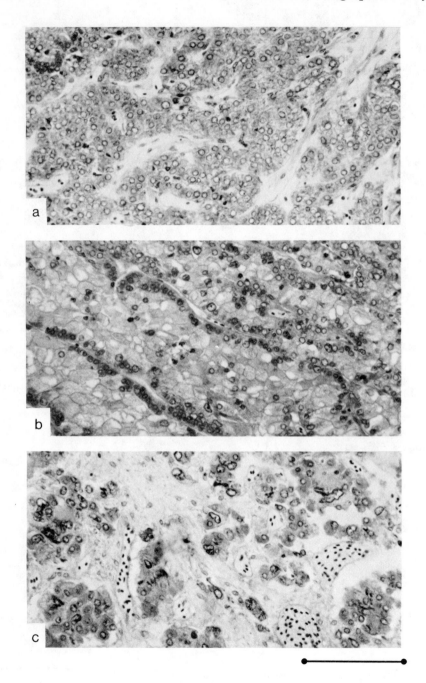

No experimental studies have been made to confirm the identity of the cell types in the various zones of the pituitary of arawana, and the tentative identifications that follow are based on analogy with kelesa.

The rostral *pars distalis* (fig. 4*a*) contains mainly adrenocorticotropic and luteotropic cells, partly compartmented by strands of connective tissue and associated blood vessels. The luteotropic cells are not arranged in follicles, as they are, for example, in salmonids, and are histologically difficult to distinguish from the adrenocorticotropic cells, though the latter seem generally to lie in more intimate contact with the neurohypophyseal branches. Somatotropic cells also occur in the rostral *pars distalis,* mostly in its posterior and lateral regions, and they extend deep into the proximal *pars distalis,* chiefly along the connective tissue partitions.

The proximal *pars distalis* (fig. 4*b*) contains, besides the somatotropic cells referred to above, the gonadotropic cells. In ripe fish these are very large, and their growth during gonad maturation results in a massive increase in the total bulk of the proximal *pars distalis.*

The *pars intermedia* (fig. 4*c*) consists largely of neurohypophyseal tissue, with relatively few cells, perhaps of two different types. Extremely prominent in immature fish, the *pars intermedia* comprises relatively less of the total pituitary volume as the proximal *pars distalis* grows during maturation.

REFERENCES

ALFRED, E.
1964.   The fresh-water food fishes of Malaya, 1: *Scleropages formosus* (Müll. & Schl.).   Fed. [Malaya] Mus. Journ., new ser., vol. 9, pp. 80-83.
1969.   Conserving Malayan fresh-water fishes.   Malayan Nat. Journ., vol. 22, pp. 69-74.
BALL, J. N., and BAKER, B. I.
1969.   The pituitary gland: Anatomy and histophysiology.   Pp. 1-110 *in* "Fish Physiology," vol. 2, W. S. Hoar and D. J. Randall, eds.   Academic Press, London.
GREENWOOD, P. H.
1973.   Interrelationships of osteoglossomorphs.   *In* "Interrelationships of Fishes," P. H. Greenwood, R. S. Miles, and C. Patterson, eds.   Suppl. no. 1, Zool. Journ. Linnean Soc., vol. 53, pp. 307-332.

FIG. 4.   Sagittal sections, 5 microns, of pituitary gland of same mature ♂ *Osteoglossum bicirrhosum* as in fig. 3*b*. Scale line corresponds to 50 microns. Masson's trichrome stain. *a*, Rostral *pars distalis,* showing neurohypophysis ramifying among luteotropic and adrenocorticotropic cells; *b*, Proximal *pars distalis,* showing gonadotropic cells, and somatotropic cells arranged along strands of connective tissue; *c*, *Pars intermedia,* showing extensive neurohypophyseal ramification among at least two types of cell. Blood vessels are conspicuous.

GREENWOOD, P. H.; ROSEN, DONN E.; WEITZMAN, STANLEY H.; and MYERS, GEORGE G.
    1966.   Phyletic studies of teleostean fishes, with a provisional classification of living forms.   Bull. Amer. Mus. Nat. Hist., no. 131, pp. 341-455.

INTERNATIONAL UNION FOR THE CONSERVATION OF NATURE (IUCN)
    1969.   The red data book, 4: Pisces; fresh-water fishes.   IUCN, Morges, Switzerland.

NELSON, GARETH J.
    1969.   Infraorbital bones and their bearing on the phylogeny and geography of osteoglossomorph fishes.   Amer. Mus. Novitates, no. 2394, 37 pp.

SCOTT, DAVID B. C.
    1974.   The reproductive cycle of *Mormyrus kannume* Forsk. (Osteoglossomorpha, Mormyriformes) in Lake Victoria, Uganda.   Journ. Fish Biol., vol. 6, pp. 447-454.

SCOTT, DAVID B. C., and FULLER, JOAN D.
    1976.   The reproductive biology of *Scleropages formosus* (Müller and Schlegel) (Osteoglossomorpha, Osteoglossidae) in Malaya, and the morphology of its pituitary gland.   Journ. Fish Biol., vol. 8, pp. 45-53.

DAVID B. C. SCOTT

Volcanic Correlations Across the Gulf of California

Principal Investigator: R. Gordon Gastil, San Diego State University, San Diego, California.

Grant No. 1110: To study basement rock and Tertiary volcanic correlations across the Gulf of California.

After nearly a decade of geologic mapping and mineral dating in the Peninsula of Baja California and northern Sonora in Mexico, I wished to broaden my understanding of geology along those coastal areas of the Gulf of California with which I was not familiar. This meant looking at southern Sonora, Sinaloa, Nayarit, and the southeastern coast of Baja California. Several groups at American universities and the scientific community of Mexico were concerned with the study of Sinaloa, and we therefore limited our work in Sinaloa to visiting described localities. A former student doing graduate work at the University of California at Santa Barbara was beginning work in the northwestern corner of coastal Jalisco and southwestern corner of Nayarit. We chose to concentrate our effort in central coastal Nayarit.

Central Nayarit is situated at the juncture of the trans-Mexican volcanic belt and the northwest-trending axis of the Gulf of California. Several authors had suggested that the fundamental structural element of the Gulf continued onto the mainland beneath the trans-Mexican belt.

Work in Mexico. We spent several days collecting material for potassium-argon dating in western Sonora, where I had previously mapped with graduate students (1970-1972). Approximately one month was spent in Mexico City researching the work done by students at the universities, obtaining maps and photographs, and establishing cooperative arrangements with Mexican geologists.

Two and a half months were spent in Nayarit and northwestern Jalisco doing reconnaissance geologic mapping. A collection of rocks for dating and chemical analyses was shipped back to San Diego. A week was spent in Sinaloa, and then two weeks in the southern part of Baja California. The collections made in Baja California supplemented work done by a co-investigator there in 1971-1972.

Laboratory Work. Several hundred rocks were thin-sectioned and studied petrographically. Approximately 50 were selected for mineral dating, but

231

for various reasons successful dates were obtained on only about 35. Chemical analyses were obtained for 20 dated rocks. A considerable delay in the completion of the work was caused by the necessity of waiting for completion of potassium-argon dating before selecting rocks for chemical analysis.

Publication and Presentation of Results.   Papers were presented at the second San Andreas Fault Symposium (published: Gastil and Jensky, 1973); the Circum-Pacific batholith project, Santiago, Chile, 1973 (Gastil and Krummenacher, 1974); the biannual meeting of the Geological Society of Mexico, Guanajuato, 1974 (Krummenacher and Gastil, 1977); the American Association of Petroleum Geologists, Pacific Section Meeting, San Diego, 1974; the Geological Society of America, Cordilleran Section Meeting, Las Vegas, 1974 (Gastil and Krummenacher, 1977); and were published (Gastil, Krummenacher, and Minch, 1979). The principal work on the geology of Nayarit was published in the Geological Society of America Bulletin and accompanying map series (Gastil, Krummenacher, and Jensky, 1979).

Some of the research initiated in the southern part of the Peninsula of Baja California is being pursued by John Minch, Saddleback College, Mission Viejo, California, and will be published in the years to come.

Significant Results.   One of our objectives was better to delineate the pattern of plutonic rock types and plutonic rock ages which I had earlier proposed (Gastil et al., 1972; Krummenacher et al., 1975). Combined with the work of Jensky (1975) we identified the cooling ages in the Nayarit-Jalisco batholith belt. Data in Nayarit are too fragmentary to establish a coherent picture. More work is needed in Jalisco and farther to the southeast in Mexico before regional patterns can be clearly delineated.

We learned that the distribution of trans-Mexican volcanic rocks in Nayarit is 0 to 4.5 million years. We also discovered a province of bimodal (basalt-rhyolite) volcanic rocks at circa 10 million years. The Sierra Occidental ignimbrite sequence failed to yield dates in the 23-35 million-year range, as found by others farther north in Sinaloa-Durango, but rather ages of 18-21 million years. We suspect that the older sequence may have been erosionally removed prior to the deposition of this Miocene sequence.

We discovered what may be an extensive terrane of Cretaceous rhyolite-dacite in northern Jalisco (and probably Nayarit). We believe that these rocks have in the past been confused with Oligo-Miocene volcanic rocks.

We did not find evidence of active strike-slip movement through the trans-Mexican volcanic belt. And in fact I think we can say that no significant strike-slip motion has occurred in the past 10 million years. On the basis of major provinces of pre-10 million-year rocks there is a suggestion of major right lateral offset, but we are hard pressed to identify the approximate trace of such a fault zone. In Gastil, Krummenacher, and Jensky (1979) we suggest a plausible position for such a fault zone, but it is placed through areas of almost unknown geology, and additional mapping could eliminate even this possibility.

The basement rock terrane south of La Paz, Baja California, includes some elements not common to other areas of the peninsula. Mafic gneisses were dated as old as Paleozoic, and a pyroxene-bearing granitic gneiss with horizontal foliation is extensively exposed south of Todos Santos. In the Loreto, Baja California, area we discovered weakly metamorphosed volcanic-volcaniclastic rocks of Cretaceous age. This is the first time that this terrane had been identified on the east coast of the Peninsula. Finally, Triassic (?) ammonoids and other poorly preserved fossils were collected in the metamorphosed carbonate terrane east of El Mármol, Baja California. These were the first Triassic fossils so far discovered in the Peninsula. Triassic fossils have since been identified at San Hipólito in the southern half of the Peninsula (Minch et al., 1975).

As with many research projects the discoveries opened more avenues for further investigation than they provided satisfactory answers for questions already asked.

REFERENCES

GASTIL, R. GORDON, and JENSKY, WALLACE A.
1973.   Evidence for strike-slip displacement beneath the trans-Mexican volcanic belt. Proceedings of the Conference on Tectonic Problems of the San Andreas Fault system, Robert L. Kovath, ed.   Stanford Univ. Publ. Geol. Sci., vol. 13, pp. 171-179.
GASTIL, R. GORDON, and KRUMMENACHER, DANIEL
1975.   Reconnaissance map of coastal Sonora between Puerto Lobos and Bahia Kino.   Geol. Soc. Amer. Map and Chart Ser. MC-16.
1977.   Reconnaissance geology of coastal Sonora between Puerto Lobos and Bahia Kino.   Geol. Soc. Amer. Bull., vol. 88, pp. 189-198.
1978.   A reconnaissance geologic map of the south central part of the State of Nayarit, Mexico.   Geol. Soc. Amer., Map and Chart Ser. MG-24.
GASTIL, R. GORDON; KRUMMENACHER, DANIEL; DOUPONT, JOAN; and BUSHEE, JONATHAN
1974.   The batholith belt of southern California and western Mexico.   Pacific Geol., vol. 8, pp. 73-78.
GASTIL, R. GORDON; KRUMMENACHER, DANIEL; DOUPONT, JOAN; BUSHEE, JONATHAN; and BARTHELMY, DAVID
1976.   La zona batolítica del sur de California y el occidente de México.   Bol. Soc. Geol. Mexicana, vol. 37, pp. 84-90.
GASTIL, R. GORDON; KRUMMENACHER, DANIEL; and JENSKY, WALLACE A.
1979.   Reconnaissance geology of central-west Nayarit, Mexico.   Geol. Soc. Amer. Bull., vol. 90, pt. 1 (January), pp. 15-18, illus.

GASTIL, R. GORDON; KRUMMENACHER, DANIEL; and MINCH, JOHN C.
  1979.   The record of Cenozoic volcanism around the Gulf of California.   Geol.
          Soc. Amer. Bull., vol. 90, pt. 1, pp. 839-857.
GASTIL, R. GORDON; MORGAN, G. J.; and KRUMMENACHER, DANIEL
  1978.   Mesozoic history of the peninsula of Baja California and related areas of
          the Gulf of California.   Pp. 107-116 *in* "Mesozoic Symposium," David
          G. Howell and Kristin A. McDougall, eds.   Pacific Section, Society of
          Economic Mineralogists and Paleontologists.
GASTIL, R. GORDON; PHILLIPS, RICHARD P.; and RODRIGUEZ-TORRES, R.
  1972.   The reconstruction of Mesozoic California.   Proc. 24th Int. Geol.
          Congr., sect. 3, pp. 217-229.
JENSKY, WALLACE A.
  1975.   Reconnaissance geology and geochronology of the Bahia de Banderas
          area, Nayarit and Jalisco, Mexico, 80 pp.   M.S. thesis, University of
          California, Santa Barbara.
KRUMMENACHER, DANIEL; GASTIL, R. GORDON; BUSHEE, JONATHAN; and
          DOUPONT, JOAN
  1975.   K-Ar apparent ages, peninsular ranges batholith, southern California
          and Baja California.   Geol. Soc. Amer. Bull., vol. 86, pp. 760-768.
MINCH, JOHN C.; GASTIL, R. GORDON; ROBINSON, J.; and FINK, W.
  1976.   Geology of the Vizcaino Peninsula.   *In* "Aspects of the Geologic Histo-
          ry of the Continental Borderland," D. G. Howell, ed.   Pacific Section
          AAPG Misc. Publ. 24.

                                                            R. GORDON GASTIL

Survey of the Tana River Colobus and Mangabey

Principal Investigator: Colin P. Groves, Australian National University, Canberra, Australia.

Grant No. 1080:   For a survey of the Tana River red colobus and the agile mangabey.

The purpose of the investigation, conducted during July-September 1972, was primarily to survey the habitat of two rare primates, whose distribution and numbers were previously unknown, and to make recommendations for their preservation. At the same time, the scientific neglect of the Tana River region itself made it imperative to undertake a brief ecological survey of the river's environs (analysis of vegetation types and soils, observation of birds, trapping of small mammals) for a better understanding of the factors controlling the distribution and life history of the two monkeys and pertinent to their survival.

The Tana River red colobus *(Colobus rufomitratus)* is not closely related to other species of "red" colobus, although it superficially resembles *Colobus pennantii tephrosceles* from the eastern forests of the Western Rift. The Tana River mangabey *(Cercocebus galeritus)* is most closely related to Central African forms but, like the colobus, is specifically distinct from them, according to new studies by C. P. Groves (1978). Both are therefore quite isolated, geographically as well as morphologically.

The Tana River (see fig. 1) rises in Mount Kenya and the Aberdares, flowing initially north but soon turning south by southeast toward the Kenya coast. Only its upper third receives tributaries; the lower two-thirds of the course flows through dry country, with increasingly marked meanders, until it reaches the sea at Kipini. Because of evaporation its flow near its mouth is only one-half of that at the Hargazo Falls, near the point of confluence with the last permanent tributary.

During the upcountry wet season, the Tana's flow is much increased, and it may flood in its lower reaches. Although there are two wet seasons annually inland, the Tana floods on average once every two years. The flood plain ex-

[1] In this survey I was assisted by Peter Andrews, British Museum (Natural History), London, England; Jennifer F. M. Horne, Nairobi, Kenya; and John Kinyanjui, National Museums of Kenya, Nairobi, Kenya. Also assisting were Jan Gillett, Samuel Kibua, and Alec Forbes-Watson of the National Museums of Kenya.

tends upriver as far as Wenje (see fig. 1) and reaches a maximum breadth of some 4 kilometers on each side of the river in the region of Hewani (fig. 2). We were told that in November and December 1972, after we left, the river flooded to a depth of about 75 centimeters at Munazini and had left, when it receded, a deposit of mud, clay, and sand 23 centimeters thick through the forest there.

The instability of the environment caused by the flooding regime has another consequence: the river undergoes continual changes in course, mostly minor but every so often involving a shift of its bed for 10-20 kilometers. Some of the abandoned courses, which form a network over the flood plain, still support forest blocs; one of them still holds permanent water and is known as Lake Giritu.

The vegetation of the flood plain is mostly open edaphic grassland, which changes sharply to bushland on the edge of the flood plain. Scattered through the grassland, but mostly along the river itself, are patches of forest, which we classified into six types (table 1); it is here—and not in the continuous gallery forest upriver, or in the swamp forest near the mouth—that the colobus and mangabey live.

Red colobus occupy some 648 hectares of forest, and we estimated their total number, by extrapolation from counts in certain selected forests, at around 1,760, of which two-thirds would live in the 10-kilometer strip along both sides of the river from Munazini north to Makere ya Gwano (see fig. 3). As colobus are easy to see, and fairly easy to count when jumping a gap, as when the whole troop crosses one after the other, we feel fairly confident that this total is of the right order of magnitude.

Mangabeys occupy a larger area of forest than colobus, about 733 hectares (as we estimated in our dry-season survey); they are found, for instance, in the forest at Maziwa along Lake Giritu (see fig. 2) and in the Wenje forest (see fig. 3); the latter is their northernmost outpost, but colobus appear not to extend so far north. We suggest a mean of about 2,245 mangabeys, but as mangabeys are shy and difficult to see, this figure could be much higher or much lower; indeed Katherine M. Homewood (1975), who was a part-time visitor to our camp and remained to undertake a long-term study of mangabey behavior, favors a figure of only 1,000 to 1,500; and she notes that because of the wide range of some mangabey troops the total amount of forest utilized by them in the rainy season is about double that for the dry season.

The straight distance from Wenje (see fig. 3) to the Garsen-Lamu road, the southernmost boundary of both colobus and mangabey, is about 56 kilometers; so this is the whole range of the Tana River mangabey, that of the red colobus falling about 8 kilometers short of this.

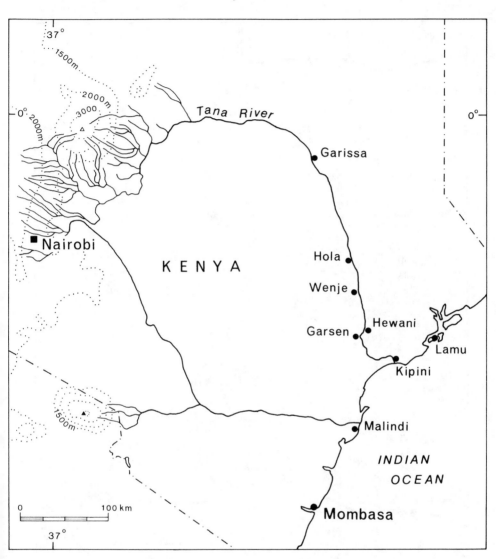

FIG. 1.   Course of the Tana River in Kenya.

Both species seem to occur at higher densities in the small patches of "cultivation forest" (regrowth after abandonment of cultivation) than in primary forest. This may be because of greater food abundance or because of the presence of a single troop of either species with no restriction on movement, or a

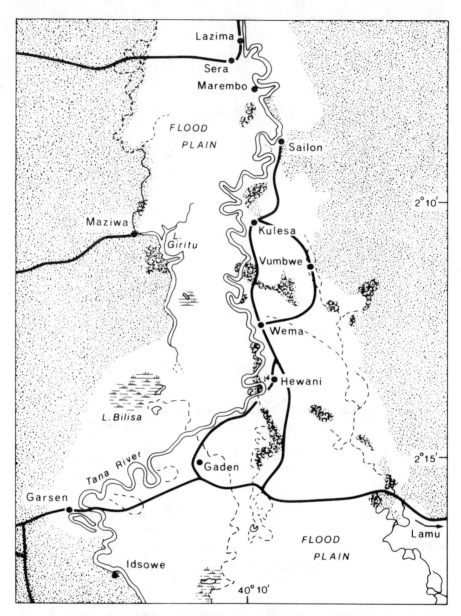

Fig. 2.   Flood plains along the Tana River are an instable environment, for the Tana floods on average once every two years.

combination of factors. Mangabeys, however (Homewood, 1975), wander from one to another of these patches; whether the more highly arboreal colobus do so we could not discover. However, as there are not more than 17 hectares of "cultivation forest" within the flood-plain area, the number of colobus and mangabey inhabiting them is hardly significant.

For the other categories of forest and woodland, it appears that mangabeys are most abundant in forests with either plentiful leaf litter (through which they forage for food—probably insects, fungi, and seedlings) or with dense undergrowth, or both. They are consequently present in quantity in forests with a single dominant tree species, where there is a heavy continuous canopy, as well as in very open *Acacia* woodlands where sunlight penetrates to the ground over wide areas. On the other hand, colobus prefer forests with the wide variety of tree species their diet requires (Clutton-Brock, 1975) and with a fair selection of emergents where they can sit and sun themselves.

Other mammals in the area include five species of primates (baboon, vervet, Sykes monkey, and two species of galago), elephant, buffalo, topi, water-

TABLE 1. Classification of Forest and Woodland Types of the Tana Flood Plain (This table is somewhat oversimplified, especially in that most forest blocs that are primarily mixed evergreen incorporate zones of single-dominance, woodland, or cultivation forest.)

Type	Total area (hectares)	Location on flood plain	Floristic variety	Canopy	Shrub layer	Presence of [1]	
						colobus	mangabey
Acacia/Mimusops woodland	100	upstream	fair	open	thick	xx	xx
Cynometra/Garcinia woodland [2]	10	downstream	poor	closed	sparse	few	few
Mixed evergreen forest [3]	485	throughout	rich	varies	varies	xx	x
Garcinia forest	45	Maziwa only	poor	closed	poor	no	xx
Pachystela forest	50	Munazini only	rich	fairly	fair	x	x
Cultivation forest	20	throughout	rich	open	thick	xx	xx

[1] x, occurs; xx, often abundant.

[2] The total amount of *Cynometra/Garcinia* woodland on the flood plain is at least double that indicated, but colobus and mangabey occur in only some 10 hectares of it.

[3] Although colobus are abundant in most Mixed Evergreen forest patches, in one (Wenje) they are absent; due perhaps to rarity of flooding, more closed canopy, and some tendency for *Sorindeia* to dominate.

buck, and hippopotamus. All the ungulates feed primarily on the flood-plain grasslands (the elephants feed also in the forest) and retire into either forest or bushland in the heat of the day. The red duiker *(Cephalophus natalensis)* is common in the forests and sometimes feeds at the forest edge. Strikingly, however, there are almost no specifically forest-adapted species beyond the colobus and mangabey. The common rodents are the tree rat *(Grammomys dolichurus)*, spiny mouse *(Acomys subspinosus)*, and Huet's bush squirrel *(Paraxerus ochraceus)*, all of them found in the flood-plain forests of the Tana, but in other parts of their range they are preferentially bush-living species; the multimammate rat *(Praomys natalensis)*, which lives wherever there is a grassy ground-cover; and the grass mouse *(Arvicanthis niloticus);* as well as commensal rats, which we caught in a village. The red bush squirrel *(Paraxerus palliatus)* seems to occur sporadically in forest country. In general, even species occurring in the nearest forest country to the south, the Arabuko-Sokoke and Gedi forests near Malindi, fail to occur along the Tana; we specifically searched for the golden-rumped elephant shrew *(Rhynchocyon chrysopygus)*, which leaves characteristic signs on leaf-litter, but did not find it. We concluded that the flooding regime of the Tana has resulted in the elimination of the more typical forest mammalian fauna and their replacement in the forests by intrusive rodents, and by monkeys adapted to just such conditions (Homewood, 1975, demonstrates that the Tana mangabey depends on an unstable environment for its survival).

It is instructive, too, to note what species are absent from the flood-plain grasslands. Zebras and Grant's gazelle, both encountered in more open areas in the bushland zone, appear never to enter the grassland—a finding that emphasizes the special position of Africa's edaphic grasslands and highlights the contrast with the more familiar East African Plains country, where zebras and gazelles are abundant. The latter grasslands (according to Vesey-Fitzgerald, 1970) are most likely fire-induced, degraded bushland.

Among the birds, too, the forest inhabitants include few specifically forest forms, but many intrusive, from other habitats. The richest bird fauna was to be found in those forests that, being rarely or incompletely flooded, had much undergrowth (such as the big forest at Wenje).

As an indirect result of the expedition, and more directly due to the interest of the late L.S.B. Leakey and the cooperative efforts of K. M. Homewood and C. Marsh, the Kenya Government has now created a game reserve in much of the area in question—between Makere and Munazini on the west bank, and between Wenje and Kitere on the east bank. This is the area containing the highest concentration of colobus and mangabey, as well as a good cross section of other fauna. However, the implementation of a 40,000-acre

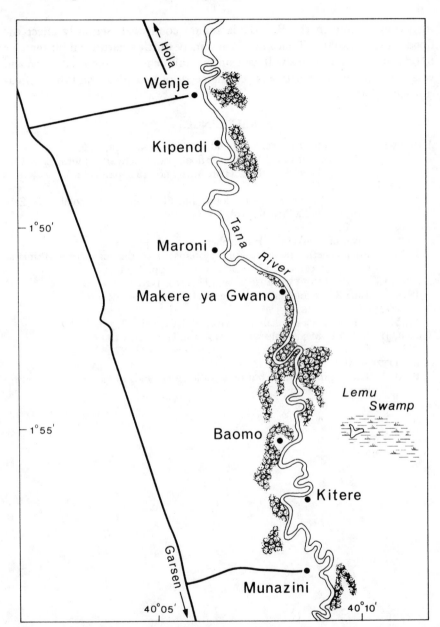

FIG. 3. Range of the Tana River mangabey and the red colobus, showing forest areas they inhabit.

irrigation scheme in the Bura-Hola region could well seriously affect the flooding regime of the Tana and its constantly shifting nature; and it remains to be seen what effect this will have on the unique forests and their fauna and what balance can be struck between the needs of agriculture and those of nature conservation.

REFERENCES

ANDREWS, PETER; GROVES, COLIN P.; and HORNE, JENNIFER, F. M.
    1975.   Ecology of the lower Tana River flood plain (Kenya).   Journ. East African Nat. Hist. Soc., Nat. Hist. Mus., no. 151, pp. 1-31.
CLUTTON-BROCK, T. H.
    1975.   Feeding behavior of red colobus and black and white colobus in East Africa.   Folia Primat., vol. 23, pp. 165-207.
GROVES, COLIN P.
    1976.   River of monkeys.   Hemisphere, vol. 20, pp. 28-32.
    1978.   Phylogenetic and population systematics of the mangabeys (Primata: Cercopithecoidea).   Primates, vol. 19, pp. 1-34.
GROVES, COLIN P.; ANDREWS, PETER; and HORNE, JENNIFER F. M.
    1974.   Tana River colobus and mangabey.   Oryx, vol. 12, pp. 565-575.
HOMEWOOD, KATHERINE M.
    1975.   Can the Tana mangabey survive?   Oryx, vol. 13, pp. 53-59.
HORNE, JENNIFER F. M.; ANDREWS, PETER; and GROVES, COLIN P.
    1975.   Still an explorer's river.   Africana, pp. 19-20, 27, 30, 38.
VESEY-FITZGERALD, D. F.
    1970.   The origin and distribution of valley grasslands in East Africa.   Journ. Ecol., vol. 58, pp. 51-75.

COLIN P. GROVES

Geochronology and Paleoenvironments of the Murray Springs Clovis Site, Arizona

Principal Investigator: C. Vance Haynes, Jr., University of Arizona, Tucson, Arizona.

Grant No. 1092[1]*:*   In support of continuing studies of the paleoecology at the Murray Springs archeological site in Arizona.

The Murray Springs Clovis site was exposed by tributary head cutting in Curry Draw some time between 1958 and 1965 when an exposure of mammoth bones was found in the course of mapping late Quaternary deposits of the upper San Pedro Valley in southeastern Arizona. Curry Draw is a discontinuous gulley or arroyo tributary of the San Pedro River that is typical of the many channels entrenched into late Quaternary alluvium of the Southwest since the middle of the 19th century. The resulting archeological discoveries and the dispute over whether overgrazing or climatic change caused the gullying led to the geologic investigations that continue today.

Curry Draw is one of many arroyos in the upper San Pedro Valley that reveal a similar succession of sediments for the region. The older valley fill, named the St. David Formation and composed of late Tertiary and early Pleistocene alluvium and lacustrine deposits (Gray, 1967) is beveled by the Tombstone pediment (Bryan, 1926) and covered in places by the Nexpa gravels, part of which occupy strath terraces (fig. 1).

The Millville alluvium occupies channels cut into the St. David Formation (fig. 2) and represents the oldest post-St. David aggradation in the upper San Pedro Valley. It contains a Rancholabrean fauna and is older than the 45,000-year range of carbon-14 dating. Erosion of the Millville alluvium led to the formation of numerous springs along many San Pedro tributaries, and these produced the Sobaipuri clay and Coro marl between 30,000 and 13,000 years ago. Desiccation of these shallow-water or marsh deposits led to erosion and deposition of the Graveyard channel sand between 13,000 and 11,000

---

[1] Archeological investigations at Murray Springs, since their inception in 1966, have been supported by the National Geographic Society, and geochronological investigations in the San Pedro Valley including the Murray Springs site have been supported by the Earth Sciences Section of the National Science Foundation (Grants GP-5548, GA-1288, GA-12772, and DES72-01582 A01).

243

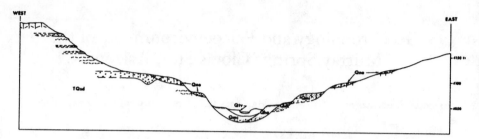

FIG. 1. Generalized geologic cross section of the San Pedro Valley in the vicinity of Horsethief Draw, Arizona, showing St. David Formation (TQsd), Nexpa gravels (Qne), Millville alluvium (Qmi), Weik alluvium (Qwk), Hargis alluvium (Qha), McCool alluvium (Qmc), and Tevis alluvium (Qtv). Valley width ca. 2 miles.

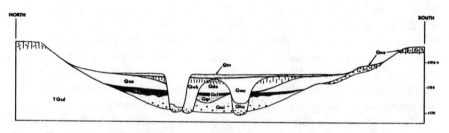

FIG. 2. Generalized geologic cross section of Curry Draw at Murray Springs Clovis site, Arizona, showing St. David Formation (TQsd), Nexpa gravels (Qne), Millville alluvium (Qmi), Sobaipuri mudstone (Qso), Coro marl (Qco), Graveyard sand (Qgr), Clanton clay (Qcl), Donnet silt (Qdo), Weik alluvium (Qwk), Hargis alluvium (Qha), McCool alluvium (Qmc), and Tevis alluvium (Qtv). Valley width ca. 0.25 mile.

years ago when the area was visited by hunters belonging to the Clovis culture. Their occupation of the Naco, Lehner, Escapule, and Murray Springs Clovis site was followed by the deposition, between 11,000 and 9,000 years ago, of the Clanton clay, a black wet-meadow or cienega deposit which preserved bone and lithic remains in some places on undisturbed living floors. Between 9,000 and 7,000 years ago, the tributary valleys were filled with the Donnet silt, a clayey, loesslike silt that formed relatively shallow flat-floored valleys. Human occupation of the San Pedro Valley is not obvious during this time, but Sulphur Springs-stage artifacts occur in contemporaneous deposits of the adjacent Sulphur Springs Valley.

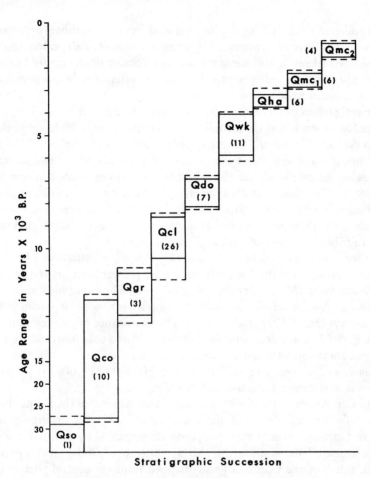

FIG. 3. Radiocarbon age range of strata, upper San Pedro Valley, Arizona. Dashed
lines indicate extensions due to one standard deviation.

The first evidence of Holocene arroyo cutting in the buried record occurs
in the form of poorly sorted and mixed alluvium occupying deep channels cut
approximately 7,000 years ago. Arroyo cutting and filling occurred at least
four times between then and cutting of the present arroyos since the 1880's.
Geochronology of these units is shown in the accompanying histogram (fig.
3), which is based upon 74 stratigraphically controlled radiocarbon dates.

With this geochronology as a background, I will attempt to reconstruct,
from the limited data available, the geoclimatic events before, during, and after Clovis occupation.

In addition to the geologic processes read from the sediments, paleoenvironmental data have been provided by investigations of fossil pollen, charcoal, mollusks, vertebrates, and ancient soils, but because of the limited extent of these studies to date, only preliminary interpretations can be made and many problems remain to be solved.

Investigations of fossil springs, discovered with a backhoe in 1969, indicate the feeder sands and the associated vertebrate fauna to be facies of the Sobaipuri clay and Coro marl. Both the molluscan fauna (Russell, 1971) and the occurrence of large vertebrate remains in the spring conduits and along clay partings in the marl indicate that these deposits were formed in spring-fed ponds or marshes that were shallow enough at one time or another to permit mammoths, horses, camels, bison, tapir, bear, and their predators (Saunders and Kelso, 1971) to traverse them and some to get caught in the quicksand at the springs between 30,000 and 23,000 years ago.

Pollen investigations of these units have not been successful because of poor preservation, but the few grains that were preserved suggested a full pluvial environment (Mehringer and Martin, personal communication), which would mean downward displacement of vegetation zones of between 300 and 1,000 meters (Mehringer et al., 1967). The dominance of grazing animals in the vertebrate fauna, in conjunction with the limited palynological data, suggests that some sort of wooded parkland may have extended from the base of the Huachuca Mountains to San Pedro River 30,000 to 13,000 years ago. The site area is now desert grassland and desert scrub.

The channel deposits of the Graveyard sand member of the Lehner Formation occupy a relatively small shallow channel, cut after drying-up of the ponds and marshes, which must have been accompanied by a drop in the water table of at least 3 meters. During this 13,000- to 12,000-year-old period of erosion, much of the Coro marl was stripped from the central part of Curry Draw, leaving an irregular erosional surface and exposing the inactive spring conduits in the base of the Sobaipuri clay. This is the surface upon which Clovis people hunted and camped 11,000 years ago.

The inactivity of the springs of area 8 before this time is indicated by the fact that the conduit sands are truncated by the erosional contact at the base of the Clanton clay, and there is no evidence of any relationship to the F_1 channel as would be expected if discharge had been reactivated upon exhumation of the old feeders. This indicates that the springs lost their hydrostatic head long before the water table had dropped enough to allow entrenchment of the Coro marl by the F_1 channel. This sequence of events suggests a marked reduction in recharge sometime before 13,000 years ago and a general decline in the water table between 13,000 and 11,000 years ago when Clovis hunters found the

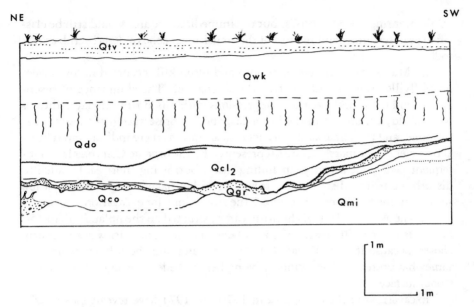

FIG. 4. Stratigraphy of the southeast wall, area 3, Murray Springs Clovis site, Arizona, showing irregular depressions in the Graveyard sand (Qgr) that are believed to be mammoth tracks in a shallow well.

F_1 channel almost inactive in area 1 where mammoth tracks along the channel were not obliterated by subsequent flow. In fact there is evidence that Graveyard channel-sand may have been excavated by mammoths to make a water hole (fig. 4) in the same manner as African elephants do today (Iain and Oria Douglas-Hamilton, 1975, p. 97).

The relatively shallow channel configuration of the Graveyard sand, which is obviously winnowed from the Millville formation, and the gently sloping banks suggest that it was an effluent or perennial stream being fed by seepage from the more permeable sand and gravel zones in the Millville formation.

Charcoal from the upper part of the Graveyard sand has been identified as *Fraxinus* sp. (ash), which is a common riparian species today along seep-fed channels such as Government Draw on the opposite side of the San Pedro from Curry Draw.

Fossil pollen samples from marl in the top of the Graveyard sand at the Lehner site 12 miles south of Murray Springs indicate that the time of Clovis occupation was one of more effective moisture than today, in that pine, oak, and juniper zones were closer to the site than now (Mehringer and Haynes,

1965; Mehringer et al., 1967), but the immediate site area would still be classified as desert grassland instead of the transitional zone to desert scrub as it is today.

At Murray Springs the mammoth and bison kills occurred in low swales on Millville alluvium adjacent to the F_1 channel. The abundance of bison-hoove- and mammoth-foot-size depressions with raised rims of clay indicates wet, muddy conditions in the low areas, and the preservation of these tracks, the bone, and the remarkable artifact concentrations there indicate rapid burial by a cienega or marsh deposit represented by the organic Clanton clay. Subsequent pedogenic activity, including insect burrowing, noticeably failed to disturb the artifact distribution. It is this rapid burial of the Clovis occupation surface by the black mat that makes the site unique for excavation.

At the associated Clovis hunting camp, situated on the uplands 30 to 150 meters from the kill areas, an eroded bench of the Coro marl was apparently chosen because it was (1) flat, (2) close to water and the kill areas, and (3) somewhat protected from wind by being below the level of an upland (Tombstone) surface.

Excavations at the camp area in 1970 and 1971 have revealed a shallow, complex stratigraphy disturbed by 11,000 years of bioturbation in the form of root growth, insect and rodent burrowing, and the digging of prehistoric pits or wells. Clovis artifacts still occur in clusters, and concentrations of flakes from a given biface or tool are disoriented from their original position and commonly intermixed with artifacts of Cochis age in slope wash and colluvial fillings of voids of the riddled deposits (fig. 5). A few of the Clovis artifacts were found in what is believed to have been their original position on the contact between the eroded Coro marl and the overlying Donnet silt which, in this higher ground, may be a pedogenic facies of the Clanton clay.

After Clovis occupation of the site, the black mat (Clanton clay) formed as a wet-meadow or cienega soil, thickest in the low areas of the site, between 10,000 and 9,000 radiocarbon years ago, and some of the lowest areas apparently were covered by shallow water in which lamina of soft, white, powdery calcium carbonate were deposited as an intercalated facies of the black, organic Clanton clay (fig. 4). At this time the site may have looked like the cienega near Curtis Ranch does today. The thickest exposures of these organic clays and interbedded marls have provided the best samples for radiocarbon dating the time of Clanton clay deposition.

Sometime between 9,000 and 8,000 years ago, there was sufficient discharge down the swale to erode the Clanton clay, and in some areas to reactivate the F_1 channel. This new channel, referred to as F_3, contains redeposited animal bones and is filled with black, organic, sandy clay redeposited from the

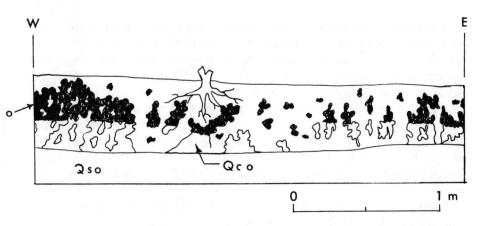

FIG. 5. Cross section along line 5–2, station EE, area 7, Murray Springs Clovis site, Arizona, showing remnants of Coro marl (Qco) and Donnet silt (Qdo) within a bioturbational mixture of these units and colluvium.

Clanton clay and Graveyard sand, such that there is an inversion of the radiocarbon dates from organic clays in the F_3 channel.

Between 8,000 and 7,000 years ago the valley was filled with calcareous silt of the Donnet member, which is apparently mostly eolian with some slope-washed sediments. The aggradational soil profile in the Donnet silt shows decreasing organic matter and increasing secondary carbonates toward the top, indicating less effective soil moisture conditions. By 7,000 years ago, Curry Draw must have resembled the dry grassy swales that typified the San Pedro tributaries before modern arroyo cutting. The valley of Knipe cienega near Canelo may be a modern example.

Ancient arroyo cutting began sometime between 7,000 and 6,000 years ago when Curry Draw was entrenched to a depth of about 15 feet, and filling of the arroyo occurred sometime over the next 2,000 years between 6,000 and 4,000 years ago. The Weik alluvium, consisting of coarse, clastic channel sands and lag gravels overlain by pond clays and a gray cienega soil, contains a pollen record from the pond clays indicating the most mesic period in the postpluvial pollen record of the Southwest. Mehringer et al. (1967) consider 300 meters to be a reasonable estimate of the degree of depression of life zones during the period 5,000 to 4,000 B.P.

The subsequent Hargis and McCool alluvial deposits indicate that similar arroyo cut and fill cycles occurred at least three more times before the modern cutting began in the 1880's, but the vegetation changes, while real, did not significantly shift boundaries of the local life zones. Such change must, however, have been great enough to affect local plant covers and water table levels and thus affect cutting and filling. During this time it is apparent that the dominant aggradational processes are (1) pond clay deposition and (2) slope wash deposition followed by soil formation.

The last event before modern dissection was the deposition of as much as 2 feet of red sand and gravel of the Tevis alluvium on top of the swale floor in the lower reaches of Curry Draw. Some of this alluvium came from a head cut 0.7 mile above the Murray Springs site and indicates that discontinuous gullying began before headward retreat from the San Pedro River had progressed very far upstream.

Over the past six years of excavation at Murray Springs the most erosive rainstorms have been during the winter months. A winter rain in late 1966 caused the headcut at the site to retreat 10 feet, and a summer thunderstorm in 1967 caused calving of the sides and further retreat exposing the bison kill site. In late 1971 extensive erosion occurred at the site and would undoubtedly have resulted in at least as much headward retreat as the 1966 winter storm had not open trenches and workings directed the flow, causing caving of trench walls and stripping of several areas above the main headcut. At present there is no evidence that the modern epicycle of erosion is over.

REFERENCES

BRYAN, KIRK
   1926.   San Pedro Valley, Arizona, and the geographic cycle.   Bull. Geol. Soc. Amer., vol. 37, pp. 169-170 (abstr.).
DOUGLAS-HAMILTON, IAIN and ORIA
   1975.   Among the elephants, 285 pp., illus.   Viking Press, New York.
GRAY, R. S.
   1967.   Petrography of the upper Cenozoic non-marine sediments in the San Pedro Valley, Arizona.   Journ. Sed. Petr., vol. 37, no. 3, pp. 774-789.
MEHRINGER, PETER J.
   1970.   Early Man in the San Pedro Valley, Arizona, 236 pp.   Ph.D. dissertation, University of Arizona, Tucson.
MEHRINGER, PETER J., and HAYNES, C. VANCE, JR.
   1965.   The pollen evidence for the environment of Early Man and extinct mammals at the Lehner mammoth site, southeastern Arizona.   Amer. Antiq., vol. 31, pp. 17-23.
MEHRINGER, PETER J., JR.; MARTIN, PAUL S.; and HAYNES, C. VANCE, JR.
   1967.   Murray Springs, a mid-postglacial pollen record from southern Arizona. Amer. Journ. Sci., vol. 265, pp. 786-797.

RUSSELL, R. H.
   1971.   Biogeography of Late Cenozoic Mollusca from the San Pedro Valley. Paper presented at Physical Science Section, Southwestern and Rocky Mountain Division, American Association for the Advancement of Science and Arizona Academy of Science, Tempe, Arizona.
SAUNDERS, J. J., and KELSO, G. K.
   1971.   Fossil mammals in a spring conduit, Cochise County, Arizona.   *Idem.*

C. VANCE HAYNES, JR.

Fossil Amphibians and Reptiles of Nebraska and Kansas

Principal Investigator: J. Alan Holman, The Museum, Michigan State University, East Lansing, Michigan.

Grant Nos. 1039,   For study of amphibians and reptiles of northeastern Nebras-
1213, 1560.   ka (upper Miocene and middle Pliocene) and of the Wa-
Keeney local fauna (lower Pliocene) of Trego County, Kansas.

I. Research in Trego County, Kansas

The WaKeeney local fauna, Trego County, Kansas, has produced the largest lower Pliocene herpetofauna known. The collecting was done from a single site that represented a small stream basin filled with fine-grained cross-bedded sands. The WaKeeney local fauna was discovered by Lester F. Phillis in about 1941. After the discovery, parties from the University of Michigan and from the University of Kansas collected at the site, but these collections were made at the surface and no systematic excavations were attempted. In 1966 Richard L. and Jan Wilson removed about 250 "small" sacks of matrix (I interpret this as about $2\frac{1}{2}$ tons) from the site and wet-screened the material in a nearby spring. The vertebrate fauna from the work was published by Wilson (1968). Shortly after, the Wilsons moved to the West Coast, and the late Dr. Claude W. Hibbard of the University of Michigan suggested that I continue excavations at the site, in view of the potentially large herpetofauna. Collecting was done in the summers of 1969, 1970, 1972, and 1973. The last two trips were financed by grants from the National Geographic Society.

Previously published references to the site include Hibbard and Phillis (1945), Hubbs and Hibbard (1951), Brodkorb (1962), Feduccia and Wilson (1967), Wilson (1968), Hibbard and Jammot (1971), and Holman (1971).

Location and Geology. All Michigan State material and most of the Wilsons' material came from a single site (UM-K6-59), which is on the Lowell Hillman Ranch 2,350-2,500 feet south and 75 feet east of the NW corner Sec. 22, R22W, T11S, Trego County, Kansas. The elevation at the site is 255 feet. The general regional picture of the area is as follows. The Saline River has eroded into the chalky limestone and calcareous shale beds of the Upper Cretaceous Niobrara Formation (upper Smoky Hill chalk member and lower

Fort Hays limestone members). The outcrops of these eroded beds form the "bluffs" that are the picturesque landmarks of the area. These Cretaceous beds are unconformably overlain by the Pliocene Ogallala Formation. The Ogallala beds are of unconsolidated clastic sediments which greatly vary in particle size. In this part of Kansas they are mainly unfossiliferous, but the WaKeeney site (UM-K6-59), representing a small basin in a stream in the Ogallala Formation, contains small vertebrate fossils. Above the Ogallala formation are Pleistocene sediments of eolian or fluviatile origin; overlying the Pleistocene sediments are Recent soils. Wilson (1968) figured a measured section through UM-K6-59.

Based on his study of the mammalian fossils of the site, Wilson (1968) believes that the WaKeeney is best assigned to the middle or late Clarendonian (lower Pliocene) provincial age.

Methodology. It was determined that the bones of the site were almost entirely confined to a cross-bedded sand lens that ranged in thickness from about 6 inches to about 3 feet. This lens, which averaged about 2 feet thick, was quarried laterally into the side of a hill until it finally gave way, in 1973, to unfossiliferous bluish clay. Material was gathered in burlap sacks, each containing about 45 pounds of matrix. A sample of one-half ton would be collected at each visit to the site, and this material was taken by truck to a nearby washing site on the Saline River or one of its tributaries. The material was then put on special wooden racks (Hibbard, 1949) to dry. The dried concentrate invariably contained small clay balls that had to be rewashed after they were thoroughly dried. After the clay balls were rewashed the concentrate was now ready to pick through for vertebrate fossils. Each field season our efficiency in processing matrix increased. The quantity processed in 1969 was 13.24 tons; in 1970, 20 tons; in 1972, 36 tons; and in 1973, 39 tons. In all, 75 tons of matrix were processed during the period of support by the National Geographic Society grants. In 1972 and 1973 we were greatly aided by use of a small front-end-loader for the removal of overburden.

Personnel. Student workers were key personnel in collecting the fossils. These include Merald Clark and William Rainey in 1969; Merald Clark, Bernie Franks, and Carl Steinfurth in 1970; James Fowler, Frederick Heineman, and Maria O'Hare in 1972; and Joseph Holman, Richard McArthur, Margaret Mead, Jason Potter, and Vincent Wilson in 1973. Dr. Robert Weigel of Illinois State University came out to the site and worked on the project in 1969, 1970, and 1972.

Location of WaKeeney Fossils Collected. WaKeeney fossils collected by Michigan State University have been placed in the Museum, Michigan State

University, and have been given Michigan State University-Vertebrate Paleontology numbers (MSU-VP). Dr. Robert Weigel of Illinois State University
is studying the birds. The late Dr. Claude W. Hibbard of the University of
Michigan and his student D. Jammot described two new shrews from the
MSU WaKeeney material (Hibbard and Jammot, 1971); but the remainder of
the mammalian material remains unstudied in the Museum at Michigan State
University.

   Scientific Results.   A paper (Holman, 1975) on the WaKeeney local herpetofauna appeared in a volume in honor of the late Dr. Claude W. Hibbard.
The WaKeeney local fauna yielded a herpetofauna consisting of at least 2 salamanders, 15 anurans, 5 turtles, 4 lizards, and 8 snakes. About half (48.2 percent) of these are indistinguishable from species living today, and most genera
and families are extant, but some forms are holdovers from earlier times and
some are unique to the fauna.

   A checklist of the WaKeeney herpetofauna follows:

Class Amphibia
   Order Urodela
      Family Ambystomatidae
         Ambystoma tigrinum (Green)
         Ambystoma maculatum (Shaw)
         Ambystoma sp. indet.
   Order Anura
      Family Pelobatidae
         Scaphiopus hardeni Holman (new species)
      Family Tregobatrachidae (new family)
         Tregobatrachus hibbardi (new genus and species)
      Family Bufonidae
         Bufo cognatus Say
         Bufo marinus (Linnaeus)
         Bufo hibbardi Taylor
         Bufo pliocompactus Wilson
         Bufo valentinensis Estes and Tihen
      Family Hylidae
         Acris sp. indet.
         Hyla cf. *H. cinerea* (Schneider)
         Hyla cf. *H. gratiosa* LeConte
         Hyla cf. *H. squirella* Sonnini and Latreille
         Hyla sp. indet.
         Pseudacris cf. *P. clarki* (Baird)
      Family Ranidae
         Rana cf. *R. areolata* Baird and Girard
         Rana cf. *R. pipiens* Schreber
         Rana sp. indet.

Class Reptilia
  Order Chelonia
    Family Kinosternidae
      Sternotherus odoratus (Latreille)
    Family Emydidae
      Terrapene cf. *T. carolina* (Linnaeus)
    Family Testudinidae
      Geochelone orthopygia (Cope)
      Geochelone sp.
    Family Trionychidae
      Trionyx sp. indet.
  Order Sauria
    Family Anguidae
      Ophisaurus attenuatus Baird
      Gerrhonotus mungerorum Wilson
    Family Teidae
      Cnemidophorus cf. *C. sexlineatus* (Linnaeus)
    Family Scincidae
      Eumeces hixsonorum Holman, new species
  Order Serpentes
    Family Boidae
      Tregophis brevirachis Holman, new genus and species
      Ogmophis pliocompactus Holman, new species
    Family Colubridae
      Nerodia hillmani Wilson
      Thamnophis sp. indet.
      Paleoheterodon sp. indet.
      Coluber or *Masticophis*
      Elaphe sp. indet
      Lampropeltis similis Holman

Unique forms in the fauna include a new species of *Scaphiopus*, a new family, genus, and species of frog, a new species of *Eumeces*, a new genus of boid snake, a new species of *Ogmophis*, and an extinct species of watersnake *(Nerodia hillmani)*. Modern species appearing for the first time in the fossil record include *Ambystoma maculatum*, *A. tigrinum*, *Bufo cognatus*, *Sternotherus odoratus*, *Terrapene* cf. *T. carolina*, *Ophisaurus attenuatus*, and *Cnemidophorus* cf. *C. sexlineatus*.

Habitats represented by the herpetofauna include a basin in a sluggish stream, a marshy area, mesophytic woodlands, and xerophytic woodlands. A subtropical climate with mild winters and temperatures seldom if ever reaching the freezing point and with vegetation similar to that of the Texas Gulf Coastal Plain today is indicated.

Differences between upper Miocene herpetofaunas in Nebraska and Saskatchewan and the WaKeeney local fauna were many, including (in the Wa-

Keeney) lack of large cryptobranchid salamanders, lack of xenosaurid lizards, lack of archaic natricine and colubrine snakes, and presence of large numbers of living species (about one-half).

II. Research in Northeastern Nebraska (1976)

At present I am involved in the study of herpetofaunas from temporally equivalent sites (upper Miocene, lower Valentine Formation) from north-central, northeastern, and southeastern Nebraska. It is hoped that ultimately a regional paleoecological picture of the amphibian and reptile life of this period of time over a broad geographical area in Nebraska may be presented.

Although I had been extensively involved in collecting fossils in north-central Nebraska before 1976, I had only briefly visited the sites in northeastern Nebraska in 1971 and 1974. Dr. Michael Voorhies, vertebrate paleontologist at the University of Nebraska State Museum, invited me to return to northeastern Nebraska in 1976 to excavate, personally, some of the fossils. For this purpose a grant was requested from the National Geographic Society and was funded.

When I arrived in Orchard, Nebraska, in August 1976, with two student assistants, Lisa Griggs and Mark Podell, the group was taken on a tour of sites in northeastern Nebraska by Dr. Voorhies. After some preliminary collecting at various sites, it was decided to concentrate collecting at the Annies Geese Cross (abbreviated AGC, representing upper Miocene) and Devils Nest Airstrip (abbreviated DNA, representing middle Pliocene) sites because they were both quite productive and could be worked effectively at the same time.

I am grateful to the National Geographic Society for providing the grant that funded this trip to northeastern Nebraska. My assistants in the field, Lisa Griggs and Mark Podell, rendered invaluable service. And I thank Dr. Michael Voorhies of the University of Nebraska State Museum, who helped our group in many ways and visited the site several times to lend a hand with the collecting.

THE ANNIES GEESE CROSS (AGC) SITE, UPPER MIOCENE

Location and Age. The AGC site was discovered by Dr. Michael Voorhies in a road-cut 10 miles northwest of Crofton, Knox County, Nebraska. Dr. Voorhies has been collecting fossil mammals from the site for several years, and plans to report on the geology and mammalogy of the site in a future publication. Dr. Voorhies's stratigraphic work has shown that the AGC site is equivalent in age to the lower part of the Valentine Formation and is thus of upper Miocene age.

Methodology. The matrix at the AGC site was a weakly cross-bedded, fine-grained sand that was rather wet when quarried. Thus, a washing and screening technique was used to collect the fossils. Matrix was dug out of the bank at the site, put into burlap bags, and then transported by truck to a shallow bay at the nearby Lewis and Clark Reservoir. Here the matrix was washed through boxes with screen sides and bottoms, a process similar to the one described by Hibbard (1949). The concentrate from the matrix was then sun-dried after being placed on towels on top of a large tarp. When the concentrate was dry it was sorted through for fossils in the trailer which was rented as our base of operation.

A list of fauna from the AGC site as of May 11, 1978, follows:

Class Amphibia
   Order Anura
      Family Pelobatidae
         Scaphiopus sp. (Spadefoot)
Material: Ilia and sacrococcyges
Remarks: This small burrowing frog probably lived in sandy areas on land. The bones are most similar to those of *Scaphiopus bombifrons,* a common frog of the High Plains of the United States today.
      Family Hylidae
         Hyla sp. (Tree Frog)
Material: Ilia
Remarks: The ilia are similar to those of several modern tree frogs of small to moderate size, but specific determinations await further study.
      Family Bufonidae
         Bufo sp. (Small Toad)
Material: Ilia
Remarks: Several ilia indicate the presence of small toads, quite contrasting in size to the "giant toad" ilia found at the DNA site.
      Family Ranidae
         Rana sp. (Grass Frog)
Material: Ilia
Remarks: These ilia indicate a small species of *Rana* very similar to the modern leopard frog, *Rana pipiens.* The presence of this species indicates a grassy marsh in the proximity of the site.
Class Reptilia
   Order Squamata
      Family Iguanidae
         Leiocephalus sp. (Curly-Tailed Lizard)
Material: Dentaries
Remarks: Mr. Carl Wellstead has reported on these important fossils in his master's thesis at the University of Nebraska and plans to discuss them in a forthcoming publication. The genus *Leiocephalus* is confined to the West Indes today, except for a small colony which has been introduced into Florida. The present-day tropical distribution of this lizard indicates that the climate of northeastern Nebraska must have been

much warmer in upper Miocene times than at the present.
    Family Colubridae
        Paleoheterodon tiheni (Extinct Hognose Snake)
Material: Trunk vertebrae
Remarks: This snake has specialized rear-teeth that were very long and knifelike for puncturing the bodies of inflated toads. An almost complete specimen of this snake was recently reported from the upper Miocene of southeastern Nebraska (Holman, 1977). This is the first published record of this genus and species for northeastern Nebraska.
        Elaphe sp. (Rat Snake)
Material: Trunk vertebrae
Remarks: The presence of a rodent-eating snake in the fauna is not surprising in the light of the occurrence of small rodents among the mammalian fossils from AGC.
        Thamnophis sp. (Gartersnake or Ribbonsnake)
Material: Trunk vertebrae
Remarks: This snake genus has species that are often found in grassy or marshy areas.

THE DEVIL'S NEST AIRSTRIP (DNA) SITE, MIDDLE PLIOCENE

    Location and Age.   The DNA site was discovered by Dr. Michael Voorhies and occurs in the eroded surface of an abandoned airstrip at the Devil's Nest development Area 12 miles north-northwest of Crofton, Knox County, Nebraska. Dr. Voorhies has been collecting fossil mammals from the site for several years and plans a report on the geology and mammalogy of the locality. Dr. Voorhies's stratigraphic work has shown that the fossil-bearing bed is a Hemphillian (middle Pliocene) channel in the Valentine Formation.

    Methodology.   Collecting methods at the DNA site included picking up material at the surface of this extensive deposit and dry-screening at the site. This fitted very well into our schedule, as we could visit the DNA site during times when we were waiting for the AGC concentrate to dry or on weekends. The DNA site turned out to be rich in vertebrate fossils, especially in turtle material.

    A list of fauna from the DNA site as of May 11, 1978, follows:

Class Amphibia
    Order Anura
        Family Bufonidae
            Bufo sp. (Giant Toad)
Material: Ilia
Remarks: This is an important fossil find for the material represents a toad that appears to be identical to the modern "giant toad," *Bufo marinus*, which today ranges from extreme southern Texas south into Mexico and Central America. The presence of this species also indicates a much warmer climate for northeastern Nebraska in the middle Pliocene than at present.
        Family Ranidae
            Rana sp. (Grass Frog)

Material: Ilia

Remarks: This frog, also very similar to the modern leopard frog, *Rana pipiens*, indicates the presence of a grassy marsh in the area.

Class Reptila

  Order Chelonia

    Family Chelydridae

      Chelydra sp. (Snapping Turtle)

Material: Shell fragments

Remarks: This species indicates the presence of a slow-moving or still permanent body of water.

    Family Emydidae

      Pseudemys sp. (Cooter or Slider Turtle)

Material: Nuchal plates and other shell material

Remarks: The presence of these large aquatic turtles indicates the presence of a permanent body of water, probably a slow-moving river or large pond.

      Clemmys sp. (Spotted Turtle Relative)

Material: Nuchals and shell matrial

Remarks: These turtles are semiaquatic and today live in grassy marshes.

    Family Testudinidae

      Geochelone sp. (Small Rugose Land Tortoise)

Material: Numerous pieces of shell

Remarks: This rough-shelled small land tortoise is certainly a member of the "tugida" group of *Geochelone* species. This group was rather widespread in the High Plains of North America in the late Tertiary.

    Family Trionychidae

      Trionyx sp. (Softshelled Turtle)

Material: Several pieces of shell

Remarks: This is perhaps the most aquatic genus of freshwater turtles living in the United States today so a permanent body of water, probably a slow-moving river, stream, or a pond, is indicated.

  Order Squamata

    Family Teidae

      Cnemidophorus sp. (Racerunner Lizard)

Material: Dentary

Remarks: The lizards of this genus all live in sandy habitats today, thus such a habitat must have been in the vicinity of the fossil site in the middle Pliocene.

    Family Colubridae

      ? *Heterodon* (Hognose Snake)

Material: Vertebrae

Remarks: At this time I am not sure whether this isolated vertebral material represents the extinct genus *Paleoheterodon* or the living genus *Heterodon*. Modern hognosed snakes prefer dry, sandy habitats.

      Salvadora sp. (Patchnosed Snake)

Material: Trunk vertebrae

Remarks: This genus occurs hundreds of miles to the south of the area today and thus is another form that indicates a warmer climate for northeastern Nebraska in the middle Pliocene. Members of this genus mainly prefer dry, terrestrial habitats today.

Elaphe sp. (Ratsnake)
Material: Trunk vertebrae
Remarks: This rodent-eating species probably fed on mice and small rats that were present as substantiated by the mammalian fossils from the DNA site.

GENERAL CONCLUSIONS

On the basis of herpetological fossils identified, it would appear that northeastern Nebraska had a much warmer climate in both the middle Pliocene and upper Miocene than at present. I would venture to guess that the climate was similar to that of the Gulf Coast of Texas today. Certainly the Curly-Tailed Lizard in the AGC fauna and the "Giant Toad" and southern turtles and snakes in the DNA fauna would indicate such a possibility.

The depositional environments of the two sites appear to be different. The weakly cross-bedded, small-grained sand that forms the AGC matrix would indicate a low energy transport situation, possibly a small "hole" in a gently flowing stream. The lack of animals with permanently aquatic habits might indicate a seasonal stream or pond. A dry, sandy, terrestrial habitat is also indicated by some of the AGC herpetofauna.

On the other hand, the large number of turtles that require a permanent aquatic habitat at the DNA site indicate the presence of a permanent large stream, river, or pond. Other faunal elements also indicate the presence of a rather dry, perhaps sandy, terrestrial habitat.

PRESENT STATUS OF THE PROJECT

At present (1980), several people are continuing to study the AGC and DNA material collected in 1976.

1. Carl Wellstead (whose University of Nebraska master's thesis discusses lizards of the AGC site) is preparing a report on upper Miocene lizards which will detail some of the AGC *Leiocephalus* material.

2. Dale Jackson, a graduate student at the University of Florida, is studying the aquatic emydid turtles from the DNA site.

3. J. Alan Holman is studying the remainder of the herpetological material from both sites and will incorporate Wellstead's and Jackson's work into a final publication on the amphibians and reptiles of the two faunas.

4. Michael Voorhies of the University of Nebraska State Museum is studying the mammalogical material from the site.

One of the most spectacular finds, if not the most spectacular find, in the 1976 collection from the DNA site was the complete skull of the large insectivore, *Meterix (Plesiosorex)*. Dr. Voorhies has informed me that this is the only skull known of this animal that has been known previously only on the basis of teeth. This hedgehog-size insectivore has been illustrated by University of Nebraska artists and will be featured in a separate scientific publication because of its importance.

REFERENCES

BRODKORB, P.
   1962.   A teal from the lower Pliocene of Kansas.   Quart. Journ. Florida Acad. Sci., vol. 25, no. 2, pp. 157-160.
FEDUCCIA, J. A., and WILSON, R. L.
   1967.   Avian fossils from the lower Pliocene of Kansas.   Occ. Pap. Mus. Zool. Univ. Michigan, no. 655, 6 pp.
HIBBARD, C. W.
   1949.   Techniques of collecting microvertebrate fossils.   Contrib. Mus. Paleont. Univ. Michigan, vol. 8, no. 2, pp. 7-19.
   1960.   An interpretation of Pliocene and Pleistocene climates in North America.   Michigan Acad. Sci. Arts, Letts. 62d Ann. Rept., pp. 5-30.
HIBBARD, C. W., and JAMMOT, D.
   1971.   The shrews of the WaKeeney local fauna, lower Pliocene of Trego County, Kansas.   Contrib. Mus. Paleontol. Univ. Michigan, vol. 23, no. 24, pp. 377-380.
HIBBARD, C. W., and PHILLIS, L. F.
   1945.   The occurrence of *Eucastor* and *Eipgaulus* in the lower Pliocene of Trego County, Kansas.   Univ. Kansas Sci. Bull., vol. 30, no. 16, pp. 549-555.
HOLMAN, J. A.
   1971.   Small vertebrate fossils from the WaKeeney local fauna in Trego County, Kansas.   Amer. Phil. Soc. Yearbook for 1971, pp. 323-324.
   1975.   Herpetofauna of the WaKeeney local fauna (lower Pliocene: Clarendonian) of Trego County, Kansas.   Pp. 49-66 *in* "Studies of Cenozoic Paleontology and Stratigraphy in Honor of Claude W. Hibbard," Univ. Michigan Pap. Paleont., no. 12.
   1977.   Upper Miocene snakes (Reptilia, Serpentes) from southeastern Nebraska.   Journ. Herpetology, vol. 11, no. 3, pp. 323-335.
HUBBS, C. L., and HIBBARD, C. W.
   1951.   *Ictalurus lambda,* a new catfish based on a pectoral spine from the lower Pliocene of Kansas.   Copeia, 1951, no. 1, pp. 8-14.
WILSON, R. L.
   1968.   Systematics and faunal analysis of a lower Pliocene vertebrate assemblage from Trego County, Kansas.   Contrib. Mus. Paleont. Univ. Michigan, vol. 22, no. 7, pp. 75-126.

J. ALAN HOLMAN

Geology and Vertebrate Paleontology of the Agate Fossil Beds National Monument and Surrounding Region, Sioux County, Nebraska (1972-1978)

Principal Investigator: Robert M. Hunt, Jr., The University of Nebraska, Lincoln, Nebraska.

Grant Nos. 1069, 1763. In support of an integrated geological and paleontological study of the Agate National Monument and surrounding region, and the excavation of an Early Miocene faunal assemblage (Harper Quarry).

The Tertiary rocks of the central Great Plains physiographic province (Darton, 1905, pl. 2) constitute a thick wedge of sediment that extends eastward nearly to the Missouri River from the Rocky Mountain front ranges. These beds are one of the most prolific sources of vertebrate fossils in the Western Hemisphere. Much of our present understanding of the evolution of North American mammals, deciphered by paleontologists during the past 120 years, is based on fossils derived from the continental Tertiary rocks of this region.

Gradual dissection of this sediment wedge by the rivers of the central Great Plains has exposed much of the rock record in western Nebraska and adjoining parts of South Dakota, Wyoming, and Colorado, providing the paleontologist with one of the more complete sequences of continental Tertiary sediments in North America. So basic to the vertebrate paleontology of the continent are these sediments and their contained fossils that the Wood Committee (Wood et al., 1941) of the Paleontological Society, at the time that they defined a provincial time scale for the North American continental Tertiary, designated type localities for 5 of the 18 provincial ages in western Nebraska.

In order to evaluate the fossil mammals collected in western Nebraska and adjoining regions during the previous century, it is essential to understand the geologic relations of the various Tertiary rock units. Despite the considerable importance of the Tertiary of western Nebraska to an understanding of North American mammal evolution, geologic mapping has been limited to reconnaissance studies by N. H. Darton (1899, 1902, 1903, 1905) and G. I. Adams (1902) of the United States Geological Survey, and by A. L. Lugn

(1939) of the University of Nebraska at map scales ranging from 1:125,000 to 1:2,500,000.

The Arikaree of N. H. Darton (1899)

The continental Tertiary rocks of the Great Plains were separated into three great divisions by N. H. Darton. His pioneer work receives validation today in the general approval given these divisions by many geologists. In his first major report, Darton (1899) recognized the (1) White River beds, (2) Arikaree beds, (3) Ogallala beds.

Our work has centered on the Arikaree of Darton in an attempt to clarify the geologic relationships of these fossiliferous rocks in their type area in western Nebraska. There has been relatively little disagreement in identification of White River or Ogallala sediments in the central Great Plains, but the Arikaree has been somewhat controversial for several reasons: (1) the Arikaree as originally mapped by Darton (1899) is subject to subdivision into smaller rock units, more so than either the White River or Ogallala—early attempts at subdivision were ill-defined without clearly indicated boundaries, either stratigraphic or geographic, yet the names of the subdivisions persist in the literature and were employed in the collection of fossil mammals; (2) the White River and Ogallala beds have been maintained without significant alteration in concept since Darton's report of 1899, but the Arikaree has suffered an unfortunate emendation (Lugn, 1939) that obscures the unity of Darton's initial concept by removal of the upper part of the Dartonian Arikaree to a new stratigraphic unit (Hemingford Group) that has never been adequately defined; (3) the geographic relationship of the type Arikaree and type Ogallala in western Nebraska is such that the oldest stratigraphic units of the Ogallala are not directly superposed on the youngest Arikaree, thus the temporal relationship of oldest Ogallala to youngest Arikaree must be established through fossil correlation and radiometric dating.

Darton's original concept of the Arikaree as set forth in his report of 1899 is worth careful consideration. The relationship between the Arikaree and Ogallala beds in their type area in western Nebraska, according to Darton, was that between a lower rock unit (Arikaree) of more northerly outcrop area, comprising loose to fairly compact fine-grained sands containing a large amount of volcanic ash intermixed with the sands and as local ash beds, unconformably overlain by an upper rock unit (Ogallala) of more southerly outcrop area comprising carbonate-cemented sands and clays intermixed with crystalline debris from the Rocky Mountains.

In essence, Darton's conception of the Arikaree is that of a fine-grained semiconsolidated sand with abundant volcanic glass shards intermixed. The Ogallala comprises clastic rocks of more varied textures intermixed with crystalline debris, and implicitly without significant volcanic glass. Darton wrote, "In studying the geology of this region it was found that several formations contained extensive deposits of volcanic ash. There is a general admixture of ash as well as a number of thick beds of it in the Arikaree formation . . . So far as observed, it is rare in the Ogallala formation. The Arikaree formation contains a sprinkling of ash almost throughout its extent . . . The ash in these formations was probably derived from volcanoes in the Rocky Mountain region, for there is no evidence of Tertiary volcanoes in the vicinity. . . ."

To be sure, there are channel facies within the Arikaree of Darton with abundant crystalline granule to pebble gravel but these igneous and metamorphic clasts occur within laterally restricted channel deposits, not diffused through the formation as in the Ogallala.

The Arikaree of Sioux County, Nebraska

Darton's maps (1899, pls. 82, 84) indicate that the Arikaree beds are exposed primarily in the four northwestern counties of Nebraska (Sioux, Dawes, Box Butte, Sheridan, fig. 1). The most complete superpositional sequence of Arikaree rocks occurs in Sioux County. These beds likewise are rich in fossil mammals, providing a record of Early Miocene mammal evolution unexcelled elsewhere on the North American continent.

Arikaree units form most of the surface outcrops of Sioux County (fig. 1), geomorphically expressed as an elevated tableland that extends from the Pine Ridge escarpment (the northern limit of the Arikaree in western Nebraska) on the north to the North Platte River valley on the south. The stratigraphically lowest five Arikaree formations (fig. 3) comprise the bulk of surface outcrops in Sioux County, whereas the three stratigraphically highest formations are very restricted in geographic area of exposure within the county.

In the early part of this century, when most of the Arikaree rock units were originally defined, the lack of topographic maps or aerial photography made detailed mapping and clarification of stratigraphic relationships difficult; the recent availability of topographic maps as well as aerial and satellite photoimagery has allowed us to relate detailed mapping to the regional geologic setting in a manner not possible for earlier paleontologists.

My current view of the stratigraphic sequence of rock units comprising Darton's Arikaree is shown in figure 3 (for the present, a subdivision of the

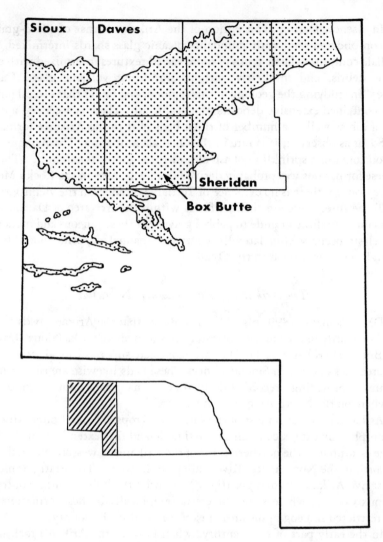

FIG. 1. Geographic distribution of the Arikaree beds of N. H. Darton in western Nebraska as originally defined and mapped in 1899.

Arikaree of Darton into Arikaree and Hemingford groups is not accepted, based on Lugn's [1939] inability to objectively define Hemingford rocks in lithic terms). In Sioux County, the White River beds of Meek and Hayden are overlain by the Arikaree of Darton (including the Gering Formation of Darton) along the Pine Ridge escarpment in Monroe Creek Canyon. Here 600 feet of Arikaree forming the escarpment were divided into three formations by J. B. Hatcher in 1902. The Gering and Monroe Creek Formations constitute a single depositional episode, beginning at the base with stream-deposited fine- to medium-grained sands, crystalline gravels, and intertonguing silt-stones that grade upward into massive sand and silt with abundant volcanic ash intermixed in the sediment. Very few fossils have been collected from the Gering-Monroe Creek sequence, because of heavy plant cover, steep cliff-forming outcrops, and poor exposures at the Pine Ridge escarpment, where these formations are best exposed. The Harrison Formation disconformably overlies the Monroe Creek Formation, the former distinguished by a slight increase in grain size and change in weathering characteristics. A contact between the two formations can be mapped in Sioux County along the Pine Ridge escarpment, but it is often covered by vegetation and difficult to locate. At the head of Monroe Creek Canyon (sect. 21, T32N, R56W), the Harrison Formation is about 120 feet thick, and the combined thickness of the Gering-Monroe Creek interval is about 480 feet.

The Gering, Monroe Creek, and Harrison Formations in central Sioux County are predominantly fine to very fine grained grayish semiconsolidated sands, rich in volcanic glass shards and other grains of volcanic origin intermixed with the sand,[1] and lacking in crystalline gravel or other epiclastic materials (except in local laterally restricted channel facies). The regional geometry of these formations markedly differs from the simple tabular form depicted by Peterson (1907, 1909) and others in the early 20th century.

The Upper Harrison Beds of O. A. Peterson (1907, 1909)

Perhaps the most significant geological result of my study of the Arikaree of central Sioux County is the regional definition of the geometry of the Upper Harrison beds (Peterson, 1907, 1909), summarized by the geologic profile of figure 2 from the Pine Ridge escarpment to the Agate Fossil Beds National Monument. A thin veneer of ash-rich sand, a few to 45 feet thick, with thin lenticular interbedded freshwater limestones and silica-cemented land surfaces (siliceous grits of Hatcher, 1902) at particular levels, overlies the Harrison Formation along the crest of Pine Ridge north of the town of Harrison (sects. 21, 22, 27, 28, T32N, R56W). This is the youngest stratigraphic unit along the Pine Ridge escarpment in this area, and can be mapped southward into the Niobrara Canyon (figure 2) about 8 miles southwest of the town of

---

[1] Herein called volcaniclastic sands, fide Pettijohn et al., 1972, p. 261.

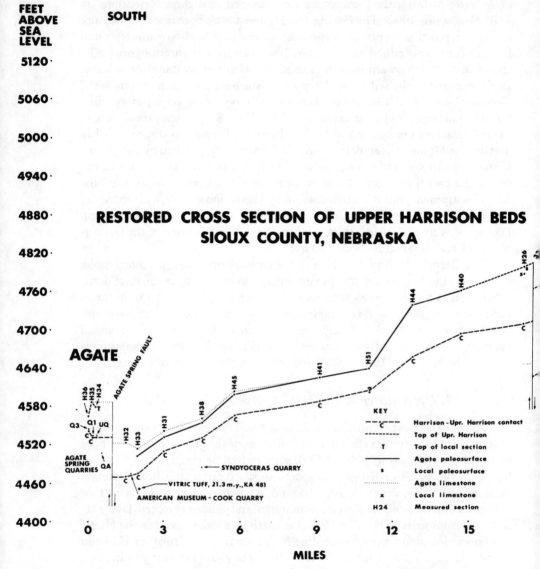

FIG. 2. Geologic restored cross section of the Upper Harrison beds of O. A. Peterson (1907, 1909) from the Pine Ridge escarpment to the Agate Fossil Beds

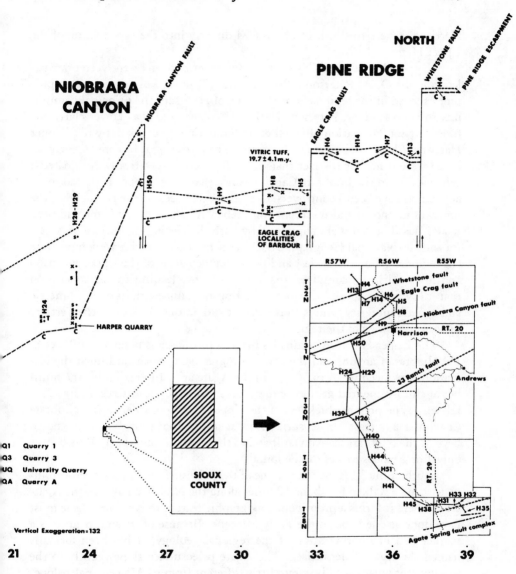

National Monument, showing the location of the principal fossil quarries, dated volcanic ash beds, and faults (modified from Hunt, 1978).

Harrison, where this unit can be traced directly into the type section of the Upper Harrison beds.

"Upper Harrison beds" is an unfortunate term given by the vertebrate paleontologist O. A. Peterson (1907, pp. 22-23) to the youngest stratigraphic unit exposed in the region about the town of Harrison, the principal community in Sioux County. Peterson (1907, 1909) conceived of a "Lower Harrison" (the Harrison Formation of Hatcher) in Sioux County overlain by his "Upper Harrison," hence the origin of the name. The term might be conveniently ignored were it not for the fact that in 1909 Peterson specifically designated a type locality in the Niobrara Canyon. Since that time, Upper Harrison rocks and faunas have been a controversial topic, largely because the geometry of the unit was unknown and no recent comprehensive study of the fauna had been made. Based on our work supported by both the Geological Society of America and the National Geographic Society, it has been possible to demonstrate the regional geometry, facies, and petrographic nature of the Upper Harrison and to establish its contained mammalian fauna, leading to our conclusion that it is without doubt a distinct formation-rank unit with its own geometric and genetic integrity, and is an important and unique element in the Tertiary historical geology of the region.

The Upper Harrison attains its maximum thickness of about 160 feet in the Niobrara Canyon, and then thins progressively southward until the formation is reduced to 20 to 50 feet in the Agate area. Interestingly, the number of silica-cemented geomorphic surfaces (called 'paleosurfaces' in fig. 2) is related to the present thickness of the Upper Harrison beds. In the Niobrara Canyon area at least 5 paleosurfaces occur in superposition, but to the north beyond the Niobrara Canyon fault and to the south beyond the 33 Ranch fault only 1 or 2 paleosurfaces can be found.

South of the 33 Ranch fault, one of the paleosurfaces of particular prominence can be walked for about 12 miles along the Niobrara River to the Agate area, where it forms a prominent topographic feature today, much as it must have done at one time in the Early Miocene. Because of its significance as a marker bed in interpretation of the regional geology, it has been formally named the Agate paleosurface. The Agate paleosurface slopes gently to the southeast at what could be a rate little different from its Miocene paleoslope.

The Upper Harrison beds and Harrison Formation constitute nearly all surface outcrops in Sioux County from the Pine Ridge escarpment south to the 33 Ranch fault. In its type area north of the fault, the Upper Harrison is composed of thin channel deposits of ephemeral streams (Harper Quarry occurs in such a deposit) at the base of the formation overlain by massive silty sands with thin interbedded freshwater limestones and the silica-cemented paleosurfaces. The Niobrara Canyon area seems to preserve an ancient shallow Upper Harrison paleovalley, perhaps structurally controlled, that filled at first by means of a very limited volume of ephemeral stream deposits succeeded by the major volume of volcaniclastic sand, chiefly an aeolian deposit. The limestones represent very shallow yet widespread ephemeral ponds with little resident fauna other than freshwater ostracods. The land surface must have been periodically stabilized by the formation of the successive paleosurfaces rich in animal burrows and plant root casts.

As one travels south from the Niobrara Canyon toward Agate along the Niobrara River (fig. 2, measured sections H40, H44, H51, H41), volcaniclastic massive sand beneath the prominent Agate paleosurface comprises the entire Upper Harrison and the channel deposits of ephemeral streams are absent. However, upon reaching the Agate area, cross-bedded stream deposits again appear (fig. 2, measured sections H31-36, H38, H45) both intertongued with and overlain by the massive sands with freshwater limestone (Agate limestone) and the Agate paleosurface. These appear to be the deposits of a major ephemeral drainage several miles in width but of little depth, gauged by the thickness of the channel deposits which do not exceed 30 feet. These channel sands and related deposits in which occur the Agate Spring Quarries constitute a second paleovalley (Agate paleovalley) distinct from that in the Niobrara Canyon.

The Younger Tertiary Formations of Sioux County

The youngest stratigraphic unit of Tertiary age north of the 33 Ranch fault in Sioux County is the Upper Harrison of Peterson, but south of the 33 Ranch fault in the Agate area the Runningwater Formation (Cook, 1965) overlies the Upper Harrison. The Runningwater Formation includes not only a massive volcaniclastic sand facies but also a major channel facies occupying the Whistle Creek valley south of Agate, rich in granitic gravel and sand. Cook in his description of the Runningwater said that "pebbles up to one-half inch in diameter of various granitic rocks were noted in the conglomeratic phases of the Runningwater . . . the first such known . . . to occur in several hundred feet of antecedent Miocene sediments in this part of Nebraska [above the crystalline gravel of the Gering Formation]. . . ."

Runningwater deposits cover a large area in central Sioux County south of the 33 Ranch fault and north of the divide between the North Platte and Whistle Creek valleys. To the east, particularly in Box Butte and Dawes counties, the Runningwater is overlain by the Box Butte Formation (Galusha,

1975). On the high divide between the North Platte and Whistle Creek valleys, the Runningwater Formation is overlain by deposits of the Sheep Creek, Olcott, and Snake Creek Formations (Skinner et al., 1977) within the very small geographic area of less than 10 square miles in which these last 3 formations are exposed in Sioux County. Whereas the Upper Harrison beds are pyroclastic sands and silt associated with ephemeral channel facies that demonstrate reworking of the primary pyroclastic materials, the Runningwater Formation preserves the largely epiclastic channel facies of a major regional drainage, having at least seasonally continuous flow of varying discharge, associated with massive volcaniclastic sands which suggest both aeolian and fluvial influences in their deposition.

Nearly all the Tertiary surface rocks of Sioux County (excluding the White River beds) can be assigned to one of the formations in the sequence from Gering through Runningwater; in fact, most surface rocks belong to either the Harrison, Upper Harrison, or Runningwater Formations. The formations above the Runningwater beds in figure 3 occur either in a few isolated outcrops in east-central Sioux County (Box Butte Formation, Galusha, 1975, fig. 1), or in a small area of about 8 square miles on the high divide between the North Platte and Whistle Creek valleys (the classic Sheep Creek-Snake

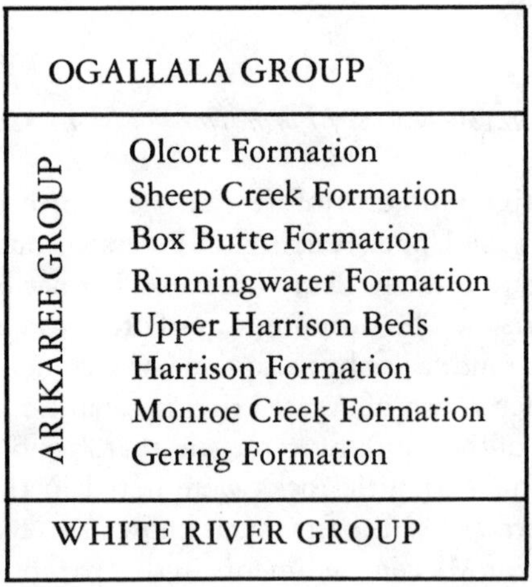

OGALLALA GROUP
ARIKAREE GROUP — Olcott Formation Sheep Creek Formation Box Butte Formation Runningwater Formation Upper Harrison Beds Harrison Formation Monroe Creek Formation Gering Formation
WHITE RIVER GROUP

FIG. 3.   Stratigraphic sequence of Tertiary formations in western Nebraska as recognized in the present study. Formations above the White River Group and below the Ogallala Group are tentatively included in an Arikaree Group that better corresponds to Darton's original Arikaree concept than the current restriction of the term to the lowest three formations.

Creek area, Skinner et al., 1977, Sheep Creek Formation, Olcott Formation). Because of their geographically limited exposures, these formations are not likely to have figured significantly in Darton's concept of the Arikaree.

Darton's Arikaree Concept Relative to Current Work

It is of interest to ask whether the principal surface formations recognized within the area that Darton mapped as his type Arikaree do in fact, in the light of recent work, conform to his original concept of the lithic nature of the Arikaree as originally defined in 1899. In Sioux County this seems to be true. Petrographic work by my colleague, Dr. John Breyer, Texas Christian University, Fort Worth, Texas, has shown that the very-fine to fine-grained sands of the Gering through Runningwater contain a large portion of volcanic glass intermixed with the sediment. The mineralogy of these Early Miocene formations is similar, averaging nearly 40 percent vitric lithic fragments (glass shards of diverse type), and slightly more than 30 percent each of feldspar and quartz. Besides the vitric lithic fragments, many of the framework grains appear to be of volcanic origin. Much of the quartz is of the strain-free monocrystalline variety; resorption features and an occasional bipyramidal form are seen. Feldspar euhedra, especially those with attached glass, also suggest a volcanic origin. Among the potassium feldspars, sanidine is conspicuous by its abundance, microcline by its near complete absence. Thus the fine-grained clastic sediments of the type Arikaree in Sioux County are predominantly volcaniclastic sands. More specifically, the type Arikaree of Sioux County can be characterized as air-fall pyroclastic debris admixed with varying, and often small, amounts of epiclastic debris from nearby uplifts. Original accumulation of these sediments as a blanket of air-fall debris is indicated by the composition and sorting of the sediment, by the angularity of the grains and shards, by the apparent lack of primary sedimentary structures (other than trace fossils), and by the regional uniformity of the deposit. After initial deposition but before lithification, the sediments were reworked in some cases by fluvial and/or aeolian processes. These reworked sediments exhibit horizontal stratification and both large and small scale cross-stratification.

Stream deposits within these pyroclastic beds have distinctive cut-and-fill geometries and constitute only a small volume of the type Arikaree exposed in Sioux County. Their chief paleontological importance lies in the frequent concentrations of mammal bones they contain. The stream deposits are readily divided into two types, based on the predominance of epiclastic or pyroclastic debris in the channel fill: (1) local ephemeral channel sands characterized by reworked pyroclastic material; (2) channel sands that appear to be the fill of major through-going streams, characterized by much crystalline epiclastic debris.

Within Sioux County, the relationship between epiclastic and volcaniclastic facies is observable through study of outcrops of the Gering and Runningwater Formations. In these outcrops the epiclastic facies often can be seen to intertongue with the volcaniclastic facies, with crystalline pebbles and sands occurring as thin lenses and as isolated clasts in the volcaniclastic fine-grained sands near the channels.

In summary, the Sioux County Arikaree can be divided into three commonly encountered facies: (1) Widespread massive pyroclastic fine-grained sands and silts, with evidence of periodic stabilization (burrows, root casts of plants, duricrust) as a land surface at numerous horizons; (2) local volcaniclastic stream deposits, representing the sandy fill of ephemeral drainages comprising chiefly reworked pyroclastic debris; (3) epiclastic stream channel sands and gravels, indicative of influx of crystalline debris from the Rocky Mountains and adjacent uplifts. Finally, the thin micrite limestones containing ostracods and gastropods (fig. 2) that occur chiefly in the Upper Harrison in Sioux County constitute a fourth relatively minor facies; the Agate limestone is the most prominent of these shallow freshwater carbonate deposits.

The great volume of the Arikaree in Sioux County and throughout its type area in western Nebraska is volcaniclastic in character, with the epiclastic lithotype a minor component. Recognition of the predominantly volcaniclastic nature of the type Arikaree focuses on the same diagnostic property explicitly mentioned by Darton (1899) in his original description of the unit: "The formation includes a large amount of volcanic ash, as a general admixture in its sediments as well as in beds of considerable extent and thickness." A strong argument can be made to include all formations from Gering through Upper Harrison in the Dartonian Arikaree, as well as the mappable extensions of these chiefly volcaniclastic sands outward to geographically more distant areas.

The internal facies relationships of the Runningwater Formation (a major epiclastic channel facies associated with a volcaniclastic sand facies) and its stratigraphic relationship to the four Arikaree formations beneath it offer insight as well as several potential solutions to the Arikaree-Hemingford problem. Presently no known evidence contravenes Cook's (1965) oft-quoted statement that the Runningwater gravels mark the first major influx of crystalline debris into the central Great Plains since the basal Arikaree gravels of the Gering Formation. Despite the mineralogical similarity between the volcaniclastic sand facies of the Runningwater and the four older Arikaree units, the influx of crystalline material from the Rocky Mountains might be used as a convenient base for a revised Hemingford Group. Alternatively, the volcaniclastic character of the fine-grained sand facies could be emphasized as a basis for an extended Arikaree Group that includes the Runningwater Formation.

Are the stratigraphically highest formations of limited geographic exposure in Sioux County and surrounding region (Box Butte, Sheep Creek, Olcott Formations, fig. 3) also of similar character? Can they also be included within an Arikaree Group defined chiefly in terms of volcaniclastic sands as the primary lithotype? Although much evidence is not yet evaluated, field observations suggest that several of these formations include a significant volcaniclastic component in their fine-grained sand facies, and despite the presence of epiclastic channel sands as important facies within these units, volcaniclastic sediments are associated with the epiclastic phase, and possibly comprised a much greater portion of the formation before recent erosion reduced these units to their present geographically limited exposures.

Regardless of the final disposition of the Box Butte, Sheep Creek, and Olcott Formations, the concept of a Hemingford Group appears to have little value as defined by Lugn (1939), because the Upper Harrison and Runningwater are indistinguishable in their volcaniclastic character from the remainder of the type Arikaree (Gering, Monroe Creek, Harrison), and these two formations were an integral part of Lugn's Hemingford concept under the term "Marshland Formation."

Cenozoic Faulting and Regional Structure

During the early part of the present century, Darton's concept of the Arikaree was adopted and modified by vertebrate paleontologists whose chief aim was to secure fossils in these Miocene rocks (Peterson, 1904, 1907, 1909; Hatcher, 1902; Osborn, 1918; Cook, 1915). The Tertiary units of Sioux County were visualized as tabular regional sheets of relatively uniform thickness. In this light, the geological framework of the fossiliferous beds seemed to be quite simple. Our recent work shows that this view ignored not only the complex regional geometry and facies relationships of the formation-rank units, but also the influence of regional structure.

Most important in modifying the classic view of the Tertiary of northwest Nebraska is my discovery of a pattern of major northeast-southwest trending faults (fig. 2), aligned in parallel, and of about the same magnitude of apparent vertical displacement. The zone of faults has a width of about 30 miles, extending from the Pine Ridge escarpment on the north to the high divide between North Platte and Whistle Creek valleys on the south. Satellite photo-imagery shows that two of the faults, the Niobrara Canyon and 33 Ranch, can be traced southwestward into Wyoming where they join the Whalen Fault System. Both the Niobrara Canyon and 33 Ranch faults have prominent topographic expression, with an elevated southern block forming a regional scarp that is evident both on satellite photoimagery and in the field.

These surface faults possibly are a northeastward extension of the Mullen Creek-Nash Fork shear zone, recently discussed by Warner (1978) as part of a major tectonic feature of North America named by him the Colorado Lineament. Warner suggests that the Colorado Lineament is a Precambrian wrench fault system more than 1,100 kilometers long that extends through the Rocky Mountains from the Colorado Plateau northeastward to Minnesota, possibly representing a fault system characteristic of the marginal zone of an ancient continental plate. In southeast Wyoming, the northern margin of the lineament is said to be the Mullen Creek-Nash Fork shear zone. A possible extension of the shear zone onto the central Great Plains is represented by the Richeau-Jay Em fault zone (Droullard, 1963), mistakenly called the Hartville Fault by Warner (1978, fig. 1). The Richeau-Jay Em fault zone includes the Whalen Fault which can be traced northeast to the Niobrara Canyon and 33 Ranch faults of Sioux County, thereby demonstrating the extension of the shear zone from the Rocky Mountain front ranges to the northwestern Nebraska high plains.

In Sioux County, the faults cut all Arikaree units up to and including the Runningwater Formation on direct field evidence, and on indirect evidence appear to offset proboscidean-bearing Tertiary sandstones called by Peterson (1909) the Spoon Butte beds. Thus, faulting must postdate volcanic ash near the stratigraphic top of the Runningwater Formation, dated at 16.9 ± 1.7 m.y.B.P. by the fission track method,[2] and probably postdates the first occurrence of gomphothere proboscideans in the Great Plains, i.e., younger than about 15 million years B.P. Recognition of the faults introduces a significant change in concept from earlier views of the regional structural setting of the Miocene continental strata, and has an influence on the interpretation of the succession of mammal faunas in the region.

---

[2] Vitric tuff, SW$\frac{1}{4}$, NE$\frac{1}{4}$, NE$\frac{1}{4}$, sect. 30, T.28N, R.51W, south rim of Niobrara River valley, Box Butte County, Nebraska, 30-35 feet beneath top of Runningwater Formation in its type area, fission-track dated bulk glass shards, determined as average of 3 separate samples (one determination each), $\bar{x}$ [1σ] $= 16.91 \pm 1.69$ m.y.B.P., Sample Nos. MT-1A, 1B, 1C-72, radiometric data used in calculation available upon request from Dr. J. D. Boellstorff, Conservation and Survey Division, University of Nebraska, Lincoln, Nebr. 68588.

Mammalian Biostratigraphy

A primary aim of our research is the development of a refined mammalian biostratigraphy for the region. The accuracy of the result heavily depends on how well the fossiliferous sites are integrated with the study of the regional geological context. Without attention to geologic mapping, petrography and sedimentology, structural geology and geochronology as well as paleontology, a necessary perspective as to the *raison d'être* of the fossil sites is lost. Accordingly, a mammalian biostratigraphy for the region that truly explains fossil occurrence in terms of paleoecology, taphonomy, and environment of deposition relative to the geologic history is a final rather than early result of such a study.

The development of a preliminary biostratigraphy for the region has centered on the Arikaree formations most extensively exposed: the Harrison, Upper Harrison, and Runningwater. A summary of the distribution of fossil mammals collected from these formations is presented in table 1 (a more detailed listing will be published elsewhere). Fossil mammals in the collections of several museums, in particular the American Museum of Natural History, New York, and the Carnegie Museum, Pittsburgh, have been used to develop table 1, in addition to new material collected in northwest Nebraska during the eight years 1971-1978.

A principal result of the study was the discovery that the Agate Spring Quarries, one of the major Miocene mammal sites in North America, are located in the base of the Upper Harrison beds, and are not found in the Harrison Formation as previously believed (fig. 2, Quarry 1, Quarry 3, University Quarry). This significantly alters the concept of the Harrison fauna in western Nebraska, since the current understanding of that fauna was based mainly on the fossil mammals from the Agate Spring Quarries. The only presently known major sites that occur within the Harrison Formation of Sioux County are the Stenomylus Quarry of F. B. Loomis, Syndyoceras Quarry of H. J. Cook, and Quarry A (the first of the Agate Quarries excavated by O. A. Peterson in 1904), all situated in the Niobrara River valley within or near the Agate Fossil Beds National Monument.

The principal Upper Harrison quarries of western Nebraska occur in central Sioux County in geographic and stratigraphic proximity above the Harrison quarries in the Agate area, with the exception of Harper Quarry (Hunt, 1978) located in the Niobrara Canyon. The Upper Harrison quarries in the Agate area (Agate Spring Quarries with the exception of Quarry A, American Museum-Cook Quarry) and in the Niobrara Canyon (Harper Quarry) are found in very-fine to fine-grained volcaniclastic sands deposited in ephemeral

TABLE 1.   Preliminary Biostratigraphy of the Harrison Formation (Hatcher, 1902), Upper Harrison Beds (Peterson, 1907, 1909), and Runningwater Formation (Cook, 1965), Northwest Nebraska and Southeast Wyoming

	Harrison Formation	Upper Harrison Beds	Running- water Formation
CARNIVORA:			
Procyonidae			
Zodiolestes	X	—	—
Edaphocyon	—	—	X
Bassariscus	—	?	X
Canidae			
Phlaocyon	X	X	X
Cynarctoides	—	X	X
Tomarctus	X	X	X
Leptocyon	X	—	X
Amphicyonidae			
Daphoenodon	X	X	X
Ysengrinia	—	X	—
Cynelos	—	X	X
Amphicyon	—	—	X
New genus	—	X	—
temnocyonines	X	X	—
Ursidae			
Cephalogale	—	X	X
Mustelidae			
Potamotherium	—	—	X
Brachypsalis	—	—	X
Leptarctus	—	—	X
Oligobunis	X	X	X
Promartes	X	X	?
Megalictis	?	X	—
Felidae	—	—	—
PERISSODACTYLA:			
Rhinocerotidae			
Menoceras	?	X	X
Diceratherium	X	X	—
Chalicotheriidae	X	X	X
Tapiridae	X	X	X
Equidae			
Parahippus nebrascensis	—	X	—
Parahippus wyomingensis	X	X	—
Parahippus pawniensis	—	—	X
Parahippus cognatus	—	—	X
Archaeohippus	—	—	X
anchitheres	X	X	X

	Harrison Formation	Running-water Formation	Upper Harrison Beds
ARTIODACTYLA:			
Tayassuidae			
Cynorca	—	X	—
Desmathyus	X	X	X
Anthracotheriidae			
Arretotherium	—	—	X
Hypertragulidae			
Nanotragulus	X	X	—
Entelodontidae			
Dinohyus	X	X	X
Protoceratidae			
Syndyoceras	X	X	?
Protoceras	X	—	—
Camelidae			
Stenomylus	X	X	?
Moschidae			
Blastomeryx advena	—	X	—
Blastomeryx olcotti	—	X	—
Blastomeryx sp.	—	—	X
Dromomerycidae			
Aletomeryx	—	—	X
Barbouromeryx	—	—	X
Oreodonts			
Promerycochoerus	X	X	—
Merycochoerus	—	X	X

stream channels cut into the Harrison Formation. To date, accumulations of mammal bones numerous enough to justify a quarry have been found only in the basal Upper Harrison channel fills and not in the stratigraphically higher massive volcaniclastic sands that appear to be largely if not entirely pyroclastic in origin. These higher sands produce only isolated specimens.

The mammalian fauna from the Harrison Formation of central Sioux County and the immediately adjacent area in Niobrara County, Wyoming, includes amphicyonid, canid, and mustelid carnivores, and among the herbivores, representatives of the major perissodactyl families, as well as peccaries, hypertragulids, entelodonts, protoceratids, camels, and oreodonts among the artiodactyls. Although the Harrison mammals have not been studied in depth, it appears that many genera continue into the Upper Harrison beds without significant faunal break (table 1).

The mammalian fauna from the Upper Harrison is derived chiefly from central Sioux County and contiguous areas in Goshen and Niobrara counties,

Wyoming. The fauna includes the mammalian assemblages from the Agate Spring Quarries, American Museum-Cook Quarry (Hunt, 1972), and Harper Quarry (Hunt, 1978) from channel deposits within the base of the formation. These quarries produce a similar mammal fauna that includes chalicotheres, rhinos, entelodonts, horses, and amphicyonid carnivores as common elements. The vertical stratigraphic range of these mammals within the formation is under study. The uppermost part of the Upper Harrison at its type locality in the Niobrara Canyon yields a major faunal assemblage as isolated specimens derived from outcrops along the south rim of the canyon; in general, the same taxa seem to be present as in the channel deposits at the base of the formation with the exception of oreodonts *(Merycochoerus, Merychyus)* and the artiodactyl *Blastomeryx,* unknown from the quarries in the base of the formation (1977 excavation at Harper Quarry produced astragali that possibly represent *Blastomeryx).*

The Upper Harrison beds include the first occurrence of not only *Merycochoerus* and *Blastomeryx* but also the carnivores *Megalictis, Cynelos, Ysengrinia, Cephalogale,* and *Cynarctoides,* and the last occurrence of the carnivores *Megalictis* and the temnocyonine amphicyonids *(Temnocyon, Mammocyon),* the rhinoceros *Diceratherium* and primitive species of parahippine horses *(Parahippus nebrascensis* and *P. wyomingensis),* and the artiodactyls *Nanotragulus* and *Promerycochoerus.*

There is a recognizable and significant difference between the fossil mammals of the Upper Harrison and Runningwater Formations in this region (not between the Harrison and Upper Harrison as suggested by Schultz, 1938, p. 443, and Lugn, 1939, p. 1254) that is expressed in the last appearance of many mammalian lineages and the first appearance of new forms (table 2). It is this faunal and lithic discontinuity between Upper Harrison and Runningwater that Lugn (1939) mistakenly has referred to as "the most significant and important structural and erosional unconformity within the Miocene series in western Nebraska," but Lugn confused the unconformity at the base of the Runningwater Formation for one at the base of the Upper Harrison, thus leading to his belief that the critical horizon was the boundary between Harrison and Upper Harrison units.

The Runningwater Formation marks the first occurrence of the bearlike carnivore *Amphicyon* and several mustelids *(Leptarctus, Potamotherium, Brachypsalis),* of advanced parahippine horses *(Parahippus cognatus, P. pawniensis)* and *Archaeohippus,* of antilocaprids and dromomerycid artiodactyls *(Aletomeryx, Barbouromeryx),* and probably the camel *Michenia* (here restricted to species with fused metapodial bones).

TABLE 2.   Comparison of the Fossil Mammals of the Upper Harrison Beds and Runningwater Formation, Western Nebraska and Southeast Wyoming

Genera Common to Upper Harrison and Running-water Formations	Genera Exclusive to Upper Harrison and Older Formations	Genera Exclusive to the Runningwater and Younger Formations
?*Bassariscus*	*Ysengrinia*[1]	+*Edaphocyon*
Phlaocyon	*New amphicyonid genus	+*Amphicyon*
Cynarctoides	*temnocyonine amphicyonids	
Tomarctus		+*Potamotherium*
?*Leptocyon*		+*Brachypsalis*
Daphoenodon[2]	*Promartes*	+leptarctine mustelids
Cynelos	*Megalictis*	
Cephalogale		
Oligobunis		
Menoceras	*dicerathere rhinos	
Parahippus[3]		+*Archaeohippus*
anchitheres		
chalicotheres		
tapirs		
Desmathyus		
Dinohyus	*Nanotragulus	+*Arretotherium*
	Syndyoceras[4]	
Stenomylus[5]		
Oxydactylus		+*Michenia*
Blastomeryx		+*Aletomeryx*
		+*Barbouromeryx*
Merycochoerus	*Promerycochoerus	
Merychyus		+antilocaprid

Comments: Genera marked with asterisk (*) are last known occurrence in Great Plains. Genera marked by cross (+) are first occurrences.

[1] *Ysengrinia* is known from the Bridgeport Quarries together with a faunal assemblage that appears to be equivalent to the Runningwater fauna. The lithic unit that these quarries are found in is not named.

[2] The species of *Daphoenodon* from the Upper Harrison and Runningwater are very different, probably representing long separate lineages, thus this is probably not a direct continuation of a lineage from one formation to the next.

[3] Species of *Parahippus* in the two formations are distinct.

[4] Fragmentary remains suggest remote chance this artiodactyl occurs in the Runningwater Formation but this is very doubtful.

[5] The large type specimen of *Stenomylus crassipes* is very likely from the fine-grained facies of the Runningwater Formation in the area northeast of Agate. These small camels, however, are very rare in this formation.

FIG. 4. Working surface of Harper Quarry, Upper Harrison beds, Niobrara Canyon, Sioux County, Nebraska, on July 1, 1977, during excavation sponsored by the National Geographic Society. Bone level indicated by large entelodont humerus (indicated by arrow) in left foreground.

Although our paleontological fieldwork has explored much of the Arikaree surface outcrop in Sioux County, the discovery of Harper Quarry (Hunt, 1978) in the Upper Harrison in its type area in the Niobrara Canyon is our most significant paleontological achievement. An opportunity thus was afforded to examine in detail the depositional setting of a bone deposit of a kind similar to the Agate Spring Quarries. Harper Quarry (fig. 4) can be considered an excellent example of an attritional bone deposit. It is an accumulation in a single stratum of a mass of disarticulated (fig. 5) mammal bones, chiefly of very young and old individuals of a number of different species, both carnivores and herbivores, which shows evidence of subaerial weathering and damage caused by carnivores. The fossil bed itself is a graded deposit, with very fine sand and silt mixed with ash and lime mud surrounding the mammal bones in the lower part of the deposit, becoming finer grained upward until only pyroclastic debris, lime mud and ostracod valves are found in the upper part. Other than mammals, the only other biota from Harper Quarry is an ostracod-diatom-charophyte algal assemblage. Taphonomic analysis of mammal bones and bone fragments in the deposit led to the conclusion that mov-

FIG. 5.   Disarticulated bones and bone fragments constitute the fossil mammal assemblage from Harper Quarry, exemplified by this large entelodont humerus 22 inches in length, presently the largest bone found in the quarry (this bone appears in fig. 4).

ing water must have aligned certain bones and produced considerable wear on others, but that a current of sufficient energy to align these bones would have removed lime mud and ash. Thus the aligned bones must have been present prior to the filling of the site with the fine-grained sediments that comprise the bulk of the deposit. It is probable that the Harper Quarry bone deposit formed in an ephemeral stream channel, with bones aligned by periodic floods, possibly accumulating skeletal elements over a considerable time, until the channel segment became separated from the main channel and thus became an ephemeral pond that gradually filled with lime mud and pyroclastic debris.

In future years, as the biostratigraphy and paleoecology of fossil mammals in these Miocene rocks is further refined, building on the geological and paleontological information that has been worked out in the initial phase of this study, a more complete and accurate picture of the ancient environments and their successive faunas will result. This can then be applied to problems outside the local area in regions geographically distant from the central Great Plains.

REFERENCES

ADAMS, GEORGE I.
1902.   Geology and water resources of the Patrick and Goshen Hole Quadrangles in eastern Wyoming and western Nebraska.   U. S. Geol. Surv. Water Supply and Irrig. Pap. no. 70, 50 pp.

COOK, HAROLD J.
1915.   Notes on the geology of Sioux County, Nebraska, and vicinity.   Bull. Nebr. Geol. Surv., vol. 7, pt. 11, pp. 59-75.
1965.   Runningwater Formation, Middle Miocene of Nebraska.   Amer. Mus. Novitates, no. 2227, 8 pp.

DARTON, NELSON H.
1899.   Preliminary report on the geology and water resources of Nebraska west of the one hundred and third meridian.   U. S. Geol. Surv. 19th Ann. Rpt., 1897-1898, pt. 4 (Hydrography), pp. 719-785.
1902.   Camp Clarke and Scotts Bluff Geologic Quadrangles.   U. S. Geol. Surv. Map Folios nos. 87, 88.
1903.   Preliminary report on the geology and water resources of Nebraska west of the one hundred and third meridian.   U. S. Geol. Surv. Prof. Pap. no. 17, 69 pp.
1905.   Preliminary report on the geology and underground water resources of the central Great Plains.   U. S. Geol. Surv. Prof. Pap. no. 32, 433 pp.

DROULLARD, E. K.
1963.   Tectonics of the southeast flank of the Hartville Uplift, Wyoming.   Pp. 176-178 *in* "Guidebook to the geology of the northern Denver Basin and adjacent uplifts," 295 pp., D. W. Bolyard and P. J. Katich, eds., Rocky Mountain Assoc. of Geologists, Denver, Colorado.

EVERNDEN, J. F.; SAVAGE, D. E.; CURTIS, G. H.; and JAMES, G. T.
1964.   Potassium-argon dates and the Cenozoic mammalian chronology of North America.   Amer. Journ. Sci., vol. 262, p. 178.

GALUSHA, TED
1975.   Stratigraphy of the Box Butte Formation, Nebraska.   Bull. Amer. Mus. Nat. Hist., vol. 156, art. 1, pp. 1-68.

HATCHER, JOHN B.
1902.   Origin of the Oligocene and Miocene deposits of the Great Plains.   Proc. Amer. Philos. Soc., vol. 41, pp. 113-131.

HUNT, ROBERT M., JR.
1972.   Miocene amphicyonids (Mammalia, Carnivora) from the Agate Spring Quarries, Sioux County, Nebraska.   Amer. Mus. Novitates, no. 2506, 39 pp.
1978.   Depositional setting of a Miocene mammal assemblage, Sioux County, Nebraska (U.S.A.).   Palaeogeogr., Palaeoclimatol., Palaeoecol., vol. 24, pp. 1-52.

LUGN, ALVIN L.
1939.   Classification of the Tertiary System in Nebraska.   Bull. Geol. Soc. Amer., vol. 50, pp. 1245-1276.

McKenna, Malcolm C.
  1965.   Stratigraphic nomenclature of the Miocene Hemingford Group, Nebraska.   Amer. Mus. Novitates, no. 2228, 21 pp.
Osborn, Henry F.
  1918.   Equidae of the Oligocene, Miocene, and Pliocene of North America; iconographic type revision.   Mem. Amer. Mus. Nat. Hist., new ser., vol. 2, pt. 1, pp. 1-330.
Peterson, Olaf A.
  1904.   Osteology of *Oxydactylus*.   Ann. Carnegie Mus., vol. 2, no. 3, pp. 434-475.
  1907.   The Miocene beds of western Nebraska and eastern Wyoming and their vertebrate faunae.   Ann. Carnegie Mus., vol. 4, no. 1, pp. 21-72.
  1909.   A revision of the Entelodontidae.   Mem. Carnegie Mus., vol. 4, p. 75.
Pettijohn, P. J.; Potter, P. E.; and Siever, Raymond
  1972.   Sand and sandstone, 618 pp., illus.   Springer-Verlag, New York.
Schultz, C. Bertrand
  1938.   The Miocene of western Nebraska.   Amer. Jour. Sci., vol. 35, pp. 441-444.
Skinner, M. F.; Skinner, S. M.; and Gooris, R. J.
  1977.   Stratigraphy and biostratigraphy of late Cenozoic deposits in central Sioux County, western Nebraska.   Bull. Amer. Mus. Nat. Hist., vol. 158, art. 5, pp. 263-370.
Warner, Lawrence A.
  1978.   The Colorado Lineament: a middle Precambrian wrench fault system.   Bull. Geol. Soc. Amer., vol. 89, pp. 161-171.
Wood, H. E.; Chaney, R. W.; Clark, J.; Colbert, E. H.; Jepsen, G. L.; Reeside, J. B., Jr.; and Stock, C.
  1941.   Nomenclature and correlation of the North American continental Tertiary.   Bull. Geol. Soc. Amer., vol. 52, pp. 1-48.

Robert M. Hunt, Jr.

Vegetation Patterns of an Emperor Goose Nesting Area near Kokechik Bay, Western Alaska

Principal Investigator: Marion T. Jackson, Indiana State University, Terre Haute, Indiana.

Grant No. 1067:   For a botanical study of the Kokechik Bay area, Alaska.

A vegetation survey was conducted during the summer of 1973 to describe the plant communities and flora of an emperor-goose nesting study site located in the Clarence Rhode National Wildlife Refuge some 135 airline miles west of Bethel, Alaska (fig. 1). The project leader was Dr. Charles M. Kirkpatrick of Purdue University,[1] to whom the grant was originally made. The study area was a transect 1/2 mile (0.8 kilometers) wide with the long axis extending $3\frac{1}{2}$ miles (5.63 kilometers) southward from Kokechik Bay. The 1.75-square-mile (453-hectare) tract comprises the eastern half of sections 12, 13, 24, and 25, T. 18 N., R. 92 W.

Tundra vegetation patterns in western Alaska are incompletely described. Hopkins and Sigafoos (1951) evaluated the effects of frost action on vegetation in the Seward Peninsula. Hanson (1951, 1953) extensively studied vegetation-soil relationships in several western Alaska areas, not including the Yukon-Kuskokwim Delta region. Detailed studies by Johnson et al. (1966) of the Ogotoruk Creek area at Cape Thompson, located several hundred miles north, covered some similar habitats to those at Kokechik Bay, but this was the first quantitative plant ecological study of the coastal tundra of the Yukon-Kuskokwim River Delta.

Since a major objective was to describe the vegetation units of the area, particularly as they relate to the nesting patterns and success of the emperor geese (Eisenhauer and Kirkpatrick, 1977), the criteria of Johnson et al. (1966) were used in which repeating patterns of species associations were identified

---

[1] Thanks are extended to Byron P. Hollett who served as field assistant. Taxonomic determinations made by plant specialists are gratefully acknowledged as follows: Dr. John Thomson, University of Wisconsin at Madison, lichens; Dr. William C. Steere, New York Botanical Garden, mosses and hepatics; Dr. Leslie A. Viereck, University of Alaska, shrubs; and Dr. David F. Murray, University of Alaska, herbaceous vascular species. Logistic support was provided by Dr. Calvin J. Lensink and Jerry Hout of the Clarence Rhode National Wildlife Refuge. David I. Eisenhauer and Carl A. Strang generously shared their field camp headquarters.

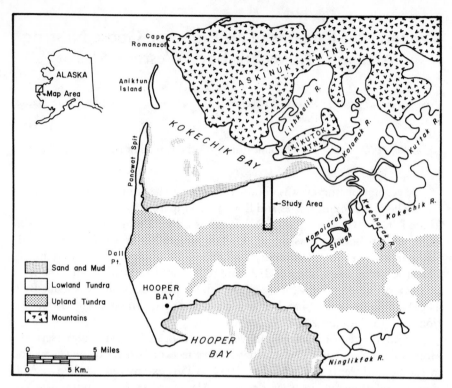

FIG. 1.   Location of the field study site near Kokechik Bay at the edge of Bering Sea. The study transect, 1/2 mile (0.8 kilometer) by 3½ miles (5.63 kilometers), extends southward from the tidal wash zone onto upland tundra.

and named. Vegetation units usually coincided with the larger, well-defined physiographic units. A series of repeating patterns was considered as a single discrete vegetation type or mapping unit.

Methods

The limits of 15 terrestrial vegetation units plus the boundaries of aquatic habitats were recognized and mapped at an approximate scale of 1:3,600. Field mapping was facilitated by a rough water-land distribution map prepared earlier by Eisenhauer and Frazer (1972) and oblique aerial photographs taken by the author. Ponds, surface features, and plant communities as small as about 8 meters in diameter were mapped as separate units.

Quantitative plant-community data were taken by the line-intercept method for 11 of the most prevalent plant-community types. A 50-meter steel tape was laid out along random compass directions from points chosen randomly within the mapping units. The long transect lines were divided into ten 5-meter segments, and the cover intercepting the first meter of each segment was measured and recorded to the nearest centimeter. The intercepted total cover in centimeters was recorded separately for each species. Very small vegetation units, such as *Hippuris* marshes and hummock tops, were sampled by 5-meter lines, rather than the usual 50-meter lengths. Sixty meters of total intercept distance were recorded for major communities, with 30 in minor types and 100 in the upland tundra. A total of 57 long transects were taken in all 11 community types.

Relative cover values for individual species were based on percent of vegetative cover, rather than percent of total cover. Frequencies were based on decimeter segments of each meter tallied. For example, a species with cover intercepted in 9 decimeters of a given meter was recorded as having a frequency of 90 percent. Relative frequencies were also computed. Importance values were calculated by averaging the relative values of vegetative cover and frequency. Density determinations were not made because of the enormous number of stems involved for many species and the indefinite limits of many individual plants.

A floristic list of vascular plants was compiled for the entire study site. Nomenclature for most vascular species follows Hultén (1968); that for shrubs follows Viereck and Little (1972). All questionable species were verified by experts in the respective botanical fields.

Vegetation Types

The entire 1.75-square-mile (453-hectare) study site was one-third water and two-thirds vegetated. Fifteen vegetation types were recognized, but only 11 are described below. Two *Elymus*-dominated types were combined when sampling, as were two short sedge units. Two small types (Willow Coppice and Upland Grass Meadow), which totaled only 4.2 percent of the vegetated area, were not sampled. Five types (Grass-sedge Meadow, Tall Sedge Marsh, Upland Tundra, Short Sedge Meadow, and *Elymus* Meadow) comprised 88 percent of the 295 vegetated hectares.

WET-TUNDRA COMMUNITIES

The wet-tundra communities are those low-lying areas (located generally in the northern part of the study area near Kokechik Bay) that rise 1-2 meters or less above the normal high-tide levels. Storm tides place most of them awash at some times of the year, and daily tidal influence is felt throughout much of the area via long sloughs that usually fill and empty twice daily (fig. 1).

Species diversity is low in wet-tundra vegetation. The 6 communities sampled averaged only 13 species each, and 4 had 11 or fewer species. Low diversity is due, in part, to nonutilized biomass that accumulates on the surface as plant litter. Slow rates of decomposition during the short growth season favor litter build-up. The featureless topography of the wet tundra fails to trap deep snows, which would protect shrubs and taller broadleafed herbs typical of sheltered habitats. Perennially wet soils and saline tidal wash apparently exclude many species.

Wet tundra is largely dominated by carices, grasses, and broadleafed herbs. The four major plant communities averaged 52, 24, and 22 percent importance for those life forms, respectively. Lichens were not recorded; mosses, ericads (Ericaceae plus *Empetrum*), ferns et al., and shrubs were of minor importance.

Short Sedge Meadow. Extensive continuous meadows of up to several hectares each occupy the inter-slough flats at the north end of the study area near Kokechik Bay. Most of the area is less than 1 meter higher than daily high tides.

The community of seven species was dominated by carices less than 1 decimeter tall. *Carex rariflora* was the overwhelming dominant at 71 percent importance; *Potentilla egedii* contributed 22 percent importance; and two grasses, *Elymus arenarius* and *Puccinellia phryganodes,* had a combined importance of 6 percent.

Grazing by geese keeps the plants short, and copious avian fecal wastes seem to be an important nutrient source.

Soils are very poorly drained and continually wet at the surface; permafrost averaged 45 centimeters deep. Tidal flow keeps soil salinity high. Lower lying mud flat areas interspersed with the sedge communities contain exceedingly sticky clay. Vegetation is excluded from the mud flats because of seasonal ponding or daily tidal action.

Elymus Meadow. Narrow bands of grass meadow dominated by *Elymus arenarius* cover the natural levees that flank the tidal sloughs. Nearly pure stands of *Elymus* occupy the levee tops, but at lower elevation and farther inland the community grades into Short Sedge Meadow or Grass-sedge Meadow. *Elymus arenarius* at 37 percent importance and *Puccinellia phryganodes* at 11 percent were the grass dominants. *Carex rariflora* was the most important sedge at 19 percent importance, and *P. egedii* the only dominant broadleafed herb at 28 percent. Low utilization of the coarse-textured *Elymus* by geese or other fauna results in a dense sod and thick litter accumulation. Apparently the warmer tidal flow melts the permafrost to about 0.5 meter along slough margins. Such warming action, plus nutrient deposition by the tides, permits noticeably more rapid vernalization along the sloughs. By late summer *Elymus* heads at nearly knee height towered above the other species, which were usually less than 20 centimeters tall.

Soils are sandy and moderately well drained along the slough margins, grading imperceptibly into poorly drained clay in low swales. Turf development is much stronger than in the Short Sedge Meadow.

Grass-sedge Meadow. Grasses and sedges shared dominance nearly evenly (35 versus 41 percent total importance) in the slightly higher, better-drained inland areas to the south. This second largest community type (64 hectares) was variable in species composition but quite uniform in physiognomy. Most stands were 20-30 centimeters tall at maturity, with scattered grass and forb emergents.

Greater habitat variation increases species diversity. Dominance was evenly shared by *Carex rariflora* and *C. glareosa,* plus *Puccinellia phryganodes* and *Poa eminens,* which total 58 percent importance. *Poa lanata* was a high-fidelity species but had low importance because of its delicate small size. Sixteen species had nearly 2 percent or greater importance. Swales were dotted with such wildflowers as *Primula* spp. and *Trientalis europaea* in late June and early July, while *Sedum rosea, Empetrum nigrum, Achillea borealis,* and *Petasites frigidus* were more common on higher ground. Extensive mats of prostrate willow (*Salix fuscescens*) occurred locally and seemed to be important nurseries for seedling establishment during succession.

Soils are strongly gleyed above the permafrost layer, which averaged 39 centimeters deep. All soils tend to high surface wetness.

Tall Sedge Marsh. Low-lying areas in the central part of the study area, which are permanently wet and subject to storm tides, contain broad expanses of nearly pure stands of *Carex lyngbyaei.* Ten other species were recorded, all sparingly except *Stellaria monantha* at 9.3 percent importance. Only three grasses (*Puccinellia phryganodes, Deschampsia caespitosa,* and *Dupontia fischeri*) and two broadleafed herbs (*Potentilla palustris* and *Rumex arcticus*) extend into the sedge canopy.

The tall sedges commonly reach 0.5-0.75 meter at fruiting time. Utilization of the available biomass was negligible, except by muskrats. As a result, coarse litter accumulates to 10-15 centimeters. The water table remains at the surface until evapotranspiration lowers the level in late summer.

Soils are highly organic, with rooting of the coarse sedges most abundant at 8-20 centimeters in a peaty layer. Permafrost averaged 37 centimeters deep. Methane and hydrogen-sulphide odors were strong when soil pits were dug.

The topography is essentially flat, with perhaps 1-2 meters elevation change per kilometer. Drainage is very sluggish. The only breaks in the sedge monotony are lakes and low hummocks.

Artesian Marsh. Near the south edge of the Tall Sedge Marsh, meltwaters from snowfields along a north-facing bluff edge (see below) create a plant community dominated by *Sphagnum* moss and *Potentilla palustris.* Meltwater presumably flows downslope along the permafrost interface at the base of the bluffs, then upwells in the *Sphagnum* zone. A person walking on the saturated vegetation mat steps in half knee-deep, breaking through in places to near hip-boot tops. Permafrost begins below 1 meter deep.

The interesting plant community contains three willow species ($<$ 1/2 meter tall), which totaled 18 percent importance. *Carex aquatilis* was the most abundant sedge, followed by *C. saxatilis; C. lyngbyaei,* dominant in adjacent Tall Sedge Marsh, dropped to 1.8 percent. Two species of *Eriophorum* totaled 3.8 percent, and *Equisetum fluviatile* contributed 3.1 percent. Northern water-carpet, *Chrysosplenium tetandrum,* was sparingly collected only in this type. Cranberry, *Oxycoccus microcarpus,* was regularly recorded.

Hippuris Marsh. At the edges of shallow ponds and mud-flat margins dense stands of the emergent aquatic mare's-tail *(Hippuris tetraphylla* and *H. vulgaris)* begin growing in early summer. By fall these communities enlarge substantially as the ponds shrink from evapotranspiration, until extensive *Hippuris* stands 20-30 centimeters tall surround the shallower water bodies. The two species of *Hippuris* comprised 75 percent of stand importance, with the coastal species, *H. tetraphylla,* predominating. *Hippuris vulgaris* was more common in small snow-melt ponds on pingo tops and around fresh-water lakes in the upland tundra.

DRY TUNDRA COMMUNITIES

Dry tundra communities occupy topographic features that rise above normal tide levels. The greater relief improves soil drainage, but profiles remain moist throughout the growth season. Permafrost layers are generally shallower because of improved insulation by the lichen-heath-moss vegetation mats.

Species richness was much higher and dominance more uniformly shared than in wet-tundra types. The five communities sampled averaged 38 species, compared to an average of 13 for 6 wet-tundra types; the leading dominant species averaged only 19 percent importance, compared to 50 percent in wet-tundra communities.

Surface litter cover was much less extensive in the dry communities ($\bar{X}$ = 14 percent) than at wet sites ($\bar{X}$ = 36 percent). Apparently these low-growing communities increase their photosynthetic surface by horizontal expansion over more of the ground area; whereas the taller life forms of wet-tundra types have greater leaf area exposed vertically.

Dry-tundra habitats were dominated by ericads, lichens, mosses, and shrubs, in that order of importance. The contribution of carices, grasses, and broadleaf herbs was minor, except for several Hummock and Bluff Edge communities where broadleafed herbs dominated.

Hummock Community.   At numerous locations in the Tall Sedge Meadow, but rarely in other vegetation types, ice lenses wedge upward, raising oval or elongated mounds 1-2 meters above the featureless sedge plain. They range from about 5 to 30 meters long and some 2-5 meters wide. Several appeared to be of very recent origin, with bare clay surfaces nearly devoid of plant cover. Others were older and well vegetated by an array of broadleafed herbs seldom found elsewhere.

Thirty-five species of all life forms comprised the Hummock Community. No species was predominant, as 17 species contributed 2 percent or greater importance. *Ligusticum scoticum, Trientalis europaea, Artemisia tilesii,* and *Barbarea orthoceras* had a combined importance of 30 percent. Lichens contributed negligible cover.

Soils are poorly developed with the extruded clay surfaces showing only the beginnings of soil structure. The absence of insulating litter and the greater surface area exposed by the convex configuration permit thawing to about 1 meter. As hummocks enlarge and increase in height from continued frost wedging, they grade into low pingos. Plant succession aids in this transition as the surfaces become stabilized.

Low and High Pingo Communities.   Pingo tundra consists of extensive reaches of low mounds interspersed with swales covered by Grass-sedge Meadow. Better drainage and reduced snow accumulation on pingo tops result in increases in lichens and heaths. Surfaces are frequently ruptured by frost cracks up to 1/2 meter wide and several meters long.

Low pingos are usually raised only 2-3 meters above the surrounding terrain and are less than 100 meters across.

High pingos, appearing from the air as huge cushions or pillows, are generally much larger and extend 3-6 meters above surrounding low-lying areas. The largest grade into high, level expanses similar topographically and vegetatively to upland tundra.

Species diversity was 40 and 33 species, respectively. *Empetrum nigrum* was the leading dominant in both types, reaching 39 percent importance on Low Pingos. Lichens collectively contributed 12 and 29 percent importance, respectively, with *Cetraria islandica* the most important species. *Rubus chamaemorus* forms extensive colonies, but grasses, carices, and broadleaf herbs afford minor contributions.

Vegetation height rarely exceeds a decimeter except for scattered emergent grasses or such herbs as *Petasites frigidus, Ligusticum scoticum, Sedum rosea, Achillea borealis,* or *Pedicularis* spp.

Extensive areas of High Pingos are upholstered with nearly pure lichen-moss stands, whose individual plants extend no more than 5 centimeters above the general surface, but the litter mat accumulates to 15-20 centimeters deep. On Low Pingos the mat is thinner and composed of *Empetrum, Rubus chamaemorus,* and *Salix fuscescens,* intermixed with smaller clumps of lichen and mosses. *Sphagnum fuscum,* which sometimes grows in large clumps and appears as orange blotches when viewed from a low-flying plane, is a major mat former in High Pingos, at 4 percent importance, but is essentially absent from Low Pingos, at 0.4 percent.

Soils of both types averaged 25 centimeters (range 20-34) to permafrost and had similar profiles. Root zones averaged 16 and 12 centimeters on High and Low Pingos, respectively.

Upland Tundra.   Near the south end of the study site steep bluffs rise 20-25 meters above the general level of the Tall Sedge Marsh. Above the bluffs upland tundra undulates southward in long swells for several miles toward Hooper Bay. Lakes are fewer, more regular in outline, and frequently temporary, filling and drying in response to precipitation and snow-melt patterns.

Thirteen species of lichens, topped by *Cladonia mitis* at 21 percent and *Cetraria islandica* at 11 percent importance, collectively comprised 44 percent stand importance. In all, 40 plant species were recorded. Ericads had a collective importance of 32 percent, with *Ledum palustre* (11 percent) and *Empetrum nigrum* (6 percent) the most common. Patches of orange *Sphagnum fuscum* 2-3 decimeters across were quite common.

Most of the vegetation is less than a decimeter tall, particularly on exposed ridges where snow blows free or has only thin accumulations. The species composition changes rapidly as microrelief differs by 5-10 centimeters. Lichens and ericads are more common on small hillocks, with mosses (particularly *Sphagnum fuscum*) in moist microdepressions.

Large grazing animals were exterminated from the region by Eskimos several decades ago, so the Upland Tundra type is remarkably free from disturbance.

Soils are very similar to those of High Pingos. The thick insulating vegetation mat (X̄ of 9.0 centimeters) plus a rooting zone of decaying organic matter to an average of 16 centimeters prevent melting of permafrost below a mean of 27 centimeters (range 22-35).

Bluff Edge.   Although this type covers only 3 hectares along the bluff faces toward the south end of the study area, it contains the greatest species diversity and is a most interesting area botanically. Forty-four species were recorded in only 30 sample plots, as compared to 40 species in 100 plots in Upland Tundra. Shrubs contributed 14 percent importance with *Spiraea beauverdiana* and *Salix pulchra* most common. *Lycopodium alpinum, L. annotinum, Equisetum arvense,* and *Dryopteris dialatata* totaled 9 percent.

Deep snow accumulates in the bluff ravines and recesses and persists in the deepest cavities on north slopes until about August 1. Such microenvironments protect a series of species found at no other location in the study area and allows every life form to be well represented. *Geranium erianthum* is second in importance and grows in showy clumps to 3 decimeters tall. Fireweed (*Epilobium angustifolium*), the fern *Dryopteris dialatata, Sanquisorba stipulata,* the grass *Hierochloe alpina, Solidago multiradiate,* and *Sibbaldia procumbens* were recorded only in the Bluff Edge habitat.

Soils are friable, coarse textured, well drained, and well aerated. Litter cover is minimal.

Floristic Composition

The vast majority of the nearly 650 separate collections taken during the summer of 1973 were from the emperor-goose study site. A few collections were made in the Askinuk Mountains and at some wet-tundra locations elsewhere in the Clarence Rhode National Wildlife Refuge.

A total of 105 species of plants contributed cover to the line transects within the 11 community types sampled. Fifty-four other species were collected within the study area to bring the total collection to 159 species. The collection of lichens, mosses, and hepatics totaled 29 species, all but four of which were recorded in the sample plots. No special effort was made to complete a floristic list of cryptogams. The remaining 130 of the total species were vascular plants, representing 83 genera in 37 families. This collection does not represent the complete vascular flora of the 1.75-square-mile study area, but most species were encountered.

The breakdown of the 105 species taken within the plots by life form follows: Lichens 16, mosses and hepatics 9, ferns et al. 5, grasses 11, carices 12, shrubs 8, heaths 8, and broadleaved herbs 36.

A complete set of all collections is housed in the Indiana State University Herbarium.

REFERENCES

EISENHAUER, DAVID I., and FRAZER, DAVID A.
  1972.   Nesting ecology of the emperor goose (*Philacte canagica* Sewastianov) in the Kokechik Bay region, Alaska.   2d Ann. Rpt. Dept. Forestry and Conserv. Purdue Univ., 82 pp. (mimeo).
EISENHAUER, DAVID I., and KIRKPATRICK, CHARLES M.
  1977.   Ecology of the emperor goose in Alaska.   Wildlife Monogr., no. 57 (October 1977), 62 pp.
HANSON, H. C.
  1951.   Characteristics of some grassland, marsh, and other plant communities in western Alaska.   Ecol. Monogr., vol. 21, pp. 317-378.
  1953.   Vegetation types in northwestern Alaska and comparisons with communities in other Arctic regions.   Ecology, vol. 34, pp. 111-140.
HOPKINS, DAVID M., and SIGAFOOS, ROBERT S.
  1951.   Frost action and vegetation patterns on Seward Peninsula, Alaska.   U. S. Geol. Surv. Bull. 974-C, pp. 51-100.
HULTÉN, ERIC
  1968   Flora of Alaska and neighboring territories; a manual of vascular plants, 1,008 pp.   Stanford University Press.
JOHNSON, ALBERT W.; VIERECK, LESLIE A.; JOHNSON, ROSS E.; and MELCHIOR, HERBERT
  1966.   Vegetation and flora.   Chap. 14 (pp. 277-354) *in* "Environment of the Cape Thompson Region, Alaska," N.J. Willomovsky and J. N. Wolfe, eds., 1,250 pp.   U. S. Atomic Energy Comm. Div. Techn. Inf., Oak Ridge, Tennessee.
VIERECK, LESLIE A., and LITTLE, ELBERT L., JR.
  1972.   Alaska trees and shrubs. Agr. Handb. no. 410, 265 pp., illus.   Forest Service, U. S. Department of Agriculture, Washington, D. C.

MARION T. JACKSON

Foraging in Optimum Light as a Niche Dimension for Neotropical Frogs

Principal Investigator: Robert G. Jaeger, State University of New York at Albany, Albany, New York.

Grant No. 1127:   To investigate the illuminations under which five species of Panamanian frogs forage to test whether foraging is correlated with phototactic behavior.

During April 1973 Dr. Jack P. Hailman, of the University of Wisconsin, Linda S. Jaeger, and I studied the foraging behavior of six species of terrestrial frogs on Barro Colorado Island, Smithsonian Tropical Research Institute, Panama Canal Zone. It was our intention to test in the field for the first time several hypotheses that Hailman and I had previously proposed concerning the phototactic behavior of frogs, as documented through laboratory experiments, and the illumination under which frogs forage in natural habitats. The three hypotheses are briefly as follows, the last one being directly pertinent to the present study, but derived from the other two: (1) Every species of frog has an optimum ambient illumination (O.A.I.) toward which individuals will move in preference over all other available intensities of white light. The hypothesis was derived from the phototactic responses in the laboratory of 121 species of anuran amphibians from 16 of the order's 17 families, in which some species chose very high intensities of light, others very low intensities, and the remaining formed a continuum between these extremes (Jaeger and Hailman, 1973). (2) A frog, when situated in light at its O.A.I., has maximal visual discrimination of objects, and such discrimination decreases as the ambient light becomes either more or less intense (Hailman and Jaeger, 1976). Thus, a frog can best distinguish objects of slightly differing reflected intensities of light when the ambient illumination is optimum for the species. (3) A frog, when foraging, should move to a place in its habitat that approximates the species' O.A.I., since the frog would best be able to detect the movement of prey in that place (Jaeger and Hailman, 1973).

To test the third hypothesis above, we selected for study six sympatric species of terrestrial frogs in Panama: *Bufo typhonius* and *Bufo marinus* (family Bufonidae), *Physalaemus pustulosus* and *Leptodactylus pentadactylus* (Leptodactylidae), *Dendrobates auratus* and *Colostethus nubicola* (Dendrobatidae). We had previously determined the phototactic preferences of all but the last of these

297

species in the laboratory, by methods reported in Jaeger and Hailman (1973). In the field study, we measured activity and foraging of the frogs in three ways: (1) Ten 1-square-meter quadrats were placed along Lutz Creek and these were censused hourly for 24 hours to determine activity periods of *Colostethus nubicola*. We measured illuminance in the quadrats hourly using a Science & Mechanics model 102 photometer and an ISCO spectroradiometer. (2) Several habitats on the island were censused hourly for 24 hours on many occasions to determine the activity periods of the other five species, and illuminance was monitored at each census. (3) Illuminance was measured throughout the month at the eye-position of frogs of all species just after they were seen to ingest a prey item, or perform some other activity. By these methods we could determine the times of day, the habitats, and the ambient illuminations at which the different species were active and, during active periods, at which they were feeding. In total, illuminance was measured photometrically during the above studies on 768 occasions.

The results are summarized in table 1, and detailed data may be found in Jaeger et al. (1976) for *Colostethus nubicola* and in Jaeger and Hailman (1980) for the other species. The species with the lowest O.A.I. as determined by phototactic preference in the laboratory (*Leptodactylus pentadactylus*) is also active under the dimmest light conditions in the field, as predicted by our hypothesis. This species probably also fed under very dim illuminance while active, although we could not determine this empirically because of our inability to see clearly at night. This species is strictly nocturnal, remaining under forest ground litter from the first light of dawn to evening darkness. Even when active the frog remains in the closed-canopy forest where illuminance from moonlight is minimal.

Dendrobates auratus has a somewhat higher O.A.I. value than the previous species, and it is active and forages under appropriately higher illuminances, as predicted by our hypothesis. It becomes active shortly after the first light of morning and continues to forage until after sunrise. A second period of activity begins before sunset, and feeding continues until just after sunset. This species appears typically to hide in holes in the ground, where individuals remain at night and during the bright daylight period. Frogs of this species were variable in habitat, being found from open to closed-canopy conditions, although they were normally near streams.

Physalaemus pustulosus has a high O.A.I. value, higher than we were able to measure in our phototactic testing apparatus in the laboratory. As predicted by hypothesis its activity ranges into bright daylight illuminances, unlike the previous two species. It also forages under conditions of bright light through the midday period. Individuals of the species are active throughout the 24-hour period, but their activity can be divided into two subsets. From later afternoon through the night and into midmorning, males call and pairs can be seen in amplexus, making foam nests for deposit of eggs. Calling ceases during the midday period, when ambient light is at its brightest, and this period is given over to extensive foraging. Breeding occurs in any body of still water. Feeding occurs while sitting on objects in and beside the water under closed-canopy conditions. The frogs do not remain in water during the day when exposed to full sunlight.

Bufo typhonius also has a high O.A.I. value, which corresponds well to the natural illuminances under which the frog is active and feeding, as predicted by our hypothesis. We were unable accurately to census the activity periods of this frog over 24 hours, because of the wide dispersal of the individuals. However, it is clear that the species is diurnal and feeds through the brightest part of the day, albeit in the shade of the closed canopy forest. This is evident in table 1, when comparing the maximum illuminances under which *B. typhonius* and *Physalaemus pustulosus* feed. Both forage at midday, but the maximum illuminance for the former species is considerably less in the forest than that for the latter species in the more open water habitat.

Bufo marinus possesses a high O.A.I. value, yet it feeds at night under very dim illumination, contrary to our hypothesis. The species is generally nocturnal, but not strictly so, since it has been found moving in open-canopy areas under extremely high illuminances, as shown in table 1. While feeding at night the marine toad remains in open-canopy habitats, as on mud flats or open fields. We at first thought that its high O.A.I. value might reflect visual perception under bright moonlight conditions in these open areas. However, spectroradiometric measurements of near full moonlight at night, recorded by Jack P. Hailman, show that such moonlight nowhere nearly approaches the species' O.A.I. of at least 90 lux. We now feel that the toad's high O.A.I. value is related to its infrequent diurnal activity. During the day these toads hide under fallen leaves or in bushes, but for some reason as yet undetermined they occasionally hop, in the brightest sunlight, from one hiding place to another. Apparently individuals will feed at night under intense illumination when it is available, since this was the only species to sit under outdoor flood lights in the laboratory compound on Barro Colorado Island, where the toads caught large insects attracted to the light. *Bufo marinus* probably also uses nonvisual perception in locating prey at night. Jaeger (1976) reported that one toad was seen to move in the direction of a group of breeding *Physalaemus pustulosus* every time the latter called, but to stop moving when the frog chorus ceased. Finally the marine toad located the *P. pustulosus,* which were not originally in the toad's line of vision, and ingested several of the frogs. This miscellaneous observation throws doubt on the idea of Straughan (1973) that an anuran hears best in a frequency bandwidth approximating that of the call of its own species.

Although we have not been able to obtain an O.A.I. value for *Colostethus nubicola,* results of the 24-hour quadrat census show that this species is bimodal in activity (table 1), hiding in ground litter at night and during the brightest midday period. As with *Dendrobates auratus,* this form of bimodal activity allows the frog to be active within a rather restricted range of ambient illuminances in the forest.

The above results of our field studies show that our hypothesis is a viable one: Species of frogs do tend to forage and/or be otherwise active under natural ambient illuminations approximating their O.A.I. values. In the present study we cannot show a quantitative match between the two, but we do show a rank-order match; i.e., species with low O.A.I. values do forage under dimmer conditions of light than species with higher O.A.I. values. In the one exception reported here it is shown that the species will forage under brighter conditions (artificial lighting) than are normally available and that the species occasionally moves through open canopy places under extremely bright light. In sum, all but one of the species studied support the hypothesis, and the exceptional species does not refute the hypothesis. Data from tadpoles also support the hypothesis, since a species that has a high O.A.I. value forages on aquatic plants in ponds under natural conditions of light approximating that value (Jaeger and Hailman, 1976).

This research is the first in the long history of the study of phototaxis to suggest and attempt to demonstrate an ecological adaptation for phototactic behavior. Most previous work has treated phototaxis as an artifact of laboratory testing or as a "nonadaptive" behavior. To the contrary, we feel that phototactic movements by a frog play an important part in its ability to locate and capture prey objects and, perhaps, to detect the approach of predators, a factor not yet tested by us. The results of our present study are necessarily crude determinations of the light *perceived* by frogs while foraging. This is true for various technical reasons that cannot yet be controlled in the field. For example, we cannot determine at any given time the retinal adaptational state of the frog or its pupillary dynamics, both of which are important to the frog's visual perception. We hope, in future fieldwork, to have better control over such physiological variables, in which case we expect to find a better quantitative match between illuminance at foraging and the species' O.A.I.

We now consider phototaxis as only one factor used by a frog for placing itself in the most favorable ambient illumination. Diel rhythms in many spe-

TABLE 1.   Phototactic Preferences of Frogs Compared with Range of Illuminances Under Which Activity Occurred in Panama

Species	O.A.I. (lux)	Illuminance of activity (lux)	Illuminance of feeding (lux)	Time of feeding	Habitat of feeding
L. pentadactylus	<0.04	<0.01	<0.01 ?	Nocturnal	Forest
D. auratus	0.13	0.59-53	2.07-47	Morning and evening	Forest and open canopy
P. pustulosus	>90	<0.01-148	11-129	Diurnal	Forest and open canopy
B. typhonius	>90	8.48-114	12-86	Diurnal	Forest
B. marinus	>90	<0.01-320	<.01-2.57	Nocturnal	Open canopy
C. nubicola	—	0.23-68	15-19	Morning and evening	Forest

cies control the periods of activity throughout a day, allowing a frog to forage when the light is generally near the species' O.A.I. (night, midday, morning and evening, etc.). Once the frog is active, physiological mechanisms in the pupils and retinae control the amount of light entering the eyes and stimulating the photoreceptors. When these physiological mechanisms are unable to cope with rapid changes in surrounding light, then the frog must use phototaxis in seeking a place at which the light approximates the species' O.A.I.

The diversity of O.A.I.'s among species of frogs yields a clue to the possible ecological significance of phototaxis. Of the 55 species of frogs from temperate regions, for which we have determined O.A.I. values in the laboratory, all but one have preferences for high intensities of white light. However, of the 66 species from tropical and subtropical regions that we have tested, 23 percent prefer low intensities of light (Jaeger and Hailman, 1973). Since species of frogs are known to be much more densely packed in tropical than in temperate areas (Crump, 1974), a greater diversity of O.A.I.'s in the tropics may indicate a greater degree of space and time partitioning during activity periods there.

Our hypothesis, that a frog will forage in light approximating its O.A.I., has both temporal and spatial components, since light intensity varies through both time and space. The intensities of light under which members of a species will forage is a dimension of that species' niche, and it may be an important one in communities where species are densely packed and food niche partitioning occurs. For example, two species of similar size that forage at the same time of day may be faced with potential overlap of prey species. Such an overlap can be greatly reduced if one species has a high O.A.I. and forages in open places while the other species has a low O.A.I. and forages in densely vegetated places; this is exactly what happens with *Bufo marinus* and *Leptodactylus pentadactylus,* respectively, in Panama. Therefore, within a given temporal period, phototactic behavior could allow two species to partition habitats. Within a given habitat, phototactic behavior, along with circadian rhythms, can favor the foraging of two species at different times. *Bufo typhonius* and *Dendrobates auratus* are roughly the same size, but the former forages at midday when the latter is quiescent, while the latter species forages in dimmer morning and evening light. Further field studies may enable us to determine just how important phototactic behavior is as a niche dimension in a community matrix of competitive interactions.

REFERENCES

CRUMP, MARTHA L.
  1974.   Reproductive strategies in a tropical anuran community.   Univ. Kansas Mus. Nat. Hist. Misc. Publ., vol. 61, pp. 1-68, illus.
HAILMAN, JACK P., and JAEGER, ROBERT G.
  1976.   A model of phototaxis and its evaluation with anuran amphibians. Behaviour, vol. 56, pp. 215-249, illus.
JAEGER, ROBERT G.
  1976.   A possible prey-call window in anuran auditory perception.   Copeia, 1976, pp. 833-834.
JAEGER, ROBERT G., and HAILMAN, JACK P.
  1973.   Effects of intensity on the phototactic responses of adult anuran amphibians: a comparative survey.   Zeitschr. Tierpsychol., vol. 33, pp. 352-407, illus.
  1976.   Ontogenetic shift of spectral phototactic preferences in anuran tadpoles. Journ. Comp. Physiol. Psychol., vol. 90, pp. 930-945, illus.
  1980.   Activity of neotropical frogs in relation to ambient light.   Biotropica, in press.
JAEGER, ROBERT G.; HAILMAN, JACK P.; and JAEGER, LINDA S.
  1976.   Bimodal diel activity of a Panamanian dendrobatid frog, *Colostethus nubicola,* in relation to light.   Herpetologica, vol. 32, pp. 77-81, illus.
STRAUGHAN, IAN R.
  1973.   Evolution of anuran mating calls: bioacoustical aspects.   Pp. 321-327 *in* "Evolutionary Biology of the Anurans: Contemporary Research on Major Problems," 470 pp., illus.   University of Missouri Press, Columbia, Missouri.

ROBERT G. JAEGER

The Origin and Ancestry of Wheat

Principal Investigator: B. Lennart Johnson, University of California, Riverside, California.

Grant No. 1059:   To study the origin and ancestry of wheat.[1]

For more than five decades a quest for the wild progenitors of cultivated wheat has been fostered by the need for a source of genes for conventional wheat improvement and by the more distant prospect of essentially resynthesizing cultivars from improved versions of their parental genomes.

Bread wheat *(Triticum aestivum* L. em. Thell.) evidently originated under cultivation in the early foredawn of historical times somewhere in the vast area between the Tigris and Indus Rivers. It is a hexaploid (2n=42) carrying three genomes in duplicate (AABBDD), each genome comprising seven chromosomes. Two of the genomes (A and B) clearly were derived from cultivated emmer (AABB), a tetraploid wheat (2n=28) that had been domesticated by Stone Age man from wild emmer, *T. dicoccoides* Körn. Schweinf. The wild species is endemic mostly in the western arm of the fertile crescent from the upper Jordan Valley to Southeastern Anatolia (fig. 1). The third genome (D) can be traced to the wild diploid Goat Grass, *Aegilops squarrosa* L. (2n=14) (McFadden and Sears, 1946) which still persists as a weed in wheat fields eastward from the Tigris. Thus, *aestivum* × emmer hybrids consistently show 14 pairs of chromosomes and 7 univalents (14II + 7I), while *aestivum* × *squarrosa* hybrids exhibit (7II + 14I). Furthermore, the protein band pattern obtained by electrophoresis of crude seed extracts of *T. aestivum* can be duplicated by a mixture of seed extracts from emmer and *Ae. squarrosa* (Johnson, 1973).

That bread wheat originated after the domestication of emmer may be inferred from the fact that all hexaploid wheats like cultivated emmer and all other cultivated wheats have nonshattering ears that can be harvested intact,

---

[1] Field studies and seed collecting were expedited by FAO (Food and Agriculture Organization of the United Nations), the Ford Foundation, Beirut, and the Hebrew University of Jerusalem, Rehovot. Material from Transcaucasia was obtained through the N. I. Vavilov Institute, Leningrad. Hybridization and cytological studies were made at the University of California, Riverside, California, and the Institute of Plant Breeding, University of Bari, Bari, Italy.

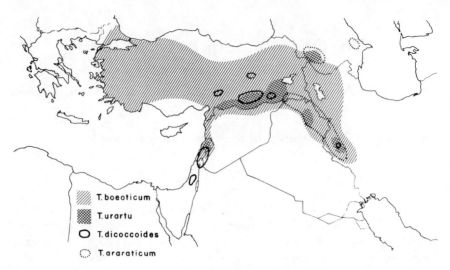

FIG. 1. Geographic distribution of the wild wheats.

whereas all wild wheats disperse their seeds individually as they ripen. *Non-shattering* mutations resulting in higher yields of harvested grain presumably were unconsciously favored by the harvesting methods used by Neolithic farmers. Apparently, as emmer spread eastward in primitive agriculture into the natural range of *Ae. squarrosa,* the two species hybridized spontaneously and, as a result of chromosome doubling, the first hexaploid arose.

Origin of the Tetraploids

The tetraploids which originated as wild wheats present a more complex problem involving the evolutionary time scale. Besides the emmer group derived from the wild *T. dicoccoides* (fig. 2), they include also the more obscure *timopheevii* group which was domesticated from the wild *T. araraticum* Jakubz. (fig. 2), a species distributed from Transcaucasia and Eastern Anatolia southward through the Kurdish Uplands of Iraq and Iran (fig. 1).

One of the parents of both *T. dicoccoides* and *T. araraticum* is thought to be the morphologically similar wild diploid wheat, *T. boeoticum* Boiss. (2n=14) (fig. 2). The most widely dispersed of the wild wheats (fig. 1), it ranges from Greece to Transcaucasia and southward throughout the fertile crescent, and occurs in all areas where tetraploid wheats are indigenous. It was presumed to be the donor of the seven chromosomes arbitrarily designated as the A genome

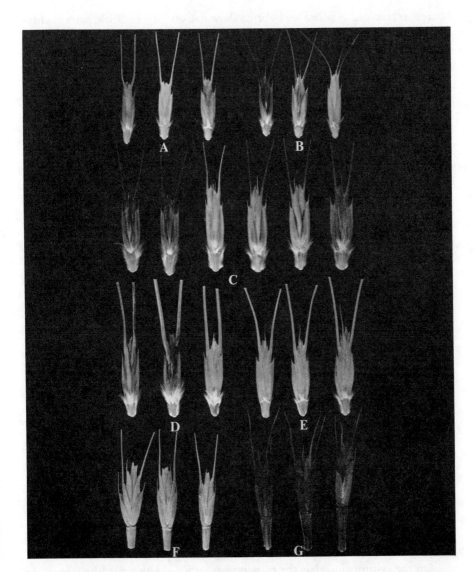

FIG. 2.   Spikelets of the wild wheats and synthetic amphiploids: A, *T. boeoticum* (2n=14). B, *T. urartu* (2n=14). C, synthetic *T. boeoticum-T. urartu* amphiploids (2n=28). D, *T. dicoccoides* (2n=28). E, *T. araraticum* (2n=28). F, synthetic *T. monococcum-Ae. speltoides* amphiploid (2n=28) [*T. monococcum* is a cultivated derivative of *T. boeoticum*]. G, synthetic *T. urartu-Ae. speltoides* amphiploid (2n=28).

because tetraploid × *boeoticum* hybrids show 4-6 out of 7 possible pairs of chromosomes. But the evidence from chromosome pairing has proved to be inconclusive owing to the fact that various diploid (2n=14) species of *Aegilops* which show high pairing with *T. boeoticum* (about 5II) also show about 5II in crosses with the tetraploid wheats (Kihara, 1937; Sears, 1956).

The most enigmatic question regarding the origin of the tetraploids, however, has been the identity of the other parent, the presumed donor of the seven chromosomes designated at the B genome. These chromosomes normally fail to pair with those of any diploid species. As a consequence, the concept soon emerged that the second parent may be extinct or that B is a modified genome of hybrid origin comprising segments from two or more diploid genomes. Following the theory of Sarkar and Stebbins (1956), *Aegilops speltoides* Tausch has been generally regarded as the donor of the B genome or the major contributor to it.

The possibility that the missing parent of the tetraploids might be another diploid wheat was largely rejected, presumably because the wild diploids were thought to compose a single species, *T. boeoticum,* which showed no evidence of genomic diversity. A second wild diploid wheat, *T. urartu* Tum. (fig. 2) was reported by Jakubziner (1958); however, if indeed accepted by Western geneticists as a distinct species, it was not posed as the missing parent, probably because it was known only as a restricted Armenian endemic far removed from the presumed center of origin of the emmer tetraploids.

More recently, a series of studies by the authors and co-workers on seed protein electrophoretic patterns in *Triticum* and *Aegilops* indicated that the missing parent of the tetraploid wheats was not a species of *Aegilops* (see Johnson, 1972, for references), but more probably an unrecognized diploid wheat. All species of *Aegilops* were characterized by a fast moving band that had no counterpart in the protein pattern of the tetraploid wheats.

Exploration and Experimentation

The National Geographic Society Near East Expedition to Study the Origin and Ancestry of Wheat was undertaken specifically to explore the area of endemism of wheat in an effort to find the missing parent.

On the assumption that the missing parent would be most likely to occur where wild tetraploid and diploid wheats are sympatric, exploration was concentrated in Southeastern Turkey at the midpoint of the tetraploid range, in the Zagros Mountains of Iraq and Iran and in the Rift Valley and Mt. Hermon areas of Lebanon and Israel. More than 1,450 accessions of wild wheats were assembled (table 1) and subjected to protein-electrophoretic, morphological, and cytogenetic examination.

More than 500 crosses (table 2) were made among the diploid and tetraploid species using biotypes of each from various geographic areas. Most of these crosses were fully fertile. Seeds of certain crosses were found to germinate only under *in vitro* embryo culture. Such seeds are referred to as nonviable. Other crosses gave viable seed which yielded sterile plants.

TABLE 1.   Number of *Triticum* Accessions Assigned to the
Various Species After Final Identification

The authors are indebted to the following persons: DR. E. KJELQVIST for 41 accessions of the Turkish collections; DR. D. ZOHARY for 4 accessions of the Iranian collections; DR. M. M. JAKUBZINER, DR. P. A. GANDILIAN, and the late PROFESSOR P. M. ZHUKOVSKY, for the entire Transcaucasian collection.

Collection area	Diploids		Tetraploids	
	T. boeoticum	*T. urartu*	*T. dicoccoides*	*T. araraticum*
Greece-Turkey	279	71	133	3
Lebanon-Israel	14	72	132	—
Iraq	379	1	—	255
Iran	36	4	2	10
Transcaucasia	41	6	—	18
Totals	749	154	267	286

TABLE 2. Seed Viability in Intra- and Interspecific Crosses
among Diploid and Tetraploid Species of *Triticum*

[This table was condensed from data given in Johnson and Dhaliwal (1976) and includes unpublished data from A. Blanco.]

Cross		Number of crosses made	Number of successful crosses	Percent success	Percent seed viability
Female	Male				
boeoticum	*boeoticum*	84	73	86.9	100
urartu	*urartu*	46	32	69.5	100
boeoticum	*urartu*	181	85	47.0	100
urartu	*boeoticum*	46	32	100.0	0
within both tetraploid species		130	111	85.4	100
reciprocals between tetraploid species		38	37	97.4	100
		525	370	70.5	

PROTEIN PATTERNS

On the basis of the seed protein electrophoretic pattern, the tetraploids, consistent with their disjunct geographic ranges and their taxonomic classification into two species, were separable into two classes. Diploids from Greece to Central Anatolia (fig. 1) showed the typical pattern of *T. boeoticum,* but those from the area of the tetraploids (Eastern Anatolia, Transcaucasia, and the Fertile Crescent) unexpectedly showed two patterns, that of *T. boeoticum* and a pattern previously observed in two accessions of *T. urartu* from Armenia, the only verified material of that species previously examined.

Having classified the diploids on the basis of protein pattern, those with the *urartu* profile were found to comprise a morphologically homogeneous group with the diagnostic characters of *T. urartu* as described by Gandilian (1972). Thus, *T. urartu,* for the first time, was found to be widely dispersed outside of Armenia throughout the natural range of the wild tetraploids. It became highly suspect as the missing parent of both *T. dicoccoides* and *T. araraticum* (Johnson, 1975).

Subsequently, seed extracts electrophoresed with SDS (sodium dodecyl sulfate) added to the medium were found to give very similar protein patterns for both diploid and tetraploid species (Dhaliwal and Johnson, 1976b). The effect of SDS was to dissociate the albumins which otherwise were differently complexed in each species giving each a characteristic protein pattern.

MORPHOLOGY

Except for their greater spikelet size, the wild tetraploids are remarkably similar to the wild diploids (fig. 2). The spikelets of both, unlike those of the closely related genus *Aegilops,* have a short hairy basal rachis segment and sharply keeled glumes. The average anther length of each tetraploid (2.9 millimeters) falls midway between that of *T. boeoticum* (3.6 millimeters) and that of *T. urartu* (2.2 millimeters) (Johnson and Dhaliwal, 1978). In other respects the tetraploids combine species specific characters of the diploids in different ways. For example, *T. araraticum* like *T. urartu* (fig. 2) has a short third awn between the two major ones, whereas *T. dicoccoides* like *T. boeoticum* typically lacks a third awn. Also with regard to the mode of anther dehiscence, *T. araraticum* resembles *T. urartu* and *T. dicoccoides* resembles *T. boeoticum* (Dhaliwal and Johnson, 1976a). But *T. dicoccoides* like *T. urartu* has glabrous leaves while *T. araraticum* like *T. boeoticum* has prebescent leaves (Johnson and Dhaliwal, 1978). Such differences between the tetraploid species could be accounted for by genetic segregation in their presumed amphiploid progenitor *(T. boeoticum-T. urartu)* as a result of residual pairing between *boeoticum* and *urartu* chromosomes. They could not be similarly accounted for by an amphiploid involving either *T. boeoticum* or *T. urartu* and any species of *Aegilops*.

INITIATION OF AMPHIPLOIDY

Among plants in general, the initiation of amphiploidy entails duplication of differentiated parental genomes; and such differentiation is contingent on reproductive isolation of the parental species, involving partial or complete sterility of their F_1 hybrid (Stebbins, 1947).

The data in table 2 show that barriers to gene exchange exist between *T. boeoticum* and *T. urartu*. Crosses between plants within each diploid and tetraploid species (table 2) as well as reciprocal crosses between the two tetraploid species gave fully viable seed, but reciprocal crosses between the diploid species behaved very differently. Crosses using *T. boeoticum* as the female parent gave viable seed, but crosses involving *T. urartu* as the female gave shrivelled nonviable seed. Thus, half of the potential crosses between the two diploid species fail to produce progeny in the F_1 generation where such failure is most effective as a reproductive isolating mechanism (Johnson and Dhaliwal, 1976).

Reproductive isolation at the diploid level clearly led to effective differentiation of the *boeoticum* and *urartu* genomes. Whereas intraspecific F_1 hybrids among plants of either *T. boeoticum* or *T. urartu* (table 3) were highly fertile, those hybrids which were obtained between the two species (i.e., the F_1 hybrids involving *T. boeoticum* as the female parent and *T. urartu* as the male) were sterile (9.9 percent stainable pollen and 0.0 percent seed set). Therefore,

TABLE 3. Pollen Stainability and Seed Set in Intra- and
Interspecific Hybrids of *T. boeoticum* and *T. urartu*
[This table was condensed from data given in Johnson and Dhaliwal (1976)
and includes unpublished data from A. Blanco.]

Female	*Male*	*Number of crosses*	*Percent pollen stainability*[a]	*Percent seed set*[b]
boeoticum	*boeoticum*	7	86.4	80.7
urartu	*urartu*	11	92.8	79.9
boeoticum	*urartu*	19	9.9	0.0
urartu	*boeoticum*	1[c]	10.8	0.0

[a]Stained with iodine potassium iodide (I_2KI).

[b]Percent of spikelets bearing at least one seed.

[c]This hybrid was obtained by in vitro culture of the excised embryo.

possible perpetuation of the *boeoticum* × *urartu* hybrid in the wild would depend essentially on fortuitous amphiploidy (a doubling of the chromosome number) which would provide each chromosome with an identical undifferentiated pairing homologue.

SYNTHETIC TETRAPLOID WHEATS

The sterile *boeoticum* × *urartu* hybrids (table 3) when treated with colchicine in the seedling stage produced some ears bearing from one to many seeds. The seeds gave rise to plants with the tetraploid (2n=28) number of chromosomes. These synthetic amphiploids proved to be highly fertile under optimum conditions in the field where seed setting averaged 95 percent (Johnson and Dhaliwal, 1978).

The *boeoticum-urartu* amphiploids (table 4) showed preferential chromosome pairing with an average of 8.12 bivalents per cell and an equivalent bivalent frequency of 13.59 out of a possible maximum of 14. While an average of 2.51 pairs associated to form quadrivalents, the chromosomes tended to separate regularly at anaphase I where 82.60 percent of the cells showed normal 14:14 chromosome disjunction. The regular disjunction pattern undoubtedly accounts for the high level of fertility of the amphiploids. Evidently, the *boeoticum* and *urartu* chromosomes involved in quadrivalent formation can substitute for one another to form viable gametes. Such substitutions in the primary amphiploid could have led to the segregation of different parental traits to the presumed tetraploid derivatives, *T. dicoccoides* and *T. araraticum,* as noted above in the discussion of morphology.

Most of the *boeoticum-urartu* amphiploids exhibited heterosis with regard to spikelet size, the spikelets being larger than those of either parent and equal to those of *T. dicoccoides* and *T. araraticum* (fig. 2).

Morphologically, the *boeoticum-urartu* amphiploids were virtually indistinguishable from the wild tetraploid wheats with respect to diagnostic spikelet characters long recognized by taxonomists (fig. 2), notably the short hairy rachis segment and the sharply keeled glumes. With reference to the same characters, the synthetic amphiploids *Ae. speltoides-T. monococcum*[2] and *T. urartu-Ae. speltoides* (fig. 2) were markedly different from the tetraploid wheats. Also, the anthers of the tetraploid wheats were equal in length to those of the *boeoticum-urartu* amphiploid, but significantly different from those of various *boeoticum-Aegilops* amphiploids (Johnson and Dhaliwal, 1978). Little doubt seems to remain that *T. boeoticum* and *T. urartu* are the progenitors of the tetraploid wheats.

---

[2]*T. monococcum* is a cultivated derivative of *T. boeoticum.*

TABLE 4. Mean Chromosome Association and Chiasma Frequency
in *Boeoticum-Urartu* Amphiploids

Number of amphiploids	Number of PMC's per amphiploid	Chromosome association					Number of chiasmata per PMC	Percent anaphase I cells with 14:14 disjunction
		I	II		III	IV		
			Ring	Rod				
7	58	0.49	6.28	1.84	0.30	2.51	24.23	82.60

TABLE 5. Chromosome Association in Triploid Hybrids Between
Tetraploid *(T. timopheevii* and Emmer) and
Diploid *(T. boeoticum* and *T. urartu)* Wheats

Triploid hybrids	Number of hybrids	Chromosome association[a]					Number of chiasmata per PMC
		I	II	III	IV	V	
timopheevii × *boeoticum*	3	8.40	5.06	0.60	0.12	0.02	8.40
emmer × *boeoticum*	2	8.80	5.75	0.24	—	—	10.04
timopheevii × *urartu*	4	8.22	5.27	0.67	0.13	0.19	8.92
emmer × *urartu*	5	8.80	6.12	0.08	—	—	10.04

[a]An average of 50 PMC's (pollen mother cells) per hybrid was examined.

CHROMOSOME PAIRING HOMOLOGIES

The genomes of the two diploid species showed equal pairing affinity with chromosomes of the tetraploids. In crosses with *T. timopheevii* and emmer wheat *T. boeoticum* gave 5.06 and 5.75 bivalents respectively (table 5), and *T. urartu* gave 5.27 and 6.12 bivalents. In the absence of further evidence, these results could be interpreted to indicate that the *boeoticum* and *urartu* genomes pair each with a different genome of the tetraploids. However, by using telocentric chromosomes visibly recognizable at MI (meiotic metaphase I) Chapman et al. (1976) and Dvořák (1976) showed that the *urartu,* like the *boeoticum* chromosomes, paired with the A genome of the tetraploids. Neither of the diploid genomes paired with B. Thus, on the basis of chromosome pairing at MI, the A genome of the tetraploids is ambiguously identifiable with both of the diploid wheats as well as with diploids of the genus *Aegilops,* whereas the B genome has not been similarly identified with any species.

The anomalous pairing behavior of the A and B genomes is clearly due, in part, to the effect of the gene *PH* which is located on the long arm of chromosome 5B. This gene is known to suppress pairing of B with A as well as with other genomes (Okamoto, 1957; Riley and Chapman, 1958). In the absence of 5B virtually complete pairing occurs between the A and B genomes (Riley, 1960; Mello-Sampayo, personal communication). Further evidence reviewed by Johnson and Dhaliwal (1978) shows that A as well as B comprises chromosomes that have differentiated at the tetraploid level with respect to pairing affinity. It follows from this evidence that if one of a pair of homoeologues (a pair consisting of the corresponding but genetically somewhat dissimilar chromosomes from each parent) differentiated sufficiently so that it no longer pairs with the other, then it would not be expected to pair with the corresponding chromosome of either parent. Consequently, without regard to their parental origin, the seven less modified homoeologues (the A genome) would be expected to pair with the chromosomes of either parent, while the seven more modified ones (the B genome) would not be expected to pair at all with either parental genome. The anomalous pairing behavior of the tetraploid genomes is thus simply explained, and it is not inconsistent with the other evidence pointing to *T. boeoticum* and *T. urartu* as the parents of the tetraploid wheats.

REFERENCES

CHAPMAN, V.; MILLER, T. E.; and RILEY, R.
  1976.   Equivalence of the A genome of bread wheat and that of *T. urartu*. Genet. Res., vol. 27, pp. 69-76.
DHALIWAL, H. S., and JOHNSON, B. L.
  1976a. Anther morphology and the origin of the tetraploid wheats.   Amer. Journ. Bot., vol. 63, pp. 363-368.
  1976b. SDS-electrophoretic patterns and the origin of the tetraploid wheats. Genet. (Suppl.), vol. 83, p. 20.
DVOŘÁK, J.
  1976.   The relationship between the genome of *Triticum urartu* and the A and B genomes of *Triticum aestivum*.   Canadian Journ. Genet. Cytol., vol. 18, pp. 371-377.
GANDILIAN, P. O.
  1972.   On the wild growing *Triticum* species of the Armenian S.S.R.   Bot. Journ., vol. 57, pp. 173-181.
JAKUBZINER, M. M.
  1958.   New wheat species.   Proc. First Int. Wheat Genet. Symp., Winnipeg, pp. 207-217.
JOHNSON, B. L.
  1972.   Protein electrophoretic profiles and the origin of the B genome of wheat. Proc. Nat. Acad. Sci., U.S.A., vol. 69, pp. 1392-1402.
  1973.   Seed protein patterns and the gene resources of wheat.   Proc. Symp. Genet. and Breeding of *Durum* wheat, Bari, Italy, pp. 153-164.

JOHNSON, B. L.—continued
  1975.   Identification of the apparent B-genome donor of wheat.   Canadian Journ. Genet. Cytol., vol. 17, pp. 21-39.
JOHNSON, B. L., and DHALIWAL, H. S.
  1976.   Reproductive isolation of *Triticum boeoticum* and *Triticum urartu* and the origin of the tetraploid wheats.   Amer. Journ. Bot., vol. 63, pp. 1088-1094.
  1978.   *Triticum urartu* and genome evolution in the tetraploid wheats.   Amer. Journ. Bot., vol. 65, pp. 907-918.
KIHARA, H.
  1937.   Genomanalyse bei *Triticum* und *Aegilops*. VII. Kurze Uebersicht über die Ergebnisse der Jahre, 1934-36.   Mem. Coll. Agric. Kyoto Imp. Univ., vol. 41, pp. 1-61.
MCFADDEN, E. S., and SEARS, E. R.
  1946.   The origin of *Triticum spelta* and its free threshing hexaploid relatives. Journ. Hered., vol. 37, pp. 81-89, 107-116.
OKAMOTO, M.
  1957.   Asynaptic effect of chromosome V.   Wheat Inf. Serv., vol. 5, p. 6.
RILEY, R.
  1960.   The diploidisation of polyploid wheat.   Heredity, vol. 15, pp. 407-429.
RILEY, R., and CHAPMAN, V.
  1958.   Genetic control of the cytologically diploid behavior of hexaploid wheat. Nature (Lond.), vol. 182, pp. 713-715.
SARKAR, P., and STEBBINS, G. L.
  1956.   Morphological evidence concerning the origin of the B genome in wheat. Amer. Journ. Bot., vol. 43, pp. 297-304.
SEARS, E. R.
  1956.   The B genome of *Triticum*.   Wheat Inf. Serv., vol. 4, pp. 8-10.
STEBBINS, G. L.
  1947.   Types of polyploids. Their classification and significance.   Adv. Genet., vol. 1, pp. 403-428.

B. L. JOHNSON
H. S. DHALIWAL
A. BLANCO

The Reconstruction of the Kyrenia Ship, 1972-1975

Principal Investigator: Michael L. Katzev, Oberlin College, Oberlin, Ohio.

Grant Nos. 1098,   In support of the reconstruction of the Greek merchant ship
1462.   sunk off Kyrenia, Cyprus, sometime in the latter third of the
fourth century before Christ.

With the permission and support of the Department of Antiquities of the Republic of Cyprus, work on the Kyrenia ship continued during 1972-1973 under the aegis of Oberlin College and was completed between 1974 and 1975 with the assistance of the American Institute of Nautical Archaeology. In addition to these institutions' sponsorship, financial aid was received from the National Endowment for the Humanities, the John Brown Cook Foundation, Cyprus Mines Corporation, the National Geographic Society, UNESCO, and the American Council of Learned Societies. Cyprus Mines Corporation also provided aid through its facilities on the island. The United States Embassy in Nicosia rendered assistance in innumerable ways; and following the Turkish invasion and occupation of northern Cyprus in 1974, Ambassador William R. Crawford and his staff were constantly at the disposal of the project's needs. Finally, a profound expression of gratitude is extended to the project's personnel, who so devotedly dedicated themselves to the successful restoration of the Kyrenia Ship, particularly Robin C. M. Piercy, Assistant Director; J. Richard Steffy, Ship Reconstructor; Susan Womer Katzev, Photographer and Artist; Frances Talbot Vassiliadou, Conservator; Robert K. Vincent, Jr., Assistant; Gay Donati Piercy, Assistant to the Conservator.

Background

In 1965, while picking sponges at a depth of 30 meters, Andreas Cariolou accidentally discovered a mound of amphoras on the seabed. He graciously showed the mound to archeologists from the University of Pennsylvania Museum who were searching for shipwrecks off the coasts of Cyprus during the autumn of 1967. They surveyed the site and determined that a fair-size merchant ship had sunk off Kyrenia sometime in the latter third of the fourth century before Christ (Katzev, 1974a).

During two seasons of excavation, in the summers of 1968 and 1969, the Pennsylvania group completed the recording and recovery of material from

315

316

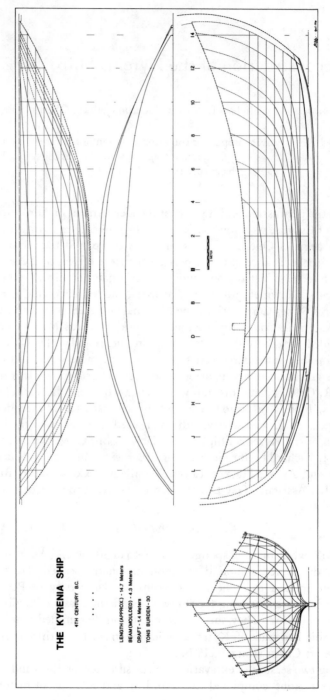

THE KYRENIA SHIP

4TH CENTURY B.C.

· · · · ·

LENGTH (APPROX.) - 14.7 Meters
BEAM (MOULDED) - 4.3 Meters
DRAFT - 1.4 Meters
TONS BURDEN - 30

FIG. 1.   The Kyrenia ship's lines. (By J. Richard Steffy.)

the site. The ship's principal cargo consisted of approximately 400 amphoras, which can be associated with ports of call at Samos and Rhodes. Almonds were another commodity carried aboard, and over 10,000 amazingly well-preserved specimens were found. Some 29 hopper-type grain mill blocks, surrounded by fist-size stones and bedded in gravel and beach sand, served as the ship's ballast. From fore and aft cabins the black-glazed crockery used by the crew of four on the Kyrenia ship's last voyage was raised. Seven bronze coins which were recovered indicate that the ship sank circa 300 B.C. Most fortunately about 70 percent of the merchantman's hull lay buried beneath the fine muddy sand of the seabed. After meticulously labeling and plotting each piece in situ, the excavators carefully lifted almost 5 tons of waterlogged wood to the surface (Katzev, 1970, 1973, 1975, 1976, 1978).

Every piece of wood was then the subject of detailed cataloguing, photographing of inner and outer faces, as well as drawing of these surfaces at full scale, in order to insure against the loss of any information should the timbers suffer during preservation treatment. After a year of research and experimentation, it was clear that a program of treatment using the water soluble compound polyethylene glycol (PEG) of molecular weight 4000 and gradually increasing the concentration of the solution to almost 100 percent would yield bulked, dimensionally stable wood. Tanks of galvanized steel, their interiors coated with fiberglass, were made and equipped to heat and circulate the PEG solution. And in the summer of 1971 large-scale treatment of the ship's timbers began. The rate at which the PEG was absorbed depended in part on the condition of the wood, its species, and particularly the piece's cross-sectional dimensions. Time of treatment, therefore, varied from a minimum of 8 months to a maximum of 2 years. When taken from the tanks (the last piece was removed during December of 1973), the timbers were slowly dried and cooled to room conditions. Then the wood's surfaces had to be laboriously cleaned of the congealed PEG, at which point a piece was at last ready to be used in the reassembly of the Kyrenia ship. For 99 percent of the timbers this process of treatment successfully preserved the wood without any shrinkage or warpage (Katzev, 1974b, 1979, 1980).

Reconstruction

Correlating the in situ plan of the hull on the seabed, the detailed catalogue of the wood, and the full-scale drawings of each piece (manually reduced to 1:10 scale), Richard Steffy analyzed and interpreted the data, producing a set of preliminary drawings of the ship's lines. These were graphically projected at full scale on the walls of the ship's gallery in the Crusader Castle at

Kyrenia, and this process—not dissimilar to "mold lofting"—yielded pertinent alterations to the projections. The results were then subjected to further scrutiny and criticism through building a 1:5 scale research model. From these experiences Steffy was able to prepare a more accurate version of the ship's original contours. He confirmed that the Kyrenia ship had a curved, rocker-shaped keel; and his work revealed a shallow, broad, double-ended vessel, 14.7 meters in length, 4.3 meters abeam (beam/length ratio of 1:3), and 1.4 meters in draft: a merchantman of slightly less than 30 tons burden.

Sufficient evidence for the ship's sailing rig survived to enable us to construct a model destined for sea trials. Made of fiberglass at 1:5 scale, the model was large enough to be manned. Equipped with dual steering oars, she carried a broad "square" sail, fitted with guide rings for brail lines. (Calculations indicated that the original ship had a sail measuring approximately 10.7×6.0 meters, or 64 square meters, with over 180 lead brail rings.) Through a series of tests we obtained vital information about the steering and handling of the ancient merchantman. For example, by manipulating the two steering oars, the helmsman found her extremely responsive to his touch; she would turn or could be stopped almost within her own length. And, while actually sailing this model, it was learned that under the best of conditions—a following wind—the Kyrenia ship might have made 4 or 5 knots. But, surprisingly enough, because the mast was set relatively far forward amidships, with one edge of her sail swung round and brailed-up she could also make amazingly good headway when pointing as close as 6 points off the wind.

The Kyrenia ship was built in the shell-first manner. To appreciate better this technique of construction, a full-scale section of the hull was built for a length of 2 meters aft amidships. In this replica the modern-day researchers used materials and tools similar to those of the ancient shipwright. The pine keel was adzed, and mortises were chiseled into the lower faces of its rabbets. After shaping a garboard strake, mortises were cut in its lower edge to match those of the keel. Then this garboard was edge-joined to the keel by oak tenons inserted in the mortises, and these tenons were locked in place with pegs. Strake by strake the hull was built up using the same tenon and peg joinery. Above the turn of the bilge the first of two thicker planks was set. The girding function of this wale evidently was fully understood by the ancient shipwright, for he placed this large plank where it was needed most—at the waterline. A cap rail provided additional stiffening at the top of the hull. In the original ship some 8,000 mortises had been cut, their bottoms carefully squared to receive 4,000 tenons. These tenons served as "mini" frames, each contributing strength to the shell construction; and our replica of the hull was indeed quite rigid before any internal framing was installed.

FIG. 2.   Mr. Steffy fitting a plank to the port side of the 1:5 scale research model. In the background work proceeds on the replica—a full-scale section of the hull. (Photo by Susan Womer Katzev.)

FIG. 3.   The 1:5 scale fiberglass model during sea trials off the Crusader Castle.
(Photo by Susan Womer Katzev.)

Not until the entire shell was completed were the frames inserted. Cut from naturally curved timbers, the alternating floors and half frames were finely adzed to fit the shape of the hull; and above these, futtocks and top timbers were placed. All the frames were secured by pure copper spikes. Copper rod (generously supplied by Rome Cable, a division of Cyprus Mines Corporation) was forged into spikes and hand-hardened, driven from the outside through pine treenails to insure water tightness, and clenched over with their tips bent back and hammered down into the interior of the frames to provide their sure holding. For added strength to the hull, a stringer and limber strake were attached to the frames. Backing the main wale, the stringer served as an internal clamp as well as a shelf, supporting the few athwart beams. Similarly, the limber strake served a dual purpose, for it was rabbeted to support the limber boards. Between the stringer and limber strake, ceiling planks were laid down to protect the frames from wear and tear by cargo and ballast. Finally plates of thin lead sheathing were applied to the exterior of the hull and held in place by a myriad of copper tacks. This lead sheathing had been a last attempt to make the Kyrenia ship watertight.

With the knowledge gleaned from these reconstructions, we were better prepared to reassemble the Kyrenia ship using the preserved, original wood.

FIG. 4.   The completed replica with Robin Piercy serving as "scale." (Photo by
Susan Womer Katzev.)

Down the length of the ship's gallery a concrete pedestal was poured 12.00
meters long, 1.00 meter high, 0.30 meter wide at the bottom, and 0.20 meter wide at the top. On this pedestal an elaborate oak structure was made, simulating a dry dock shipway. The first piece of the keel was laid on September
29, 1972. This phase of the reassembly—relaying the 10-meter-long keel—
was the most exacting challenge in the whole operation; for, if the curvature of
the keel were off by more than 1 centimeter, such an error would have been
compounded at least tenfold by the time the upper wale was reached. To support the strakes a temporary wooden scaffolding of complicated units, placed
1 meter apart perpendicular to the keel's pedestal, was built. These units were
adjustable so that initially battens delineating the sheer lines of the hull could
be set to trace true curves, and subsequently the contours of the strakes could
be altered to follow their original sweep. In reassembling the strakes each of
thousands of pieces required individual attention. Mortises, tenons, pegs, and
edge-angles had to be aligned before planks could be precisely secured one to
another. Since the ancient mortise-tenon joinery could not be reutilized, we
manufactured customized fasteners from stainless steel wire 2 millimeters in
diameter. Broken frames had to be mended. After deep holes were drilled into
the breaks, the pieces were heated in a large "homemade" oven. Just below its

melting point of 55°C. the polyethylene glycol preservative softened and became malleable. Upon removing the pieces from the oven, long wooden dowels soaked in polyethylene glycol were inserted into the holes; these dowels served as "reinforcing rods" as the pieces were joined, while the cooling polyethylene glycol slowly solidified to serve as a kind of "glue" sticking the pieces together. Also during this process the pliable frames could be rebent to their original curvatures. In adding the frames to the reassembly, their nails had to be oriented with the nail holes in the strakes before the frames could be accurately set and secured—again using stainless steel wire—within the hull. Slowly, painstakingly, the reassembly progressed; but each day the modern reconstructors were struck anew by the skill and craftsmanship of the ancient shipwright. On November 9, 1973, the last frame was put in place. However, due to the interruption in our work caused by the Turkish invasion and occupation of northern Cyprus during the summer of 1974, we were not able to complete finally the reassembly by adding the interior planks until May 19, 1975.

Fortunately, approximately 70 percent of the ancient Kyrenia ship survived to be included in this modern restoration of the oldest seagoing hull yet recovered. Through the process of reassembly much was learned about the hull's design and construction not otherwise obtainable. It was revealed that the port side had a slightly different cross-sectional shape than the starboard. In fact, remarkably enough, the port had 5 percent more wetted surface and indeed one more strake than the starboard. Careful inspection of the workmanship on each side of the keel suggests that this imbalance was the result of two teams of shipbuilders working side by side. Evidence came to light that in the stern there was a deck upon which the helmsman stood and below which there was a locker. Most probably in the bow there was a comparable deck, serving as a platform for heaving the anchors, below which was a cuddy. Between the bow and stern decks, however, absolutely no evidence was found for decking; rather, the cargo of the Kyrenia ship seems to have been ladened into an undecked hold. During the reassembly it was also possible to observe and evaluate various repairs made to the hull in antiquity. The ship had been subjected to major overhauls on at least three separate occasions. These repairs included the replacement of damaged floors in the bow and the application of a thin wood sheathing over much of the bow's exterior in order to seal opening seams; the replacement of rotten strakes in the bow and the application of lead patches over splitting seams in the bow's interior to make them watertight; and finally sheathing the entire outer hull with thin sheets of lead as a last attempt to cover the leaking seams and prolong the life of the ship. It is not clear how many years lapsed between these repairs, but one may conjecture that in

FIG. 5.   The reassembled Kyrenia ship. (Photo by Michael L. Katzev.)

all they must have encompassed decades. Furthermore, after the lead sheathing was applied, parts of the keel's worn shoe were replaced as many as three times, reinforcing the supposition that the Kyrenia ship had seen many years of service.

Exhibition

In Kyrenia's Crusader Castle the Department of Antiquities finished restorations in the three galleries allocated as a museum for the ship's excavation. The partly destroyed arch dividing the northernmost gallery was restored, and half of the second floor in this gallery was rebuilt to provide additional display space. Reconstruction of the collapsed groin vault in the middle gallery was completed. The walls and vault of the southernmost gallery—the Ship Gallery—were sprayed with a special compound (Lewin LSP I formula) to consolidate the soft limestone and minimize the fall of sand-size crystals onto the reassembled ship. And the floors in all three galleries were relaid with flagstone paving. The reassembly's temporary wooden scaffolding was replaced by an iron cradle, whose rows of stanchions were set 2 meters apart, providing strong and permanent support for the ship. The government of the Republic of Cyprus provided the equipment necessary for air conditioning the Ship Gallery. Under the direction of the UNESCO advisor to Cyprus, Jacques Dalibard, this equipment was installed by UNFICYP personnel during the spring of 1976. Now a selection of finds from the excavation, culminating in the display of the reassembled ship, may be seen in these three galleries of Kyrenia's Crusader Castle.

Recording and Conservation

The preliminary recording of the contents of the Kyrenia ship, undertaken during the excavation season of 1968 and 1969, was thoroughly reviewed and completed. This work included the recataloging, photographing, and drawing of all the material to a standard suitable for its final, scholarly publication. The approximately 400 amphoras were reinspected toward better describing the color and quality of their fabrics. The 29 grain mill blocks were photographed and weighed, their total weight being 1,652 kilograms; also the fist-size ballast stones were weighed, and the weight of those stones recovered during the excavation totaled 230 kilograms. Further mending of the crew's crockery produced 20 more vases for documentation. Additions to the repertory of plates, bowls, and pitchers included 4 casserole pots and a tiny votive lamp.

Iron decomposes rapidly under water. A concretelike formation builds up around the object. Within this "concretion" a mold is formed of the iron

FIG. 6.   A selection of iron blooms. Scale is marked in lengths of 1 centimeter.
(Photo by Michael L. Katzev.)

FIG. 7.   The deadeyes. Scale is marked in lengths of 1 centimeter. (Photo by Susan
Womer Katzev.)

FIG. 8.   The wooden bow drill extracted from the large concretion. Scale is marked
in lengths of 1 centimeter. (Photo by Michael L. Katzev.)

FIG. 9.   Replicas of the spearheads. Scale is marked in lengths of 1 centimeter.
(Photo by Michael L. Katzev.)

original. Also, as the concretion builds up, it entraps any other objects in the
environs of the iron. To determine what the iron object was originally, it is
necessary to saw the concretion in half and make a cast from the mold. And to
release any objects entrapped in the concretion, it is necessary to break up the
concretelike formation. Using a lapidary saw and a polysulphide rubber compound, replicas of the iron objects from the Kyrenia ship were cast; and using
a vibrotool, all the other entrapped objects were released from the concretions.

In the stern locker of the Kyrenia ship some 30 iron blooms had been
stacked. They formed a concretion weighing approximately 600 kilograms.
Entrapped in this concretion were: a bronze ladle whose handle ends in an ele-
gant duck's head, a small lead bowl, 57 lead guide rings for brail lines, a wood

toggle, 3 wood deadeyes, various fragments of rope, a bow drill, 11 knuckle-bones, a portion of a garlic clove, 18 olive pits, 764 grape seeds, 14,760 fig seeds, more almonds, pistachio and hazel nuts, et cetera. The wealth of material painstakingly extracted from this "mine" of a concretion cannot be overestimated. Its detailed analysis and interpretation will add immensely to our knowledge of seamanship and the habits of seafarers in antiquity.

Smaller concretions yielded an additional 45 replicas of iron implements. Among the most interesting objects were the supports of several gridirons, a complex key with 8 teeth, a ship's slice, a hammer, the fluke of an anchor, and 8 spearheads. These latter weapons might explain why the Kyrenia ship came to grief. No spears were recovered from within the hull; the excavators found all of them beneath the hull, and some were bent from impact. Valuable objects were not found in the wreck, nor were any of the sailors' personal effects. These circumstances suggest a pirate attack, the looting and scuttling of the Kyrenia ship more than 22 centuries ago.

Documentary Film

With the permission and encouragment of the National Geographic Society, the Cyprus Broadcasting Corporation shot footage focusing on the various phases of the reconstruction. The result was a premiere on March 23, 1977, in Nicosia, Cyprus, of a 54-minute, 16-mm, sound, color film entitled "With Captain Sailors Three: The Ancient Kyrenia Ship," produced by the Cyprus Broadcasting Corporation in cooperation with the National Geographic Society. This documentary film, covering the project from the wreck's discovery through the ship's reassembly, is now available in Greek, English, and French editions and is actively being distributed worldwide to educational, cultural, and historical institutions.

Conclusion

The Kyrenia ship project has provided a vivid picture of a fourth century B.C. ship and her crew. What we see is a merchantman of slightly less than 30 tons burden. Well built, she was nevertheless the "tramp" vessel of her day. Trading through the Aegean and eastern Mediterranean, she had called at Samos, Nisyros, Rhodes, and perhaps Cyprus to take on and discharge cargoes as varied as wine, millstones, almonds, iron, or other more perishable materials. Undoubtedly she had made many similar voyages throughout the lifetime of Alexander the Great, her open hold filled with comparable cargoes. Indeed, for several generations of mariners it seems she had successfully plied the seas in such commerce. But luck ran out on her last crew of four. Around the year 300 B.C. we believe pirates suddenly ended the sailing life of the Kyrenia ship. However, to our good fortune the sea yielded these secrets over 2,200 years later. Through the dedication of sponsors and project members, after 8 years of labor, this the oldest seagoing hull yet recovered has been resurrected. It is hoped that in the years to come visitors and scholars will find reward in the exhibit of the Kyrenia ship.

REFERENCES

KATZEV, MICHAEL L.
  1970.   Resurrecting the oldest known Greek ship.   Nat. Geogr. Mag., vol. 137, no. 6, pp. 840-857, illus.
  1973.   Resurrecting a Greek ship 2,300 years old.   Pp. 35-40 *in* "Men, Ships, and the Sea," by Alan Villiers, 436 pp., illus. National Geographic Society, Washington, D. C.
  1974a. Cyprus underwater archeological search, 1967.   Nat. Geogr. Soc. Res. Rpts., 1967 Projects, pp. 177-184, illus.
  1974b. Last port for the oldest ship.   Nat. Geogr. Mag., vol. 146, no. 5, pp. 618-625, illus. [with Susan Womer Katzev].
  1975.   Resurrecting an ancient Greek ship.   Explorers Journ., vol. 53, no. 1, pp. 2-7, illus.
  1976.   Cyprus underwater archeological search, 1968.   Nat. Geogr. Soc. Res. Rpts., 1968 Projects, pp. 177-188, illus.
  1978.   Cyprus underwater archeological search, 1969.   Nat. Geogr. Soc. Res. Rpts., 1969 Projects, pp. 289-305, illus.
  1979.   Conservation of the Kyrenia ship, 1970-1971.   Nat. Geogr. Soc. Res. Rpts., 1970 Projects, pp. 331-340, illus.
  1980.   Conservation of the Kyrenia ship, 1971-1972.   Nat. Geogr. Soc. Res. Rpts., 1971 Projects, pp. 417-426, illus.

MICHAEL L. KATZEV

The Microdistribution of Small Mammals at the Coniferous-Deciduous Forest Interface

Principal Investigator: Gordon L. Kirkland, Jr., Shippensburg State College, Shippensburg, Pennsylvania.

Grant No. 1052: For a study of the microdistribution of small mammals at the coniferous-deciduous ecotone.

Microhabitat selection in small mammals is most easily observed and studied in regions of sharply defined habitat interfaces. This phenomenon is well illustrated in comparisons of forest and grassland habitats where certain species exhibit a decided preference for one habitat and are absent or seldom encountered in the other. The meadow jumping mouse, *Zapus hudsonius* (Whitaker, 1972), the least shrew, *Cryptotis parva* (Golley, 1962), and the prairie deer mouse, *Peromyscus maniculatus bairdii* (Hooper, 1942), are restricted primarily to grassland habitats and are seldom or never encountered in adjacent woods. The red-backed vole, *Clethrionomys gapperi* (Hamilton, 1963), the woodland deer mouse, *Peromyscus maniculatus gracilis* (Klein, 1960), the woodland jumping mouse, *Napaeozapus insignis* (Whitaker and Wrigley, 1972), and the southern flying squirrel, *Glaucomys volans* (Grimm and Roberts, 1950), are more or less restricted to forests to the same extent.

In certain regions of the Northeastern United States, sharp habitat breaks occur between two other major habitat types, the coniferous forest and the deciduous forest. The steep altitudinal and moisture gradients in the Adirondack Mountains of New York State produce numerous sharp breaks between these forest types. Boreal coniferous forests are restricted to the cooler upper slopes and the poorly drained lowlands, while deciduous forests cover the intermediate slopes. This paper reports the results of research designed to determine whether any ecological sorting of species or microhabitat selection occurs in mammals at the coniferous-deciduous ecotone. In addition to this report, a previous treatment of these data by Kirkland and Griffin (1973) is recommended.

Personnel and Acknowledgments

Data for this research were collected with the assistance of students from Shippensburg State College. Rebecca J. Griffin was a student field coordinator in 1972.

I am indebted to the staff of the Huntington Wildlife Forest Station, Newcomb Campus, State University College of Forestry, for their assistance in 1971 in providing laboratory facilities and access to lands under their supervision. In 1972 Walter M. Chapman, manager, and Robert Hampson, lands manager, of the MacIntyre Development of N L Industries, Inc., furnished sleeping and laboratory space and admittance to lands of the MacIntyre Development at Tahawus, New York.

This research was supported by a grant from the National Geographic Society in 1972 and by Shippensburg State College.

Materials and Methods[1]

Data were collected at two different sites in Essex County, New York. During August 1971 the investigation was conducted on the northeast slope of Catlin Mountain on the Huntington Wildlife Forest Station of the State University College of Forestry at Newcomb. A grid of 200 Sherman LFA live-traps ($3\frac{1}{2}$ by 3 by 9 inches, folding aluminum) was established along a moderate-to-steep (45°+) slope near Huntington Forest grid line J-13, at an elevation of 2,200 to 2,400 feet. Stations, at intervals of 40 feet, were arranged in a 20-by-10 pattern, with one trap per station. The trap site was centrally located within each grid section. The trapping area included both upland coniferous and lowland deciduous forest components, with a well-defined break. The deciduous portion contained American beech *(Fagus grandifolia)*, striped and sugar maple *(Acer pennsylvanicum* and *A. saccharum)*, and yellow birch *(Betula alleghaniensis)* as dominants, and was generally dry. Undergrowth consisted of club moss *(Lycopodium* sp.), fancy fern *(Dryopteris intermedia)*, cinnamon fern *(Osmunda cinnamomea)*, hobblebush *(Viburnum alnifolium)*, clover, and saplings of the above-mentioned tree species. The coniferous area was dominated by a dense stand of mature red spruce *(Picea rubens)* and was more moist than the deciduous zone. Moss-covered rocks and logs were plentiful, and at most sites the irregular forest floor was sufficiently overgrown with mosses to create large subsurface cavities. The trapping grid was run from August 10 to 13 and from August 16 to 20; the interval was to permit repeatedly caught individuals to recover from prolonged exposure in the live-traps. The total number of trapnights was 1,674. Traplines were checked once daily between 8 and 10 a.m.

A grid of 130 Sherman live-traps was established during August 1972 in a low moist area south of Lake Sally on the MacIntyre Development of N L Industries, Inc., at Tahawus (Santanoni Quadrangle). The plot, with trap sta-

---

[1] Descriptions of field techniques and sites are taken from Kirkland and Griffin (1973).

tions at 40-foot intervals, located in the center of each grid section, consisted of 12 rows of 10 traps each and 2 rows of 5, and was located at an elevation of approximately 1,800 feet. Although a well-defined break occurred between coniferous and deciduous zones, a few isolated pockets of conifers were present within the deciduous area. The grid was bordered on three sides by waste rock from the open-pit mining operations of the MacIntyre Development. The co-niferous areas were predominantly wet and contained northern white cedar *(Thuja occidentalis),* red and black spruce *(Picea mariana),* and balsam fir *(Abies balsamea).* Undergrowth varied from sparse to heavy and consisted for the most part of sphagnum mosses, grasses, ground pine, clover, ferns, horsetails, and other herbs. Maple seedings and shrubby trees as well as fallen trees and logs were common at many sites. The deciduous portions consisted of Ameri-can beech, sugar and red maple *(Acer rubrum),* and yellow birch and were gen-erally drier, although certain of the trap stations within the zone were described as wet. The forest floor was generally covered with leaf litter, and wood sorrel, ground pine, and other herbs were common. Fern undergrowth

TABLE 1. Capture Totals and Diversity Indices for the 1971 Catlin Mountain and 1972 Tahawus Trapping Grids

Species	1971	1972
Sorex cinereus Kerr	12	4
Sorex fumeus Miller	7	—
Sorex dispar Batchelder	1	—
Blarina brevicauda Say	17	15
Tamias striatus (Linnaeus)	7	5
Tamiasciurus hudsonicus (Erxleben)	1	1
Peromyscus maniculatus (Wagner)	44	14
Clethrionomys gapperi (Vigors)	34	34
Microtus pennsylvanicus (Ord)	—	2
Napaeozapus insignis (Miller)	4	22
Totals	127	97
Shannon Index (H)	2.48	2.43
Index of Equitability (H/Hmax)	.78	.81

varied from light to heavy, and sproutlings and saplings of the deciduous and fir species were sometimes numerous. Berry bushes *(Rubus* sp.) and fallen trees or logs were present at several stations. The 1972 grid was, in general, much more moist than the 1971 grid. The grid was established on August 8 and was run for 9 days with a break of 2 days (August 12 to 14), for a total of 1,170 trapnights. Traps were checked twice daily, between 8 and 9 a.m. and 4 and 5 p.m.

Mammals captured alive during the two trapping periods were sexed, aged, measured, and marked by toe-clipping. After the coordinates of the capture sites were recorded, the individuals were released as close as possible to the trap station, the only exceptions being those individuals that appeared to be suffering from prolonged exposure in the traps. These were released in sunlit areas to speed recovery from hypothermia.

Within each trapping grid the microdistribution of small mammals was analyzed on the basis of the distribution of trap stations at which each species was captured. Expected values for X^2 analysis were based on the proportion of sites that were coniferous and deciduous on the two study plots. The ratio of coniferous to deciduous stations was 46:154 in 1971 and 55:75 in 1972. The 0.05 level of significance was used in all cases.

Results and Discussion

Ten species of small mammals were captured in the two study areas in 1971 and 1972 (table 1). Although 7 species were common to both plots, their relative abundances differed. Spearman Rank Correlation analysis (Siegel, 1956) of the rankings of the 7 species produced an r_s of 0.46, indicating that there was no significant correlation between the rankings of the seven species in the study areas at the 0.05 level. The complementary abundances of the woodland deer mouse, *Peromyscus maniculatus gracilis* (LeConte), and the woodland jumping mouse, *Napaeozapus insignis* (Miller), contributed to the lack of correlation.

In spite of the differences in relative abundances of species in the two mammal communities, the species diversity of the two samples, as measured by the Shannon Index of Diversity (Shannon and Weaver, 1963), was nearly identical (table 1).

The remainder of this section will consist of brief descriptions of the abundance and distribution of captures of these 10 species. These will be divided into the four families represented.

SORICIDAE. The short-tailed shrew, *Blarina brevicauda* (Say), was the most common insectivore in both 1971 and 1972. Seventeen individuals were captured a total of 21 times in 1971, while 15 individuals were captured a total of 17 times in 1972. In both years, this species was taken more frequently in the deciduous portions of the plots. It was taken in conifers in only 1 of 21 captures in 1971 and in 5 of 17 captures in 1972. Although the preference was significant at the 0.05 level in 1971 ($X^2 = 3.89$, $df = 1$), it was not significant in 1972.

Throughout its range *Blarina brevicauda* occupies a wide variety of habitats; however, Hamilton (1963) notes that it is most abundant in regions of heavy leaf mold. The noticeable absence of this substrate in the coniferous areas, particularly on Catlin Mountain, may partially explain the low capture rate in the coniferous zones.

Only one specimen of the rare long-tailed shrew, *Sorex dispar* Batchelder, was taken during the 2 years of study. The habitat at the trap site, consisting of moist moss-covered rocks in a coniferous zone, is similar to that described for this species by Hamilton (1963), Handley (1956), Holloway (1957), and Mansueti and Flyger (1952).

The smoky shrew, *Sorex fumeus* Miller, was taken only on Catlin Mountain in 1971 when 2 specimens were captured in the coniferous zone and 5 specimens in the decidous zone. Its absence in 1972 cannot be explained, since *S. fumeus* is known to occur in, if it does not prefer, damp woods and bogs (Paradiso, 1969).

The masked shrew, *Sorex cinereus* Kerr, was the only member of the genus *Sorex* captured on both study areas (12 specimens in 1971 and 4 in 1972). Throughout its range, this species occupies a broad range of habitats and Hamilton (1963) describes it as "a true cosmopolite." Thus its presence on both sampling areas was not unexpected. Although insufficient specimens were captured to permit meaningful statistical analysis, the distribution of captures indicated that *Sorex cinereus* did not exhibit a pronounced preference for either forest zone.

SCIURIDAE. The eastern chipmunk, *Tamias striatus* (Linnaeus), exhibited a marked preference for the deciduous zone. In 1971 all 8 captures (7 individuals) were in the deciduous area, while in the 1972 study 13 of 14 captures (5 individuals) were in the deciduous zone.

One red squirrel, *Tamiasciurus hudsonicus* (Erxleben), was captured in each of the two years. Single captures were made in the deciduous zone in 1971 and in the coniferous zone in 1972.

CRICETIDAE. The meadow vole, *Microtus pennsylvanicus* (Ord), is primarily a grassland species and its presence on the 1972 grid was somewhat unexpected. The two individuals captured in the coniferous zone were subadults and probably transients.

The status of the red-backed vole, *Clethrionomys gapperi* (Vigors), as a forest dweller is in marked contrast to the normal grassland preference of most microtine rodents. In 1971 *C. gapperi* was the second most common species, and it was the most common in 1972. In 1971, *C. gapperi* exhibited a marked preference for the coniferous portions of the grid, both in single capture ($X^2 = 13.9$, $df = 1$) and multiple capture ($X^2 = 10.3$, $df = 1$) analyses. In 1972 this species was distributed throughout the grid and exhibited no habitat preference.

The explanation for these data may be found in the moisture requirements of this species. The preference of *C. gapperi* for moist habitats has been noted by Getz (1968). In addition, work by Odum (1944) on laboratory specimens found that *C. gapperi* had a daily consumption of water nearly six times that of other similar-sized forest-dwelling rodents. In 1971 the upland coniferous zone had a conspicuously moist floor with dense moss and moist rocks. The deciduous zone was noticeably drier. In 1972 the entire grid was more moist with trap stations near standing water scattered throughout. Thus it appears that moisture is the prime factor in influencing the microdistribution of *C. gapperi*. Selection for the coniferous zone in 1971 was in response to the more abundant moisture in the conifers. In the absence of sharp moisture gradients associated with breaks in vegetation, this species exhibited no preference for either coniferous or deciduous zones.

The woodland deer mouse, *Peromyscus maniculatus gracilis,* was the most abundant species in 1971; however, in 1972, it ranked fourth (table 1). This reduction in abundance was accompanied by a more restricted distribution in 1972 as compared to 1971. In 1971 *P.m. gracilis* exhibited no preference for either forest zone. This contrasted with a significant preference for the deciduous zone ($X^2 = 17.2$ for all captures; $X^2 = 9.3$ for initial captures, $df = 1$) in 1972.

The data from 1972 may be interpreted in two ways: (1) *P.m. gracilis* avoided the lower wet coniferous zone and/or (2) competition from the *Napaeozapus insignis* may have excluded *P.m. gracilis* from most of the grid. Although Whitaker and Wrigley (1972) indicate that there is no evidence of *P. maniculatus* and *N. insignis* adversely affecting each other, the data from this study reveal a nearly perfect negative distribution of captures in these species. In the two summers both species were captured at the same trap station at only 2 out of 112 stations where either species was caught.

ZAPODIDAE.   The woodland jumping mouse, *Napaeozapus insignis,* exhibited markedly different abundances in the two study areas (table 1). In 1971 all four individuals were trapped in the deciduous zone. Its scarcity on the upland site in 1971 was in marked contrast to its abundance in the lowland site in 1972 where it was the second most common species. An examination of the 1972 distribution of this species with respect to the major vegetational types revealed no preference for the deciduous zone based on sites of initial capture; however, the distribution of multiple captures indicates a preference for hardwoods $(X^2 = 4.94, df = 1)$. There was a decided preference for sites judged to be dry for both initial and multiple captures $(X^2 = 7.8$ and $X^2 = 5.2, df = 1)$. The data from this study indicate that although N. *insignis* may prefer moist habitats, as previously noted by Preble (1956) and Whitaker and Wrigley (1972), it appears to frequent drier sites within the damp areas.

Summary

In August 1971 small mammals were sampled at the sharply defined interface between the higher altitude coniferous forest and the midslope deciduous zone. Similar sampling was conducted in August 1972 at the interface between the deciduous zone and the coniferous forest occuping low, poorly drained areas. Comparison of data collected at the two sites revealed small-mammal community differences between the two forest interfaces sampled. Although 7 of 10 species were common to both plots, there was a marked difference in abundances of some species at the two sites. On the well-drained upland site, *P.m. gracilis* was the most common small mammal while *C. gapperi* was somewhat restricted to the coniferous zone and N. *insignis* was rare. In the poorly drained lowland site, *C. gapperi* was the most common species and was distributed throughout the zone. N. *insignis* was common and had a distribution of captures complementary to that of the less frequently captured *P.m. gracilis.*

These results indicate that microhabitat selection can be detected at the coniferous-deciduous interface. In the case of *T. striatus,* the forest-type per se appears to be the proximal factor. In other species, however, such as *C. gapperi,* moisture may be controlling, whereas in others competitive interactions may play a deciding role.

REFERENCES

GETZ, LOWELL L.
    1968.   Influence of water balance and microclimate on the local distribution of the red-backed vole and white-footed mouse.   Ecology, vol. 49, pp. 276-286.
GOLLEY, FRANK B.
    1962.   Mammals of Georgia, 218 pp.   University of Georgia Press, Athens.
GRIMM, WILLIAM C., and ROBERTS, HARVEY A.
    1950.   Mammal survey of southwestern Pennsylvania, 99 pp.   Pennsylvania Game Commission, Harrisburg.
HAMILTON, WILLIAM J., JR.
    1963.   Mammals of the Eastern United States, 432 pp.   Hafner Publishing Co., New York.
HANDLEY, CHARLES O., JR.
    1956.   The shrew *Sorex dispar* in Virginia.   Journ. Mamm., vol. 37, p. 435.

HOLLOWAY, H. L.
  1957.   *Sorex dispar* at Mountain Lake, Virginia.   Journ. Mamm., vol. 38, p. 406.
HOOPER, EMMET T.
  1942.   An effect on the *Peromyscus maniculatus* Rassenkreis of land utilization in Michigan.   Journ. Mamm., vol. 23, pp. 193-196.
KIRKLAND, GORDON L., JR., and GRIFFIN, REBECCA J.
  1973.   Microdistribution of small mammals at the coniferous-deciduous forest ecotone in northern New York.   Journ. Mamm., vol. 55, pp. 417-427.
KLEIN, HAROLD G.
  1960.   Ecological relationships of *Peromyscus leucopus* and *P. maniculatus gracilis* in central New York.   Ecol. Monogr., vol. 30, no. 4, pp. 387-407.
MANSUETI, R., and FLYGER, VAGN F.
  1952.   Long-tailed shrew *(Sorex dispar)* in Maryland.   Journ. Mamm., vol. 33, p. 250.
ODUM, EUGENE P.
  1944.   Water consumption of certain species of mice in relation to habitat selection.   Journ. Mamm., vol. 25, pp. 404-405.
PARADISO, JOHN L.
  1969.   Mammals of Maryland.   North Amer. Fauna no. 66, 193 pp.   U. S. Bureau of Sports Fisheries and Wildlife, Washington.
PREBLE, NORMAN A.
  1956.   Notes on the life history of *Napaeozapus insignis*.   Journ. Mamm., vol. 37, pp. 196-200.
SHANNON, CLAUDE E., and WEAVER, WARREN
  1963.   The mathematical theory of communication, 117 pp.   University of Illinois Press, Urbana.
SIEGEL, SAMUEL
  1956.   Nonparametric statistics for the behavioral sciences, 312 pp. McGraw-Hill Book Co., New York.
WHITAKER, JOHN O., JR.
  1972.   *Zapus hudsonius*.   Mammalian Species no. 11, 7 pp.   American Society of Mammalogists.
WHITAKER, JOHN O., JR., and WRIGLEY, ROBERT E.
  1972.   *Napaeozapus insignis*.   Mammalian Species no. 14, 6 pp.   American Society of Mammalogists.

GORDON L. KIRKLAND, JR.

Reproductive Performance of Ospreys (*Pandion haliaetus*) in Northwestern California

Principal Investigator: James R. Koplin, Humboldt State University, Arcata, California.

Grant No. 1087: In support of studies on reproduction of ospreys.

In 1970, I initiated a study on the distribution, abundance, and reproductive status of ospreys breeding in northwestern California. In 1971, an associate, Jon M. French, joined me and we completed the study in 1972 (Koplin, 1971; French, 1972; French and Koplin, 1977). The objective of the study was to obtain information on reproductive performance of ospreys nesting in Pacific coastal and stream environments for comparison with similar information previously obtained from oligotrophic and mesotrophic lakes (Koplin, 1978, 1980).

Area of Study

The area of study included streams, bays, lagoons, and estuaries of Humboldt and Del Norte Counties, and northwestern Mendocino County; and streams in western Trinity County. Surveillance was concentrated on the lower reaches of the watersheds of the Trinity and Van Duzen Rivers; the lower reaches of the watersheds and estuaries of the Smith, Klamath, and Eel Rivers; the entire watersheds and the estuaries of Redwood and Usal Creeks and Little, Mad, and Mattole Rivers; Humboldt Bay and watersheds of inlet streams—Jacoby, Freshwater, and Salmon Creeks and Elk River—to Humboldt Bay; Lakes Tallowa and Earl; Freshwater, Stone, and Big Lagoons; and Shelter Cove (French, 1972; French and Koplin, 1977).

Mountains dominate the topography of northwestern California. The only level terrain is along the Pacific coastal plains and deltas of large streams. The region is drained by numerous streams in precipitous, narrow canyons. The majority of these streams originate in northwestern California. The Klamath River originates in central Oregon.

Precipitation in the area studied falls mainly in the winter between November and May; summers are characteristically dry. Consequently, stream flow fluctuates seasonally, with high runoff during winter and low runoff during summer. These runoff patterns are moderated by impoundments on the

337

Klamath, Trinity, Mad, and middle fork of the Eel Rivers. All other streams in the study area are free-flowing. Mean annual precipitation at Eureka is 36 inches (U. S. Department of Commerce, 1960), with precipitation increasing from south to north and west to east to the crest of the first mountains east of the Pacific Ocean.

Summers on the coast are cool and often accompanied by dense fogs; high temperatures and clear weather are common inland of the crest of the first mountains east of the Pacific. Winters throughout the area are characteristically overcast and rainy. Northwesterly onshore winds characterize the spring months, the transition period from the wet winter to the dry summer.

The majority of streams in the area of study drain forested watersheds. The Klamath, Mattole, and lower reaches of the Eel Rivers drain localized agricultural areas as well as forested watersheds.

Humboldt Bay; Freshwater, Stone, and Big Lagoons; and Lakes Earl and Tallowa are shallow coastal bodies of water. All but Freshwater Lagoon are permanently or temporarily connected to the Pacific Ocean during the year. Shelter Cove is a small cove approximately 0.5 mile in length.

With the exception of limited agricultural areas, the vast majority of the area of study is forested. At lower elevations and along the Pacific coast, redwood (*Sequoia sempervirens*) is the predominant tree. At higher elevations and farther inland, Douglas fir (*Pseudotsuga menziesii*) is the predominant tree. Willows (*Salix* sp.) and red alder (*Alnus rubra*) are common streamside shrubs, although the high annual rainfall characteristic of the area tends to obliterate the distinction between riparian and forest vegetation.

Streams in the area of study are known to be inhabited by 31 species of fishes, 14 of which are considered common (DeWitt, 1964). Humboldt Bay is known to be inhabited by at least 52 species of fishes (Skeesick, 1963). Species of fishes in Stone and Big Lagoons and in Shelter Cove are less well known but presumably are similar to those in Humboldt Bay. Freshwater Lagoon is stocked regularly with hatchery-reared rainbow trout (*Salmo gairdnerii*) of catchable size; these constitute the major bulk of the fish fauna in the lagoon (McDaniels and Phillips, 1972).

Results

Distribution of Nesting Sites.   Ospreys built nests in the tops of dead, partially or completely live redwoods and Douglas firs. Forty-five percent of 20 nests discovered in Usal Creek and 83 percent of 105 nests discovered elsewhere in the area of study were in dead or partially live trees.

Eighty-three percent of all 125 nests were in four areas: the Klamath River, near Humboldt Bay, south fork and main Eel River, and Usal Creek. The remaining nests were found on the lower Smith, Trinity, Little, and Van Duzen Rivers, Redwood Creek, and near two small lakes. No nests were found on the middle or south forks of the Smith River, Mad River, middle fork of the Eel River, Mattole River, or at Shelter Cove.

Only three nests were within 1 mile of the Pacific Ocean, even though ospreys commonly fished the coastal lagoons, Humboldt Bay, and the Pacific Ocean at the mouth of Usal Creek. The majority of ospreys that fished these areas built nests 2 to 5 miles inland, presumably because of the deleterious influence of northwesterly winds during spring and the heavy fogs during summer.

Abundance and Productivity.   Heights of nests ranged from approximately 40 to 250 and averaged 100 feet above ground; these trees were too tall for a person to climb to examine the contents of nests. Consequently, productivity of fledglings was the only measure of reproductive success obtained.

Surveillance for active nests—those attended by ospreys—was initiated each year in March or April. Active nests discovered after early June were not included in calculations of fledgling productivity. Apparently inactive nests discovered after early June might have been abandoned by ospreys failing to lay or to hatch eggs earlier in the breeding season. Therefore, calculations of fledgling productivity including active nests discovered after early June could be biased to indicate a higher fledgling rate than actually existed. The majority of active nests discovered prior to early June were revisited at biweekly intervals; the expected numbers of fledglings produced could be tallied between mid-July and early August because by then nestlings were large enough to be seen from the ground.

As was learned during previous studies (Koplin, 1978, 1980), nesting territories of ospreys often contain two or more nests, only one of which is used during any one nesting season. Territories containing multiple nests were readily identifiable along streams since nest sites within territories were within 10 to 350 yards of one another, whereas territories were separated from one another by 2 to 10 or more miles. Nest sites where ospreys nested in loose colonies and foraged a common fishing site—the coastal lagoons, Humboldt Bay, and the mouth of Usal Creek—were in close proximity to one another, and identification of territories in these areas was difficult or impossible. No attempt was made to identify territories at Usal Creek where some pairs of ospreys nested within 100 yards of one another.

It was possible to identify a total of 65 nesting territories; 45 contained a single nest per territory and 20 contained 2 to 4 nests per territory and a total of 50 nests. It was impossible to assign the remaining 30 nests, all at Usal Creek, to territories.

Thirty of the 46 territories discovered by 1971 (65 percent) were used and 38 of the 65 territories discovered by 1972 (58 percent) were used. Ospreys at Usal Creek, undiscovered until late in the breeding season of 1971, used 20 or 30 nests (66 percent) found.

We were able to measure fledgling productivity of 63 nesting efforts, 22 in 1971 and 41 in 1972; a total of 64 fledglings was produced (1.0 fledgling per pair). Variation in productivity ranged from a low of 0.5 fledgling per pair of ospreys at Usal Creek in 1972 to a high of 1.7 fledglings per pair along the lower Klamath River in 1971.

Reproductive Status. If ospreys in northwestern California are subjected to mortality patterns similar to those of ospreys in New York and New Jersey, then the average of 1.0 fledgling per nesting pair would suffice to maintain a stable population within the area of study (Henny, 1972; Henny and Wight, 1969; Henny et al., 1970). If the data on fledgling productivity from Usal Creek are excluded, ospreys within the area of study produced an average of 1.2 fledglings per breeding pair, which is indicative of a normally breeding population of ospreys.

Factors Influencing Reproduction. Usal Creek differed from the other areas being studied in one major respect: it was being logged. Samples of surf and night smelt (*Hypomesus pretiosus* and *Spirinchus starksi*), the primary prey of ospreys at Usal Creek, were analyzed for toxic chemicals. The analyses revealed trace levels of residues of DDT and PCBs, comparable to levels of the same chemicals in the Humboldt Bay ecosystem where ospreys reproduced normally in 1971 and 1972. Further indication that logging inhibits reproduction of ospreys was the production of 20 young by 9 pairs of ospreys during 18 breeding efforts (1.1 fledglings per pair) in 1971 and 1972 at Humboldt Bay during years when there was no logging and the production of only 2 young by 5 pairs of ospreys (0.4 fledgling per pair) in 1973 when the area in which ospreys nested at Humboldt Bay was being logged (Ueoka, 1974).

Other factors known to inhibit, or suspected of inhibiting, reproduction of ospreys breeding in northwestern California included weather, predation, and various forms of human disturbance in addition to logging. Availability of suitable nest sites, chemical contaminants, and availability of food resources apparently had no inhibiting influence on reproduction of ospreys.

The heavy forests throughout northwestern California contained a superabundance of trees apparently suitable for nesting sites.

As indicated, chemical analyses of marine biota revealed only trace levels of DDT and PCB residues. Chemical analyses of fish from the Klamath River revealed only trace levels of the same chemicals (Koplin, 1971). Presumably other streams in the area of study also were uncontaminated by chlorinated hydrocarbons because reproductive rates of ospreys on these streams were comparable to reproductive rates of ospreys on the Klamath River.

Gross differences in availability of food resources can influence reproductive rates of ospreys (Koplin et al., 1977). Comparison of information from northwestern California with information from Flathead Lake, Eagle Lake, and Lake Almanor indicate that rates of reproduction of ospreys in northwestern California were not inhibited by limited availability of food resources; that is, approximately 15 percent of the nesting pairs of ospreys in northwestern California, excluding those at Usal Creek for reasons already mentioned, fledged broods of three young; 19 percent of pairs of ospreys breeding at Eagle Lake, a mesotrophic lake, fledged broods of 3 or 4 young, whereas only 10 percent of pairs of ospreys breeding at Flathead Lake and Lake Almanor, both oligotrophic lakes, fledged broods of 3 or 4 young. Furthermore, productivity of fledglings by ospreys in northwestern California, exclusive of Usal Creek, was more comparable to productivity of ospreys breeding at the mesotrophic lake (1.2 fledglings per breeding pair) than of ospreys breeding at the oligotrophic lakes (0.9 fledgling per breeding pair). Even at Usal Creek where reproduction of ospreys apparently was inhibited by disturbance from logging activities, indications were that availability of food resources was not involved. We witnessed ospreys capture two (!) fish, one in each foot, on 3 of 144 dives recorded at Usal Creek, a phenomenon that my colleagues and I have not witnessed in the 2,134 other dives of ospreys we have recorded elsewhere in the West (French, 1972; Ueoka and Koplin, 1973; Ueoka, 1974; Koplin et al, 1977). Also, daily quantities of fish delivered by parents to nests differing in size of brood in northwestern California were more similar to quantities delivered to comparably sized broods in nests at the mesotrophic lake than at the oligotrophic lake (Ueoka, 1974; Koplin et al., 1977).

Nine of 68 nests (13 percent) discovered by early 1972 were destroyed, apparently by storms, during the winters of 1970–1971 and 1971–1972. None of these nests was rebuilt during subsequent spring months, although a new nest was constructed near to one that was lost and nests were used adjacent to three that were lost.

No instances of predation were documented during the study. However, the only known losses of young occurred at Usal Creek where four nestlings, approximately 4 to 5 weeks old, disappeared from two adjacent nests. Although we were unable to determine the cause of these losses, ravens (*Corvus corax*) or crows (*C. brachyrhynchos*) may have preyed upon them. Both ravens and crows were common in the vicinity of osprey nests and were driven away by nesting ospreys on occasion. Crows frequented trees adjacent to some osprey nests to such an extent that we suspected they may have nested nearby. Ravens and crows sometimes were in osprey nests after young fledged at times when the nests were unoccupied during the day.

In addition to logging, the most common forms of human activity potentially inhibiting reproduction of ospreys in northwestern California included vehicular traffic, recreation, and shooting.

Vehicular traffic or highway construction apparently had some detrimental influence on reproduction of ospreys. A nest in a 250-foot redwood was used during and prior to 1972 when the nest was adjacent to U. S. Highway 101. It was not used after 1972 when alteration of the highway included the tree containing the nest in the median strip of the highway.

Sightseeing, camping, fishing, and swimming were the main forms of recreational activity in the area of study; there was no indication that these activities were detrimental to reproduction of ospreys in 1971 or 1972. However, only one chick fledged from 6 nests (0.2 fledgling per pair) in Humboldt Redwoods State Park, a heavily used recreation area on the Eel River, in 1975 (Foreman, 1975); 13 nesting efforts fledged 13 chicks (1.0 fledgling per pair) in the same area in 1971 and 1972 (French, 1972).

The use of firearms was common throughout the area of study. We observed young boys shooting at great blue herons (*Ardea herodias*) on the Klamath River in 1971, and we were informed that a young boy shot an osprey on the Klamath River in 1972. Local residents hunted small game, shot skeet, and target practiced on the south spit of Humboldt Bay during both years of study; gulls, shorebirds, and barn swallows were often killed on the spit. Ospreys commonly perched on elevated structures on the spit to consume prey caught in Humboldt Bay. The perched ospreys offered easy targets, and it is quite probable that they were shot on occasion. Although use of firearms was common elsewhere in the area of study, the height and isolation of most nests afforded a measure of protection from such molestation. In addition, the presence of landowners or loggers were deterrents to most would-be shooters.

Summary

The distribution, abundance, and reproductive status of ospreys breeding in northwestern California were studied between 1970 and 1972. By the end of the study, 125 nests, representing a minimum of 58 breeding ospreys, had been found in Humboldt, Del Norte, northern Mendocino, and western Trinity Counties. The majority of nests (83 percent) were in four localities near the Pacific Coast: east of Humboldt Bay, the lower reaches of the watersheds drained by the Klamath and Eel Rivers, and Usal Creek. Breeding success in terms of fledgling productivity was obtained for 63 nesting efforts during the breeding seasons of 1971 and 1972. A total of 64 fledglings was produced (1.0 fledgling per nesting effort). On the basis of the data obtained, ospreys appeared to be maintaining stable population levels in all localities in the area of study but Usal Creek. Disturbance from logging was the only factor we could identify to explain the observed reproductive inhibition of ospreys in Usal Creek. Weather, predation, shooting, and disturbance from vehicular traffic or highway construction and recreational activities also appeared to inhibit reproduction of ospreys in northwestern California. Availability of nesting sites, chemical contamination and availability of food resources apparently had no inhibiting influence on reproduction of ospreys in northwestern California.

REFERENCES

DeWitt, John W.
   1964.   The fish and fish habitats of the coastal redwood region in Mendocino, Humboldt, and Del Norte Counties in California.   National Park Service Project NPS-WASO-11-64-(4).   Mimeo report, 31 pp.
Foreman, S. A.
   1975.   Breeding success of ospreys in Humboldt Redwoods State Park.   Student report, 12 pp.
French, Jon M.
   1972.   Distribution, abundance and breeding status of ospreys in northwestern California, v +58 pp.   M.S. thesis, Humboldt State University, Arcata, California.
French, Jon M., and Koplin, James R.
   1977.   Distribution, abundance and breeding status of ospreys in northwestern California.   Pp. 221-240 *in* Proceedings of North American Osprey Research Conference. National Park Service Publ.
Henny, Charles J.
   1972.   An analysis of the population dynamics of selected avian species.   U. S. Fish and Wildl. Serv. Wildl. Res. Rpt., no. 1, 99 pp.
Henny, Charles J.; Overton, W. S.; and Wight, Howard M.
   1970.   Determining parameters for populations by using structural models. Journ. Wildl. Man., vol. 34, no. 4, pp. 690-703.
Henny, Charles J., and Wight, Howard M.
   1969.   An endangered osprey population: Estimates of mortality and production.   Auk, vol. 86, no. 2, pp. 188-198.
Koplin, James R.
   1971.   Osprey workshop: Summary of research findings and management recommendations.   Cal-Neva Wildl. Trans. 1971, pp. 114-122.
   1978.   Reproductive performance of ospreys *(Pandion haliaetus)* at Flathead Lake, Montana.   Nat. Geogr. Soc. Res. Rpts., 1969 Projects, pp. 323-332.

KOPLIN, JAMES R.—continued
1980. Reproductive performance of fish-eating birds at Eagle Lake, California. Nat. Geogr. Soc. Res. Rpts., 1971 Projects, pp. 427-443.
KOPLIN, JAMES R.; MACCARTER, DOUGLAS S.; GARBER, DAVID P.; and MACCARTER, DONALD L.
1977. Food resources and fledgling productivity of California and Montana ospreys. Pp. 205-213 *in* Proceedings of North American Osprey Research Conference. Nat. Park Serv. Publ.
MCDANIELS, K., and PHILLIPS, A.
1972. Osprey fishing success at Big, Stone and Freshwater Lagoons. Mimeo report, 11 pp.
SKEESICK, D. G.
1963. A study of some physical-chemical characteristics of Humboldt Bay, 148 pp. M.S. thesis, Humboldt State University, Arcata, California.
UEOKA, M. L.
1974. Feeding behavior of ospreys at Humboldt Bay, California, vi + 76 pp. M.S. thesis, Humboldt State University, Arcata, California.
UEOKA, M. L., and KOPLIN, JAMES R.
1973. Foraging behavior of ospreys in northwestern California. Raptor Res., vol. 7, no. 2, pp. 32-38.
U. S. DEPARTMENT OF COMMERCE, WEATHER BUREAU
1960. Local climatological data, 4 pp. Eureka, California.

JAMES R. KOPLIN

Mexican Indian Pottery

Principal Investigator: Lewis Allen Krevolin, Research Associate, Museum of the American Indian, Heye Foundation, New York, N.Y.

Grant No. 1129:   In support of a study of the reconstruction of Meso American pottery techniques.

Traditional Indian potters in Mexico, working within a technology that developed in this hemisphere around 3000 B.C., are today producing the same kinds of wares, for the same purposes, as their ancestors did. Often of mixed ancestry, or mestizo, traditional potters still live and work in isolated communities in which the fabric of their lives indicates a relationship to the Indian cultures that existed prior to contact with Europeans. Beliefs based on ancient mythologies still permeate Indian life and dominate pottery production as well.

The field study that was carried out in central, western, and southern Mexico was designed to bring me in contact with traditional potters so that I could observe and document the actual production cycle—clay preparation, forming, decorating, and firing methods. Approximately, 3,000 photographs were taken. Tools used by potters as well as finished work were collected to enhance the value of the photographic documentation and create a unique combination of study material.

The combined collection of tools, pottery, and photographs provide a more incisive comparison between archeological and modern regional production and forms. This combination of methods provides the basis for reconstruction of pre-contact pottery technology.

Historically, potters generally have lived in separate villages situated near good sources of clay and fuel. If potters live in larger, mixed communities today they are likely to live in a separate *barrio,* or neighborhood.

The traditional potter is usually a woman, although where it is customary for men to make pottery the women generally do not. Working in a technique handed down to her by a female member of her family, the potter is not an artist but a craftswoman making wares in a prescribed manner for a traditional use. The forms she makes were invented hundreds, perhaps thousands, of years ago. She may be one of several women in the village who, working independently of one another, produce exactly the same forms. She is the prime producer of pottery, along with other female members of her family. Her husband will often help in obtaining clay and fuel, and with the firing; since she is not likely to speak Spanish, he will also market the finished ware for her.

The potter's work cycle usually lasts from 7 to 14 days. Production is directly related to the specified market days of the area, with the firing taking place the day before the wares are to be taken to market. Much of the potter's work is done outdoors, in open spaces or under trees or lean-tos, as part of the regular household activities. Consequently, production is limited during the rainy season.

Just as the pattern of Indian life has evolved slowly over the centuries, so have traditional clay pottery forms evolved in the same manner. A containing vessel is not an expression of the potter's esthetic sense, but a utilitarian item that will be judged in the marketplace for its technical quality and the familiarity of its form and finish. The function it serves will have changed little over the generations.

Along with techniques of construction, method, and prescribed day of firing, the potter inherits a folk "patent" on style, shape, and size. Particular families, *barrios,* and villages seem to specialize in distinctive wares. Difference in color, size, and function must have originally stemmed from the inherent properties of local clays and local firing techniques. The time-honored specialization is maintained by custom. Size, shape, color, and decoration are all parts of the recipe given the potter during her apprenticeship. She may make subtle changes of her own, but for all intents and purposes her ware will be exactly as prescribed by her mentor.

Potters continue to work with the same tools their ancestors used—an array of stone, wood, reed, and calabash implements. Tools made from pieces of gourd, shells, and fired clay are generally referred to as potter's ribs and scrapers. Corncobs are used as rollers and smoothers, and scraps of leather, fabric, and plastic are used to smooth rims, handles, and legs. Each potter has her own bowl of favorite implements—a scrap of metal, a special pebble, an odd reed or stick for special tasks, and so on. The adoption of a new tool or material does not necessarily alter the technique. Nylon fishing line, for example, is now used for trimming instead of yucca fiber, but the function of the tool has not changed.

The potter's wheel did not exist in pre-contact America, and is still not used by traditional potters, though Indian potters did invent many types of turning devices and techniques to help them produce symmetrical forms. Traditional pieces are formed by hand using various coil, slab, pinching, or molding techniques.

Molds made of clay are widely used. "Tortillas" of clay are formed between the hands, on flat stones or on wooden boards. These sheets of clay are

FIG. 1.   Corncobs were used as rollers in forming this pot, Tlapazula, Oaxaca.

then draped over or into the molds. Sections of pots made in this way are then assembled, handles are added, necks and spouts formed, and feet attached.

Many vessels, particularly larger pieces, are made freehand. Ropes or coils of clay are wound around the perimeter of a volume and then worked together to create a pot. Or the potter may take a ball of clay, make a hole in it, and then pinch or squeeze the clay up or out to form a containing vessel. This pinch technique is often combined with coil building. Numerous combinations and variations of both freehand and molding techniques are possible.

The use of the bottle gourd as a container predates the invention of pottery in this hemisphere and is basic to the development of traditional clay forms. (In some cases the bottle gourd is still used for water storage and cooking.) Ultimate usage and handling partly determine the shape of the finished vessel, together with a subtle combination of qualities inherent in the clay. Its workability, strength, color, and texture are not related to the function of the finished pot.

Much of the traditional ware made today is undecorated. Those pieces which are more elaborately constructed and decorated often have a ceremonial or decorative use.

Many different decorating techniques are used. Frequently clay legs or handles, many with zoomorphic or human forms, are built into pots. Clay stamps resembling butter molds are pressed into a wad of clay and attached to a vessel to create a raised repeat pattern. Found objects such as screws, nuts, or twigs may be pressed into the damp pot to produce repeated linear or geometric patterns.

Linear patterns can be cut into a vessel with a sharpened needlelike instrument when the clay is wet. Scratching into the surface is also done after the pot has been fired. Known as post-fire incising, this ancient technique works best if slip of a different color is applied to the surface of the pot so that the incised pattern will be of a contrasting color. Piercing is a decorative device which grew from a functional requirement for pots in which corn was soaked before it could be ground. Patterns are often cut into the surface of a mold in which pots are formed. Pots that have been fired are often decorated with nonceramic paints applied with reeds, feathers, or brushes made of animal hair.

Accidental byproducts of the firing can also be decorative elements. Fire clouds, caused by the burning of fuel in direct contact with the pot during firing, often take on imaginary shapes and enhance the appearance of the pot. Simple variations of color occurring on an unevenly fired pot can enliven the surface. For the most part these flash marks can be controlled or eliminated by careful stacking of fuel and vessels in the fire. Some potters seem to avoid them, others accept them, while still others appear to like the effect.

Burnishing, or rubbing a pot before it is fired to create a patina, was perfected rather early in history. It probably began as a way of strengthening the surface of the clay. The compacting of the surface particles of clay prevents dusting and makes the pot more waterproof. The results are not only practical

FIG. 2.   Revolving a clay form on a *molde,* Coyotepec, Oaxaca.

but beautiful, for a burnished piece can take on the glow of glazed ware if carefully polished. Burnishing is time-consuming, however, and only minimal effort is expended on most common pottery.

Contemporary Indian potters use the bowl of a spoon, a piece of glass, or a highly polished stone. Some of these stones have been used by a family for generations and take on a gemlike quality. In some areas of Mexico, *brunito,* or polishing, is accomplished by the use of a lump of ore—usually iron. In Tzinizunizan, the ore is attached to a wooden handle to create a pummel-like tool called a *brunedore.* In Coyotepec, the carbon core of a battery is used, thereby not only burnishing but also heightening the color of the pot.

A traditional container is unglazed (its surface is burnished instead). Fired at low temperatures (600° to 800° F.) for short periods of time, the ware is sintered, not vitrified. The clay is heated to the point at which it is stabilized (will not disintegrate in water) but not fused. This is because the ware is to be used over an open fire and must remain elastic in order to respond to the rapid expansion and contraction caused by an open flame. If the clay were vitrified or fused at higher temperatures, it would crack upon contact with the flame.

The burnished, sintered wares are made of local common clays containing various quantities of iron oxides. The amount of metal oxides occurring naturally in the clay, together with the firing technique, determines the color of the finished pot. The same clay vessel could come out red if fired in an oxidizing fire, black in a reduction fire.

For all practical purposes, Indian potters do not use permanent kilns as we have come to know them. The kiln is created when the ware and the fuel are stacked for the fire. (This may be why archeologists have not found any precontact kilns or at least have been unable to identify them positively).

The first step in the traditional firing process is the proper drying of the ware. Often the prefire takes a much longer time than the firing itself. The finished pots are allowed to dry slowly, usually somewhat protected from direct sun or wind. The length of time varies with weather conditions and time of year. When they are completely dry, the pots may be fired in one of several ways: in an open fire on the ground, in pits of varying depth and configuration, or in an open kiln using some form of raised hearth surrounded by a low wall of rock or adobe brick.

Firing is done the day before market day, with everyone in the village firing at the same time. On market day the finished wares are transported by donkey, wagon, backpack, or on top of buses—or any combination of the above, depending on the distance between potter and market. The potter rarely brings her wares to market herself. Instead, a male relative does this for her, or the pots may be sold to a pottery merchant at the marketplace. In some cases, middlemen have arrangements with potters in the area to buy all their productions and bring them to market themselves. In some larger towns, such as Patzcuaro, a special pottery market is held on Fridays which draws potters and buyers from the region.

After her wares are marketed, the potter begins her production cycle all over again, continuing an ancient technology which, despite its simplicity, has produced some of the master works of the potter's craft.

Results produced by my fieldwork in Mexico have been published by Crafts Horizon, in October 1976. The National Endowment for the Humanities funded the exhibition "Traditional Pottery of Mexico" held at the Museum of the American Indian, Heye Foundation, New York. The exhibition showed approximately 200 pieces of pottery and pottery-making tools collected in Mexico. Approximately 200 photographs explain the modern technology and help delineate the archeological specimens in the museum's collection.

The complete collection of pottery, pottery-making tools, and all documentations were given to the Museum of the American Indian as a study collection to be made available to scholars as well as the general public.

Work is presently under way in the preparation of a book, *Indian Pottery Technology of Mexico*.

Acknowledgments

A vital part of any field survey is the photographic record. At the suggestion of Dr. Frederick Dockstader, director of the Museum of the American Indian, Heye Foundation, the museum photographer, Carmelo Guadagno, met me in Mexico and accompanied me on most of the field trip, recording photographically almost everything we observed while I made notes and watched the potters working. The quality of the photographic record is a testament to Mr. Guadagno's skilled interest and pride in his work. I am indebted also to Dr. Frederic Dockstader and Dr. David Grove for their wholehearted support and interest in my work.

I acknowledge with gratitude the grant given me by the National Geographic Society in supplementary support of this research survey.

REFERENCES

DOCKSTADER, FREDERICK, and KREVOLIN, LEWIS
 1972.   Naked clay. 3000 years of unadorned pottery of the American Indian, 76
        pp.   Museum of the American Indian, Heye Foundation, New York,
        N.Y.
KREVOLIN, LEWIS
 1976.   Traditional pottery of Mexico. A technological continuum. 30 pp.,
        illus.   Museum of the American Indian, Heye Foundation, New York,
        N.Y.
 1972.   4000 years of American Indian Pottery.   Craft Horizon, vol. 32, no. 5,
        10 pp.
 1976.   Indian Pottery of Mexico.   Craft Horizon, vol. 36, no. 3, 12 pp.
KREVOLIN, LEWIS, and CONSTANTIVE, ELIZABETH
 1967.   Ceramics. 48 pp. illus.   Pittman Publishing Corp., N.Y.

LEWIS ALLEN KREVOLIN

Late Cenozoic Basaltic Volcanism Along the Jemez Zone, Arizona and New Mexico

Principal Investigator: A. William Laughlin, University of California Los Alamos Scientific Laboratory, Los Alamos, New Mexico.

Grant Nos. 1077, 1210.   To study the origin of ultramafic inclusions and their relationship to basalt genesis.

Basaltic volcanism has been a common occurrence along the Jemez zone between Grants, New Mexico, and Show Low, Arizona. These eruptions, which ranged from Pliocene to Holocene in age, produced both large fissure flows and more isolated cinder cones. The research described in this report had three major objectives: (1) to determine the spatial and temporal distribution of this volcanism and the petrographic and chemical nature of the resulting products, (2) to determine the magnitude of chemical and strontium isotopic variations in individual basalt flows within this area, and (3) to further characterize the nature of ultramafic inclusions from the Bandera Crater site.

Geologic Setting

The Jemez zone is a linear belt of young volcanic centers extending from northeastern New Mexico-southeastern Colorado through the Jemez Mountains, Mount Taylor, the Bandera lava field, the Zuni volcanic centers, the Springerville-St. Johns-Show Low volcanic field, and the volcanic field near Globe, Arizona, to the Pinacates region of Sonora, Mexico.

As originally defined by Mayo (1958), this zone or lineament transects five physiographic provinces: the Great Plains, southern Rocky Mountains, the Rio Grande Rift, the Colorado Plateau, and the Basin and Range Provinces. This report will discuss a short section of the zone lying within the Colorado Plateau Province and extending from Grants, New Mexico, to Show Low, Arizona.

Most of the eruptions occurred within the broad valleys and on the plains typical of this portion of the Plateau. Three volcanic centers, however, developed within the central portion of the Zuni uplift. In general the fissure eruptions were earlier, forming large flows upon which cinder cones were later developed.

353

Prior Work

Relatively little work had been done on the basaltic rocks of this area before the present research was initiated. Nichols (1946) studied the morphology of the McCartys basalt, one of the youngest flows in the Bandera field, and related it to flow mechanisms operating during extrusion. In another structural study, Hatheway and Herring (1970) examined the long lava tubes in the basalt flows, considering them possible analogs of lunar rilles. Renault (1968, 1970) and Laughlin et al. (1972b) discussed the chemistry of some of the basalts from the Bandera field, recognizing that both alkalic and tholeiitic basalts were erupted from adjacent vents within a short period of time. Laughlin et al. (1971) described a new ultramafic inclusion locality at Bandera Crater and reported the results of chemical and strontium isotopic analyses of the inclusions and host basalt. They concluded that the inclusions were accidental in the basalt and were mantle derived.

Two recent papers (Baker and Ridley, 1970, and Lipman and Moench, 1972) have described the volcanic rocks of the Mount Taylor field at the northeast end of the segment of the Jemez zone discussed herein. Baker and Ridley (1970) concluded that the basalts at Mount Taylor were mantle derived and that the rhyolites were formed by partial melting of the granitic basement. Lipman and Moench (1972) subdivided the basalts into four sequences, beginning with nepheline normative alkalic basalts, followed by two sequences of silicic alkalic basalts and finally by olivine tholeiites.

At the far southwest end of the area discussed here, almost no work has been done on the basalts of the Springerville-St. Johns-Show Low area. As part of a hydrologic study, Akers (1964) mapped this area, subdividing the basalts into several stratigraphic groups. No petrographic or chemical work was done on these basalts however. Leeman (1970) reported the results of an $^{87}Sr/^{86}Sr$ determination on one basalt sample from this area.

A general paper by Kudo et al. (1971) on the origin of basalts in New Mexico included data on several basalts from this area. They suggested that although the tholeiitic basalts originated in the mantle, they were contaminated by crustal material prior to eruption.

Analytical Methods

The work described here consisted of field and laboratory studies by the principal investigator, three academic collaborators (D. G. Brookins, P. E. Damon, and R. A. Heimlich) and four graduate students from Kent State University (John R. Carden, Francis Dellechaie, Gerald L. Gallagher, and

Mark Gawell). Samples were collected during two field trips funded by the National Geographic Society, and laboratory investigations were done during the following academic years at Kent State University, the University of New Mexico, and the University of Arizona. A portion of the work was completed after the principal investigator moved to the Los Alamos Scientific Laboratory.

Because of the objectives of these investigations, the methods of sample collection were crucial. In the studies of the McCartys flow (Carden) and the Paxton Springs and Cerro Colorado flows (Dellechaie) fresh samples were collected along the length of the flows. Where possible, samples were also collected from vertical sections through the flows. Gawell's samples, from the alignment of cinder cones, were taken from several stratigraphic horizons in each cone.

A detailed petrographic analysis was performed on all samples collected, and selected samples were prepared for chemical analysis. Analysis was by atomic absorption spectrophotometry after lithium metaborate fusion. Accuracy was monitored by the analysis of U. S. Geological Survey standard rock samples. Whole rock Rb-Sr and Sr isotopic analyses were performed by Brookins at the University of New Mexico. Damon performed K-Ar analyses on several samples to obtain radiometric ages.

Results

For the sake of brevity detailed analytical results will not be reported here, but references to the pertinent publications or theses will be cited.

Nature of Basaltic Volcanism. Basaltic volcanism along the central portion of the Jemez zone can be assigned roughly to three volcanic fields. From northeast to southwest these are the Bandera lava field, Zuni volcanic centers, and the Springerville-St. Johns-Show Low volcanic field. Much of our work has been concentrated in the Bandera field with lesser amounts in the other two areas.

The term Bandera lava field refers to the area of Holocene basalt flows described by Hatheway and Herring (1970) and Laughlin et al. (1972b), which in the main lies south and southeast of the Zuni Mountains. The field includes the major Bandera, McCartys, and Laguna flows and a number of smaller flows and associated vents. Three small volcanic centers within the Zuni Mountains and the Bluewater flow north of the Zunis are also included within this field.

The Zuni centers (Kelley and Clinton, 1968) are a somewhat older group of flows and cones southwest of the Bandera lava field and extending almost to the Arizona border. Volcanism within this field is all basaltic and some of the flows traveled a considerable distance.

The Springerville-St. Johns-Show Low field, as the name implies, is roughly encompassed by these three towns in Arizona. Eroded cinder cones sit upon a series of flows that apparently were erupted over a considerable span of time.

Although only basaltic volcanism has been recognized from this portion of the Jemez zone, the basalts have a wide compositional range (44.5 to 53 percent SiO_2). Nepheline normative basalts with SiO_2 contents as low as 44.5 percent erupted from the Bandera, Paxton Springs, and Cerro Colorado craters (Laughlin et al., 1971, 1972b; Dellechaie, 1973). Southwest of Bandera Crater, nepheline normative basaltic cinders make up some of the cones along a fracture paralleling the Jemez zone (Gawell, 1974; Gawell and Laughlin, 1975). Although only limited work has been done in the Springerville-St. Johns-Show Low field, nepheline normative basalts have also been recognized there.

More silicic basalts with SiO_2 contents of up to about 53 percent are also common throughout the region. These basalts lie within the tholeiite field on a McDonald-Katsura plot and may be either quartz or olivine normative (Carden, 1972; Gawell, 1974). In general the tholeiitic basalts are present as large fissure flows whose vents are obscured by later volcanic activity. In New Mexico, these large tholeiitic flows include the McCartys, Laguna, and Bluewater flows within the Bandera field and the Fence Lake flow from the Zuni centers. Gawell and Laughlin (1975) reported the presence of tholeiitic basalts in the cinder cone alignment southwest of Bandera Crater. To the southwest, in Arizona, the somewhat older, large basalt flows are also apparently tholeiitic in composition.

Although large differences occur in the chemical compositions of the basalts, these differences are not strongly reflected in the petrography. Both the alkalic and tholeiitic basalts are usually porphyritic with phenocrysts of olivine, plagioclase, and minor clinopyroxene (Carden, 1972; Dellechaie, 1973; Gawell, 1974). Phenocrysts commonly make up about 15 to 35 percent of the rock. The relative proportions of olivine and plagioclase in the phenocrysts varies considerably, olivine being more abundant in the alkali basalts. Plagioclase, olivine, clinopyroxene, opaques, and tachylite comprise the groundmass. Very minor apatite may be present as inclusions in the plagioclase. Secondary minerals such as calcite and limonite are present as vesicle fillings. Small xenoliths and xenocrysts of quartz are often observed in abundances of up to 0.4 percent of the rock.

Where determined, olivine compositions are remarkably constant, Fo_{85-86} with no zoning. Grains range from fresh to highly altered; the alteration consists primarily of iddingsite and hematite.

In many of the samples examined, two generations of plagioclase were present within the phenocryst population. For example, in the McCartys basalt (Carden, 1972) strongly zoned crystals with compositions averaging An_{85} are relatively rare, while moderately zoned phenocrysts having compositions ranging from An_{50} to An_{62} are more abundant. In the same rocks groundmass plagioclase is even less calcic, An_{45}.

Few optical determinations of clinopyroxene composition were made because of the small size and low abundance of this mineral. The few measurements made suggest it is calcic augite.

Our work indicates that chemical analysis is necessary to distinguish between the alkalic and tholeiitic basalts, which may occur in close proximity. No distinguishing spatial distribution of basalt type was observed.

Age of Volcanism.   In collaboration with P. E. Damon of the University of Arizona, six new K-Ar dates were obtained on basalt samples from this area. A date of 0.188 ± 0.042 million years was obtained on a widespread alkali basalt flow from the Bandera lava field. Based on geomorphological evidence this flow, which was sampled about one kilometer west of Bandera Crater, is one of the oldest flows in the field. It apparently formed a surface on which Bandera Crater and the other cinder cones developed.

West of Bandera Crater, near Zuni Pueblo, an olivine tholeiite caps an east-west trending ridge. An age of 0.68 ± 0.55 million years was obtained on this flow. The source for this flow cannot be demonstrated but it is presumed to have been among the Zuni Centers. The Fence Lake flow, which is compositionally similar to the flow at Zuni Pueblo, also had its source within the Zuni centers. It is probably the largest single exposed flow within the area, covering approximately 600 square kilometers. It was dated at 1.38 ± 0.29 million years. Because of the large error, the age of the Zuni Pueblo flow cannot be distinguished from that of the Fence Lake flow.

Three basalts from the Springerville-St. Johns-Show Low field were also dated. Two of these were exposed in a road cut on U. S. 60 a few kilometers east of Springerville. At this locality three flows are exposed with river gravels and sands separating the lowermost flow from the middle flow. The uppermost flow lies directly on top of the middle flow with no intervening sediments. The lower and middle flows were dated at 2.86 ± 0.14 and 0.801 ± 0.040 million years, respectively. Despite the age difference the two flows are compositionally identical, both being olivine tholeiites. A low silica alkali basalt which forms cliffs along a small tributary of the Little Colorado River just west of Springerville was dated at 2.98 ± 0.08 million years.

Although there are many exceptions, in general the more widespread, older basalts are tholeiitic and the younger cinder cones are alkalic.

Chemical and Isotopic Variability within a Single Basalt Flow. In the past, single samples have often been used to characterize the chemical and strontium isotopic compositions of large basalt flows. The data obtained from these samples have, in turn, been used to draw sweeping conclusions on conditions in the mantle where the basalts originated. It is clear that large scale intraflow variability of chemical or strontium isotopic composition could seriously affect these conclusions.

Chemical variability was examined in three basalt flows from the Bandera lava field (Carden, 1972; Dellechaie, 1973; Carden and Laughlin, 1974) and strontium variability was examined in one flow (Laughlin et al., 1972a; Brookins et al., 1975). In the initial study of McCartys flow, 37 samples were taken along the approximately 50 kilometers length of the flow; some from vertical sections through the flow. Petrographic and chemical analyses indicated that significant modal mineralogic and chemical variations exist laterally, but not vertically within the flow (Carden and Laughlin, 1974). Mineralogically, the flow shows an increase in modal olivine and a decrease in modal plagioclase away from the vent. The major element oxides, Fe_2O_3 and MgO, increase with distance from the vent, as do the trace elements, Cr and Zn. Decreases in SiO_2, Al_2O_3, CaO, Cu, and Sr occur over this same interval. Although these changes are not extremely large, they are sufficient to change the nomenclature of the basalt from a quartz tholeiite at the vent to an olivine tholeiite at the distal end.

The ratio $^{87}Sr/^{86}Sr$ is widely used as a criterion for distinguishing between mantle and crustal origins for volcanic rocks and as a measure of the degree of contamination by surficial crustal rocks. In order to apply this criterion, however, isotopic homogeneity within a flow must be either assumed or demonstrated. This assumption has always been made with no testing of its validity.

Earlier work by Leeman (1970) and Laughlin et al. (1972a) gave conflicting values for $^{87}Sr/^{86}Sr$ ratios from different single samples from McCartys flow. Leeman (1970) reported a value of 0.7062 for this ratio, and Laughlin et al. (1972a) reported 0.7040 for a different sample from the flow. Because of the large differences in these values, vastly different interpretations could be made of the place of origin or the degree of crustal contamination of the McCartys flow.

To examine further the $^{87}Sr/^{86}Sr$ variations within this flow, 13 additional samples of the basalt and 2 of the underlying soil (Brookins et al., 1975) were analyzed. The 15 basalt samples exhibited a range of $^{87}Sr/^{86}Sr$ ratios from 0.7037 to 0.7081 confirming the extreme Sr isotopic variability of this flow. The two soil samples from beneath the flow had $^{87}Sr/^{86}Sr$ ratios of 0.7155 and 0.7226. There were no correlations between the $^{87}Sr/^{86}Sr$ ratios of the basalt and either distance from the vent or major-element composition of the samples. A positive correlation between the ratio and the total Sr composition and the high ratios in the underlying soil suggested a very heterogeneous contamination of the basalt by the soil over which the lava flowed. Because of the rarity of observed xenocrysts and xenoliths, this could not be confirmed by petrographic examination.

Dellechaie (1973) examined lateral chemical variations within four flows of alkali basalt, two each from the Paxton Springs and Cerro Colorado volcanic centers. Flows from these centers were sampled on an approximately 800-meter grid, supplemented by samples which we thought to represent late-stage differentiates.

Petrographically, the flows from the Paxton Springs and Cerro Colorado centers are similar to each other and to other flows from the Bandera lava field (Laughlin et al., 1972b; Carden and Laughlin, 1974). They are hypocrystalline, porphyritic basalts with phenocrysts of olivine, plagioclase, and clinopyroxene. Olivine phenocrysts are subhedral to euhedral and generally less than 0.5 millimeter in diameter. Lateral compositional variations in olivine composition were not observed and the composition averaged Fo_{85}. Plagioclase phenocrysts were generally smaller than those of olivine, although some plagioclase crystals reached 0.6 millimeter in length in the Cerro Colorado flows. Compositionally, the plagioclase varied from An^{49} to An^{59} with, again, no apparent lateral variation in composition. Clinopyroxene phenocrysts were also small (usually less than 0.3 millimeter) and compositionally were calcic augites. The groundmass included olivine, plagioclase, clinopyroxene, opaques, and tachylite. Sandstone xenoliths were rare in all flows.

Field and petrographic examination indicated that two flows were erupted from each center. At the Paxton Springs center, one flow moved south from the vent and the other flowed to the north. The two flows had a combined length of about 11 kilometers; the maximum width was 1.6 kilometers. The two flows from the Cerro Colorado center moved north, east, and south through several canyons. Basalt flowing down Zuni Canyon eventually ponded just south of the present site of the town of Grants, New Mexico. The two Cerro Colorado flows lie in superposition in Bonita and upper Zuni Canyons.

Whole rock chemical analyses were performed on 49 samples of the four flows; 10 from the southern Paxton Springs flow, 14 from the northern, and 25 from the Cerro Colorado flows. Results of these analyses are reported by

Dellechaie (1973). The southern Paxton Springs was found to be chemically homogeneous with no significant lateral variation. Small chemical variations were observed in the northern Paxton Springs flow but they were not systematic with distance from the vent. In addition, no systematic variation was noted between minor oxide contents and the abundances of the major oxides SiO_2 or MgO. No significant lateral chemical variations were observed within the Cerro Colorado flows.

Chemical Variations in a Cinder Cone Alignment.   After chemical variability was examined in the three single flows, a similar study was initiated on seven cinder cones that apparently were erupted along a single fracture (Gawell, 1975). These cones extend for approximately 22 kilometers along a northeast trending line on the west side of the Bandera field, paralleling the trend of the Jemez zone. Field evidence such as depth of weathering and amount of topographic relief indicates that the cones decrease in age from southwest to northeast.

Forty-five samples collected from the major cones and several smaller subsidiary cones were subjected to petrographic and chemical analysis (Gawell, 1975; Gawell and Laughlin, 1975). Petrographically there is little difference in the basalts from the several cones. In general, they are hypocrystalline and porphyritic; subophitic textures are developed locally. Phenocrysts of olivine, plagioclase, and sparse clinopyroxene occur within a groundmass of the same minerals plus tachylite and opaques. Modal variations along the alignment were small and probably not significant. A decrease in olivine phenocryst abundance was observed from southwest to northeast (Gawell, 1975) but the range in abundances from a single cone was so large that little confidence can be placed in the trend.

The most significant chemical variation along the length of the cinder cone alignment was exhibited by the SiO_2 content. This oxide varied from 45.3 to 52.8 percent, generally increasing toward the northeast. The oxides K_2O and TiO_2, showed well-defined decreases to the northeast as the SiO_2 content increased. The variation in MgO content along the alignment was less well pronounced but a slight decrease to the northeast was apparent.

Petrography of Ultramafic Inclusion from Bandera Crater.   Laughlin et al. (1971) recognized two broad types of ultramafic inclusions in cores of volcanic bombs from Bandera Crater. One was characterized by high percentages of olivine in the mode and accessory red (Cr-rich) spinel. The second was pyroxene-rich with green (Mg-rich) spinel as an accessory mineral. These were referred to as red and green spinel lherzolites, respectively, although other ultramafic rock types were present in each suite.

Gallagher (1973) reexamined the two suites of inclusions; petrographic analyses were completed on 14 red-spinel lherzolites, 15 green-spinel lherzolites, 1 layered inclusion (one layer each of red- and green-spinel lherzolite), and 3 gabbro inclusions. Partial chemical analyses were obtained on one sample each from both the red- and green-spinel lherzolite suites.

The red-spinel lherzolite suite was relatively restricted in modal composition. Olivine was the most abundant mineral in all samples; ranging from 48 to 85 percent olivine. Second in abundance was orthopyroxene with a range of 9-43 percent. Clinopyroxene contents ranged from 2 to 9 percent. Red spinel and rarely phlogopite were present as accessory minerals. The red-spinel bearing inclusions were all characterized by morar textures with large, broken porphyroclasts of pyroxene set in an aggregate of recrystallized olivine grains.

Olivine from the red-spinel inclusions had a very small compositional range (Fo_{89-92}) as determned from the N_y refractive index. No zoning was evident and the crystals were free from inclusions. The orthopyroxene was usually buff-colored and xenoblastic or subidioblastic in habit. Compositionally the orthopyroxene ranged from En_{86} to En_{89} as determined by the measurement of the 2V angle. Exsolution of clinopyroxene parallel to (100) was common. Reaction rims, up to 0.2 millimeter in thickness and consisting of minute olivine crystals in brownish glass, were developed between the clinopyroxene and the basalt surrounding the inclusion.

Optical data obtained from the clinopyroxene indicated that it is diopside. Minor exsolution of orthopyroxene was observed in some clinopyroxene grains and inclusions of olivine and red spinel are common. Although alteration of clinopyroxene is rare, when it does occur, the products include minute xenoblastic grains of red spinel.

The green-spinel bearing suite have xenomorphic-granular or hypidiomorphic-granular textures and exhibit little evidence of stress in the solid-state. Textures are relatively open when compared to the mosaic textures of red-spinel-bearing inclusions. Variations in modal composition are much larger than in the red-spinel suite and only the Ol corner of the Ol-Opx-Cpx triangle is not represented by samples. In addition to the olivine, orthopyroxene, and clinopyroxene, spinel, phlogopite, kaersutite, and opaques are present as accessory minerals. Minor glass formed as a reaction product may be present.

Olivine compositions were obtained on five samples; Fo contents range from 80 to 85 percent. Orthopyroxene compositions, as determined from the 2V angle, range from En_{76} to En_{86}. The clinopyroxene was identified optically as diopside.

A single-layered inclusion was collected at the Bandera Crater site. This sample is almost a perfect rhombohedron consisting of a 3-centimeter-thick red-spinel-bearing layer and a 1-centimeter-thick green-spinel-bearing layer. Each layer is mineralogically and texturally similar to samples of the respective suite—except that in the green-spinel-bearing layer, all pyroxene is intensely altered. This layer also contains more accessory green spinel than do most other samples.

The three gabbroic inclusions were made up of varying proportions of plagioclase, orthopyroxene and clinopyroxene. Two of the samples had hypidiomorphic-granular textures and no observable alteration of any of the minerals. Modally, these samples contained plagioclase, 30 percent; orthopyroxene, 30 percent; and clinopyroxene, 40 percent. The third sample had an xenomorphic-granular texture and showed massive alteration of the pyroxenes. The altered gabbro contains 15 percent each of plagioclase and orthopyroxene and 70 percent clinopyroxene.

Chemical analyses were performed on one sample from each of the two spinel-bearing suites. Notable differences in the Al_2O_3, MgO, CaO, Na_2O, and K_2O contents were observed. The red-spinel-bearing inclusion was enriched in MgO and depleted in Al_2O_3, CaO, Na_2O, and K_2O relative to the green-spinel-bearing inclusion.

Texture, mineral chemistry, and whole-rock chemistry suggest that the red-spinel-bearing inclusions are xenoliths of depleted mantle material and that the green-spinel-bearing inclusions have a cumulate origin from a basaltic magma. The limited number of gabbroic inclusions hinders determination of their origin. They could be either xenoliths incorporated by the basalt or cumulates from the basalt.

Conclusions

Based on the results obtained in these investigations, the following major conclusions may be derived:
- Both alkalic and tholeiitic basaltic volcanism was common along the central portion of the Jemez zone.
- No temporal or spatial distribution patterns exist for the two basalt types.
- Volcanism has been active along the central portion of the Jemez zone from 3 million years B.P. until essentially the present. No migration of volcanism is apparent.
- Extreme strontium isotopic heterogeneity exists within the McCartys basalt associated with minor chemical variability. Extreme care should

be taken in extrapolating isotopic or chemical data from one sample to an entire flow.

- Two different types of ultramafic inclusions are present at the Bandera Crater site. These probably represent both accidental xenoliths and cognate inclusions in the basalt.

REFERENCES

AKERS, J. P.
 1964.   Geology and ground water in the central part of Apache County, Ariz. U. S. Geol. Surv. Water-Supply Paper 1771, 107 pp.
BAKER, I., and RIDLEY, W. D.
 1970.   Field evidence and K, Rb, Sr data bearing on the origin of the Mt. Taylor volcanic field, New Mexico, U.S.A.   Earth and Planetary Sci. Lett., vol. 10, pp. 106-114.
BROOKINS, DOUGLAS G.; CARDEN, JOHN R.; and LAUGHLIN, A. WILLIAM
 1975.   Additional note on the isotopic composition of strontium in McCartys flow, Valencia County, New Mexico.   Earth and Planetary Sci. Lett., vol. 25, pp. 327-330.
CARDEN, JOHN R.
 1972.   Chemical and petrographic variations in McCartys basalt flow, Valencia County, New Mexico, 77 pp.   M.S. dissertation, Kent State University. (Unpublished.)
CARDEN, JOHN R., and LAUGHLIN, A. WILLIAM
 1974.   Petrochemical variations within the McCartys basalt flow, Valencia County, New Mexico.   Bull. Geol. Soc. Amer., vol. 85, pp. 1479-1484.
DELLECHAIE, FRANCIS
 1973.   Chemical and petrographic variations in the Cerro Colorado and Paxton Springs basalt flows, Valencia County, New Mexico, 54 pp.   M.S. dissertation, Kent State University. (Unpublished.)
GALLAGHER, GERALD L.
 1973.   The petrography of ultramafic inclusions from Bandera Crater, New Mexico, 49 pp.   M.S. dissertation, Kent State University. (Unpublished.)
GAWELL, MARK J.
 1974.   Chemical and petrographic variations in the Cerro Negro-Cerrito Arizona cinder cone chain, Valencia County, New Mexico, 57 pp.   M.S. dissertation, Kent State University. (Unpublished.)
GAWELL, MARK J., and LAUGHLIN, A. WILLIAM
 1975.   Chemical and petrographic variations in the Cerro Negro-Cerrito Arizona cinder cone lineation, Valencia County, New Mexico.   Geol. Soc. Amer. Abstr. with Programs, vol. 7, p. 1084.
HATHEWAY, A. W., and HERRING, A. K.
 1970.   Bandera lava tubes of New Mexico and lunar implications.   Univ. Arizona Tucson Commun. Lunar and Planetary Lab., vol. 8, no. 152, pp. 299-327.

KELLEY, VINCENT C., and CLINTON, N. J.
1960.   Fracture systems and tectonic elements of the Colorado Plateau.   Univ.
New Mexico Publ. Geol., no. 6, 104 pp.
KUDO, ALBERT M.; AOKI, K.; and BROOKINS, DOUGLAS G.
1971.   The origin of Pliocene-Holocene basalts of New Mexico in the light of Sr
isotopic and major element abundances.   Earth and Planetary Sci.
Lett., vol. 13, pp. 200-204.
LAUGHLIN, A. W.; BROOKINS, D. G.; and CARDEN, J. R.
1972a.   Variations in the initial strontium ratios of a single basalt flow.   Earth
and Planetary Sci. Lett., vol. 14, pp. 79-82.
LAUGHLIN, A. WILLIAM; BROOKINS, DOUGLAS G.; and CAUSEY, J. D.
1972b.   Late Cenozoic basalts from the Bandera lava field, Valencia County,
New Mexico.   Bull. Geol. Soc. Amer., vol. 83, pp. 1543-1552.
LAUGHLIN, A. WILLIAM; BROOKINS, DOUGLAS G.; KUDO, ALBERT M.; and
CAUSEY, J. D.
1971.   Chemical and strontium isotopic investigations of ultramafic inclusions
and basalt, Bandera Crater, New Mexico.   Geochim. et Cosmochim.
Acta, vol. 35, pp. 107-113.
LEEMAN, W. P.
1970.   The isotopic composition of strontium in late-Cenozoic basalts from the
Basin-Range province, Western United States.   Geochim. et Cosmo-
chim. Acta, vol. 34, pp. 857-872.
LIPMAN, PETER W., and MOENCH, ROBERT H.
1972.   Basalts of the Mt. Taylor volcanic field, New Mexico.   Bull. Geol. Soc.
Amer., vol. 83, pp. 1335-1343.
MAYO, EVANS B.
1958.   Lineament tectonics and some ore districts of the Southwest.   AIME
Trans., 1958, pp. 1169-1175.
NICHOLS, ROBERT L.
1946.   McCartys basalt flow, Valencia County, New Mexico.   Bull. Geol.
Soc. Amer., vol. 57, pp. 1049-1086.
RENAULT, JACQUES R.
1968.   Variation in some Quaternary basalts in New Mexico.   Geol. Soc.
Amer. Abstr. for 1967, Spec. Paper 121, p. 247.
1970.   Major element variations in the Potrillo, Carrizozo, and McCartys basalt
fields, New Mexico.   New Mexico Bur. Mines and Min. Res. Circ.
113, 22 pp.

A. WILLIAM LAUGHLIN

Anangula and Chaluka Investigations of 1972

Principal Investigator: William S. Laughlin, Laboratory of Biological Anthropology, The University of Connecticut, Storrs, Connecticut.

Grant No. 1086: To study the Aleutian survivors of the Bering Land Bridge.

This report focuses on the excavations of 1972 at the Anangula Blade site and at the Chaluka midden site on the opposite side of Nikolski Bay. Anangula is an older Aleut form of the Aleut name for the island that is designated Ananiuliak on U. S. Coast Guard charts. Earlier, it formed the northwestern arm of Nikolski Bay on the Bering Sea side of the southern end of Umnak Island. The geographic area of focus is Nikolski Bay because it has provided evidence of continuous occupation for a minimum of 8,700 years, contained in the three archeological sites of the Anangula Blade site, the Anangula Village site, and Chaluka. Nikolski Bay enjoyed considerable marine resources of its own and provided a commanding center for exploitation of the Pacific Ocean side of Umnak Island, and the Samalga Pass area. Both the Pacific Ocean and the Islands of Four Mountains can be seen from Anangula.

Umnak Island is significant for its unique geological position and history; it was the terminus of the former southwestern arm of the Bering Land Bridge connecting Siberia and Alaska. Samalga Pass separates Umnak Island from the Islands of Four Mountains to the west and has long been an area of remarkable abundance for marine resources and birds. It was the first eastern pass into the Bering Sea until rising sea levels formed more, but shallower, passes to the east. The Umnak Lemming, like the Aleuts, appears to be a survivor of the Bering Land Bridge.

The objectives of the 1972 excavations were concerned with the sequence of events in the Blade site and also with calibration of the Blade site with the 4,000-year-old village site of Chaluka on the opposite side of Nikolski Bay. The Blade site had been discovered in 1938 by W. S. Laughlin and A. G. May while working for Dr. Ales Hrdlička on a Smithsonian Institution expedition to the Aleutian and Commander Islands. Subsequent excavations had provided radiocarbon dates of hearth material with embedded flakes (C. B. Turner, in 1962), and an increasing knowledge of the high tool density in the central portion of the site (A. McCartney, M. Yoshizaki, R. K. Nelson, and W. S. Laughlin, in 1963). The diversity of stone artifacts had also been largely developed so that the carved stone dishes, lamps, weights, lava rubbing or

365

dressing stones, red ochre and palette and grinding stones, and grooved stones for shaping shafts, were all known to occur, in addition to the predominant number of cores, prismatic blades struck from the cores, and transverse burins made on the blades.

We needed to know the character of the site margins and in particular the elevation above mean sea level, the elevation above the marine terrace that silhouettes the small (2.5 km. by 0.5 km.) island, and the density of stone tools. The problem of elevations was especially important for it appeared that the site, now too low for occupation, had earlier been higher, then relatively lowered by the rise of sea level. Interestingly, as well as crucially, the site would have been completely destroyed but for tectonic uplift. We had made a preliminary survey in 1952 but only for selected points (Laughlin and Marsh, 1954). Thus, we needed a good transit survey to develop an understanding of the geological and archeological history of the site.

Tool densities on the peripheries were needed to determine if the occupation had in fact extended to the margins, and with dates to determine if the margin was older, younger, or the same general period as the central portion of the site.

Four excavators—crew chief S. B. Laughlin, F. Ginsburg, A. Atkinson, and B. Thompson—conducted an excavation on the Nikolski Bay side of the Blade site, the protected side of Anangula facing Nikolski 7.2 kilometers to the southeast. The excavation consisted of an area 3 by 8 meters, and a 1-meter-wide trench extending over the shoulder and down into the notch of the wave cut terrace (fig. 1). The highest surface level, immediately below the sod, was 12.84 meters above mean sea level. In actual excavation it was necessary to remove the dense sod and then to remove some 2 meters of volcanic ash, some mixed with varying amounts of clay and earth, all horizontally aligned. The culture-bearing strata, termed levels 1-5, are found only between Ash III above and Ash II below. This cultural zone varies from 15-30 centimeters (fig. 2).

An examination of the stratigraphy indicates a natural "pinching out" that is consonant with this margin being near the natural or original margin of the site when it was occupied. There has been slumping, and some erosion. Ash IV (dates at some 3,000 years ago) was found in the extension trench running down to the marine terrace. The fact that Ash IV, but not the earlier Ash III, was found suggests that the terrace had not yet been cut or that it had not been elevated above mean sea level by the time Ash III was deposited (fig. 3).

The tool numbers and inventory indicated a reduced number of tools and also a lesser diversity in tool types. Chip clusters mark places where manufacturing was conducted and the radiocarbon specimens attest to fire hearths. An

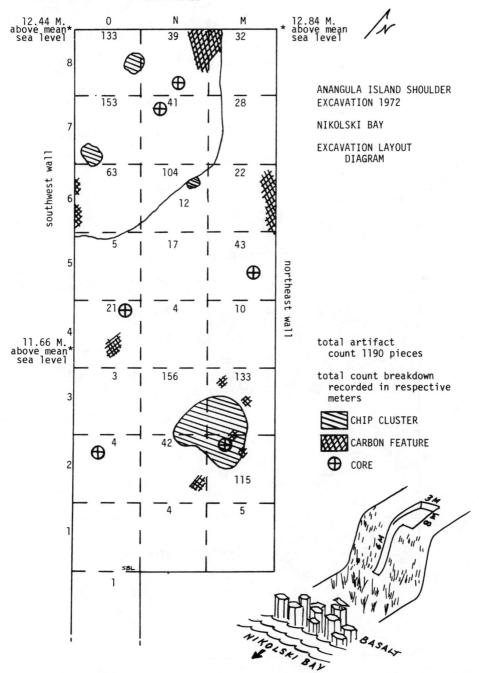

FIG. 1.   Layout diagram, Anangula Island shoulder excavation 1972 (Drawing by
S. B. Laughlin).

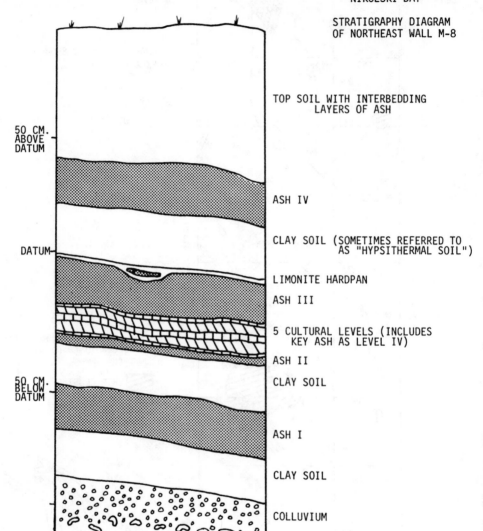

TOP SOIL WITH INTERBEDDING
LAYERS OF ASH

50 CM.
ABOVE
DATUM

ASH IV

CLAY SOIL (SOMETIMES REFERRED TO
AS "HYPSITHERMAL SOIL")

DATUM

LIMONITE HARDPAN

ASH III

5 CULTURAL LEVELS (INCLUDES
KEY ASH AS LEVEL IV)

ASH II

CLAY SOIL

50 CM.
BELOW
DATUM

ASH I

CLAY SOIL

COLLUVIUM

GLACIAL TILL

I METER

Fig. 2.   Stratigraphy of northeast wall section M-8, Anangula Island shoulder excavation (Drawing by S. B. Laughlin).

FIG. 3.   Sara Laughlin in extension trench running from Anangula blade site excavation down onto marine terrace. Boulders in lower right rest on the wave cut terrace on Nikolski Bay side of Anangula Island (1972 photo by Laughlin).

interesting fact is revealed in the finding of 19 burin spalls and only 9 burins. This relatively larger number of burin spalls calls attention to the fact that burins were rejuvenated in the same way that cores were rejuvenated by removal of a battered striking platform and preparation of a fresh one (table 1).

The low frequency of stone tools is further highlighted by comparison with the results of an excavation on the opposite or Bering Sea side of the Blade site (table 1). The tool count is some four times as great and included a lamp and features not present on the Nikolski Bay side. The significance of this lies in illustrating the fact that the concentration of settlement was in the middle and on the Bering Sea side, the side which has suffered the most erosion from storm waves. Estimates are difficult to make but it appears that some one-fourth or even one-third of the site was destroyed by marine encroachment. The site covers an area of some 25,800 meters. If an average of only 110 tools are found in each square meter the total artifact count is 2,838,010. It is the richest archeological site in the northern hemisphere. More important, the large number of stone tools is congruent with the span of occupation, some 1,500 years.

Dating

The 1972 excavation was important to dating the Blade site occupation for it provided additional dates, including the oldest date, and these at the periphery of the site. It is not possible to demonstrate that one portion is older than another though we can now say that the protected side of the site was more sparsely occupied. The large number of stone tools indicate a long period of occupation and the large number of radiocarbon dates derived from fire hearths is congruent with the tool numbers. The actual range of radiocarbon years, their distribution in time, and their continuity without hiatus provides basic information on the occupation of the early marine hunters.

As indicated in figure 2, the five levels, or strata, of the tool-bearing stratum vary in their thickness. Level 5 was absent in the 1972 excavation and it is known that here, as elsewhere, most of the tools are found above level 3. Level

TABLE 1.   Anangula Blade Site, Coastal Margin Excavations,
Artifact Numbers and Densities, 1972 and 1973

(Note: The cultural horizon throughout the blade site is approximately 15 to 30 cm. thick.)

Artifact counts	*1972 Excavation* *30 m^2 on S.E. margin*		*1973 Excavation* *10 m^2 on S.W. margin*	
	Number	*% of total*	*Number*	*% of total*
Total	1146		1515	
Chips	354	30.89	394	26.01
Non-core artifacts[1]	9	0.79	21	1.39
Core-derived artifacts[2]	783	68.32	1100	72.61
Breakdown of core-derived artifacts[2]				
Blades[3]	104	13.28	242	22.00
Flakes	618	78.93	765	69.55
Cores	6	0.77	5	.45
Tablets	27	3.45	51	4.64
Burins	9	1.15	22	2.00
Burin spalls	19	2.43	15	1.36
Average density (using total artifact count)	38.03/sq. m		151.5/sq. m	
Average density (core-derived artifacts[2])	26.1/sq. m		110/sq. m	

[1] Pumice abraders, hammerstones, lamps, bowls, anvil stones.
[2] Including cores and excluding chips.
[3] 1972: 10 of the blades (9.6%) are at least 90% complete. 1973: 44 of the blades (18.2%) are at least 90% complete.

4 is a white ash, known as Key ash, and is an especially valuable marker in identifying the ash sequence at other places, such as Chaluka. It has not been possible to discriminate dates and tools for the five levels. The total thickness (15-30 cm.) is too small to permit detection of any differences or trends, though all tools are recorded at removal by the level in which they lie. Since

TABLE 2.   Anangula Blade Site Dates

(Based on 33 specimens from between Ashes II and III and 2 specimens directly on the Ash II interface and below. The first specimen, GX 2232, is included to indicate the size of the Ash III hiatus. Letter prefixes to specimen numbers denote the laboratory where the analysis was performed. Abbreviations: S.D., standard deviation of the mean; S.E., standard error of the mean.)

Specimen	Date (years ago)		Specimen	Date (years ago)	
	Libby half-life (5570 years)	Penn half-life (5740 years)		Libby half-life (5570 years)	Penn half-life (5740 years)
0. GX 2232	6600 ± 320	6798 ± 330	23. P 1104	8129 ± 96	8373 ± 99
			24. SI-2182	8140 ± 485	8384 ± 500
Hiatus (Ash III)			25. GX 2240	8170 ± 240	8415 ± 247
1. P 1836	6992 ± 91	7202 ± 93	26. P 1103	8173 ± 87	8418 ± 90
2. P 1835	7000 ± 91	7210 ± 93	27. SI-2179	8235 ± 125	8482 ± 129
3. GX 2233	7070 ± 240	7282 ± 247	28. GX 2239	8280 ± 220	8528 ± 227
4. GX 2235	7120 ± 240	7334 ± 247	29. GX 2231	8290 ± 240	8539 ± 247
5. GX 2241	7175 ± 240	7390 ± 247	30. SI-2176	8390 ± 95	8642 ± 98
6. GX 2237	7180 ± 250	7395 ± 258	31. I 715	8425 ± 275	8678 ± 283
7. GX 2243	7260 ± 320	7478 ± 330	32. GX 2809	8435 ± 500	8688 ± 515
8. P 1108	7287 ± 87	7506 ± 90	33. GX 2230	8480 ± 350	8734 ± 361
9. SI-2177	7360 ± 100	7581 ± 103			
10. GX 2246	7395 ± 160	7617 ± 165	*Hiatus (Ash II)*		
11. SI-2180	7600 ± 100	7828 ± 103	34. SI-2178	9055 ± 95	9327 ± 98
12. P 1107	7657 ± 95	7887 ± 98	35. GX 2244	9805 ± 480	10099 ± 494
13. W 1180	7660 ± 300	7890 ± 309	Summary (specimens 1 to 33)		
14. P 1102	7701 ± 93	7932 ± 96	Range	6992-8480	7202-8734
15. P 1837	7793 ± 116	8027 ± 119	Actual span	1488	1532
16. I 1046	7796 ± 230	8030 ± 237	Mean	7785	8019
17. GX 2234	7870 ± 260	8106 ± 268	S.D.	460.5	474.3
18. SI-2181	7885 ± 335	8122 ± 345	S.E.	80.5	82.6
19. SI-2175	7920 ± 100	8158 ± 103	Statistical		
20. P 1105	7932 ± 497	8170 ± 512	range[1]	6864-8706	7070-8968
21. GX 2229	8055 ± 160	8297 ± 165	Statistical		
22. GX 2238	8060 ± 240	8302 ± 247	span	1842	1898

[1] ± 2 S.D.

many of the tools are large they exceed the size of their stratigraphically defined level.

Dr. A. B. Harper approached this problem in the search for an objective solution to defining good dates and rejecting bad dates by using the natural distribution of all the dates, 33, which are not separated from each other by more than 200 years. Arrayed from latest to earliest they extended continuously from 7202 ± 93 to 8734 ± 361 (Penn half-life). This cluster of dates is separated by Ash III from younger and by Ash II from older dates (see table 2). The mean age is significant only for calculating standard deviations, which indicate confidence that may be placed in these dates, i.e., that the occupation has been adequately dated.

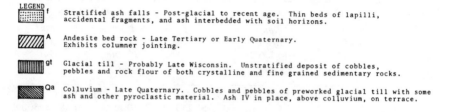

LEGEND

f   Stratified ash falls - Post-glacial to recent age. Thin beds of lapilli, accidental fragments, and ash interbedded with soil horizons.

A   Andesite bed rock - Late Tertiary or Early Quaternary. Exhibits columner jointing.

gt   Glacial till - Probably Late Wisconsin. Unstratified deposit of cobbles, pebbles and rock flour of both crystalline and fine grained sedimentary rocks.

Qa   Colluvium - Late Quaternary. Cobbles and pebbles of preworked glacial till with some ash and other pyroclastic material. Ash IV in place, above colluvium, on terrace.

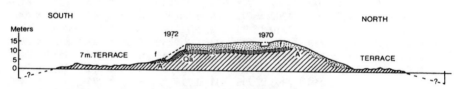

FIG. 4. Profile of South end of Anangula (drawing by S. B. Laughlin, survey by Bruce Thompson and S. B. Laughlin). Published in the Russian volume of 1976, and in the Danish *Folk* 1974/1975.

The transit survey across the southern end of Anangula, through the Blade site (fig. 4) illustrates the extensive marine terrace that encircles the entire island in relation to the surface area available for occupation. Recognizing the fact that the southern tail of Anangula is too low for occupation at present, and that there has been erosion of the periphery of the site on the Nikolski Bay side, and even more on the more exposed Bering Sea side, it is logical to suggest that rising Holocene sea levels terminated the occupation of the site by encroaching on both shores and drenching the actual site periphery. Thus, the people inhabiting this Blade site were forced to retreat uphill to the higher and more protected Village site. Ash III, and other ashfalls, were deposited after the people had begun moving their headquarters to the Village site.

In the reconstructions the figure of 22 meters was used as the minimum elevation above mean sea level for the Blade site. The surface of the lower end of the Village site some 0.5 kilometers north of the Blade site is 22 meters above sea level. It was occupied well into the Russian period, and occasionally used for camping and fishing into the beginning of the 20th century.

The physical situation is well bounded with time markers. Deglaciation and rising sea level were constant processes with their effects observable in the wave cut terrace and erosion of the peripheries of the site. The 7-meter terrace registers the sea level when the terrace was cut. Further terrace cutting, and therefore the destruction of the site, was necessarily, and fortunately, halted by tectonic uplift. Seven meters was the obvious minimum amount of uplift (table 3). The continuing rise of sea level was not halted by this tectonic event. An estimate of 10-12 meters uplift is also a minimum estimate but it does allow for the continuing rise of sea level at the rate indicated in the table.

Chaluka

Excavation of an old stone based house, well under the 3,000-year Ash IV, in the Chaluka village mound provided an opportunity to continue on through the floor of the occupation and confirm the ash sequence on this side of Nikolski Bay, as well as to enlarge our fragmentary knowledge of the early stone-based houses. These early houses are of interest because they are the earliest type of Aleutian house for which there is clear delineation and because they differ markedly from the houses described by Captain Cook in 1778 and by earlier Russian discoverers. This excavation was carried out by W. S. Laughlin, R. Sternbach, J. B. Jørgensen of the University of Copenhagen, and K. Elbaum, with some valuable participation by Dr. D. Hopkins of the U. S. Geological Survey, who also visited Anangula. S. B. Laughlin came over from Anangula with F. Ginsburg to do the stratigraphy of the suboccupation pit and to certify the immediate comparison with the Anangula stratigraphy.

The Aleut occupation begins with a layer of sea urchin tests and spines which is imposed directly upon a soil layer frequently typed as "hypsithermal" soil. The inhabitants then built a stone based house, using imported large, flat stones (figs. 5 and 6). This house was built some 3,400 years ago. Two radiocarbon dates from the base of the house yielded 3905 ± 120 years ago (GX 2798), and 3430 ± 205 years ago (GX 2802). The house contents were typical of the early Chaluka Aleut culture, including stone lidded chambers in the floor, large carved stone dishes, and some lamellar tools with the bifacially flaked tools.

A total of 44 radiocarbon dates for Chaluka, currently being analyzed by A. B. Harper, indicates that initial occupation began 4,000 years ago, at the eastern end, where this excavation was made, and continued through the arrival of the Russians, to the present. The distribution of radiocarbon specimens

TABLE 3. Sequence of Events, Nikolski Bay, Umnak Island

Libby half-life years BP	Sea level (below present)	Elevation of Anangula shoulder (in m.) above MSL	Anangula	Common events	Chaluka
000		12m	Anangula Village abandoned		Nikolski Village Medvedev massacred
200					(AD 1764)
500					
1,000					
1,500					
2,000					West Chaluka occupied
2,500					
3,000				Ash IV	
3,500					
4,000	Present level	+ (11-13)m			East Chaluka occupied
4,500	−(2-4)m	+ (13-15)m			Inner Nikolski Bay refilled
5,000	−(5-8)m	+ (15-17)m			
5,500	−(8-11)m	+ (17-19)m		Tectonic uplift (10-12 meters)	Nikolski Bay drained
6,000	−(0-2)m	+ (5-7)m	7M Terrace cut Anangula separated from Umnak Island		Strand flat cut
6,500	−(4-6)m	+ (9-11)m			
7,000	−(8-10)m	+ (13-15)m	Anangula Village occupied	Ash III	
7,500	−(12-14)m	+ (17-19)m	Anangula blade site abandoned		
8,000	−(16-18)m	+ (21-23)m		Key Ash	
8,500	−(20-22)m	+ (25-27)m	Anangula blade site occupied		
9,000	−(24-26)m	+ (29-31)m		Ash II	
9,500	−(28-30)m	+ (33-35)m		Ash I	
10,000	−(32-34)m	+ (37-39)m		Deglaciation	

is not uniform because we submitted many more specimens above and below Ash IV in order to bracket the sterile ash as closely as possible in our effort to secure as precise a dating as possible of that calibrating, volcanic event. Some two thousand years ago the Aleuts had extended their occupation to the west end of the Chaluka midden, and it is in the western portion that the Russian party of Dennis Medvedev, massacred there in A.D. 1764, was found in 1970.

FIG. 5.   David M. Hopkins standing inside Paleo-Aleut stone-based house, eastern portion of Chaluka site, Nikolski, Umnak Island. One house wall on his left is made of vertically placed stones. Sea urchin tests and spines make up a large part of the occupational debris of later occupants responsible for the accumulation of debris (1972 photo by Laughlin).

FIG. 6.   Jørgen Balslev Jørgensen excavating on floor of Paleo-Aleut stone-based house. Laminations of sea urchin shell and obtruding pieces of whalebone are visible in excavation wall of overlying debris (1972 photo by Laughlin).

We excavated on down to the original Holocene surface of the rise on which Chaluka was founded, and thus made direct comparison with the Anangula Blade site stratigraphic sequence. The same sequence of ashes and soils was found (fig. 7), notably, Ash III, Key Ash (white), Ash II, Ash I, and the various clays descending to glacial till.

In addition to the stratigraphic and archeological problems addressed in this season's researches, J. B. Jørgensen and W. S. Laughlin laid out a protocol for the study and recording of measurements and observations on the Paleo-Aleut skull. Our objective was to insure standardized treatment of Aleut and Eskimo skulls between Greenland and the Aleutians. We also discussed the ways in which the high isolation of Greenland and of the Aleutian Islands affected the population history of these two refugia and their significance as population anchors for the chain of Eskimo isolates between the Aleutians and Greenland. This research is reflected in the chapter, "Aleuts and Eskimos:

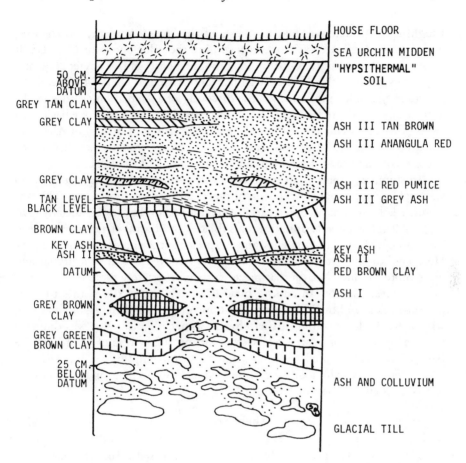

FIG. 7.   East wall of test pit No. 2, underneath Chaluka midden, Chaluka Mound excavation. Tan level corresponds to level I and black level corresponds to level II in Anangula shoulder excavation.

Survivors of the Bering Land Bridge," by W. S. Laughlin, J. B. Jørgensen, and Bruno Frøhlich, in *The First Americans: Origins, Affinities and Adaptations,* published in 1979.

In this brief report of the 1972 field excavations it should be noted that the information secured in 1972 provided the basis for a paper, "Holocene History of Nikolski Bay, Alaska, and Aleut Evolution" delivered at the Conference on the Bering Land Bridge and Its Role for the History of Holarctic Floras and Faunas in the Late Cenozoic, at Khabarovsk, USSR, May 10-15, 1973. At this conference Academician A. P. Okladnikov expressed interest in actual excavation at the Anangula Blade site. He invited W. S. and Ruth

Laughlin to Academgorodok, as guests of the Soviet Academy of Sciences, where more ideas were exchanged concerning the value of a joint USA-USSR excavation. Accordingly, Okladnikov brought a party of five Soviet archeologists to excavate with our American party on Anangula in 1974. One of the results of that joint program was the discovery of a Transition culture in the Village site, a culture that had added bifacially flaked points to the basic unifacial burin and blade technology. The long, continuous history of Aleut occupation of Nikolski Bay was thus found to be registered in the three key sites, Anangula Blade site, Anangula Village site, and Chaluka.

In summary, there is an impressive and meaningful correlation between sea level, occupational elevation, tool types, and radiocarbon dates. The Anangula Blade site was occupied early, when the sea level was substantially lower, by Aleuts who made unifacial tools (blades and burins struck from cores). They occupied the site long enough to experience the encroachment of rising Holocene sea level and as a consequence they moved uphill to a higher and more protected location. In that place, with appropriately more recent radiocarbon dates, they began adding bifacially flaked projectile points to their unifacial blade and burin industry. Tectonic uplift raised the island and preserved the Blade site from further erosion. Inner Nikolski Bay was drained, with the exposure of a large reef system during this period of uplift. As the Bay refilled and approached the salmon stream emptying Umnak Lake, Aleuts founded Chaluka on a protected ridge. This occupation continues today as the southern part of Nikolski Village.

REFERENCES

LAUGHLIN, W. S.
   1973.   Holocene history of Nikolski Bay, Alaska, and Aleut evolution.   Pp. 211-215 *in* "The Bering Land Bridge and Its Role for the History of Holarctic Floras and Faunas in the Late Cenozoic."   Academy of Sciences of USSR, Far-Eastern Scientific Centre, Khabarovsk. (Abstract).
   1974-75. Holocene history of Nikolski Bay, Alaska, and Aleut evolution.   Folk, vol. 16-17, pp. 95-115.
   1975.   Aleuts: Ecosystem, Holocene history and Siberian origin.   Science, vol. 189, no. 4202, pp. 507-515.
   1976.   Holocene history of Nikolski Bay, Alaska, and Aleut evolution.   Beringia in Cenozoic, Theses of the reports of All-Union Symposium, The Bering Land Bridge and Its Role for the History of Holarctic Floras and Faunas in the Late Cenozoic, Khabarovsk, May 10-15, 1973, V. L. Kontrimavichus, ed., pp. 492-508. (In Russian.)
   1980.   Aleuts: Survivors of the Bering land bridge.   New York, Holt, Rinehart & Winston, 1980 (in press).

LAUGHLIN, W. S.; JØRGENSEN, J. B.; and FRØHLICH, B.
  1979.   Aleuts and Eskimos: Survivors of the Bering Land Bridge Coast.   Pp.
           91-103 *in* "The First Americans: Origins, Affinities and Adaptations,"
           W. S. Laughlin and A. B. Harper, eds.   Gustav Fischer New York,
           Inc., New York.
LAUGHLIN, S. B.; LAUGHLIN, W. S.; and McDOWELL, M. E.
  1975.   Anangula Blade site excavations 1972-1973.   Anthrop. Pap. Univ.
           Alaska, vol. 17, no. 2, pp. 39-48.
LAUGHLIN, W. S., and MARSH, G. H.
  1954.   The lamellar flake manufacturing site on Anangula Island in the Aleu-
           tians.   American Antiquity, vol. 20, no. 1, pp. 27-39.

WILLIAM S. LAUGHLIN
SARA B. LAUGHLIN

Field and Taxonomic Studies of
Tropical American Raccoons

Principal Investigator: James D. Lazell, Jr., The Conservation Agency, Jamestown, R.I. Formerly at Center for Action on Endangered Species, Ayer, Massachusetts.

Grant No. 1134:   In aid of a study of the ecology and relationships of isolated tropical raccoons.

As a result of my extensive zoogeographic studies in the Antillean-Caribbean region (Lazell, 1972a, and works cited therein), and my field experience with the isolated nominal species of tropical raccoons (Lazell, 1972b), I embarked on a taxonomic revision of the genus *Procyon* Storr. My fieldwork in the Caribbean and Mexico was supported by the National Geographic Society, and in the Southeastern United States by the Edward John Noble Foundation, the American Museum of Natural History, and the Massachusetts Audubon Society.

Four named island species were investigated.

Procyon pygmaeus of Isla Cozumel was studied and photographed on that island for about 3 weeks during early 1974. Two specimens, one a completely preserved individual in alcohol, were collected to augment the considerable extant museum material (skins and skulls only). Although the pigmy raccoon is a fascinating and delightful animal in its own right, and certainly deserving of a complete autecological study, its taxonomic position seems noncontroversial. It is a broad-skulled, short-furred form closely resembling the native tropical races of *Procyon lotor* in Mexico and Central America. It is a spectacularly miniaturized form and absolutely distinct from all its mainland congeners on quantitative characters of skull and tooth size.

Two taxonomic conclusions derive from my study of *P. pygmaeus:* (1) The pigmy raccoon is an autochthonous endemic on Isla Cozumel fully deserving full species rank. (2) The morphological differences between *Procyon pygmaeus* and *P. lotor lotor* (for example) are as great or greater than the morphological differences between *Procyon cancrivorus* and *P. lotor crassidens* (for example); therefore, placing *P. cancrivorus* in a separate subgenus *"Euprocyon"* is unwarranted.

Field investigation of the three other putative species opened a veritable Pandora's box of systematic confusion. These named forms are *gloveralleni* of Barbados, *minor* of Guadeloupe, and *maynardi* of New Providence. I am fully

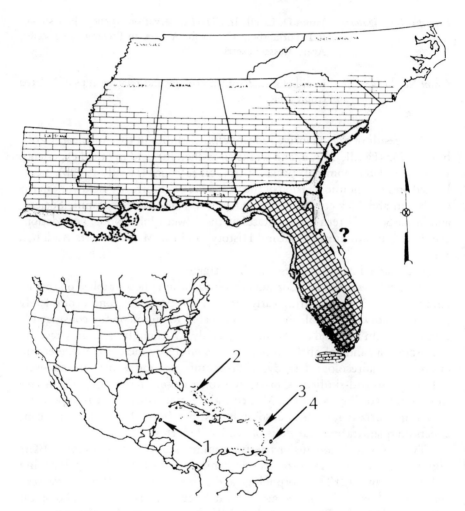

FIG. 1.   Known distributions of various raccoons *(Procyon)*. Large blocking indicates part of the range of small, small-toothed raccoons on the southeastern coastal
plain. Fine hatching indicates the primarily coastal range of the small, large-
toothed raccoon known as *Procyon lotor marinus*. Cross-hatching indicates the range
of the large, broad-skulled, high-browed Florida form known as *P. l. elucus*. Note
that *marinus* and *elucus* occur together in Florida south of Lake Okeechobee; it is not

convinced that all three were introduced from what is today the United States and represent races subsequently named and described again on the mainland.

National Geographic Society support made possible extensive field study and specimen collecting of *minor* and *maynardi* in 1973. Whole preserved specimens, complete skeletons, and the more conventional skins and skulls were obtained. These two forms are small and have relatively small teeth; they resemble the continental race currently called *P. lotor varius* of the Atlantic and Gulf inland coastal plain. Both *maynardi* and *minor* are older names than *varius*. At least *minor* seems to have undergone differentiation in the direction of miniaturization since its introduction to Guadeloupe. Such rapid, post-Columbian evolutionary changes have been meticulously documented in other exotic species established on Caribbean Islands (*e.g.,* Ashton and Zuckerman, 1951, and works cited therein).

All my material of *minor* and *maynardi* has been catalogued, tagged, labeled, and stored. I have concentrated my efforts on unraveling the problems of the small, rangy, large-toothed raccoons of the coastal Southeast and far-flung Barbados.

Procyon gloveralleni was described from the remote oceanic island of Barbados by Nelson and Goldman (1930). There are four known topotypic specimens and the Barbadian population is now apparently extinct. The type specimen, Museum of Comparative Zoology (MCZ) 18591, is a juvenile with incompletely erupted dentition. Two adult skulls, U. S. National Museum (USNM) 26780-1, are damaged; important measurements (*e.g.,* condylobasal length) can only be approximated. The only known complete skull of an adult from Barbados is within a mounted specimen on public exhibit, known as "the Barbados Museum specimen." After negotiations with Ronald Taylor, director, and Sir Frank Hutson, president, of the Barbados Museum, I obtained four whole skull X rays and three occlusal dental X rays with the co-operation of Dr. John Blewett, senior radiologist, Queen Elizabeth Hospital, Barbados. In return for these plates, my assistant, Numi C. Spitzer, and I collected and prepared exhibit mounts of scaled pigeon, mongoose, and green

---

known which occupies the central east coast. Small blocking indicates the range of small, pale, high-browed raccoons in the Middle and Lower Keys of Florida; these are apparently all *P. l. auspicatus.*

Arrows indicate the islands occupied by Caribbean isolates: (1) *Procyon pygmaeus* of Cozumel, a distinctive miniature species; (2) *Procyon maynardi* of New Providence, a form doubtfully recognizable; (3) *Procyon minor* of Guadeloupe, a small form, with small teeth, quite like that of the inland southeastern coastal plain; and (4) *Procyon "gloveralleni"* of Barbados, apparently identical to *P. l. marinus* of the Georgia Sea Islands.

monkey for the Barbados Museum. We subsequently presented them with a mounted summer tanager, donated by the Massachusetts Audubon Society.

Fieldwork in 1974 on the Georgia Sea Islands, sponsored by the Edward John Noble Foundation and the American Museum of Natural History (AMNH), confirmed the suspicion that *gloveralleni* is the same as the small, rangy, long-tailed form with disproportionately large teeth occurring there. Examination of museum specimens (at AMNH, USNM, MCZ, Louisiana State University, University of Connecticut, University of South Alabama, Mississippi Museum of Natural Science, University of Florida, and other institutions) leads to the conclusion that this form is identical with populations named *littoreus, solutus, megalodous,* and the South Florida mangrove raccoon, *P. lotor marinus* (all names, and their formerly known ranges, appear in Hall and Kelson, 1959).

The accompanying map shows geographic ranges as they are presently understood by me. Much work was done during the 1975-76 winter season in Florida and the Gulf coast region. Blood proteins of sympatric Everglades forms *(elucus* and *marinus)* were compared to each other and to the dichopatric *P. l. auspicatus* (including the seemingly identical *"incautus"*) of the Middle and Lower Florida Keys. Specimens of *marinus* were obtained all along the Gulf coast from southern Florida to Louisiana, demonstrating its continuous range. Several hundred AMNH specimens of *marinus* from the peculiar inland corridor across Georgia were examined. Fossil material at the University of Florida, much of it collected since the work of Arata and Hutchison (1964), was examined and a speculative history of the origin and development of the Florida situation has emerged.

Much work remains to be done. The Canaveral region and much of the Florida east coast remain unknown; possibly relevant material is in the U. S. National Museum. More extensive and more refined blood protein analyses are called for in view of the dramatic differences our preliminary samples showed (Lazell and Rosenbaum, in press). The Guadeloupéen form *minor,* possibly the same as our small-toothed coastal plain form called *"varius,"* has gained sudden importance because of the eruption of La Soufrière on Guadeloupe; the optimum habitat of this population is in those mountains.

Raccoons are abundant, extremely popular, economically important, and delightful animals. Their classification should not remain in its present, reprehensible condition.

REFERENCES

ARATA, ANDREW A., and HUTCHISON, J. H.
  1964.   The raccoon *(Procyon)* in the Pleistocene of North America.   Tulane Stud. Zool., vol. 2, no. 2, pp. 21-27.
ASHTON, E. H., and ZUCKERMAN, SOLLY
  1951.   The influence of geographic isolation on the skull of the green monkey *(Cercopithecus aethiops sabaeus)* IV.   Proc. Royal Soc. London, ser. B, vol. 138, pp. 354-374.
HALL, E. RAYMOND, and KELSON, KEITH R.
  1959.   The mammals of North America, vol. 2, pp. 884-891.   Ronald Press Co., New York.
LAZELL, JAMES D.
  1972a.   The anoles (Sauria: Iguanidae) of the Lesser Antilles.   Bull. Mus. Comp. Zool., vol. 143, no. 1, 115 pp.
  1972b.   Raccoon relatives.   Man and Nature, Sept. 1972, pp. 11-15.
LAZELL, JAMES D., and ROSENBAUM, R. A.
  _____.   Sympatric south Florida raccoons: Blood protein electrophoresis. 1976 Ann. Rep., Office, Chief Sci., U. S. Nat. Park Service.   (In press.)
NELSON, EDWARD W., and GOLDMAN, EDWARD A.
  1930.   Six new raccoons of the *Procyon lotor* group.   Journ. Mamm., vol. 11, pp. 453-459.

JAMES D. LAZELL, JR.

Archeological and Paleontological Investigations at Olduvai Gorge, Tanzania, 1972

Principal Investigator: Mary D. Leakey, Centre for Prehistory and Paleontology, Nairobi, Kenya.

Grant Nos. 1063,   To continue the study of prehistoric archeology at Olduvai
1076, 1102.[1]   Gorge.

Research.   Excavation during 1972 was almost entirely devoted to slowly and carefully uncovering the pits discovered in Bed III at the end of 1971. This proved a lengthy and most meticulous task, since it was essential that no part of the original surface be damaged.

At the end of the year an area of approximately 60 square meters of the deposit containing the pits had been cleared of the overlying beds and treated with soil preservative. Some of the best-preserved areas were cast by Dr. R. J. Clarke, formerly technician at the Centre for Prehistory, Nairobi.

The purpose of the pits and the associated runnels still remains obscure, but it now appears that the removal of the deposit was the primary consideration. This could have been for a variety of reasons, but the fact that the deposit is unusually saline suggests the possibility that salt was, perhaps, being exploited. However, this hypothesis must be regarded with caution since the deposit may have become impregnated with salt subsequent to the digging of the pits. Should it be correct, the runnels connecting the pits may have been for carrying water into them, in order to soften the deposit so that it could be more easily dug out.

The large area exposed revealed that all the pits were not dug at the same time. There are several examples of more recently dug pits cutting into earlier ones that had already silted up. This is similarly demonstrated by the runnels, and there are a number of cases in which the later runnels cut across earlier examples, often at right angles.

Two of the larger pits contained up to 100 small bone chips and flakes of quartzite and lava, but no tools. The occurrence of these artifacts suggests the proximity of a contemporary living site, and it was planned to dig exploratory trenches in order to try to locate it.

---

[1] Grants 1076 and 1102 were made to Louis S. B. Leakey in support of his work. Dr. Leakey died on October 1, 1972.

The six pits first discovered, which were damaged before their significance was appreciated, were removed in blocks encased in wooden crates, ready for transportation to the National Museum, Dar es Salaam. Their removal permitted further excavation in the lower levels of this trench, where it is possible that additional parts of the unusual hominid H.34 may come to light.

Mr. R.I.M. Campbell twice visited Olduvai to make a photographic record of the pits, as they were uncovered.

Dr. Richard Hay (University of California, Berkeley) and Dr. Allan Cox (Stanford University, California) both took large numbers of oriented samples from Olduvai for paleomagnetic studies. Final results were not yet available at the end of the season, but two samples from above the pits showed reversed polarity, indicating that they belong within the last major Reversed Epoch (Matuyama) that came to an end about 700,000 years B.P. Thus, the pits appear to belong to Bed III.

Publications. Dr. M. Leakey analyzed and partially prepared for publication the material from four sites excavated during the 1971 season, namely FLK Masek Beds, HEB/East, HK, and JK; work continued on the last site. A proportion of the faunal material from Beds III and IV was listed and identified by Dr. F. Symons, but she was unable to complete the study in the time available.

Dr. D. A. Roe, from the Pitt Rivers Museum, Oxford, measured all the handaxes available from Olduvai at the camp and in the National Museums at Nairobi and Dar es Salaam. His metrical analysis will be included in the monograph on Beds III and IV.

Dr. M. Leakey compiled the greater part of a small book on Olduvai intended for nonspecialists, to enable the average reader to understand better the scientific results that have been obtained at Olduvai.

Dating. A relatively new method of dating fossil bones, based on amino acids, was tried experimentally on samples from Olduvai. The figures obtained so far appear to be too young, in relation to other lines of evidence, but it is likely that this method eventually will prove to be of value, particularly in cases where neither the potassium-argon nor the carbon-14 dating method can be applied.

Buildings. A substantial stone building was erected at site DK to protect the stone circle in Bed I. It was financed by Mr. Gordon Hanes.

Also, a laboratory has been built at the camp for storage of excavated material and to enable it to be studied on the spot. This proved to be of inestimable value.

Camp.   The cessation of water haulage by the Ngorongoro Conservation led to an alarming increase of expenditure on vehicle maintenance, fuel, and repairs. Four 1,000-gallon tanks for storage of rainwater were installed and it was planned to install 6 more tanks, in order to reduce the haulage from Ngorongoro, 27 miles distant from camp.

A Toyota Land Cruiser was purchased to replace the Land-Rover that was written off by the driver but it did not prove a satisfactory vehicle.

Visitors.   A total of 23,651 persons visited the Gorge during 1972, of which 712 were students. This is an increase of 5,791 over the 1971 figures. Donations amounted to $928 and sales of books, slides, and postcards to $7,871.

MARY D. LEAKEY

The Taxonomy, Distribution, and Ecology of Australian Freshwater Turtles (Testudines: Pleurodira: Chelidae)

Principal Investigator: John M. Legler, University of Utah, Salt Lake City, Utah, and University of New England, Armidale, New South Wales, Australia.

Grant Nos. 1131,   For the study of the taxonomy, distribution, and ecology of
1289, 1676.   Australian freshwater turtles.

The unique turtle fauna of Australia consists almost entirely of side-necked turtles (S. O. Pleurodira) belonging to the Family Chelidae. Aside from the chelids in New Guinea the closest relatives of Australian chelids are in South America. Both groups are poorly known. Most Australian chelids were described prior to 1900 but as late as 1971 little was known about them.

The broad objective of this project is a biosystematic analysis of Australian chelids to elucidate their origin, evolution, and their relationships and to permit intelligent comparison of their biology with that of northern hemisphere turtles. The approach is broad (continental), consists of combined field and laboratory work, and has a basic taxonomic orientation.

Research on Australian chelids has consisted of two substantial periods of residence in Australia interspersed with periods of study in the United States of America. Periods in Australia were: December 1972-July 1974 and September 1976-January 1977 (685 days total). In these periods we made 52 trips to a total of 207 localities to gather specimens and data (total of 294 days in the field). Localities visited included most of the regions and drainage systems in which turtles were known or suspected to occur (fig. 1). In most cases field transportation consisted of a long wheel-base Land-Rover with small cargo trailer and a small aluminum boat. On longer trips specimens were sent periodically by air to our base at the University of New England, Armidale, New South Wales, Australia.

While in Australia we assembled a collection of approximately 3,000 specimens of turtles. Approximately 60 percent of these specimens were preserved whole (injected), 20 percent are complete skeletons, and 20 percent are dissections of some kind in which soft parts and viscera are stored in liquid preservative and the shell and certain skeletal elements are dried. Representa-

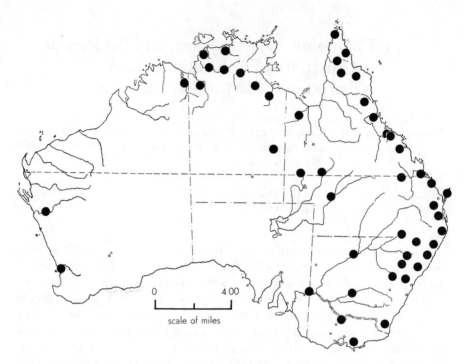

FIG. 1.   Map of Australia showing the general regions in which collections and
observations were made from 1973-1975.

tive live specimens are maintained at the University of Utah. There are also
approximately 10,000 photos (chiefly color transparencies) of habitats and
live specimens and several volumes of detailed field notes. Nearly all existing
specimens of chelids were examined in Australian museums (Australian Museum, Queensland Museum, National Museum of Victoria, Western Australian
Museum).

Specimens are now stored at the University of Utah; the collection has
been divided between the University of Utah and several Australian institutions. All holotypes will be assigned to Australian collections.

Results to Date

The aforementioned bank of specimens and data has made it possible to
begin preparation of a definitive biological account of the unique Australian
chelid fauna. Results thus far have been rapid and fairly dramatic. In my opinion, our own efforts since 1973 have produced more than half the available

knowledge on Australian chelids. Much of this knowledge remains to be organized, analyzed, and published.

My thinking on the biology of Australian chelids is set forth below in three categories. (1) Published conclusions based on careful analysis; these are in the minority because this study has only recently reached the productive stage. (2) Conclusions that are well conceived and documented by data analysis but are unpublished (as of early 1979). (3) Well-founded working hypotheses which have resulted from field and laboratory observations—a first-hand experience with a turtle fauna which may not be unique but is certainly unusual. Nearly all the specimens and data considered in these working hypotheses were obtained and prepared by me personally or by someone working closely with me. Although the taking of data is still incomplete, enough has been recorded and analyzed in each situation to give my initial thinking a substantial direction.

Taxonomy

Distribution maps are shown in figure 2.

ELSEYA

Study of all usable phenotypes in approximately 800 specimens suggests that the genus *Elseya* Gray is in need of revision and contains two genera which overlap and occur sympatrically in northeastern Australia. These are provisionally referred to as the *Elseya dentata* and *Elseya latisternum* "generic groups" (Legler and Cann, 1979). The type species is *E. dentata* Gray, type locality "Victoria River, Northern Territory."

Elseya dentata group. These animals have been recorded in only a few of the places (Cogger, 1975) where I know them to occur and they probably occur much more extensively than I am aware. We have recently demonstrated their occurrence in both Burnett and Fitzroy drainage systems (Legler and Cann, 1979). It is virtually certain that the species complex does not occur south of the Burnett River. It is likely, however, that *Elseya dentata* occurs in the Burdekin and other drainages northward toward Cooktown. Based on all the knowledge and specimens now available, there are at least 3 (more likely 4 or 5) distinguishable allopatric populations in Australia which are now referred to as *Elseya dentata*, as follows: (1) populations in the Ord, Victoria, and Daly River systems (possibly eastward to the Alligator drainages of the Van Diemen Gulf); (2) the Roper and Nicholson-Leichhardt drainages of the Southern Gulf of Carpenteria; (3) the North Johnstone River system of the Atherton Tableland; (4) all other populations south of the Atherton Tableland (now known from the Fitzroy and Burnett Rivers); and (5) *Elseya novaeguineae* is known from most coastal regions of New Guinea and is most closely related to populations of *Elseya dentata* near Darwin.

Elseya latisternum *group.*   Turtles now recognized as *E. latisternum* occur more or less continuously in eastern coastal streams from the tip of the Cape York Peninsula (lat. 10°42'S.) to the Richmond Drainage of New South Wales (lat. 29°20'S.); it is not yet clear whether this constitutes a single poly-typic species or a series of allopatric species. Closely related populations occur in the headwaters of the Murray-Darling system and there is an undescribed species that occurs in 2 isolated populations in the coastal region of New South Wales (lat. 32°30'S.).

Relationships of the two groups of Elseya.   It is uncertain whether the two genera included in *Elseya* are more closely related to one another than either is to *Emydura* (but the former seems more likely). The new species in New South Wales is probably a relict. In some respects it bridges the morphological gap between all three of the groups mentioned. The species deserves intensive study as a possible ancestral condition from which the *Emydura-Elseya-Rheo-dytes* complex could be derived.

EMYDURA

The genus *Emydura* is recognized as distinct and consisting of a series of allopatric species; sympatry with other shortnecks occurs but *not* with other species of *Emydura* despite the statements of Cann (1972) and Cogger (1975). All subgeneric taxa bear an initially confusing superficial similarity. The type species, *E. macquarii,* occurs throughout the Murray-Darling system, demon-strates a wide range of geographic variation, and is probably polytypic. *Emy-dura kreffti* (type locality "Burnett River") occurs from the Brisbane region northward to Princess Charlotte Bay and is then replaced on both sides of the Cape York Peninsula by *Emydura australis,* which occurs in many isolated populations across tropical northern Australia. *Emydura* also occurs, almost continuously, in eastern coastal streams from Brisbane southward to 33° lat.; several species or subspecies are represented in this region. None of these pop-ulations has been properly described. There is an undescribed species of *Emy-dura* far inland in permanent pools of the Lake Eyre drainage system. We obtained good series of specimens from Cooper's Creek near Windorah, Queensland. This species is seemingly more closely related to *Emydura austra-lis* in the north than to *E. macquarii* immediately to the south.

Fig. 2.   Maps of Australia and New Guinea showing approximate geographic dis-tributions of genera and generic groups of chelid turtles. See text for species in each group.

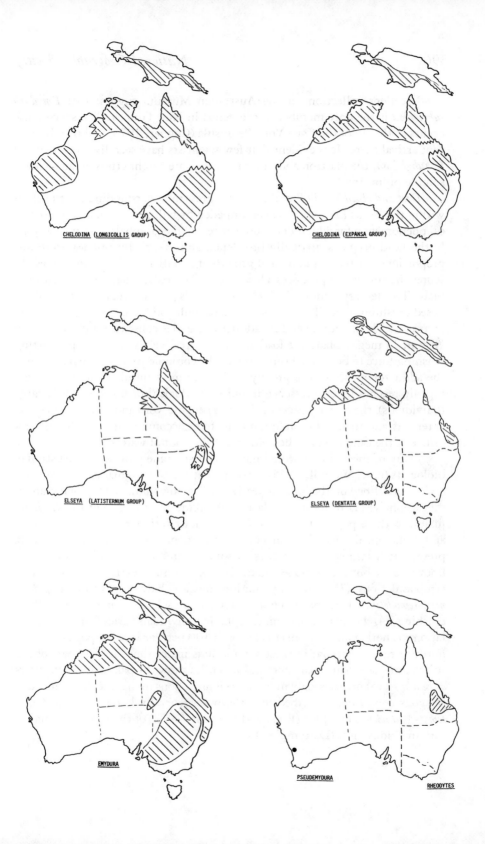

CHELODINA (LONGICOLLIS GROUP)

CHELODINA (EXPANSA GROUP)

ELSEYA (LATISTERNUM GROUP)

ELSEYA (DENTATA GROUP)

EMYDURA

PSEUDEMYDURA

RHEODYTES

Excellent collections at the Australian Museum suggest that *Emydura subglobosa* is the only member of the genus in New Guinea. The species also occurs at the tip of the Cape York Peninsula (Cogger, 1975) and may be a recent arrival there. It is evident that few scientists have seen live specimens of *E. subglobosa;* the plastron and gular markings are bright crimson (an alcohol-soluble pigment).

Diet and Head Size in Emydura.   Progress in understanding relationships within the genus *Emydura* has been impeded by failure to recognize a biological phenomenon for which I now use the term "megacephaly." In megacephaly the head becomes gradually broadened and eventually reaches grotesque proportions; posterior and medial growth of maxillary and palatine bones obscures the vomer and produces a heavy secondary palate that acts as a crushing plate. The dentary symphysis thickens, extends posteriorly, and acts as an opposed crushing plate. The size of the mandibular adductor muscles is greatly increased. The mandible and its adductor muscles constitute a class III lever system. In megacephaly the load arm is progressively shortened, permitting crushing force to be exerted very close to the coronoid process (the insertion of the adductor muscles) and greatly increasing mechanical advantage. Megacephaly reaches its quintessence in old individuals (but not necessarily large individuals): the cutting edges of the jaws become worn and no longer occlude anteriorly and the head is often too large to be accommodated by the anterior orifice of the carapace or to be held erect when out of water.

Many of these things were known at least vaguely by several Australian biologists (e.g., Worrell, 1945); part of what I now recognize as *Emydura australis* was defined on the basis of head size. We now know the following about megacephaly: (1) in most populations it occurs in only *some* of the *adult* females; in these populations there is continuous variation between "normal" and megacephalic females and none of the megacephalic characteristics are present at hatching; (2) it occurs to some degree in all species of *Emydura* known to me but is commonest in *E. australis* and most extreme in northwestern populations; (3) in most populations megacephaly results from an *ontogenetic remodeling* of dermal bone and striated muscle in response to mollusk crushing; (4) the incidence of megacephalic individuals varies from one population to another and it seems to approach 100 percent in some populations in northwestern Australia; in these populations males show at least part of the suite of megacephalic characters and juveniles show the palatal characteristics *at hatching;* (5) megacephaly in *Emydura* is analogous to megacephalic-malacophagous conditions described (or otherwise generally known) in the *Graptemys-Malaclemys* complex (Ernst and Barbour, 1972) of the Emydidae and in certain Trionychids (Dalrymple, 1977).

The immediate significance of these findings is taxonomic; megacephalic *Emydura* have probably been regarded as specifically distinct from other members of the same gene pool for at least a century (Gray, 1841, 1842; Cann, 1972; Cogger, 1975). The biological significance of megacephaly is even more interesting. I have hypothesized that individual females develop the habit of feeding on mollusks, possibly as an extra source of calcium during eggshell production (see Moll and Legler, 1971 for precedent in Panamanian *Pseudemys*). Some of these females might then continue to take mollusks, graduating to larger and larger sizes, as an extremely rich, abundant, and easy to get food (certainly more so than most of the other things in the omnivorous diet of *E. australis* [Legler, 1976]). The modifications of the head seen in megacephaly constitute a relatively easy way for a generalized turtle to become a carnivore. I have found it productive to view malacophagy as carnivorous grazing. Megacephaly in *Emydura* is regarded as one of the most exciting problems to emerge from this study to date.

RHEODYTES

In 1974 John Cann and I examined a poorly preserved specimen of a short-necked chelid that had died in captivity and we were impressed with its distinctness. In 1976 we obtained series of specimens and biological data on this new taxon in the Fitzroy drainage near Rockhampton, Queensland. A paper describing *Rheodytes leukops* new genus and species and its natural history has been completed (Legler and Cann, 1979). The paper reviews the four generic groups of short-necked chelids I recognize *(Emydura,* two groups within *Elseya,* and *Rheodytes)* in eastern Australia. *Rheodytes* is most unusual in being a fast-water specialist, subsisting almost completely on aquatic insect larvae, and having huge cloacal bursae with a highly vascular, villous mucosal lining.

PSEUDEMYDURA

All previous attempts to relate *Pseudemydura* to other Australian chelids have failed (Siebenrock, 1901, 1907; Williams, 1958; Burbidge et al., 1974), chiefly because the monotypic genus has no close relatives in Australia (personal observation). I have examined all museum specimens in existence (ca. 50) except the holotype and have been permitted to dissect and skeletonize a few (plus some experience with live specimens). *Pseudemydura umbrina* can be regarded as an incipient "box turtle" by virtue of its modified limbs and weakly kinetic shell. It is the only terrestrial trend I have noted in Australian chelids. Pseudemydura lays large eggs (i.e., much larger than the effective posterior orifice of the shell). *Pseudemydura* shares all these characters with the South American genus *Platemys* (as well as being superficially very similar to that genus). Much further work, especially skeletal comparison, remains to be done on the problem. *Pseudemydura* is however so rare and rigidly protected that studies of any kind are likely to be difficult.

CHELODINA

We have gathered significantly less information on long-necked chelids of the genus *Chelodina*, although specimens of all known species are in the collection or available for examination. In general, I regard the genus as divisible into at least two groups (more or less as suggested by Goode, 1967): *Chelodina expansa* group—*C. expansa, C. rugosa,* and *C. oblonga; Chelodina longicollis* group—*C. longicollis, C. novaeguineae, C. steindachneri. Chelodina expansa* and *C. rugosa* both have geographic ranges considerably greater than previously known and both contain undescribed forms. *Chelodina longicollis* is probably a polytypic species and deserves a thorough study of variation. It is one of the commoner species in Australia and as a result has been neglected in favor of more spectacular tropical taxa.

Karyotypes

Karyotypes were determined and analyzed for all recognized species of Australian chelids (plus all other pleurodiran genera) (Bull and Legler, 1979). There are two basic karyotypes in Australian chelids as follows: $2N = 50$— the short-necked chelids—*Elseya* (both groups), *Emydura, Rheodytes,* and *Pseudemydura;* $2N = 54$—*Chelodina,* all species. Karyotypes do not provide practical taxonomic information. In groups with nearly indistinguishable karyotypes (chromosomal morphology *and* diploid number) there are clearly recognizable genera (e.g., all the short-necked genera listed). A major conclusion was that karyotypes of chelids are stable and conservative and that the chelid karyotype is similar to an hypothetical ancestral pattern. Conversely, pelomedusid turtles have highly reduced (derived) karyotypes.

Recent Distribution

The following distributional phenomena were previously unknown or poorly documented. (1) The occurrence of *Chelodina expansa* in Queensland, from the Brisbane River system an undetermined distance northward; (2) the occurrence of members of the *Elseya latisternum* group in the headwaters of the Murray-Darling system and in small eastern coastal streams as far south as 32° latitude; (3) the occurrence of *Emydura* sp. in eastern coastal streams southward to 33° latitude. Quite aside from the fact that many or all of these populations constitute unrecognized taxa, their distributions provide the preliminary outline of a very interesting case of evolution and dispersal in relatively recent times.

At present, *Elseya latisternum* and *Emydura* sp. occur sympatrically north of 29° latitude (roughly the Queensland-New South Wales border). Although both taxa occur to the south, they are never sympatric there. In the Murray-Darling streams, *Elseya* occurs only in the headwaters either above 600 meters or above major falls. *Emydura* occurs at lower elevations and below falls. Thus far we have not found *Elseya* and *Emydura* in the same eastern drainage systems south of 29°31' latitude. *Emydura* occurs at altitudes of up to 1,050 meters on the eastern tableland, but only in streams which reach the coastal plain without flowing over major falls. In several places on the eastern tableland (e.g., near Glen Innes and Tenterfield) headwaters of the Murray-Darling system and of eastern coastal streams are separated by less than 5 kilometers; these headwaters are substantial streams and the Continental Divide separating them is insignificant. These factors in combination with preliminary studies of variation (i.e., character analyses from the coastal reaches of a stream to its headwaters) strongly suggest that both *Emydura* and *Elseya latisternum* have crossed the Continental Divide at least once in relatively recent times. It is probable that the presence of *Chelodina expansa* on both sides of the dividing range can be explained in a similar manner.

Reproduction

For nearly all taxa some data are available on eggs (size, weight, texture), number of eggs and clutches per year, incubation times, size at sexual maturity, size of hatchlings, and season of breeding. Some of the data on reproduction were presented at a symposium (Legler, 1975) and a more comprehensive paper is in preparation (see also Legler and Cann, 1979).

With few exceptions Australian chelids lay several clutches of eggs per breeding season. Within some species incubation time at a constant temperature varies latitudinally (fig. 3). Considering all available information, it is possible to characterize breeding patterns of Australian chelids as follows:

(1) *South Temperate.*—Relatively small eggs, laying in spring, short incubation time, hatching before autumn; *Chelodina longicollis* group, *Emydura*, *Elseya latisternum* group, *Rheodytes*.

(2) *Tropical.*—Relatively large eggs, laying in early dry season, moderately long incubation time, hatching before onset of wet season floods; *Chelodina expansa* group, *Elseya dentata* group (and *Carettochelys*).

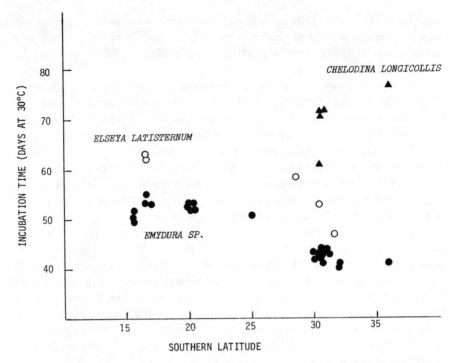

FIG. 3.   The relationship of latitude to incubation time at 30°C. under controlled
laboratory conditions in closely related turtles. The small sample of *Chelodina longicollis* was taken from various altitudes over a narrow latitudinal range and this may
explain the lack of correlation.

(3) *Autumnal.*—Occurs in south temperate region only; relatively large
eggs, laying in autumn or early winter, long incubation time, emergence in
autumn or early winter 1 or 2 years later; long incubation time first reported
by Goode and Russell (1967); *Chelodina expansa.*

The South Temperate and Tropical patterns are quite analogous to those
described for northern hemisphere cryptodires (Moll and Legler, 1971) and
the latitudinal variation in incubation time is analogous to unpublished data
for a few north temperate cryptodires (M. A. Ewert, personal communication;
Legler, personal observation).

The autumnal pattern demands explanation. I have constructed a number
of hypotheses to explain autumnal breeding; most of these were concerned
with predator avoidance or with interspecific nesting competition and all have
been rejected. *Chelodina expansa* has its closest relatives in the North (*C. rugosa*

and other populations of *C. expansa*). I think that *C. expansa* entered the Murray-Darling drainage by crossing the Continental Divide in southern Queensland. With some slight shifts, *C. expansa* at latitude 36°S. may be following essentially the same reproductive scheduling as *C. rugosa* at latitudes of 12-13°S. or *C. expansa* at intermediate latitudes, "beginning" its laying in the southern autumn (being roughly equivalent to the northern dry season) and laying a variable number of clutches.

New or Unusual Techniques

The following techniques were developed in direct relation to the Australian fieldwork: Stomach flushing (Legler, 1977; Legler and Sullivan, 1979); hormonal induction of oviposition (Ewert and Legler, 1978); diving with facemask and snorkel—not a new or unique technique but probably used more extensively in our Australian studies for collecting and observation than previously (Cann, 1972; Legler, 1978). Stomach flushing and the use of hormones to obtain eggs have greatly increased the quantity and quality of dietary and reproductive data we can obtain without sacrificing live animals.

Related Projects

In a study of this magnitude and scope one often finds unexpected and fascinating side problems. A few of these are mentioned below.

Eyelids and Nictitating Membranes. It has been assumed that all chelonians have a nictitating membrane (Underwood, 1970). Actually, chelids and several other kinds of turtles lack a nictitating membrane; this is probably a derived condition (personal observation; Legler and Cann, 1979). Also most Australian chelids have a transparent to translucent lower eyelid through which the eye can be clearly seen. Brief mention of eyelid translucency was made by Walls (1942) and Gadow (1909).

Cloacal Bursae. Cloacal bursae are diverticula of the cloaca in some turtles. Their occurrence (Smith and James, 1958) has been surveyed but their structure and function have not. In general, the mucosal lining of cloacal bursae is complex (villous) in short-necked chelids and is relatively simple in *Chelodina*. In short-necks the size of cloacal bursae and the complexity of the mucosal lining seems directly correlated with preferred habitat, being largest and most complex in species inhabiting fast, clear, and often relatively cool water. Bursae are relatively poorly developed in *Emydura*, show variable development in the *Elseya latisternum* group, are well developed in the *Elseya dentata* group, and reach the quintessence of their development in *Rheodytes* where they are large and have a very complex branched villous mucosa. The smallest divisions of the villi achieve a water-blood barrier of two cell layers. Adults and juveniles can be observed to pump water in and out of the cloacal bursae at rates of 15 to 60 times per minute. Adults and juveniles occasionally come to the surface but they do not demonstrate typical breathing mechanics; if they do breathe at these times the oxygen so obtained would seemingly be insufficient to sustain them in long periods (observed) of routine activity. (Legler, 1979.) Preliminary experiments (unpublished data) suggest that cloacal bursae are highly efficient cloacal gills in *Rheodytes leukops*.

Esophageal Glands. It was discovered in the course of many dissections that all Australian chelids have esophageal glands that undergo a seasonal hypertrophy. These glands lie in the submucosa and, at the height of their development, they increase the total diameter of the esophagus to about the same diameter as the head and greatly thicken the esophageal wall. This glandular hypertrophy occurs *only in adult males* and is negatively correlated with the testicular cycle. We have obtained adequate samples of the secretion which will be analyzed in the near future. As yet we have no idea of how these exocrine glands function.

Acknowledgments

In addition to National Geographic Society support under grants 1131 (1972), 1289 (1974), and 1676 (1976), various parts of this project also were supported partly by grants from: University of Utah Research Committee; University of Utah Biomedical Support Grant Committee; Ian Potter Foundation, Melbourne; The University of New England; Allegheny Foundation Fund for Animal Behavior Studies (Carnegie Museum of Natural History, Pittsburgh, Pa.); and the Explorer's Club.

I am deeply indebted to James J. Bull, Austin F. Legler, and John Cann for companionship, advice, and assistance in the field and to the University of New England for continuing to welcome me as Visiting Professor. I am further grateful to all of the curators of herpetological collections in Australia who permitted me to examine specimens in their care and to the authorities of the states in which we were permitted to collect specimens. Messrs. R. Jenkins and R. Longmore of the National Parks and Wildlife Service were especially cooperative in arranging export permits.

REFERENCES

BULL, JAMES J., and LEGLER, JOHN M.
  1980.   Karyotypes of side-necked turtles (Testudines: Pleurodira).   Submitted to Canadian Journ. Zool., vol. 58, pp. 828-841.
BURBIDGE, ANDREW A.; KIRSCH, JOHN A. W.; and MAIN. A. R.
  1974.   Relationships within the Chelidae (Testudines: Pleurodira) of Australia and New Guinea.   Copeia, 1974, no. 2, pp. 392-409.
CANN, JOHN
  1972.   Notes on some tortoises collected in northern Australia.   Victorian Naturalist, vol. 89, no. 6, pp. 165-168.
COGGER, HAROLD G.
  1975.   Reptiles and Amphibians of Australia, 589 pp.   A. H. and A. W. Reed, Sydney.
DALRYMPLE, GEORGE H.
  1977.   Intraspecific variation in the cranial feeding mechanism of turtles of the genus *Trionyx* (Reptilia, Testudines, Trionychidae).   Journ. of Herpetology, vol. 11, no. 3, pp. 255-285.
ERNST, CARL H., and BARBOUR, ROGER W.
  1972.   Turtles of the United States, 347 pp.   The University Press of Kentucky, Lexington.
EWERT, MICHAEL A., and LEGLER, JOHN M.
  1978.   Hormonal induction of oviposition in turtles.   Herpetologica, vol. 34, no. 3, pp. 314-318.
GADOW, HANS
  1909.   Amphibia and reptiles, 668 pp.   MacMillan, London.
GOODE, JOHN
  1967.   Freshwater tortoises of Australia and New Guinea (in the family Chelidae), 154 pp.   Lansdowne Press, Melbourne.
GOODE, JOHN, and RUSSELL, JAMES
  1968.   Incubation of eggs of three species of chelid tortoises, and notes on their embryological development.   Australian Journ. Zool., vol. 16, pp. 749-761.
GRAY, JOHN EDWARD
  1841.   *Hydraspis australis* sp. nov., *Chelodina oblonga* sp. nov., *C. longicollis*. Appendix, Capt. George Grey's "Journals of an Expedition to Northern and Western Australia."   London. pp. 445-466 pls. 6, 7.
  1842.   *Hydraspis victoriae,* 55 pp.   "Zoological Miscellany," London.
LEGLER, JOHN M.
  1975.   Reproduction in Australian chelid turtles.   Invited paper ASIH Symposium entitled "Ecology and Behavior of Freshwater Turtles" June 11, 1975.   Now in preparation for publication.
  1976.   Feeding habits of some Australian short-necked tortoises.   Victorian Naturalist, vol. 93, no. 2, pp. 40-43.
  1977.   Stomach flushing: A technique for chelonian dietary studies.   Herpetologica, vol. 33, pp. 281-284.

LEGLER, JOHN M.—continued
1978.   Observations on behavior and ecology in an Australian turtle, *Chelodina expansa* (Testudines: Chelidae).   Canadian Journ. Zool., vol. 56, no. 11, pp. 2449-2453.
1979.   Cloacal gills in Australian chelid turtles.   15 min. video tape and abstract. University of Utah Educational Media Service, Salt Lake City.
LEGLER, JOHN M., and CANN, JOHN
1980.   A new genus and species of chelid turtle from Queensland, Australia. Contributions in Science, Los Angeles County Museum of Natural History, no. 324, pp. 1-18.
LEGLER, JOHN M., and SULLIVAN, LISA J.
1979.   The application of stomach flushing to lizards and anurans.   Herpetologica, vol. 35, no. 2, pp. 107-110.
MOLL, EDWARD O., and LEGLER, JOHN M.
1971.   The life history of a neotropical slider turtle, *Pseudemys scripta* (Schoepff) in Panama.   Bull. Los Angeles County Mus. Nat. Hist., vol. 11, 102 pp.
SIEBENROCK, FIEDRICH
1901.   *Pseudemydura umbrina* sp. nov. Beschreibung einer neuen Schildkrötengattung aus der Familie Chelydidae von Australien: *Pseudemydura*. Sber. Anz. Akad. Wiss. Wien, vol. 22, pp. 248, 1 pl.
1907.   *P. umbrina, Emydura subglobosa*.   Sitz.-ber. Akad. Wiss. Wien, vol. 116, pp. 1205 et seq., figs.
SMITH, HOBART M., and JAMES, L. F.
1958.   The taxonomic significance of cloacal bursae in turtles.   Trans. Kan. Acad. Sci., vol. 61, no. 1, pp. 86-95.
UNDERWOOD, GARTH
1970.   The eye.   Pp. 1-93 *in* "Biology of the Reptilia," C. Gans. Vol. 2. Morphology B,   Academic Press, N.Y.
WALLS, GORDON L.
1942.   The vertebrate eye and its adaptive radiation, 785 pp.   Bull. Cranbrook Inst. Sci., no. 19.
WILLIAMS, ERNEST E.
1958.   Rediscovery of the Australian chelid genus *Pseudemydura* Siebenrock (Chelidae, Testudines).   Breviora, No. 84.
WORRELL, ERIC
1945.   *E. australis* "Boof head" tortoise eating freshwater mussels (Propehydridellidae).   Proc. Zool. Soc. London, pp. 23-31.

JOHN M. LEGLER

Exploration for Pliocene Faunas of East Africa

Principal Investigator: Vincent J. Maglio, Princeton University, Princeton, New Jersey.

Grant No. 1048:   For exploration of Pliocene fossil localities in the Rift Valley, Kenya.

During the past decade the late Miocene and Pliocene[1] epochs in Africa have emerged as critical periods for the origin and early radiation of the classic African mammalian fauna known from the Pleistocene and Recent. This was a period of massive faunal migration between Africa and Eurasia, followed by the nearly complete replacement of resident Miocene faunas of distinctly more archaic aspect. Although it is not yet certain to what extent some groups such as hominids or some bovids participated in this interchange, it is clear that this period of time holds the key to understanding the factors leading to the establishment of the modern fauna and of the ecological relationship within it.

Prior to 1965, knowledge of earlier Pliocene faunas in Africa was extremely scant (e.g., Cooke, 1964; Leakey, 1967) and gave little real concept of an integrated faunal assemblage. The standard of comparison for African paleontological studies was the Olduvai Gorge. Other important sites, such as Kaiso, Kanam, Laetolil, and Omo, were then too poorly known and lacked radiometric age control, so that the significance of their faunas was not readily apparent. (See fig. 1.)

Between 1965 and 1968 expeditions from Harvard University discovered and worked rich fossiliferous deposits of latest Miocene and early Pliocene age in northwestern Kenya—at Lothagam Hill and at Kanapoi. Faunal and radiometric age determinations place the time of deposition at these sites at about 6.0 and 4.0 million years, respectively (Maglio, 1970). Studies of the vertebrate remains have led to a remarkable clarification of evolutionary events in Africa during this time. In addition, these sites have contributed significantly to the interpretation of geological patterns in the Northern Gregory Rift;

---

[1] For purposes of the present report the Pliocene epoch is taken to represent that period of time between 6.0 and 2.0 million years. This restricted definition is now in common use in the European Cenozoic section and will soon be fully accepted for Africa as well.

405

FIG. 1.   Map of East Africa showing Lothagam and Kanapoi within the context of the other major fossil sites of the area.

(Behrensmeyer, 1975; Cerling and Powers, 1977), which must have had far-reaching implications for vertebrate evolution and migrations (Maglio, 1975).

In recent years continued investigations at previously known sites and the discovery of new ones have enriched our concepts of the biology, geology, and chronology of the period of time between 4 and 1 million years. Bishop and his coworkers (Bishop et al., 1971) have described new localities in the Baringo basin that extend the known sequence back to 12 million years. F. Clark Howell and C. Arambourg working in the lower Omo Valley have uncovered a magnificent succession of dated faunal and hominid remains from 4.0 to 1.8 million years (Howell, 1969 a, b; Howell et al., 1969; Brown and Lajoie,

1970). R. E. Leakey has discovered vast deposits east of Lake Turkana ranging in age from 2.6 to about 1.3 million years (Maglio, 1972). These have produced important evidence for hominid and other vertebrate evolutionary patterns, the earliest human cultural events, and for the physical history of the Turkana basin (R. Leakey, 1970, 1971, 1972; Isaac et al., 1971; Vondra et al., 1971; Maglio, 1971, 1972). Research at the Olduvai Gorge continues to provide an excellent sequence of faunas and human cultural activities from early to middle Pleistocene age (1.8 to about 0.5 million years) (M. D. Leakey, 1972, and others).

In spite of these advances, known faunas prior to 3 million years remain relatively poor when compared to those of later ages. This is especially true for those between 12 and 6 million years. As a result, numerous problems in interpretation of the prehistory of Africa remain unsolved.

Objectives of the Project

It was with this problem in mind that the present exploratory expedition was undertaken. Our major goals were (1) to revisit the most productive of the Pliocene localities in Kenya (Kanapoi and Lothagam) in order to determine the relative rates of sediment erosion and thus the feasibility of further work there, and (2) to undertake wide-ranging exploration of the southwestern side of Lake Turkana in an attempt to find additional localities of these ages. No scientific party had worked this region since one of us (V.J.M.) took the last expedition to Lothagam in 1968 (Maglio, 1976). Aerial surveys in 1970 and 1971 revealed areas of sediment that might be potentially interesting both geologically and biologically.

Results

The expedition conducted field operations in Kenya from June 1 to August 20, 1972. Members of the field party included Dennis W. Powers and Anna K. Behrensmeyer (stratigrapher-sedimentologists), Charles Smart and James Everhart (paleontologists), David Kinsman (geochemist and sedimentologist), John Kioko and Joshua Kisui (camp assistants), and Vincent Maglio (project director).

During the course of the program nine localities were visited, three previously worked by members of this party and six discovered as a result of the present reconnaissance.

At each locality both geological and paleontological programs were undertaken to determine the general nature of the site, its relation to other sites, and its potential for future studies.

Lothagam Hill.   Structurally this hill is about 8 kilometers long and 2 kilometers wide, aligned roughly on a north-south axis. Previous work in 1967 and 1968 had established a basic faunal list (Maglio, 1975) and began preliminary geological investigations (Patterson et al., 1970). More detailed studies were undertaken on the present visit in order to clarify a number of stratigraphic and paleoecologic problems.

The importance of the Lothagam fauna makes it essential to determine more accurately the field relationships between the various sedimentary units and between these and the fauna. Only in this way can any possible ecological assemblages be recognized.

Sedimentary facies at Lothagam range from claystones and tuffs to conglomerates of volcanic boulders. The stratigraphic sequence (see fig. 2) appears to be as follows (from top to base of section):

(a) Red and yellow siltstones and sandstones, 100 + meters thick, representing a fluvial environment. Previously designated "Lothagam 3."

(b) Sequence of about 60 meters of bentonitic siltstones, sandstones, and tuffs representing a lacustrine deposition regime. Designated "Lothagam 2."

(c) A basaltic sill, intruded between *b* and *d,* about 30 meters thick. Previously dated by whole rock K/Ar at $3.71 \pm$ to 0.23 million years.

(d) About 400 meters of primarily fluvial deposits consisting of coarse sandstones to fine silts and analcimolites; the lower portion shows a northern prodeltaic facies. Designated "Lothagam 1."

(e) Conglomerates of volcanic debris, probably postdating *f,* but field relationships are still uncertain.

(f) Siltstones and calcareous tuffs from a basaltic sequence which is overlain by a basaltic lava flow previously dated at 8.31 ± 0.25 million years.

(g) Sequence of about 200 meters of volcanic conglomerates intercalated with basalt flows; a single K/Ar date of 16.8 ± 0.5 million years has been measured within the sequence.

Effort was directed toward discerning the relationships between microfacies within the gross sedimentary structure. A sampling program was undertaken to provide materials for detailed laboratory studies. These will be conducted at Princeton University with the aim of (1) further clarifying depositional environments and changing environmental patterns and (2) providing direction for further studies. Questions to be answered include source areas for sediments, direction of transport, base level, sedimentation rates, and depositional environments, all of which will be critical for interpreting the paleontological data. Such studies are also essential to the establishment of regional patterns of rift sedimentation and the long-range goal of a unified Lake Turkana basin history.

Samples for pollen analysis were collected in the hope of establishing firmer ecological interpretations. These are being studied by Dr. Raymond

LOTHAGAM HILL

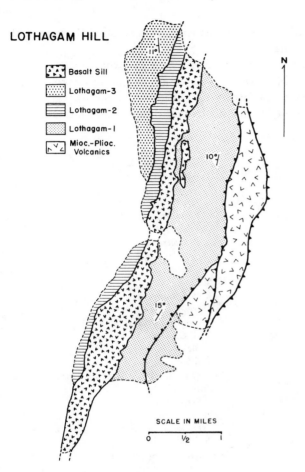

Basalt Sill
Lothagam-3
Lothagam-2
Lothagam-1
Mioc.-Plioc. Volcanics

SCALE IN MILES
0   ½   1

FIG. 2.   Geological map of Lothagam Hill.

Bonnfille, at the CNRS, Paris. Invertebrate collections from various horizons are being studied by Professor Gautier at the University of Ghent, Belgium. When correlated with samples from East Turkana and the Omo Valley, these should prove valuable for chronological and paleoecological reconstructions.

Paleomagnetic studies on the Lothagam sediments and volcanics have been started at Princeton. Similar studies are being initiated at East Turkana and the Omo and may help establish much needed cross-relationships around the basin.

One area of future investigation at Lothagam Hill is completion of detailed mapping to enable more accurate correlation of fauna with defined environments. Success with programs now in progress may make further paleomagnetic, palynological, and invertebrate analyses desirable. Most critical, however, is continued microfacies determination and distributions with respect to fossil-bearing units.

The paleontological results proved less spectacular than anticipated in terms of volume collected. Nevertheless, important new additions to the vertebrate fauna were made which contribute significantly to our understanding of this time interval. A revised faunal list by stratigraphic unit follows:

Lothagam 1 (approx. 6.0 million years)
- Primates
  - cf. *Cercocebus* sp.
  - *Australopithecus* sp.
- Rodentia:
  - Anomaluridae nov.
- Carnivora:
  - Felinae indet.
  - cf. *Homotherium* sp.
  - cf. *Civettictis* sp.
  - Hyaenidae indet.
- Orycteropodidae:
  - gen. et sp. nov.
- Proboscidea:
  - *Deinotherium* aff. *bozasi*
  - Gomphotheriidae aff. *Anancus* sp.
  - *Stegotetrabelodon orbus*
  - *Primelephos gomphotheroides*
- Perissodactyla:
  - *Hipparion* sp. nov. A
  - *Brachypotherium lewisi*
- Artiodactyla:
  - *Hippopotamus* sp. nov. A
  - *Hippopotamus* aff. *immagunculus*
  - *Nyanzachoerus tulotus*
  - *Nyanzachoerus plicatus*
  - *Nyanzachoerus* cf. *pattersoni*
  - cf. *Meteridiochoerus* sp.
  - cf. *Phacochoerus* sp.
  - *Giraffa* sp.
  - Caprini indet.
  - Antilopini indet.
  - Boselaphini indet.
  - Hippotragini indet.
  - Neotragini indet.
  - Reduncini, several taxa
  - *Tragelaphus* sp.
- Aves:
  - indet.
- Reptilia:
  - *Crocodylus niloticus*
  - *Euthecodon* sp.
  - *Podocnemis williamsi*
  - *Podocnemis pattersoni*
  - *Geochelone* sp.
  - *Trionyx* sp.
  - Pythoninae indet.
- Osteichthyes:
  - *Protopterus* sp.
  - *Lates* sp.
  - *Clarius* sp.
- Mollusca:
  - cf. *Bellanya* sp.
  - *Ampullaria wernei*
  - *Lanistes carinatus*
  - cf. *Caelatura* sp. nov.
  - *Melanoides* sp.
  - *Etheria elliptica*

Lothagam 3 (approx. 4.0 million years)
- Primates:
  - *Simopithecus* sp.
- Proboscidea:
  - *Loxodonta adaurora*
- Perissodactyla:
  - *Hipparion* sp. nov. B
- Artiodactyla:
  - *Hippopotamus* sp. nov. B
  - *Nyanzachoerus plicatus*
  - Giraffidae indet.
  - *Selenoportax nakuae*
- Reptilia:
  - *Crocodylus niloticus*
  - *Euthecodon* sp.
  - *Podocnemis* sp.
  - *Trionyx* sp.
- Osteichthyes:
  - indet.
- Mollusca:
  - *Etheria elliptica*
  - others

The most important new faunal elements are as follows:

(a) Bovidae. The bovid fauna previously reported from Lothagam 1 included four tribes, Tragelaphini, Antilopini, Reduncini, and ? Bovini. Of these only the first two were known in Africa prior to this age (i.e., 6.0 million years). Both the reduncines and bovines possibly represented the earliest members of these tribes south of the Sahara, and this can offer important data on the origin and later relationships of these elements. During the present expedition three additional tribes were recorded, Caprini, Hippotragini, and Neotragini, the latter two representing the earliest records in Africa. The morphology and relationships of this family are currently under study by Charles Smart at Princeton and should yield valuable ecological as well as evolutionary conclusions.

(b) Suidae. The genus *Nyanzachoerus* was the only suid previously known from Lothagam 1, and except for a record in the Lukeino beds (6.5 million years; Bishop et al., 1971) is the earliest African record. *Nyanzachoerus* seems to have been the first Asiatic suid immigrant into Africa after the little-understood disappearance of the archaic *Listriodon*-types of the Miocene.

Until now more modern types of suids remained unknown in sub-Saharan Africa until about 3-4 million years, whereupon new types completely replaced the previously dominant *Nyanzachoerus* fauna.

During the present field season suids close to *Phacochoerus* and *Metridiochoerus* were collected from the lowest stratigraphic units. These records, if confirmed, would double the known histories of these forms and could have important implications for the origin of the modern suid fauna of Africa. Additional material is needed before any conclusions can be drawn.

(c) Carnivora. This group remains very poorly known, but the addition of a sabretooth felid is significant in that it represents the earliest such form on the continent. Unfortunately, this specimen is too fragmentary for adequate comparisons with Eurasiatic forms.

(d) Primates. Only three teeth of the primate *Cercocebus* were collected, but again these represent the earliest records of the genus. Additional material would be essential for the determination of relationships to earlier primates in Africa.

(e) Hominidae. Two new specimens of *Australopithecus* were collected from Lothagam 1. These are an occipital fragment and a piece of parietal bone with frontal suture and a fragment of the alisphenoid attached. The specimens are too incomplete to allow meaningful deductions beyond the observation that at this early stage in hominid history the skull vault was extremely thick and very low.

The fact that two such fragments of different individuals could be recovered in only a few weeks (a mandible with ml was also collected in 1967) suggests that additional material must be present. In view of the 6-million-year age of these beds, the acquisition of further evidence of this stage in human development takes on unparalleled importance and additional effort at Lothagam would seem justified.

Naeyepunedebu Beds. These crop out along the main channel and subsidiary tributaries of the Naeyepunedebu River and are best exposed 4 kilometers north-northwest of Lothagam Hill (fig. 1). The sediments consist of westward-dipping quartz sandstones and siltstones about 500 meters thick.

The lower portion of the section exhibits superficial characteristics of coloration and fluvial sedimentation similar to those of Lothagam 1. They lie along strike from Lothagam and thus may be equivalent in age to part of that sequence.

The upper portion also consists of sandstones and siltstones, although their physical characteristics appear different from and the bedding more massive than those lower in the section. The sandstones are generally light green in color and may contain relatively less feldspar than in the Lothagam sediments. Preliminary studies indicate a westward paleocurrent direction in the upper portion of this section in contrast to the general eastward direction of the Lothagam deposits.

The uppermost portion of the Naeyepunedebu section consists of a series of gray to green lacustrine siltstones and sandstones containing algal balls in situ and an invertebrate fauna of the type associated with the so-called "220 foot beds," or Holocene deposits elsewhere around the lake. Farther to the west red siltstone units overlie this lacustrine facies. These may prove of interest in studies on the time required for the reddening of such sediments.

During the several days spent at this site a small fauna was observed in the upper portion of the section. This included *Hipparion* sp., Giraffinae indet., bovids of the tribes Bovini, Alcelaphini, and Hippotragini/or Reduncini, and *Elephas recki*. The elephant is a thin and folded enameled form comparable to stage three or four as described from Olduvai Gorge (Maglio, 1970). This would suggest a late early or early middle Pleistocene age (i.e., 1.5-0.5 million years) for at least part of the Naeyepunedebu section. The very meager fauna seen in the lower beds included unidentifiable elephant material, *Hipparion* sp., and a suid of the *Nyanzachoerus* type. The last would suggest an age older than about 3.8 million years, which is the latest known occurrence of this group in Africa.

Further field studies will be needed to enlarge the fauna and thus confirm the age of this deposit and to estabish more firmly its relationships to the Lothagam materials. If preliminary geological conclusions are confirmed, then the Naeyepunedebu and Lothagam sections combined could provide us with the longest nearly continuous sedimentary record of late Cenozoic age in Africa, with an over-all age span of from more than 8.0 million years to less than 1.0 million years. Although fossils have not yet been recovered from all portions of this section, it is clear that additional material could yield interesting evolutionary sequences. More important in terms of Lake Turkana paleohistory as a whole is the opportunity of using this as the basis for expanded studies toward a more complete reconstruction of the sedimentary and tectonic history of the region. This goal is critical if the important faunas from around the lake are to be placed in the proper perspective.

Napedet Hills. Reconnaissance of the northern flanks of the Napedet Hills, about 18 kilometers northwest of Lothagam (fig. 1), was made as part of our general survey of the area. Exposures here were previously mapped as Turkana Grits (Dodson, 1971), a generalized category of similar-looking sediments of Miocene age and of rubble derived from Tertiary volcanics. Upon examination, however, the nature of these units was unlike beds attributed to the Turkana Grits elsewhere.

The sequence consists of volcanics and tuffs, possibly of Miocene age, overlain by reddish conglomerates. Several centimeters of sandstone above the conglomerates yielded a few vertebrate fossils (see below). Overlying this unit are gray and greenish lacustrine siltstones containing fossil-fish fragments. Above this the section passes into coarse sands and unconsolidated arkosic material which may represent sediments of a more recent vintage.

The only fossils observed in these beds included *Hipparion* sp., *Hippopotamus* sp., an elephant of the *Elephas recki* type, and fish fragments. From this meager assemblage it is unlikely that the age of the fossil-bearing units could be much older than about 2-3 million years, or younger than about 0.5 million years.

The exact relationships of the Napedet beds to those of the Naeyepunedebu or other deposits are still uncertain, but further studies may reveal interesting regional correlations.

Turkwel River. Aerial reconnaissance revealed exposures of sediments along the southern banks of the Turkwel River, about 15 kilometers north of Napedet. A subsequent visit revealed a short sedimentary sequence of coarse pebble to cobble conglomerates representing a high energy gradient. Imbrication and bedding indicate a paleocurrent direction from the west; the deposit may have formed as part of an alluvial fan deposit.

A second unit consists of light-green sandstones and red siltstones perhaps 30 meters thick, apparently overlying the conglomerates. Alternatively it may lie on a fault contact. These represent a fluvial environment of sands along the main channel and silt deposits laterally or in a lacustrine related environment. These siltstones contain some gypsum indicating local evaporative conditions.

More recent lacustrine siltstones and unconsolidated sands, possibly Holocene in age, overlie the lower units. The Turkwel River beds lie on a north-south trend between the Napedet Hills to the south and the Lothodok Hills to the north and may be related to the former. The lack of fossils or of rocks suitable for radiometric dating, however, precludes any determination of age of these sediments.

Loelilia Water Hole.   Patches of sediment were observed from the air along the west flank of the Loriu Range, between Lake Turkana and the lower Kerio Valley. The main sites visited are located some 30 kilometers east of Lothagam Hill. Because of impassable terrain, a party undertook a ground exploration by boat and on foot.

Outcrops consist mainly of unfossiliferous volcanic flows and tuffs. Along their flanks were sandstones and dark-gray siltstones of lacustrine origin containing mollusks, fishes, hippopotamus, and crocodile remains of a Recent aspect. These beds appear to be similar to the Holocene "220 foot beds" at Lothagam, which have been dated at 5,000 years B.P.

Kanapoi River.   This site lies 60 kilometers south of Lothagam and was previously worked in 1966 and part of 1967 (Patterson and Howells, 1967). The site is of great importance paleontologically because of the excellent fauna and its early age of 4.0 million years. A humeral fragment discovered here in 1966 (Patterson and Howells, 1967) is the oldest hominid post-cranial remain known. Together with the Lothagam mandible, the Kanapoi hominid gives us our only glimpse of early Pliocene man. Because of this, a more detailed geological study was undertaken this year than was done previously.

The sediments along the Kanapoi River consist of 70 meters of fine tuffs and claystones to siltstones and some conglomerates. These fine sediments represent lateral facies of lacustrine and fluvial environments, which progressively moved westward during the interval of time sampled here. Depositional currents came mainly from the east. The sedimentary units are capped by a volcanic layer of basaltic composition (dated at 4.0 million years); this is most likely a flow. No sediments of any apparent antiquity overlie the flow in the Kanapoi region.

More specifically, the sediments dip slightly to the west, with the oldest exposures occurring in the eastern portion of the Kanapoi basin. The basal unit observed here consists of volcanic debris formed into a conglomerate mixed with sandstone. These immediately overlie volcanic rocks of Miocene age. The latter form several volcanic "islands" around which the Kanapoi sediments were deposited. Beds of invertebrates, primarily gastropods, grew on the flanks of these islands during early Kanapoi sedimentation. These lower beds occur in discontinuous outcrops making interpretation of lateral relationships and relative age difficult. To the east the sediments terminate on a faulted volcanic sequence.

West of the main Kanapoi exposures the capping basalt flow with occasional patches of underlying sediment can be traced for several miles in an area of low relief. Rock samples collected are being studied at Princeton in order to clarify the sedimentological features and relationships of these outcrops.

Little new vertebrate fauna was discovered this year except for the addition of a neotragine bovid and the confirmation of the suid *Notochoerus capensis*. Invertebrates and samples for pollen and paleomagnetic analyses were collected and are presently under study. The faunal list from Kanapoi follows:

Primates:
   cf. *Parapapio jonesi*
   cf. *Australopithecus* sp.
Rodentia:
   Hystrix sp.
   cf. *Tatera* sp.
Lagomorpha:
   Lepus sp.
Carnivora:
   Enhydriodon sp. nov
   Hyaena aff. *brunnea*
   Machairodontinae indet.
Proboscidea:
   Deinotherium bozasi
   cf. *Anancus* sp.
   ? *Stegotetrabelodon* sp.
   Loxodonta adaurora
   Elephas ekorensis
Perissodactyla:
   Hipparion sp. nov. B
   Ceratotherium praecox

Artiodactyla:
   Hippopotamus sp. nov. B
   Nyanzachoerus pattersoni
   Nyanzachoerus plicatus
   Notochoerus cf. *capensis*
   Okapia sp.
   Giraffa sp.
   Tragelaphus sp.
   Neotragini indet.
   Alcelaphini indet.
   Bovini indet.
Reptilia:
   Crocodylus niloticus
   Euthecodon sp.
   Podocnemis sp.
   Geochelone sp.
   Trionyx sp.
Osteichthyes:
   indet.
Mollusca:
   indet.

Kakurio River West.   Ten kilometers west of Kanapoi is a large area of sediment exposed south of the Kakurio River (fig. 1). This consists mainly of dark reddish-brown and drab sandstones and siltstones that resemble the Turkana Grits reported elsewhere in northwestern Kenya. Here, the sediments are intruded by a network of dikes that confuse the stratigraphic relationships. In the one day spent at this locality several fossils were discovered, but all were too fragmentary for identification. In view of the extensive nature of these outcrops and the paucity of Miocene faunas from the Lake Turkana area this locality would warrant additional effort, especially if its relationship to Kanapoi could be more firmly established.

Kadilinguru Hills.   About 6 kilometers south-southeast of Kanapoi limited outcrops of sediment were observed along the northern and eastern flanks of the Kadilinguru Hills. These consist of coarse sandstones and siltstones of drab coloration which seem to have a higher proportion of orthoclase feldspar than is typical of the Kanapoi sediments. This may indicate a source area different from that which furnished the Kanapoi deposits, or alternatively, these may relate to the uppermost Kanapoi conglomerates which also have an apparent high proportion of orthoclase. The environment of deposition was probably fluvial.

Very few identifiable fossils were recovered from this locality. Specimens included elephant, crocodile, and hippopotamus remains.

Ekora. This locality was originally discovered by one of us (V.J.M.) in 1966 and worked for only about one week in 1967. Exposures outcrop near the junction of the Kerio and Kalabatha Rivers, 16 kilometers north-north-east of Kanapoi.

The sediments consist of poorly indurated siltstones and claystones with some sandstones exposed near the base. A cobble conglomerate forms the uppermost exposed unit. Structurally the deposits lie in a plunging anticline of which the western limb is well exposed. A basalt exposed in the center of the anticline is believed to be the same unit that caps the Kanapoi sediments (Patterson et al., 1970). This would make the Ekora deposits slightly younger than the 4.0-million-year age of the basalt. The fauna from Ekora is compatible with this interpretation:

Proboscidea:	Reptilia:
cf. *Anancus* sp.	*Euthecodon* sp.
Loxodonta adaurora	*Podocnemis* sp.
Elephas ekorensis	*Geochelone* sp.
Perissodactyla:	Osteichthyes:
Hipparion sp. nov. B	indet.
Cerabotherium praecox	Mollusca:
Artiodactyla:	indet.
Nyanzachoerus cf. *plicatus*	

The two major observations made during the present reconnaissance were (1) sediments consisted primarily of claystones and siltstones with salt and gypsum associated in small quantity suggesting lacustrine deposition and (2) sediment transport in the coarser beds was from the west, in marked contrast to the eastern source for the Kanapoi sediments.

This sequence could provide an important sedimentological link both geographically and chronologically between Kanapoi and other major deposits in the area.

Conclusions

No new major localities for Pliocene fossils were discovered on this expedition, and the specimens collected were disappointingly few. Nevertheless, the additions to the Lothagam fauna give us a better insight into the early Pliocene vertebrates of this region than we had before. More important, in spite of the demonstrably slow rate of erosion and thus exposure of fossils at Lothagam, the discovery in a short period of time of two hominid fragments demonstrates the potential of this site for producing further evidence of this most critical period for human evolution. The same of course holds for any other vertebrate group. For example, a juvenile hippo skull collected this year, the oldest decent specimen known, shows remarkably anthrocothere-like premolars. It had been suggested that hippopotamus ancestry may lie within the anthrocothere or suid lines. This early evidence may help to clarify this question.

Equally important is the geological potential of the southwest Turkana area. The sites now known cover a vast area and represent every environment from lacustrine to deltaic to near-source fluviatile condition, and a range of time from more than 8 million years up to 5,000 years old. These can serve as the basis for a circum-Lake Turkana sedimentological history that can be of great significance to correlating and interpreting the fossil remains from the basin as a whole. Taken together, all the Lake Turkana sites contribute to the most important documentation of recent prehistory on the African Continent. Our goals are not just the discovery of additional fossils but also the understanding of these as the remains of once living biological entities that interacted with their physical environments. This goal requires the contribution of knowledge from many diverse fields.

REFERENCES

BEHRENSMEYER, ANNA K.
  1975.   Late Cenozoic sedimentation in the Lake Rudolf basin, Kenya.   Ann. Geol. Surv. Egypt, vol. 4, pp. 287-306.
BISHOP, W. W.; CHAPMAN, G. R.; HILL, A.; and MILLER, J. A.
  1971.   Succession of Cainozoic vertebrate assemblages from the northern Kenya Rift Valley.   Nature, vol. 233, pp. 389-394, illus.
BROWN, F. H., and LAJOIE, K. R.
  1970.   Radiometric age determinations on Pliocene/Pleistocene formations in the lower Omo basin, Ethiopia.   Nature, vol. 229, pp. 483-485.
CERLING, T. E., and POWERS, D. W.
  1977.   Paleorifting between the Gregory and Ethiopian Rifts.   Geology, vol. 5, pp. 441-445, illus.
COOKE, H.B.S.
  1964.   Pleistocene mammal faunas of Africa, with particular reference to southern Africa.   Pp. 65-116 *in* "African Ecology and Human Evolution," 666 pp., illus., F. Clark Howell and François Bourlière, eds.   Aldine Publishing Co., Chicago.
DODSON, R. G.
  1971.   Geology of the area south of Lodwar.   Geol. Surv. Kenya Rpt. 87.
HOWELL, F. CLARK
  1969a.   Remains of Hominidae from Pliocene/Pleistocene formations in the lower Omo basin, Ethiopia.   Nature, vol. 223, pp. 1234-1239, illus.
  1969b.   Hominid teeth from White Sands and Brown Sands, lower Omo basin (Ethiopia).   Quaternaria, vol. 11, pp. 47-64.

HOWELL, F. CLARK; FICHTER, L. S.; and BEHRENSMEYER, ANNA K.
  1969.   Vertebrate assemblages from the Usno Formation, White and Brown Sands localities, lower Omo basin, Ethiopia.   Quaternaria, vol. 11, pp. 65-88.
ISAAC, GLYNN L.; LEAKEY, RICHARD, E. F.; and BEHRENSMEYER, ANNA K.
  1971.   Archeological traces of early hominid activities, east of Lake Rudolf, Kenya.   Science, vol. 173, pp. 1129-1134.
LEAKEY, LOUIS S. B.
  1967.   Notes on the mammalian faunas from the Miocene and Pleistocene of East Africa.   Pp. 7-29 *in* "Background to Evolution in Africa," W. W. Bishop and J. D. Clark, eds.   University of Chicago Press.
LEAKEY, MARY D.
  1972.   Early artefacts from the Koobi Fora area.   Nature, vol. 226, pp. 228-230, illus.
LEAKEY, RICHARD E. F.
  1970.   Fauna and artefacts from a new Plio-Pleistocene locality near Lake Rudolf in Kenya.   Nature, vol. 226, pp. 223-224, illus.
  1971.   Further evidence of Lower Pleistocene hominids from East Rudolf, north Kenya.   Nature, vol. 231, pp. 241-245.
  1972.   Further evidence of Lower Pleistocene hominids from East Rudolf, north Kenya, 1971.   Nature, vol. 237, pp. 264-269, illus.
MAGLIO, VINCENT J.
  1970.   Early Elephantidae of Africa and a tentative correlation of African Plio-Pleistocene deposits.   Nature, vol. 225, pp. 328-332, illus.
  1971.   Vertebrate faunas from the Kubi Algi, Koobi Fora and Ileret areas, East Rudolf, Kenya.   Nature, vol. 231, pp. 248-249.
  1972.   Vertebrate faunas and chronology of hominid-bearing sediments east of Lake Rudolf, Kenya.   Nature, vol. 239, pp. 379-385, illus.
  1975.   Late Tertiary fossil vertebrate successions in the northern Gregory Rift, East Africa.   Ann. Geol. Surv. Egypt, vol. 4, pp. 269-286.
  1976.   Emergence of the Pliocene epoch at Lothagam Hill, East Africa.   Nat. Geogr. Soc. Res. Rpts., 1968 Projects, pp. 225-230.
PATTERSON, BRYAN
  1966.   A new locality for early Pleistocene fossils in north-western Kenya.   Nature, vol. 212, pp. 577-581, map.
PATTERSON, BRYAN; BEHRENSMEYER, ANNA K.; and SILL, WILLIAM D.
  1970.   Geology and fauna of a new Pliocene locality in north-western Kenya.   Nature, vol. 226, pp. 918-921, illus.
PATTERSON, BRYAN, and HOWELLS, WILLIAM W.
  1967.   Hominid humeral fragment from early Pleistocene of northwestern Kenya.   Science, vol. 156, pp. 64-66, illus.
VONDRA, CARL F.; JOHNSON, GARY D.; BOWEN, B. E.; and BEHRENSMEYER, ANNA K.
  1971.   Preliminary stratigraphical studies of the East Rudolf basin, Kenya.   Nature, vol. 231, pp. 245-248, illus.

VINCENT J. MAGLIO
DENNIS W. POWERS

Physiology and Ecology of the Topi Antelope in Masai Mara Game Reserve, Kenya

Principal Investigator: Geoffrey M. O. Maloiy, University of Nairobi, Nairobi, Kenya.

Grant No. 1083:   For a study of the topi antelope *(Damaliscus kirrigum)* in Masai Mara Game Reserve, Kenya.

Fieldwork on the topi antelope *(Damaliscus kirrigum* Ogilby) was carried out from August 1972 to July 1973. The main objective was to study the physiology, ecology, and behavior of this antelope in the Masai Mara Game Reserve. It was designed to provide information on the animal's ecology to form a context for future physiological studies of captive topi in the laboratory. The physiological characteristics of the species most relevant for future laboratory study will be defined by identifying the features of their natural environment that most importantly affect the ecology and daily activity of wild topi populations.

Topi Distribution and Environment

Topi are patchily distributed in East Africa, in discrete areas. In some cases each distribution area is inhabited by one population (e.g., Rukwa Valley in Tanzania, Alia Bay near Lake Rudolf), while in others two or more relatively independent populations can be identified. The latter is true of the topi-occupied area of the Serengeti region of Tanzania and the adjacent Mara region of Kenya, within which region several independent populations exist. The topi-occupied area formerly extended as far as Mount Elgon, but cultivation has obliterated nearly all topi north of the lands of the pastoral Masai people. A remnant population, only a few hundred strong, persists on ranches in the Endebess area of Kenya. These will probably disappear in the next few years as these ranches are being taken over for small-scale cultivation.

Within their scattered areas topi antelope occur from sea level up to an altitude of 1,700 meters, and in climates ranging from cool and equable, seasonally very hot and dry, to perennially hot and humid. The characteristic common to all distribution areas is a particular type of pasture available to them for much of the year—medium-length, fairly green, leafy swards of

419

grass. The vegetation types containing the grasses cover a wide range: *Hyphaene* palm woodland, lake-shore grasslands, open plains, *Acacia* open woodland, and vleis in ground-water forest. The species of grasses composing the swards also vary greatly. It seems to be the structure of the sward, rather than its component species, that makes it suitable for the topi antelope.

Points of interest about the species emerge from this summary. To enjoy a consistent type of pasture topi are able to tolerate a wide range of climatic conditions (temperature, humidity, radiation), in a less wide range of vegetation types (see table 1). What physiological or behavioral adaptations do they show to explain such flexibility? While the complete study hopes to answer this, this report indicates some of the lines of approach to the problem.

TABLE 1.   Climatic Data from Areas Where Topi Occur in Kenya,
Demonstrating the Range of Climates They Will Tolerate

Station No.	Mean annual rainfall	Days rain	Mean maximum	Mean minimum
85.34000	5141	26	32	22
85.36001	3074	23	32	22
88.34009	10528	77	25	11
91.35000	10436	98	25	8
91.40005	4687	63	34	22
97.40003	10944	70	29	24

Study Area and Methods

Within Kenya, the most readily accessible topi population is that on the Mara-Loita Plains in southern Masailand (Narok district). These are the only topi in Kenya presently conserved, at least in part, within a game reserve. They form a unit population within a distribution area that extends into the Serengeti National Park and adjoining regions of Tanzania (Mwanza and Musoma districts). Their seasonal movements are limited in extent. They live at an altitude, and in a climate, comparable to that of Nairobi, making them suitable as wild models with which to compare the performance of captive animals held at Nairobi. This population was chosen for the field study. It probably numbers about 3,000 animals. The fieldwork was based either at a camp on the Talek River or at the Kenya Game Department's Mara Research Station at Olemolepo, near Keekorok. Work in the Masai Mara Game Reserve was undertaken with the kind permission of the chief game warden, J. K. Mutinda; the game warden, Narok, Ole Pussy; and the senior game warden and forester, Keekorok, S. Ole Tipis.

Observational work was carried out from a Land-Rover generously lent to the project by Maj. I. R. Grimwood, with field equipment (binoculars, tape recorders, camping equipment) provided by the field investigators. One aerial survey was conducted in February 1973, using a hired aircraft, piloted by Dr. H. Croze of the Department of Zoology, University of Nairobi. Aerial photographs of the topi population were taken during this time. Local knowledge of topi distribution and movements was kindly provided by M. L. Modha, Game Department biologist, Southern Division. The major observations were made during road patrols, when the location (vegetation type, catena level, etc.), group size and composition, and activity of topi were recorded. Further activity records were collected during prolonged stationary observation of herds. Pasture samples were collected from clipped quadrats (a quarter square meter, i.e., 50 × 50 centimeters), weighed immediately in the field, and subsequently dried and reweighed. Fecal samples were similarly collected and weighed immediately in the field before drying. Chemical analyses of these samples were later on carried out in the laboratory.

Results

Distribution.   The permanent population of topi (as distinct from the Serengeti topi, which seasonally invade part of the Mara Masai Game Reserve), was found, during the first 12 months of the study, to be using a few restricted areas consistently and heavily. Each of these areas consisted of an upper plain or ridge of green grassland, a long slope toward a river, and a low-lying area of flat ground by the river, the whole area being relatively clear of trees. One of these areas of concentrated topi use was chosen for long-term observations. Topi occurred in all seasons in lower numbers scattered throughout the wooded grasslands and degenerated thicket country of the Game Reserve and surrounding country. These scattered, low-density areas showed great seasonal variations in topi occupance, an area generally being abandoned when it was very dry, or when the grass was tall and flowering. In the high-density areas there was a tendency for animals to be found on grassland high on the catena during the rains, moving downhill toward the riverine flats in the dry season. However, more prolonged fieldwork is needed to confirm these impressions.

During road counts vegetation samples were taken from pastures being used by topi and were compared with samples from pastures not being used by them. Some results of these comparisons are given in table 2. Topi were not

TABLE 2.   Characteristics of Grass Swards Where Topi Are Present or Absent.
Mean Values Are Given

Topi	Grass swards					
	Green percent	Leaf percent	Sheath percent	Stem percent	Dry crop g/m^2	Leaf table cm.
Present	46.3	45.0	32.9	21.1	291	11.6
Absent	43.5	45.5	30.3	24.2	441	38.9* or 2.7

*Leaf table values for pastures where topi were absent fell into two categories, one with tall grass, usually flower, and one with very short grass.

attracted by a high-standing crop of grass (total dry wt./m^2), or even by a high-standing crop of grass leaf; nor could their occurrence be consistently linked with a high leaf + sheath : stem ratio in the grasses. The most reliable guide to the appropriateness of pasture for topi seemed to be its height, especially its leaf table when not in flower. It was noted that at times leaf table alone was enough to distinguish pasture being used by wildebeest (and Thomson's gazelle) from that being used by topi. With further measurements, we expect to show that the pasture being used by topi is most accurately identified by a combination of height, greenness, and leaf + sheath : stem ratio.

Activity.   The records of activities of all animals noted on road patrols or during special observation periods were combined in hour classes, to obtain patterns of diurnal activity. The resulting histograms of activity frequencies are shown in figure 1, where records from August and November-December are shown separately. Daily patterns from these two seasons are closely similar. Further studies will check the possibility of seasonal variation in this daily pattern, although there is a slight indication of more diurnal time spent feeding in the August than in the November-December samples (fig. 2).

It was not always possible to observe whether a standing or lying topi was ruminating. In impala antelope, for example, nearly all standing or lying animals were found to be ruminating (Jarman and Jarman, in press), but occasional checks of resting topi showed that this was not true of this species. Many standing topi, and the majority of those lying down, were not ruminating. This apparent "waste" of ingestive-digestive time requires further investigation. Nonrumination while resting was connected particularly with certain postures, which are described and discussed below.

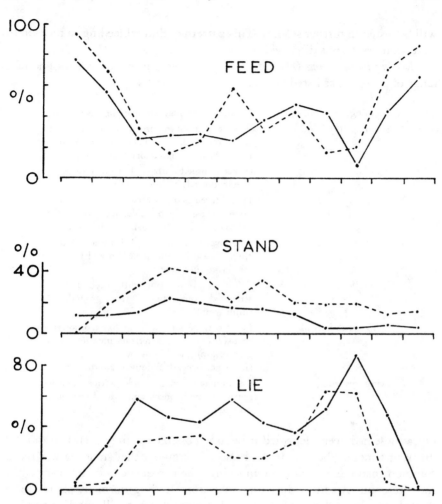

FIG. 1.   The percentages of recorded topi that were feeding, standing or lying
down, in hour classes between 0700 and 1900 hours. The solid line joins values for
November-December, and the dotted line values for August 1972.

The majority of a topi's diurnal feeding time occurs either in the early
morning or late afternoon, with a minor early afternoon peak. The resting
states—standing and lying—form the inverse of this pattern. The inference is
that feeding is suppressed by, and resting stimulated by, the higher temperature and radiation levels between 1000 and 1700 hours. These relationships

will be tested in further studies. This pattern of diurnal feeding in relation to water conservation is discussed below.

Resting Postures and Orientation.   When resting, a topi adopts one of a range of postures, as listed below.

1.	Standing, head up:	Muzzle raised; may ruminate in this posture.
2.	Standing, head down:	*Either* with neck in normal position angled upward, but with chin tucked into neck so that plane of face is angled forward and downward.
		Or neck angled horizontal or downward, with face shadowed. No rumination.
3.	Lying, head up:	Lying, forelegs under torso, hindlegs under abdomen or partly to one side; neck may be at angle to body. May ruminate in this posture.
4.	Lying, head forward:	As above, with neck angled upward, but face tilted forward, chin tucked in and face shadowed. No rumination.
5.	Lying, head on ground:	Lying as above, but with neck and chin stretched out along the ground. No rumination.
6.	Lying, head to flank:	Lying with neck turned, horizontal or lower, so that side of face rests on flank, muzzle in the region of groin, and body twisted so leg on that side is not beneath abdomen. No rumination.
7.	Lying sprawling:	Calves may lie on their sides with all four legs not under body, neck and side of face on the ground.

Once these had been identified it became possible to study their adoption at different times of the day. It can be seen in figure 1 that standing was more common than lying during the morning, their frequencies being reversed in the afternoon. An individual topi that stops feeding normally stands for a while before lying down; after a period of lying down it will stand up and begin feeding without an intervening period standing resting.

Figure 3 illustrates the frequency of the four identifiable lying postures during diurnal hours. The major change is obviously in the proportion of topi that had their heads up, as against the head being in one of the three "down" postures. Once again, these population changes reflect an individual's progression. On first lying down a topi usually has its head up and may be ruminating. After a while it will adopt one of the head-"down" postures. It does not usually revert to a head-up posture for long before standing up. The period of lying head-up before lowering the head is likely to be longer early in the morning than at midday or in the afternoon.

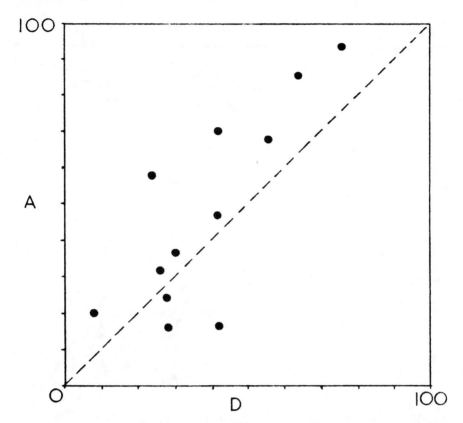

Fig. 2. A comparison between the percentages of topi feeding in the same hour classes in August (A) and November-December (D). The broken line indicates perfect correspondence. The scatter suggests higher feeding value in August.

Nearly all the topi whose activities were recorded in the Mara were in open grassland and thus were not using the shade of trees when resting. A few observed in woodland in the Mara, and many in the woodland parts of the Serengeti National Park, took advantage of the shade of trees when resting, and in these circumstances far fewer animals lay down when resting. From this it appears that lying down, and lowering the head, could be associated with resting while exposed to the sun, while standing is more characteristic of resting in shade.

Another resting posture, which is characteristic of, but by no means confined to, territorial males, is the "belvedering" attitude, in which the animal stands with the forequarters raised and the hindquarters lowered. This is exaggerated by standing on a territarium with the forequarters up the slope.

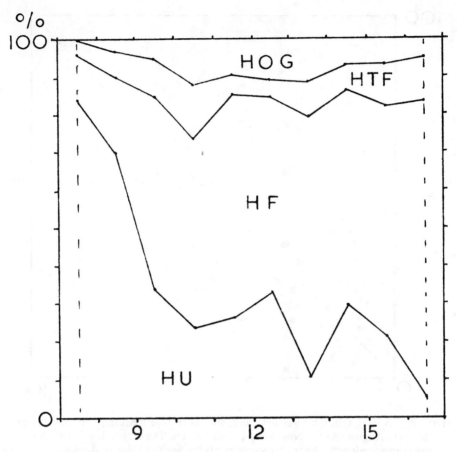

FIG. 3.   The proportions of lying topi in each of four postures in hour classes from
   0700 to 1800 hours. HOG = lying, head on ground. HTF = lying, head to flank.
   HF = lying, head forward. HU = lying, head up.

Although this is usually seen with the head held up, the individual may stand
in this position with the head forward or lowered.

   It was noted that between 1000 and 1600 hours animals resting, standing
or lying, tend to orient themselves so that the spine or at least the neck are approximately in line with the sun. This is, of course, not apparent when the sun
is at its zenith, and is more strongly apparent the less its angle of elevation,
except that orientation seems to be unaffected by the sun in the early morning
and late afternoon. Figure 4 illustrates the orientation relative to the sun of
the neck, or neck and spine if in line with each other, of 107 resting topi re-

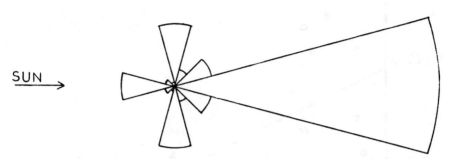

SUN →

FIG. 4. Relative frequencies of topi lying with head and neck at different orientations to the direction of the sun. Animals face outwards from the center of the diagram. Sample size = 104.

corded between 1000 and 1600 hours. The commonest position is with the head away from the sun and the neck or neck and spine approximately in line with the sun. These orientation records are necessarily approximate since methodology for accurate measurement has yet to be perfected. However, they suggest that this is an aspect of the topi's relationship with its environment that deserves further study (36 of the 107 topi held the neck at a noticeable angle to the body when resting).

Preliminary observations indicate that the topi, like its close relative the hartebeest or kongoni, is primarily a panting rather than a sweating animal. It is planned in future laboratory studies of captive animals, using a Climatic Chamber, to investigate this aspect (thermal panting) of thermal physiology as well as the response to solar radiation in the topi antelope.

Water Balance. During the study it was noted that some of the topi drank daily. At dry times of year probably all animals drank daily, usually around midday or early afternoon.

Two facets of daily water balance were revealed by the study. The first of these was that the moisture content of feces varies during the day. Measurements show a high moisture content in the early morning falling off steadily during the day (fig. 5). Seasonal variations in water content have not yet become apparent. The cause of this diurnal decline in fecal moisture is not obvious, and clearly deserves laboratory study. It is, however, postulated that this phenomena is related to the role played by the animal's colon in conserving water. When animals are without water, particularly during the dry season, the colon reduces water output while the kidney concentrates urine (Maloiy, unpublished observations). The second aspect of water balance concerns in-

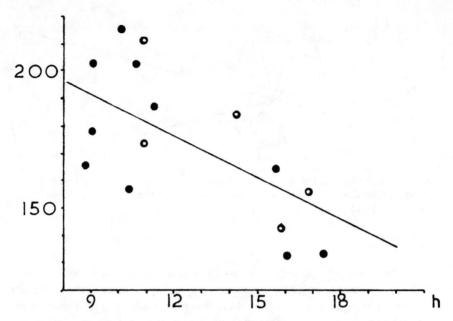

Fig. 5.   Variation in water content of feces (water content / dry weight × 100) between 0800 and 1800 hours.

take of preformed water in food. It will be seen from figure 1 that, within the period 0700 to 1900 hours, 57 percent of feeding occurs from 0700 to 0900 and 1700 to 1900 hours.

Measurements of hourly variation in the water content of pasture in the Mara show that moisture content falls steeply from dawn to 0900 hours, continues to decline until about 1400 or 1500 hours, then rises again in the afternoon and evening, so by distributing their feeding time as they do, topi are effectively improving their intake of preformed dietary water, since grass will contain three times as much water (in the early morning) as at noon.

Other Data.   In the course of the field study data have been collected on reproduction, calf survival, population structure, social grouping, and organization. Preliminary data are also available on the ability of the topi kidney to excrete such electrolytes as Na^+, K^+, Cl^-, and urea.

Discussion

From this initial study it appears that topi distribution in the study area is dictated by the animal's feeding style and the pastures most suited to it. Since such pasture is available mainly in treeless grassland (unlike that of some other topi populations), the Mara topi are exposed to high radiant heat loads during the middle of the day. This may account for their feeding activity mainly in the early morning and late afternoon, spending the middle of the day resting. Orientation when resting could help to reduce incident radiation; and lying down rather than standing would reduce the intake of reflected radiation. Decrease of fecal moisture throughout the day presumably reflects a form of water conservation through water re-absorption from the gut, implying that diurnal water intake, both in food and through drinking, is not superfluous. The timing of diurnal feeding appears to take maximum advantage of water content of grasses.

Summary of the Results to Date

1. In the Mara region of Kenya, topi distribution is closely associated with grass sward structure, especially leaf table height. Position on the catena varies seasonably to some extent.

2. Topi feed most actively (diurnally) during early morning and late afternoon. Standing gives way to lying as the resting mode during the intervening hours, and progressively more animals lie "head down" as the day progresses. Only animals with their heads up ruminate.

3. When resting there is a tendency for the neck, or neck and spine, to be oriented in line with the sun, the animal facing away from the sun. Combined with a "head down" posture, this ensures that the face is always shadowed.

4. Fecal moisture declines throughout the day (regression of fecal moisture (y) on time of day (x) gives a significant, $p < 0.001$, negative slope), $y = 236.9 - 5.04x$).

5. Times of most intensive feeding correspond with times of highest moisture content of grasses.

Future Research

Our project so far has raised many questions that we have been unable to answer. While we hope to continue doing fieldwork, we plan also to place emphasis on laboratory studies using captive animals. We plan to look at:

(a) Water and electrolyte metabolism in both heat exposed and dehydrated individuals; (b) thermoregulation and heat balance in captive topi antelopes; (c) digestion and nutrition; and (d) intestinal water and salt re-absorption in captive topi antelopes.

GEOFFREY M. O. MALOIY

West African Brachyuran Crabs

Principal Investigator: Raymond B. Manning, National Museum of Natural History, Smithsonian Institution, Washington, D. C.

Grant No. 1040:   In support of a study of Brachyuran crabs from the Gulf of Guinea.

From the standpoint of the brachyuran or true crabs, the Gulf of Guinea is one of the best known faunal areas in the world. The crab fauna of only one other area, the Mediterranean Sea, appears to be better known. In the latter area, which has been worked far more intensively for a longer time, some 125+ species of crabs have been reported. As a result of the current study, more than 215 species are now known to occur off tropical West Africa.

The West African crab fauna has been investigated in detail in the last three decades. The first of several reports was published by the Belgian zoologist A. Capart in 1951; that collection was accumulated during the course of the Belgian Oceanographic Expedition, 1948-1949, aboard the *Noordende*. In 1956 the French zoologist Monod published a review of all of the West African crabs, including a complete survey of the literature and almost 900 figures. Monod's report is still the basic reference work on the West African crabs. These two papers were followed by perhaps a score of less extensive reports published between 1956 and the present time.

In 1964 and 1965 the R/V *John Elliott Pillsbury* of the University of Miami, Coral Gables, supported in part by the National Geographic Society, made two cruises to the Gulf of Guinea as part of a research program on deep sea biology sponsored by that university (Voss, 1966). The *Pillsbury* collections—made at 179 stations, along transects in the Gulf of Guinea between Monrovia, Liberia, and Lagos, Nigeria, and including one southerly leg to the offshore islands of Annobon and Fernando Poo—formed the basis for this study. Even though these collections included representatives of only 100 of the 215 species known to occur off tropical West Africa, 16 of them proved to be undescribed. As a result of this investigation, based primarily on the *Pillsbury* collections but supplemented by other unstudied collections, 15 new genera and 23 new species have been recognized in the report on the collection prepared by me and L. B. Holthuis, of the Rijksmuseum van Natuurlijke Historie, Leiden, The Netherlands, who also participated in the *Pillsbury* cruises in the Gulf of Guinea. In that report literature records for all tropical

431

crabs in the Gulf of Guinea are brought up to date and a list of all 300+ species of crabs from the eastern Atlantic is given. In addition, original references, synonyms, and type-species citations are provided for all 144 eastern Atlantic genera, and synonymies are presented for all 36 currently recognized families of marine crabs; 26 of those families are represented in the West African fauna. One subfamily of intertidal, mud-dwelling crabs, the Camptandriinae, is reported for the first time from West Africa; there it is represented by 3 previously undescribed species, each representing a new genus.

It is not surprising that a study of a single group of invertebrates of an area considered to be relatively well known could demonstrate that more than 10 percent of the species present there were new. As pointed out by Chace (1969), it is a reflection upon our state of knowledge of marine invertebrate animals in general. In other groups or in other regions the numbers of undescribed species could be much higher. My recent study (1977) of the stomatopod Crustacea from West Africa demonstrated that 10 of the 24, or 42 percent, of the species occurring there were previously undescribed.

The Swedish zoogeographer Sven Ekman (1953) documented the existence of two major marine faunal areas as demonstrated by the distribution patterns of shallow water marine organisms: the larger Indo-West Pacific region, extending from Hawaii and Japan westward through the Indian Ocean to South Africa and the Red Sea; and the Atlanto-East Pacific region, comprising both sides of the Atlantic Ocean and the eastern Pacific, formerly connected to the Atlantic through the Panamanian region. The brachyuran crabs of the Gulf of Guinea and the eastern Atlantic in general provide additional evidence for the recognition of these major zoogeographic regions. Although only 25 species are common to the Gulf of Guinea and the western Atlantic, the former shares fewer than five with the Indo-West Pacific region, and one of those, the green crab *Carcinus maenas* (Linnaeus), appears to have been introduced where it occurs outside of the Atlantic. This figure does not include several species shared by the faunas of the Gulf of Guinea and South Africa, and which do not extend farther into the Indian Ocean. There is good evidence that at least some Atlantic species reported from the Indo-West Pacific region have been misidentified.

As John S. Garth of the Allan Hancock Foundation has pointed out (1968), and as also reported regarding some stomatopod Crustacea (Manning, 1977), strong evidence for a former Atlanto-East Pacific connection is demonstrated by the discontinuous distribution of several crabs, specifically the genera *Epixanthus, Acidops,* and *Coralliope,* each of which is represented by closely related species in the eastern Pacific and the eastern Atlantic, but is absent from the western Atlantic.

Monod (1956) considered that more than 50 Mediterranean-European species of crabs also occurred in the West African fauna. However, in several cases investigated in detail during the study of the *Pillsbury* collections, it was determined that instead of a single species occurring in the two areas, pairs of similar, closely related species occupied them. Generally this could only be recognized with adequate samples from each of the two areas. Our observations suggest that many of the species exhibiting broad distribution patterns should be studied in more detail. Further investigations of the 25 or so crabs that are now considered to be amphi-Atlantic might well demonstrate that some of them comprise two distinct species, one East American, one West African.

Even within the relatively well-known West African faunal area, our knowledge of crab species is more extensive in some geographic areas, or in some habitats, than in others. The intertidal fauna has been relatively well studied in the Cape Verde Islands and in the region around Dakar, Senegal (where Monod worked), but is relatively poorly known elsewhere. In general the shelf fauna of the Gulf of Guinea proper, from Liberia eastward to Angola, is far better known than the intertidal fauna there. The shelf fauna is fairly rich—the *Pillsbury,* for example, took 21 species at one station off the Niger River at a depth of 33 meters. In contrast the shallow-water mud and mangrove habitats need much more study, as demonstrated by the work of Powell (1976) of the University of Benin. His careful investigations in Nigeria have yielded many interesting finds, including the three new genera and species of the crab subfamily Camptandriinae mentioned above, as well as shrimps representing two new genera and species of a subfamily not previously reported outside of South America.

One of the habitats sampled by the *Pillsbury* off the islands of Annobon and Fernando Poo in the Gulf of Guinea was made up of extensive beds of coralline algae formed into hollow balls at depths between 9 and 69 meters. These balls supported an extremely rich invertebrate fauna, including 22 species of crabs, 3 of which were undescribed, and also including a number of crustaceans known only from oceanic islands in the Atlantic. A similar habitat may occur off Ascension Island in the central Atlantic; that island was visited by me in 1971 and 1976, and one beach there was found to be made up almost completely of fragmented coralline algae. Several decapod species are known to occur on Ascension and Saint Helena Islands in the central Atlantic as well as on the offshore islands of the Gulf of Guinea. Further field investigations, especially dredging operations around these islands, may well be very interesting from a zoogeographic point of view.

REFERENCES

CAPART, A.
  1951.   Crustacés décapodes brachyures.   Sci. Rés., Expéd. Océanogr. Belge,
           vol. 3, no. 1, pp. 11-205.
CHACE, FENNER A., JR.
  1969.   Unknown species in the sea.   Science, vol. 163, p. 1271.
EKMAN, SVEN
  1953.   Zoogeography of the sea, 417 pp.   Sidgwick and Jackson, Ltd.,
           London.
GARTH, JOHN S.
  1968.   *Globopilumnus xantusii* (Stimpson), n. comb., a stridulating crab from
           the west coast of tropical America, with remarks on discontinuous distri-
           bution of some West American and West African genera of brachyrhyn-
           chous crabs.   Crustaceana, vol. 15, pt. 3, pp. 312-318.
MANNING, RAYMOND B.
  1977.   A monograph of the West African stomatopod Crustacea.   Atlantide
           Reports, no. 12, pp. 25-181.
MANNING, RAYMOND B., and HOLTHUIS, L. B.
  1980.   West African brachyuran crabs.   Smithsonian Contrib. Zool., no. 306
           (in press).
MONOD, THEODORE
  1956.   Hippidea et Brachyura ouest-africains.   Mém., Inst. fr. Afr. Noire, no.
           45, pp. 1-674.
POWELL, C. B.
  1976.   Two new freshwater shrimps from West Africa: the first euryrhynchinids
           (Decapoda Palaemonidae) reported from the Old World.   Rev. Zool.
           Afr., vol. 90, pp. 883-902.
VOSS, GILBERT L.
  1966.   Narrative of the cruises.   Pp. 1-60 *in* "The R/V *Pillsbury* Deep-Sea Bio-
           logical Expedition to the Gulf of Guinea, 1964-1965," Stud. Trop.
           Oceanogr., Miami, vol. 4, pt. 1, viii + 239 pp.

RAYMOND B. MANNING

The Total Solar Eclipse of June 30, 1973, with Notes on Eclipse Expeditions of 1972, 1974, 1976, 1977, and 1979

Principal Investigators: Donald H. Menzel,[1] Harvard College Observatory, Cambridge, Massachusetts, and Jay M. Pasachoff, Williams College, Hopkins Observatory, Williamstown, Massachusetts.

Grant Nos. 1093,   In support of expeditions to observe solar eclipses in various
1126, 1198, 1270,   parts of the world, and for supplemental solar studies.
1648, 1787.

The total eclipse of June 30, 1973, was marked by an exceptionally long period of totality and by very favorable weather forecasts. Accordingly, many astronomers from the United States and abroad organized expeditions. The eclipse crossed Africa from Mauritania in the west to Kenya in the east. The National Geographic Society supported our work in part at both these sites, providing primary support for the expedition led by Donald H. Menzel to Mauritania and secondary support for a group headed by Jay M. Pasachoff as part of the National Science Foundation expedition to Kenya.

The peak of totality, with a duration in excess of 7 minutes, close to the theoretical maximum, was to take place in Mali and Niger. Drs. Menzel and Pasachoff made a preliminary reconnaissance of these sites in 1970 and provided information that proved important for later planning. The period following 1970 was followed by many years of drought in the Sahara, which led to a continuous dust haze. This, together with extreme logistical difficulties, led to the situation where almost no astronomers went to the sites where totality was the longest.

The Menzel group, with the cooperation of EEI (Educational Expeditions International), chose a site near Akjoujt, Mauritania. Scientists participating at that site, besides Dr. Menzel, included Dr. Harold E. Edgerton. Dr. Melvin M. Payne and Mrs. Mary Griswold Smith of the National Geographic Society visited the site. Dennis di Cicco, Frank Budreski, Jonathan Kern, and Sal la Riccia were among the Menzel group. Amateur participants provided as part of the EEI program were also on the site. Donald A. Cooke, a student at Williams College, represented the coordination with the Pasachoff group.

---

[1] Dr. Menzel died on December 14, 1976.

435

Robert Fischer and Berton Willard of Itek Corporation operated a search for an inter-Mercurial planet with equipment designed by Dr. James G. Baker.

A variety of experiments was planned to study various aspects of the chromosphere and corona. Two spectrographs—one of which had been featured on the expedition to Mexico described by Drs. Menzel and Pasachoff in the August 1970 *National Geographic* and the other new for the African expedition—were set to take spectra of the corona and the chromosphere. Dr. Edgerton's equipment used photoelectric detectors to measure the radiant energy output arriving at the earth's surface from the sun and corona in two energy bands. Automatic cameras were set to photograph the coronal polarization, which can be interpreted in terms of coronal electron density. Wide-field cameras with radially graded filters were prepared to photograph the corona over several solar radii.

The expedition was on site in Mauritania for 3 weeks ahead of totality to prepare the equipment; conditions often included 120°F. temperature. The National Geographic Society together with EEI has prepared a film about the expedition, together with a study package meant for schools.

The dust in the air from the long-lasting Saharan drought severely limited the experiments, and clouds added to the suspended dust to limit them even more severely. Total transparency at the time of totality was only about 10 percent. This meant, for example, that all exposure times had to be lengthened by a factor of 10. Thus the amount of data that could be gathered was severely limited. Further, the sky was not of even quality, and so the polarization data could not be used to interpret coronal structure.

Other experimenters in Mauritania suffered similar limitations. Part of the official U. S. National Science Foundation-sponsored expedition was at Chinguetti, Mauritania, and had similar problems.

Because of the weather predictions, the National Science Foundation had decided to send most of their group to Kenya, where totality was somewhat shorter, 5 minutes in duration, and the chance of clouds was somewhat higher, but the chance of dust or dust storms was lower. Dr. Pasachoff was included in this NSF group of about 75 individuals from colleges, universities, and research institutes all over the United States. Williams College students Stuart N. Vogel (subsequently admitted to graduate school at Berkeley), Daniel F. Muzyka (subsequently admitted to graduate school at Columbia), and Dan R. Stinebring (subsequently admitted to graduate school at Cornell), plus optical physicist J. Phil Schierer of Tektronix, Inc., were included in the Pasachoff group.

Their experiment was to use a new experimental silicon vidicon spectrometer developed by Schierer's group at Tektronix to observe the infrared spec-

FIG. 1.   Photograph of the 1973 total solar eclipse, taken at our site in Loiengalani,
Kenya.

trum of the corona. Silicon vidicon devices are coming into increasing use in
astronomy because of their inherently high sensitivity compared to photographic plates, the linear nature of their response, and their extended sensitivity into spectral regions where film is not sensitive. In particular, observations
were made of two infrared spectral emission lines from twelve-times ionized
iron; the ratio of these two lines is known on the basis of theoretical work to be
an extremely sensitive indicator of the coronal electron density. Other auxiliary instrumentation, supported by the National Geographic Society, included cameras to photograph the coronal chromosphere and corona.

The eclipse was observed from Loiengalani, Kenya, under favorable conditions. The results from the spectrometric experiment include limits on the
coronal electron density and enable an understanding of the contradictory results that had been gathered from prior observations using this basic method.
The results were published in an article by Pasachoff and Muzyka (1976) and

were reported to the San Diego meeting of the American Astronomical Society. Continued instrumental development of the silicon vidicon technique was also an important part of the project, and Pasachoff, Muzyka, and Schierer published an article (1976) on this subject. The expedition itself was described in Pasachoff's text, *Contemporary Astronomy* (1977).

A variety of photographs of various phases of the eclipse were also obtained by the Pasachoff group. Some were supplied to Dr. Serge Koutchmy of the Institute d'Astrophysique, Paris, who had flown for 68 minutes of totality in the supersonic Concorde in order to study possible small-scale time changes in the corona. He had landed at Chad, and so our results provided data from 1 hour farther along the eclipse path for comparison.

A year prior to the 1973 African eclipse, a total solar eclipse occurred in Prince Edward Island, Canada, and other Canadian sites. Our expedition included some of the equipment that we were to use on the 1973 expedition, and it all received a valuable checkout. In the case of the silicon vidicon photometer, it was only on the basis of its tryout in Prince Edward Island in 1972 that it was found worthy for further use. Nonetheless, heavy cloud cover prevented observation of scientific value from the 1972 eclipse, even though Dr. Pasachoff, when it became evident that the eclipse would be clouded up, was able to ascend in a small plane and obtain a photographic record of the eclipse.

The weather forecasts had not been favorable for this July 10, 1972, eclipse, nor were they favorable for the June 20, 1974, eclipse in Walpole, West Australia, or the October 22, 1976, eclipse in New South Wales, Australia. Thus, though small expeditions were launched, no elaborate equipment was set up. Dr. Pasachoff observed the 1974 eclipse, again from a small plane that took off only after the hope for ground-based observation was abandoned. In 1976, Professor Menzel was prevented from attending by his fatal illness, but he sent Dennis di Cicco and Frank Budreski in his place to operate the equipment. They were entirely clouded out.

On December 24, 1973, the sun underwent an annular eclipse at the time when Comet Kohoutek was passing near perihelion. It had been hoped that the comet would be of naked-eye brightness at that time. The eclipse was visible only at latitudes more southern than those of the United States. Menzel, in collaboration with Educational Expeditions International, headed a group in Costa Rica. Two sets of amateurs joined him there, each set for a 1-week period. The total number participating was about 100. Beside Menzel, the scientific party included di Cicco, Kern, and Fischer. Pasachoff observed the annular eclipse from a site near Bogotá, Colombia. It turned out that during perihelion Comet Kohoutek was not sufficiently bright to be seen from the ground, even during the annular eclipse, and was observed at that time only by the astronauts on Skylab. The second week of the Menzel expedition was devoted to postperihelion observations of Kohoutek, and the comet was observed by the group. A photograph taken by di Cicco appeared in the March 1974 issue of *Sky and Telescope*.

The eclipse of October 12, 1977, was observed from a ship at sea in the mid-Pacific Ocean by a group headed by Pasachoff. A 75 percent chance of clear weather had been forecast for the eclipse, which had 2.5 minutes of totality. Digitizing equipment was built for the silicon vidicon spectrometer, which was also used to take infrared spectra of the iron spectral lines to determine coronal density. Pasachoff also arranged scientific collaboration with Dr. Maxwell T. Sandford II, and with Dr. Charles F. Keller, Jr., of the Los Alamos Scientific Laboratory. Sandford brought an imaging silicon vidicon for observations of the corona in the 10,747 A infrared line of iron, for comparison with Pasachoff's spectra. Keller brought his coronal camera, with automatic polarization measurements and a radially-graded filter. Pasachoff's original group included Gavin Watson, Daniel Bruns, and Stewart Read, all students at Williams College; J. Phil Schierer, and Bruce Miller of Tektronix, Inc.; and Dennis di Cicco. Two of the main instruments were mounted on three-axis gyrostabilized mounts from Los Alamos. A large Pacific storm covered the entire eclipse path with clouds, and satellite observations and meteorological predictions directed the ship, the TSS *Fairsea,* to the place in mid-Pacific where the storm was predicted to break up. Shortly before totality, a hole did open in the clouds, and the beginning of the eclipse was satisfactorily observed. Both spectra and infrared images were recorded. The hole in the clouds closed up about 30 seconds into totality, terminating observations. Pasachoff, Sandford, and Keller described their results of the expedition at the Madison, Wisconsin, meeting of the American Astronomical Society.

Pasachoff and his group observed the total solar eclipse of February 26, 1979, from the University of Brandon in Brandon, Manitoba. New digitization for the Tektronix silicon vidicon was built. A second independent microprocessor-controlled silicon vidicon system was provided on loan from the Princeton Applied Research Corporation. Both spectrometers were directed to infrared studies. The Williams College group included John Duffield, Peter Miller, Richard Boyce, and Judith Beck, all students, and other students from Smith College, the University of Massachusetts at Amherst, and Cornell University, in addition to Schierer and Bruce Miller from Tektronix, Inc. The eclipse was satisfactorily observed in a hazy sky. The data reduction is under way.

In sum, the June 30, 1973, eclipse, "the eclipse of the century," in terms of duration of totality, was favorably observed from one of the two sites. Scientific results from this and from other eclipses were published in the relevant journals and reported on at meetings. Bad weather diminished or eliminated the scientific usefulness of the 1972, 1974, and 1976 eclipses, although the long-range weather forecasts had not been favorable in any case. Better data were obtained from the 1977 and 1979 eclipses.

Pasachoff undertook a study of the research undertaken at past eclipses as part of a larger look at the value of eclipse research in contemporary astronomy. He concluded that there were still a number of important solar research topics that can best be studied at eclipses, and that eclipse work is a significant partner to research at ground-based observatories and from space satellites. The scientific journals continue to have a flow of research articles from solar eclipse expeditions. Thus, the side of eclipse work that contributes new research results should be distinguished from the increasingly popular amateur expeditions and, in most cases, from the mere repetition of standard measurements of eclipses.

It is with great regret that I report the passing of Professor Donald H. Menzel on December 14, 1976. He has been a giant in the field of solar research for many years and had participated in about as many eclipse expeditions as anyone ever. His contributions to eclipse results and technology, including his reductions of data from the turn-of-the-century Lick eclipse expeditions and his own studies at the 1932, 1936, and subsequent eclipses, have significantly advanced the science of solar physics and the science of astronomy as a whole.

REFERENCES

ANONYMOUS
  1974.   A scientists' comet.   Sky and Telescope, vol. 47, no. 3 (March), pp. 153-158, illus. (Photograph of Comet Kohouteck by Dennis di Cicco, p. 158)
MENZEL, DONALD H., and PASACHOFF, JAY M.
  1970.   Solar eclipse, nature's super spectacle.   Nat. Geogr. Mag., vol. 138, no. 2, pp. 222-232, illus.
PASACHOFF, JAY M.
  1977.   Contemporary astronomy, 588 pp., illus.   W. B. Saunders Co., Philadelphia.
PASACHOFF, JAY M., and MUZYKA, DANIEL F.
  1975.   "Infrared Observations of the Solar Corona with a Silicon Vidicon Spectrometer," delivered at the 146th Meeting of the American Astronomical Society at San Diego; abstract: Bull. Am. Astron. Soc., vol. 7, p. 409.
  1976.   Observations of infrared (iron XIII) at the 1973 total solar eclipse. Vistas in Astronomy, vol. 19, pp. 341-353, illus.

PASACHOFF, JAY M.; MUZYKA, DANIEL F.; and SCHIERER, J. PHIL
    1976.   Silicon vidicon spectrometry and its infrared capabilities for solar research.   Applied Optics, vol. 15, pp. 2884-2890, illus.
PASACHOFF, JAY M.; SANDFORD, MAXWELL T., JR.; and KELLER, CHARLES F., JR.
    1978.   "Infrared Observations of the 1977 Total Solar Eclipse," delivered at the 152nd Meeting of the American Astronomical Society at Madison, Wisconsin; abstract: Bull. Am. Astron. Soc., vol. 10, p. 431.

JAY M. PASACHOFF

The Quintana Roo Mural Project

Principal Investigator: Arthur G. Miller, University Museum, University of Pennsylvania, Philadelphia, Pennsylvania.

Grant Nos. 1116,   In support of a long-term project to record and analyze extant
1260, 1308, 1425.   mural painting from the State of Quintana Roo, Mexico.

Beginning January 1972, a long-term project set out to record and analyze extant mural painting from a delimited region on the east coast of what was then the Territory (now the State) of Quintana Roo, Mexico. Fieldwork was carried out during 2 months of 1972, $2^1/_2$ months of 1973, 8 months of 1974, 2 months of 1975, and $1^1/_2$ months of 1976, a total of 16 months. Principal investigator and director was Arthur G. Miller. Felipe Dávalos G. served as artist, assisted by Kees Grootenboer and Eugenia Robinson. Project members, for varying periods of time, included Dolores de Silver, Marla Hires, Anthony Andrews, and Thomas Morgan. Secondino Sabido was foreman of local laborers Francisco Hau, Isidro Canul, Jorge Balam, and Antonio Sierra (mason).

From March 15-30, 1976, Frank P. Saul was engaged to write a physical anthropological study of the human skeletal remains from the 32 burials uncovered in 1974 and 1975; his report will appear as an appendix to the final monograph. During January 1977, Joseph W. Ball came to Merida, where all project pottery was stored, to carry out a ceramics evaluation of the Tancah material; his report will also appear as an appendix to the final monograph. In 1977, Anthony P. Andrews studied the archeological mollusca from the Tancah excavations and his report forms the third appendix of the Tancah-Tulum monograph.

The project was authorized by the Centro Regional del Sureste of the Instituto Nacional de Antropología e Historia, under the direction of Argl. Norberto Gongalez C. During the course of our fieldwork in Quintana Roo, we received encouragement and logistical support from the INAH and are most grateful for the part they have played in contributing to the success of the project. The individuals who aided in this project are listed in the Acknowledgments at the end of this report.

The years of most intensive fieldwork (1973, 1974, and 1975) were made possible by funds granted by the Committee for Research and Exploration of

The National Geographic Society. Major funding was also received from Dumbarton Oaks; timely supplemental support came from the Brooklyn Institute of Arts and Sciences and the Mexican-Canadian Foundation.

The purpose of this report is to highlight the scientific results obtained by the project, as well as to describe briefly the field methods and conceptual framework directing the research procedure. Detailed explication of methodology and accumulated substantive data, accompanied by conclusions regarding the cultural history and process of the East Coast Maya, may be found in the final monograph on the project research now in press at the Center for Pre-Columbian Studies, Dumbarton Oaks. The title of that volume, containing 124 figures, 25 color plates, 3 tables, and over 200 pages of text is "On the Edge of the Sea: Mural Painting at Tancah and Tulum."

Previous Research

Although Quintana Roo has been called "Mexico's forgotten quarter," our zone of study has not been entirely neglected by previous researchers. Clearly its position on the coast, exposed and accessible by sea, is the major reason the Tancah-Tulum region has had a long string of visitors. Fortunately, from the point of view of archeological preservation, people have merely visited the region and have not settled there. A sadly consistent pattern has been that where population centers develop, archeological ruins suffer, often destroyed in the process of collecting its masonry to build new structures. The Tancah-Tulum region has not been inhabited—until the recent tourist development along Yucatán's east coast—since the abandonment in 1668 of the Encomienda of Zama (the colonial name for the region) (Miller and Farriss, 1979).

As is the case for many archeological sites in Yucatán, significant exploration of the Tancah-Tulum region began in 1841 with the visit of Stephens and Catherwood (1843). The three expeditions of the Carnegie Institution of Washington to the east coast of Yucatán, under the direction of Sylvannus Morley, mark the most extensive prior research in our zone (Lothrop, 1924). The important groundwork for the analysis of the East Coast murals was laid down by the investigations of the Expedition Cientifica Mexicana which visited the region from 1937 to 1940 (Fernández, 1941, 1945a, 1945b; Fernández, Lizardi-Ramos, and Rozo, 1945). Archeologically, the research most relevant to our study was carried out by William T. Sanders (1954, 1955a, 1955b, 1960), whose major contribution was the establishment of a ceramic sequence for the Tancah-Tulum zone on the basis of his settlement pattern studies there in 1955. Various other works bear on our study, the most relevant of which are listed in the bibliography along with project reports and specialized works written by the principal investigator while the field research was in progress.

When we arrived at Tancah at the outset of our investigations, the murals were in a precarious state. At Tancah and Xelha, the new road sliced through the middle of both sites, using ancient standing architecture for road fill. Lamentably, this is a common road construction practice that has resulted in the destruction of scores of archeological sites in Yucatán; it is possible some of the dismantled structures at Tancah and Xelha originally contained mural painting. The situation was critical and fast action was required if any comprehensive record of these unique forms of visual data was to be made for generations of future scholars. Thanks to the generosity of several institutions, particularly the National Geographic Society and Dumbarton Oaks, I am happy to report here that a complete visual record of the murals of Tancah-Tulum has been formed and will be published in black and white and in color in the project monograph mentioned above.

Research Objectives

The Quintana Roo Mural Project had three major research goals: (1) Accumulation of visual data; (2) establishment of a regional chronology by stratigraphic excavation of a representative mural-bearing architectural complex; and (3) studies of Tancah-Tulum physical setting and its effect on the material culture of the region.

Only the first of these research objectives was formulated in 1972; over the years of fieldwork, each goal logically grew out of the other as it became clear that modified research strategy was necessary to answer questions raised by the one currently employed. For example, while recording on film and drawings the extant murals of the Tancah-Tulum zone, it became apparent that gradually we were coming to have a clear visual understanding of a major mural tradition of the ancient Maya. But there was no way of knowing how this tradition fitted into mural traditions elsewhere in the Maya area or how it fitted into the matrix of the archeological history of Tancah-Tulum itself. In order to begin to answer the fundamental question of art in archeological contexts, we had to establish as firmly as possible a chronology for our murals. This was formulated by three principal means: (1) Intensive stratigraphic excavations of mural-bearing Tancah Structure 44, charting changes in platform architecture and ceramic modes; (2) seriation of architectural styles and masonry techniques; and (3) seriation of mural painting styles. We also investigated the historical matrix of the murals in the Archivo General de Indias in Seville during April and May 1976. Unpublished records pertaining to the

Encomienda of Zama (Tancah-Tulum) were brought to bear on the accumulated archeological field data from the Proto-Historic period (Miller and Farriss, 1979).

The end result of this research was not one chronology but four: mural, architectural, ceramic, and documentary. As may be predicted in any area at any time, these four different chronologies did not change at the same pace and the interrelationship of each had to be carefully considered. Each of the four chronologies contributed to our reconstruction of cultural history in the Tancah-Tulum region. Perhaps the most significant result of our investigations in terms of previous chronological studies in the Yucatán Peninsula is the definition of a period of florescence of Maya civilization after 1440 lasting until 1521. It was during this period that most of the murals of the Tancah-Tulum region were painted.

After carrying out the basic groundwork of chronology, we could turn to an investigation of iconography and cultural context. Why were the murals painted? And what did they mean to the people who painted them? Here we attempted to go beyond basic description of recording and chronology to say something of what the murals may have meant for the Tancah-Tulum Maya. With our mural art in archeological contexts, we could begin to ask what the murals meant to the ancient inhabitants of this region. And, while it needs fuller explanation than possible here, meaning in the murals is partly evident in their environmental setting. This consideration led to our third area of inquiry. While the physical environment of Tancah-Tulum is something those of us who lived and worked in the region experienced in virtually all its facets, formal studies of environment helped to elucidate certain natural patterns which the Maya had incorporated and personified into their religion, as expressed in their mural art. We were aided in these environmental studies by John Griffin, a marine biologist briefly attached to the project; we were also aided by the 1974 investigations of the New Orleans Geological Society carried out in Quintana Roo (Gifford, n.d.; Weidie, 1974).

Fundamentally, the meaning of these Tancah-Tulum murals, still extant in their environmental and archeological settings, is religious. An understanding of an aspect of Maya religion in this marginal zone of Mesoamerica was at the heart of our investigations.

Our research objectives—from visual description to chronology, to the archeological context of the murals, and to the physical environment—all culminated with an analysis of meaning in the murals. We found them to be expressive of the complex Mesoamerican belief system, regionally distinct, yet related to other more fully documented zones within and beyond the Maya area. In all our investigations, the murals were our primary data, a situation unique in prehistorical studies in Mesoamerica, and one which produced unique results.

Mural Recording

In 1972, detailed study of the interior mural of Tulum Structure 5 began. I worked closely with Mexican artist Felipe Dávalos in this task which was completed during the 1973 season. For much of this century, the magnificent painting inside Structure 5 was in such an extremely poor state of preservation that an otherwise competent investigator had during the 1930's inaccurately recorded the mural (Fernández, 1945b: Lám. 18). We painstakingly reconstructed the original design by arbitrarily dividing the wall into 5-centimeter squares marked out on transparent mylar plastic temporarily placed on the painting surface. By carefully studying each demarcated square as an abstract problem the original design gradually became clear to us. The mural was then copied on paper lined with a grid reduced to one-half the scale of the mylar lines. By this means each square could be treated as a discrete problem and served to control uniformly the scale of reduction. Close field study and drawing the Structure 5 interior mural involved a total of 4 months of 8-hour days divided between the 1972 and 1973 seasons; in addition, another month was required to complete the final rendering, based on field studies, in Felipe Dávalos's studio in Mexico City. The final rendering of this important mural is shown in figure 1. Our version shows the mural to be considerably more complex than the earlier one published by Miguel Angel Fernández in 1945 (Fernández, 1945b: Lám. 18).

Beginning in 1973 and continuing into 1974, we recorded the interior paintings of Tulum Structure 16, also known as the "Temple of the Frescoes." A complicated mural divided into several horizontal bands and knitted together by a twisted cord motif delimiting these bands, the painting extends from the west wall onto the north and south exterior surfaces of the interior building. Although a complete and detailed photographic record was made of all extant painting fragments from Structure 16, only the sections surviving in best condition were rendered in final drawing (fig. 2). Five months of fieldwork were needed for this task, which resulted in the definitive rendering shown in figure 3.

We also recorded surviving exterior Structure 16 mural fragments. Earlier during this century, these exterior paintings were reported to have been in excellent condition. Attempting to preserve them, the Carnegie archeologists applied a coat of a new Dupont product called "Dulux," which resulted in an adverse chemical reaction causing the painting to flake from the wall. Study of

FIG. 1. Final rendering by Felipe Dávalos of Tulum Structure 5 interior mural.

FIG. 2.   Cut-away drawing by Felipe Dávalos showing wall painting section in Tulum Structure 16 intensively studied.

the small bits of surviving paint enabled us to reconstruct the color scheme of
the exterior wall, contrasting its brilliant polychromy with the dichromic
interior.

In 1973, we discovered two new murals at Tancah, a site located 4 kilometers north of Tulum. The painting from Structure 12 had been known since
1941 but had never been published. The murals of Structure 44 represented
an important discovery. We began recording the murals of Structures 12 and
44 toward the end of the 1973 season. Since both of these were near the new
road, there was a sense of urgency in our work; a section of the Structure 12
mural had been looted a short time before our arrival. After 2½ months of
study, we were able to reconstruct this mural as shown in figure 4.

Representing a Maya "ch'a chaac" ceremony ("summoning of the
chaacs"), the mural had a historical significance intimately related to the cultural history of the region. The painting also proved to be significant for

Fig. 3.   Final rendering by Felipe Dávalos showing Tulum Structure 16 murals; location is indicated in fig. 2.

Fig. 4.   Final rendering by Felipe Dávalos of the Tancah Structure 12 mural.

chronological reasons as it was stylistically earlier than those we had encountered in Structures 5 and 16 at Tulum. Its relatively early placement was confirmed by the temporal position of a similar painting style at Tulum which we recorded in 1973 (Str 1-Sub). Study of masonry style and stratigraphic data from the Tancah excavations all eventually confirmed our chronological placement of these murals during the Terminal Classic Period.

The newly discovered murals inside Tancah Structure 44 are what led us to the second phase of our research strategy: the excavation of the Structure 44 complex. Because these paintings (fig. 5) were similar in style and iconography to the Codex Madrid and the Codex Paris, and particularly close to the Madrid, here was an opportunity to date the Codex Madrid itself. At the very least, a solid date for Structure 44 would give a firm earliest possible date from which to make chronological assessments of murals painted on its walls and, by means of stylistic seriation, on other buildings in the region.

By 1975, all of the extant mural paintings in the Tancah-Tulum region had been carefully recorded on black-and-white and color film and in scale field drawings. In addition, we recorded several painting fragments from the site of Xelha, 20 kilometers north of Tancah, none of which had been previously known (Farriss, Miller, and Chase, 1975).

Small-scale Stratigraphic Excavations at Tancah

During 1974, intensive stratigraphic excavations were carried out in and around Tancah Structure 44 with the primary purpose of uncovering evidence to indicate when it was built. Data from platform architecture and ceramics were to provide us with an earliest possible period for the painting fragments we had discovered inside Structure 44 during 1973. We hoped that the Structure 44 murals would serve as a chronological coat hook, as it were, on which to hang the dates of stylistically determined earlier and later murals in our region. Our goal was to establish independent painting, architectural, and ceramic sequences which, after independent analysis, could be interrelated with each other to form the chronology we thought to be a sine qua non before interpretations of mural functions and meaning within Tancah-Tulum culture could be attempted. We fell short of this ideal owing to a number of factors often cited in ambitious programs of this sort: insufficient funds, staff, and time. But most of all, we did not foresee the complexity of chronologically interrelating these three manifestations of material culture. Nevertheless, we had limited success in relating independent architectural and ceramic evidence to our stylistic seriation of the murals. This success was largely due to

FIG. 5. Rendering by Kees Grootenboer of mural fragment from Tancah Structure 44 representing Maya God E. (the Maize God).

the fortunate discovery in the Structure 44 complex of 10 burials from Early Classic to Early Postclassic times, associated with platform fill; one of these platforms was directly associated with mural bearing Structure 44 itself. Also, ceramic evaluations, carried out by Joseph W. Ball, enabled us to make the most of our small collection of roughly 7,000 sherds and 13 whole vessels removed from platform fill and burial contexts.

The choice of Structure 44 for excavation was based on its small size and mural associations. We found incontrovertible evidence that the Structure 44 complex had been continuously inhabited from the Late Preclassic through the Early Colonial Periods. After evaluating our excavation, ceramic, and mural seriations, we were able to place the construction date of Structure 44 at ca. A.D. 1350. Subsequent excavation in and around an Early Colonial chapel at Tancah (Structure 71: fig. 6) carried out in 1975, produced further evidence of Early Colonial habitation there. As we later learned from documents now in the Archivo General de Indias, the site was not abandoned until 1668.

Chronology of the Tancah-Tulum Region

The regional chronology shown below was formulated after much stimulating discussion with J. W. Ball. While my primary data were murals and architecture, Ball's were ceramics. Not surprisingly, we each see different rates of change in this region, a difference which is expressed in Miller, n.d.

I refer to the A.D. 770 horizon with the somewhat clumsy designation "Terminal Classic/Early Postclassic Period" because I see no perceptible change in murals and architecture of our region during this time span.

EARLY COLONIAL	A.D. 1517-1668
LATE POSTCLASSIC	A.D. 1400-1521
MIDDLE POSTCLASSIC	A.D. 1200-1400
EARLY POSTCLASSIC	A.D. 1000-1200
TERMINAL CLASSIC	A.D. 770-1000
LATE CLASSIC	A.D. 650-770
MIDDLE CLASSIC	A.D. 550-650
EARLY CLASSIC	A.D. 250-550
TERMINAL PRECLASSIC	75 B.C.-A.D. 250
LATE PRECLASSIC	300 B.C.-75 B.C.

Ecological Studies and Conclusions

Studies of the physical environment at Tancah-Tulum were not carried out solely for their own sake, although study of the physical environment is certainly reason enough to warrant the time and money involved. Even more than that, we wanted to know how the environment affected the East Coast Maya belief system and unique world view. We found that geographical and environmental factors profoundly shaped their world view as expressed in their mural art. The fact that the aboriginal name of Tulum as revealed in 16th-century documents is *Zama* and translates as "city that looks upon the dawn" is reason enough to suspect the environmental conditioning of cultural expression in our region. Further, evidence for the worship of Venus as Morning Star is a direct factor of our zone being the easternmost region in Mesoamerica. Also, detailed studies of fresh water flow in Quintana Roo, carried out by a team of geologists, confirmed our hypothesis that the Maya understood the hydrogeology of their region of the peninsula. They gave cultural meaning to natural processes, seeing them as confirmations of religious beliefs expressed in their mural art.

This is not the place to explain just how these natural phenomena affect material culture at Tancah-Tulum. I do this in the above-mentioned monograph, focussing on the eastern location, astronomical associations, and hydrogeographic properties of the region as expressed in the iconography of their mural art. For the Tancah-Tulum Maya, murals "explain" visually the natural and cyclic phenomena which were part of their own unique physical environ-

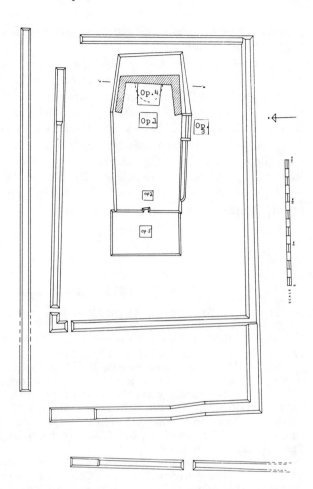

FIG. 6. Tancah Struc-
ture 71 showing loca-
tion of test pits.

ment. In this sense their painting is explanation, a visual rationalization for such fundamental phenomena as the sunrise and the Venus cycle, which the Tancah-Tulum Maya anthropomorphosized as repeating exploits of important mythmakers in their cosmology and history.

Acknowledgments

The Quintana Roo Mural Project benefited from the interest and aid of several individuals who went out of their way to encourage and in some cases tangibly to advance the success of our efforts. Full credit is given to each of these persons in the forthcoming monograph on the project. In the meantime,

I list them here in alphabetical order and gratefully acknowledge their encouragement and support:

E. W. Andrews V, George Andrews, Joann Andrews, Patty Andrews, Alberta Ball, Hal Ball, Antonio Benavides, Elizabeth Benson, Elsy Betancourt de Bush, Pablo Bush Romero, Manuel Calcaneo, Arlen Chase, Michael Coe, William Coe, Giles Constable, Gordon Ekholm, Marguerite Ekholm, Susanna Ekholm, Nancy Farriss, Marilyn Fifield, Thomas Fifield, Willie Folan, Peter Furst, Paul Gendrop, Norman Hammond, Otis Imboden, Christopher Jones, Eduardo Matos, Ursula Pariser, Rosario Parra, Cesar Portilla Rosado, Duncan Pring, Fernando Robles, Charles Rosenberg, Bertold Reise, Susan Rogers de Dávalos, Anne Schaffer, Robert Sharer, George Stuart, Gene Stuart, William Tyler, and Gordon Willey.

REFERENCES

ANDREWS IV, E. WYLLYS, and ANTHONY P. ANDREWS
    1975.   A preliminary study of the ruins of Xcaret, Quintana Roo, Mexico. Middle American Research Institute Publication 40, New Orleans.
FARRISS, NANCY M., and ARTHUR G. MILLER
    1977.   Maritime culture contact of the Maya: Underwater surveys and test excavations in Quintana Roo, Mexico. The International Journal of Nautical Archaeology and Underwater Exploration, vol. 6, no. 1, London.
FARRISS, NANCY M., ARTHUR G. MILLER, and ARLEN F. CHASE
    1975.   Late Maya mural paintings from Quintana Roo, Mexico. Journal of Field Archaeology, vol. 2, no. 1-2, pp. 5-10. Boston.
FERNÁNDEZ, MIGUEL ANGEL
    1941.   El templo num. 5 de Tulum, Quintana Roo. Pp. 155-180 *in* "Los Mayas Antiguos," Fondo de Cultura Economica, Mexico.
    1945a.   Las ruinas de Tulum, I.   Anales del Museo Nacional de Arqueologia, Historia y Etnografia, V, vol. 3, pp. 109-115, Mexico.
    1945b.   Las ruinas de Tulum, II.   Anales del Instituto Nacional de Antropologia e Historia I (1939-40), pp. 95-105. Mexico.
FERNÁNDEZ, MIGUEL ANGEL, CESAR LIZARDI-RAMOS, and ROMULO ROZO
    1945.   Las pinturas de la galeria sur del templo de las frescoes, Tulum.   Anales del Museo Nacional de Arqueologia, Historia y Etnografia, V, vol. 3, pp. 117-120. Mexico.
GIFFORD, JOHN A.
    n.d.   The geology of Lake Chunyaxche, Quintana Roo, Mexico, and its relation to the Postclassic Mayan site of Muyil.   Unpublished manuscript.
LOTHROP, S. K.
    1924.   Tulum: An archaeological study of the East Coast of Yucatan.   Carnegie Institution of Washington, Publication 335. Washington, D. C.

MILLER, ARTHUR G.
  1973.   The mural painting in Structure 12 at Tancah and in Structure 5 at Tulum, Quintana Roo, Mexico: Implications of their style and iconography.   Pp. 465-471 *in* "Atti del XL Congreso Internazionale degli Americanisti," Roma-Genova, 3-10 Settembre 1972, vol. 1. Casa Editrice Tilgher, Genova.
  1977.   The Maya and the sea: Trade and cult at Tancah and Tulum, Quintana Roo, Mexico.   Pp. 97-140 *in* "The Sea in the Pre-Columbian World." Dumbarton Oaks, Washington, D. C.
MILLER, ARTHUR G., and NANCY M. FARRISS
  1979.   "Religious syncretism in Colonial Yucatan: The archaeological and ethnohistorical evidence from Tancah, Quintana Roo, Mexico.   Pp. 223-240 *in* "Maya Archaeology and Ethnohistory," University of Texas Press, Austin and London.
SABLOFF, JEREMY A., and WILLIAM L. RATHJE
  1975.   A study of changing pre-Columbian commercial systems. The 1972-1973 seasons at Cozumel, Mexico.   Peabody Museum Monographs, no. 3. Harvard University, Cambridge, Massachusetts.
SANDERS, WILLIAM T.
  1954.   Ceramic stratigraphy of the East Coast of Yucatan.   Pp. 292-293 *in* "Carnegie Institution of Washington Yearbook no. 53." Washington, D. C.
  1955a.   Explorations on the East Coast of Yucatan.   Pp. 286-289 *in* "Carnegie Institution of Washington, Yearbook no. 54." Washington, D. C.
  1960.   Prehistoric ceramics and settlement patterns in Quintana Roo, Mexico.   Pp. 155-264, *in* "Carnegie Institution of Washington, Publication 606." Washington, D. C.
STEPHENS, J. L.
  1843.   Incidents of travel in Yucatan, vol. II. New York.
WEIDIE, A. E., editor
  1974.   Field seminar on water and carbonate rocks of the Yucatan Peninsula, Mexico.   New Orleans Geological Society, New Orleans.

ARTHUR G. MILLER

Following the Underwater Trail of a Vanishing Species—the Hawksbill Turtle

Principal Investigators: Bernard Nietschmann, University of California, Berkeley; Judith Nietschmann, Berkeley, California.

Grant No. 1058:   To study the exploitation and ecology of the hawksbill sea turtle *(Eretmochelys imbricata).*

Investigation of sea turtles presents difficult problems as the five genera of these reptiles spend almost their entire lives at sea, and each year their numbers dwindle, primarily because of human predation. One sea turtle, the hawksbill *(Eretmochelys imbricata),* is especially perplexing to study because of its very scant numbers and thinly dispersed distribution. It has been identified as "one of the most clearly endangered genera of reptile in the entire world" (Carr, 1969:74) and is listed by the IUCN as "endangered, actively threatened with extinction" (IUCN, 1973). Where it still occurs the hawksbill is highly sought after for its valuable variegated translucent shell plates (tortoiseshell), eggs, calipee, meat, and skin.

Although hawksbills are more tropically limited in distribution than other marine turtles, they do not appear in any sizable concentrations either seasonally or spatially. Instead, they are widely distributed within littoral and coral-reef environments, occurring in small groups or individually. Unlike the green turtle *(Chelonia mydas)* or ridley *(Lepidochelys),* the hawksbill does not appear to mass migrate or mass nest. Rather, its nesting pattern is spread out temporally and geographically. In the western Caribbean, hawksbills nest ungregariously on small, scattered, and isolated mainland and coral cay beaches, generally from June through November.

Very little is known about the life history, ecology, and range and movements of the hawksbill turtles. They have been so seldom studied that even some basic descriptive data are lacking. A fuller understanding of their natural history is sorely needed to plan efficient and intelligent conservation programs. For most endangered species, an inverse relationship exists between the size of the remaining population and the need for additional biological and ecological information.

The aims of our research project were to (1) locate the principal hawksbill nesting beaches and home foraging reefs; (2) gather basic descriptive information such as average size and weight, and nesting seasonality and intensity; (3)

FIG. 1.   The hawksbill, one of the least-known and most endangered of marine species. The pronounced beak, adapted for probing and digging for food in coral-reef
environments, gives the hawksbill its common English name. (Man O'War Cay.)

investigate their range, patterns of seasonal movement, and the possibility of
long-distance migration; (4) document and assess the intensity of commercial
exploitation; and (5) suggest to local and national officials appropriate conservation measures based on research results.

     To learn more about this endangered species one has to find them. How-
ever, because of their depleted numbers and diffuse distribution, a short-term
research effort focused on any one nesting beach would be inefficient and unproductive. So, rather than wait on one of the many nesting beaches for
hawksbills to come to us, we decided to go after them at sea.

     This was to be one of the first attempts to study and catch hawksbills in
their marine environment for scientific purposes.[1] When a hawksbill crawls

---

[1] One of the few other attempts to catch and tag a number of marine turtles at sea
was carried out by Schmidt (1916) in the eastern Caribbean.

FIG. 2. Setting turtle nets for hawksbills. (Miskito Cays.)

Fig. 3.   Boat and crew used during research. Here hawksbills caught off the Miskito Cays are being unloaded for weighing and tagging. (Big Sandy Bay Bar.)

up on a beach to nest, it is slow, almost helpless, and easy to catch. But in the water it is extremely quick, agile, wary, and elusive. To capture hawksbills would require considerable familiarity with their habits and habitat. For this reason it was decided to carry out the research with the aid of experienced turtlemen in tropical waters that we already knew well. We would need a boat, a skilled crew, sufficient supplies to stay at sea for long periods, and, as it turned out, a good deal of patience.

The research was conducted from May to September 1972 in the western Caribbean off the coast of Nicaragua. One of the few remaining areas in the Caribbean where appreciable numbers of green and hawksbill turtles still can be found, the reef-strewn shallow waters there are fished by the coastal Miskito Indians, probably the world's most skilled turtlemen.[2]

Working from a small diesel-powered boat crewed by four turtlemen, my wife, Judith—a coinvestigator on the project—and I traveled along the coast, among the offshore islands and reefs, from the Miskito Cays to the Río San Juan, locating and mapping hawksbill areas and nesting beaches; and catching hawksbills for measurement and tagging.[3] With the help of our crew and accompanying Miskito turtlemen, we caught hawksbills with nets set over specific coral reef spots, occasionally turned them on a small nesting beach, and captured a few underwater while skin diving. We also purchased live hawksbills from Miskito turtlemen when we visited different turtling areas.[4] A total of 60 hawksbills were caught, measured, tagged,[5] and released, as shown in table 1.

Measurements

Data on hawksbill size are conspicuously lacking in the available literature. Carr, Hirth, and Ogren (1966:4-7) provide carapace and plastron measurements from 62 mature female and 3 mature male hawksbills, noting that mean carapace length for females was 32.72 inches, and for males 31.56 inches, but they state that "no weights of hawksbills of known length" were available.

---

[2] For a description of the coastal Miskito and turtling, see Nietschmann (1973, 1974, 1977, 1979a, b).

[3] Brian Weiss, who was conducting research in a coastal Miskito village, helped greatly with logistical problems and often assisted in our research.

[4] To obtain hawksbills from the Miskito it was necessary to pay the estimated equivalent market value for the animal that could have been earned from the sale of its shell, meat, eggs, and skin.

[5] The tags were similar to the ones devised and used by Prof. Archie Carr in his research with green turtles at Tortuguero, Costa Rica (1967:25-40).

Carapace measurements and live weights were obtained for 60 hawksbills (mature and immature) during our research off eastern Nicaragua (table 2). The mean weight of 32 females was almost 120 pounds, with one huge female weighing in at 190 pounds. The males were smaller in mean size and weights. Hawksbills were once thought to be the smallest of the sea turtles, but these data suggest that the average mature hawksbill is considerably larger than the ridley (*Lepidochelys*), the smallest of the sea turtles.

Tagging Hawksbill and Tag Recoveries

Owing to the hawksbill's endangered status and sparse distribution, and the rough weather during our research, we were pleased to be able to find and tag as many as 60. As it turned out, our biggest difficulty was not catching hawksbills or riding out tropical storms, but in attempting to explain to Miskito turtlemen why we were going to so much trouble to catch or purchase such a valuable animal only to let it go again.

Subsequent recovery of some of the tags has provided new information on the possibility of occasional long-distance migration of hawksbills. Whether or not hawksbills do migrate has been a point of conjecture. Hawksbill turtlemen from Cayman Brac (Cayman Islands, B.W.I.) and from Miskito Indian villages maintain that these turtles do migrate, that each year some hawksbills leave from one area and do not reappear until several months later. Exactly where they went was a matter of conflicting claims, but that they went was agreed upon. There was simply no evidence to substantiate native migration

TABLE 1.   Methods of Capture of Hawksbill Turtles

Method of capture	*Female*	*Male*	*Total*
Turtle nets	29[a]	16[b]	45
Nesting on beach	6	—	6
Skin diving—coral reefs	4[c]	—	4
By hand—reef flat	2[c]	—	2
Harpoon	—	2	2
Shrimp boat	1	—	1
	42	18	60

[a]Including four immature turtles.   [c]All immature.
[b]Including one immature turtle.

FIG. 4.   Hawksbill captured in net while surfacing for air. Measured and tagged, it was soon released. (Miskito Cays.)

theories. Years ago, in the scientific literature, the consensus that hawksbills did not migrate was more a product of lack of data than a clear picture of hawksbill behavior: "There is a general belief that hawksbills do not migrate to any extent, and while this appears likely, it has yet to be authentically established" (Carr, 1952:369).

However, returns from tagging programs at Tortuguero, Costa Rica (Carr, Hirth, and Ogren, 1966; Carr and Stancyk, 1975), and offshore eastern Nicaragua, suggest that *Eretmochelys* may migrate or journey long distances. To date, there have been 15 tag returns from 60 hawksbills we tagged in 1972, 2 of which were international recoveries and 13 local (table 3 and fig. 5). From the 130 hawksbills tagged at Tortuguero between 1956 and 1974, Carr and Stancyk (1975) reported 7 returns, including 4 long-distance recoveries.

TABLE 2. Measurements and Weights of Hawksbills Caught off Eastern Nicaragua, 1972

Hawksbill turtles	Length of carapace—inches (cm.)	Width of carapace—inches (cm.)	Weight—pounds (kg.)
MATURE FEMALES			
Range	24.6-34.25 (62.48-87.0 cm.)	17.9-25.6 (45.47-65.02 cm.)	60.0-190 (27.22-86.16 kg.)
Mean	30.14 (76.55 cm.)	22.19 (56.36 cm.)	119.47 (54.19 kg.)
Number	32	32	32
MATURE MALES			
Range	28.125-33.5 (71.44-85.09 cm.)	20.0-33.5 (50.8-85.09 cm.)	97.0-145.0 (50-65.7 kg.)
Mean	30.64 (77.83 cm.)	22.27 (56.57 cm.)	117.76 (53.41 kg.)
Number	17	17	17
IMMATURE FEMALES			
Range	8.5-19.5 (21.59-49.53 cm.)	6.0-13.6 (15.24-34.54 cm.)	3.0-30.0 (1.36-13.61 kg.)
Mean	13.99 (35.53 cm.)	10.36 (26.31 cm.)	13.77 (6.25 kg.)
Number	10	10	10
IMMATURE MALES			
Range	16.9 (42.93 cm.)	12.2 (30.99 cm.)	19.0 (8.62 kg.)
Mean	16.9 (42.93 cm.)	12.2 (30.99 cm.)	19.0 (8.62 kg.)
Number	1	1	1

TABLE 3.   Recoveries of Hawksbill Turtles Tagged off Eastern Nicaragua, 1972

	Tag no.	Sex	Weight (pounds)	Date tagged	Place released (in Nicaragua)	Place recovered	Date	Distance
1.	N-051	F	154	8-1-72	Rio Grande Bar	Au Dakura Shoal, Nicaragua	8-13-72	15 miles
2.	N-022	F	161	7-28-72	Set Net Cays	Tyara Cay, Nicaragua[1]	8-18-72	35 miles
3.	N-039	F	150	9-2-72	Little Sandy Bay	Halfway Shoal, 8 miles east of Little Sandy Bay, Nicaragua[2]	9-3-72	Same shoal
4.	N-002	F	146	6-22-72	Sukra, Miskito Cays	Pedro Cays, Jamaica[1]	11-14-72	390 miles
5.	N-068	F	17	9-29-72	Little Sandy Bay	Halfway Shoal, Nicaragua	12-14-72	4 miles
6.	N-005	F	95	6-24-72	Sukra, Miskito Cays	Miskito Cays, Nicaragua	3-19-73	Same general area
7.	N-014	F	9	7-22-72	Set Net Cays	Set Net Cays, or Little Corn Island, Nicaragua	9-15-73	Same general area
8.	N-026	M	109	8-5-72	Little Sandy Bay	8 miles east of King's Cay, Nicaragua	3-4-74	30 miles
9.	N-069	M	129	10-20-72	Little Sandy Bay	Almirante Bay, Panama	5-10-74	275 miles
10.	N-057	M	116	8-3-72	Set Net Cays	Greytown Banks, San Juan del Norte, Nicaragua	7-31-74	105 miles
11.	N-016	M	97	7-22-72	Set Net Cays	15 miles north of Man O'War Cay, Nicaragua	11-8-74	50 miles
12.	N-015	F	135	7-22-72	Set Net Cays	Set Net Cays, Nicaragua[1]	6-7-75	4 miles
13.	N-062	F	108	9-21-72	Little Sandy Bay	Man O'War Cay, Nicaragua	10-75	10 miles
14.	N-020	F	94	7-22-72	Set Net Cays	Man O'War Cay, Nicaragua	2-24-76	40 miles
15.	N-028	F	144	8-9-72	Tyara Cay	Miskito Cays, Nicaragua	3-12-78	110 miles

[1] Nesting on beach.   [2] Returned to same shoal as where originally caught.

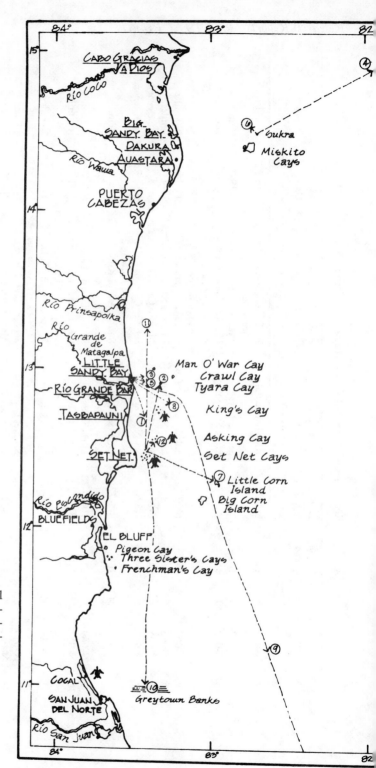

FIG. 5. Hawksbill tag recoveries. (Numbered recoveries correspond to information in table 4.)

HAWKSBILL TAG RECOVERIES

SET NET •MISKITO INDIAN
TURTLING VILLAGE

🐢 •IMPORTANT HAWKSBILL
NESTING BEACHES

0 10 20   40   60 MILES

0 10 20   40   60   80 KILOMETERS

For the western Caribbean, then, there have been but 6 reported long-distance, international tag recoveries (table 4): 4 were from hawksbills tagged at the Tortuguero, Costa Rica, nesting beach and later caught in reef foraging areas off the Miskito Cays in Nicaragua; the other 2 were tagged near these same Nicaraguan reefs—one was recovered 390 miles away, the longest recorded journey, nesting at the Pedro Cays, Jamaica, and the other, a male, was taken off Almirante Bay, Panama, near a nesting beach frequented by hawksbills (Chiriquí Beach, Panama[6]).

These tag recoveries are so few that they encourage either ultraconservative statements or wide-open speculation. Obviously, the data base is too small and the sample too limited from which to derive any solid conclusions on hawksbill migration. Nevertheless, the Nicaragua and Costa Rica tag data do lead to some strong inferences:

1. Hawksbills move around much more than previously believed.
2. Hawksbills sometimes make long-distance journeys.
3. Some of these journeys are to distant nesting beaches, bypassing locally available beaches. Even though small beaches occur within the immediate home foraging environment and are used by some female hawksbills, others still make long-distance journeys to nesting beaches. Hawksbill feeding and nesting requirements are believed to be more generalized and less specific than for green turtles, whose marine pasture foraging areas are often hundreds of miles from a highly specific nodal nesting beach. The omnivorous hawksbill, a relatively indiscriminate feeder, however, can usually find abundant sources of food in reef areas where also are found many suitable small nesting beaches. The question, then, is why do hawksbills (at least some) migrate considerable distances to a nesting beach when there are apparently available ones within their home territory? Has predation of local nesting beaches forced hawksbills to more distant beaches? Or is the inferred migration pattern simply a large-scale elaboration of the hawksbill's tendency to spread out its life cycle spatially and seasonally?
4. Hawksbill journeys may cross international boundaries. In the western Caribbean-eastern Central America area, long-distance tag recoveries indicate that at least some hawksbills do travel between feeding and nesting areas in different countries. This fact is of major significance for any conservation program aimed at protecting these rapidly disappearing marine reptiles.

The balance of our hawksbill tag returns were recovered locally in Nicaraguan waters. Of these returns, turtle number N-039 deserves special mention as it suggests a strong site fidelity and homing instinct in hawksbills similar to that described for green turtles (Carr, 1967). After being caught at a coral reef 8 miles east of the Miskito Indian village of Little Sandy Bay, this hawks-

---

[6] See Parsons (1972:58) and Carr (1956:148-152) for mention of the Chiriquí Beach.

FIG. 6.   Tagging a hawksbill. The numbered monel tags are imprinted in Spanish and English with an offer of a reward and return address.

TABLE 4.   Reported International Recoveries of Hawksbill Turtles
(Tortuguero data from Carr, Hirth, and Ogren 1966:23; Carr and Stancyk, 1975.)

Tag no.	Place tagged	Date turtle tagged	Place of recovery	Date of recovery	Approximate distance traveled (miles)
330	Tortuguero, Costa Rica	8-18-56	Auastara, Nicaragua	10-18-56	240
984	Tortuguero, Costa Rica	7-27-59	Miskito Cays, Nicaragua	7-25-60	288
8453	Tortuguero, Costa Rica	8-3-72	Miskito Cays, Nicaragua	11-73	240
H-140	Tortuguero, Costa Rica	8-26-72	Miskito Cays, Nicaragua	1-10-74	240
N-002	Miskito Cays, Nicaragua	6-22-72	Pedro Cays, Jamaica	11-14-72	390
N-069	Little Sandy Bay, Nicaragua	10-20-72	Almirante Bay, Panama	5-10-74	275

Fig. 7. Weighing hawksbill N-002, Miskito Cays. This turtle was later captured while nesting at the Pedro Cays, Jamaica, a distance of 390 miles from the release site, the longest documented hawksbill journey on record.

bill was brought to the village for measurement, weighing, and tagging before it was released. The next morning it was caught again at the same coral head at the same reef. The turtleman received a $5 recovery reward and the hawksbill was released again from the beach at Little Sandy Bay only to be caught once more the next morning, 8 miles away, at exactly the same place. Another reward was paid. The cycle of reef-village-reward-release-reef was repeated again with several variations on release sites. Nonetheless, the next morning it would appear again in the same turtleman's net at the same coral head. This one hawksbill threatened to break our National Geographic Society research fund while at the same time making one turtleman very wealthy, as he was not going to kill the turtle that carried the golden tag. If there is such a thing as waving a white handkerchief for a sea turtle instead of a brave fighting bull, we tried to do it by buying a lifetime no-more-setting-turtle-nets-at-that-reef guarantee for that hawksbill. Thinking of number N-039 hopefully still swimming around that coral head helped get me through long Michigan winters.

Hawksbill Nesting and Renesting

In the western Caribbean the nesting period for the hawksbill is spread over several months, from May to November, with the heaviest nesting occurring in July and August. All nesting takes place at night, the female usually emerging from the sea on a rising tide, and lasts approximately one hour, during which time the nest cavity is dug, some 150-160 eggs laid, and the nest site concealed.

The reproductive cycle of the hawksbill may be similar to the nonannual breeding periodicity of green turtles in the Caribbean. The very limited remigration data suggest that hawksbills may nest on a 3-4 year cycle (table 5). Of the 7 documented remigration returns, 4 were after a period of 3 years, 1 after 4 years, while 2 were recovered after 6 years, possibly representing second 3-year returns. The ecological or biological causes for such a long interval between nestings are still unknown.

TABLE 5.   Hawksbill Nesting Cycle Intervals, Tortuguero, Costa Rica, and Set Net Cays, Nicaragua

(Tortuguero data from Carr and Stancyk, 1975.)

Tag no.	Date tagged	Place tagged	Date retaken	Place retaken
306	8-15-56	Mile 5/8, Tortuguero	6-18-59	Mile 1/2, Tortuguero
783	8-25-58	Mile 1/2, Tortuguero	8-6-64	Mile 1/2, Tortuguero
2149	7-17-62	Mile $1\frac{1}{2}$, Tortuguero	8-6-65	Mile $1\frac{1}{2}$ Tortuguero
3241	8-17-64	Mile 1, Tortuguero	9-5-70	Mile 3/4, Tortuguero
4617	10-9-67	Mile 5/8, Tortuguero	9-7-70	Mile 3/8, Tortuguero
5326	9-3-68	Mile 17, Tortuguero	9-31-72	Mile $4\frac{1}{2}$, Tortuguero
N-015	7-22-72	Water Cay, Set Net Cays	6-7-75	Black Mangrove Cay, Set Net Cays, 4 miles from tag site

There is widespread consensus among native turtlemen that hawksbills nest two, three, sometimes four times during each nesting season, with a 15- to 17-day interval between each nesting. Based on a small sample of renesting returns, Carr and Stancyk (1975) found that the internesting interval was 19.82 ± 3.43 days, longer than the documented nesting period of any other species of sea turtle. Our data on 5 renesting hawksbills indicate a somewhat shorter interval, 18.5 ± 2.4 days, which is closer to the local turtlemen's estimates.

All the turtlemen we have worked with in the Caribbean insist that hawksbills renest several times within one season and usually at the same beach. During July 1972 one of the turtlemen working with us discovered a fresh hawksbill nest on a small pocket beach on one of the Set Net Cays. He made a mental note of the date, place, and tide conditions. Sixteen days later he asked us to anchor well off the same cay so that he could quietly go ashore and wait for the hawksbill to renest. Braving hordes of sand flies that night, he turned a hawksbill within 50 feet of where the first nest had been laid, verifying that it was the same one because its damaged fin left a distinctive trail.

No experimentation has been done yet on hawksbill location-finding ability to home in on a particular coral head or nesting beach. Native judgments conclude that hawksbills exhibit location-finding behavior similar to green turtles but not over such great distances. The Miskito say that hawksbills do not move in a haphazard manner whether within a coral shoal area or journeying to nest or renest. As one turtleman told me: "Hawksbill know the place. They come right to the spot. How they find it, we don't know. But they choose it right; looking out for the young."

Although hawksbills appear more spread out and less concentrated within their home range and nesting patterns, this does not mean that there are no concentrations. In the western Caribbean there are many small coral-cay pocket beaches and isolated stretches of mainland beach where hawksbills, and only hawksbills, nest. Similarly, even though hawksbills may be widely distributed over extensive coral reef areas, there are many specific coral heads and reef formations where sizable numbers of hawksbills congregate. The Miskito refer to these spots as "pure hawksbill shoals," and each has its own name.

The temporally and geographically diffuse nesting pattern spreads out survival chances over a large area and a long season. The July-August nesting peak off eastern Nicaragua also coincides with the worst weather, heavy rains and rough sea, which ordinarily would discourage human interference on the scattered nesting beaches. However, humans are too plentiful, alternative economic means are too scarce, and hawksbills are too valuable for them still to be protected by diffuse distribution and rough weather. Most of the Nicaraguan coral cays are utilized for camp sites by turtlemen, lobstermen, and, recently, Jamaican fishermen. The mainland beaches are traversed almost daily by people walking from one village to another. As a consequence, the pathways of seaside humans and marine littoral hawksbills are crossing more often and more regularly, to the detriment of the hawksbill.

FIG. 8. Miskito Indian removing hawksbill shell plates (tortoiseshell) from the bony carapace with hot water and a knife. Sold immediately for the equivalent of US$20, this one turtle supplied money equal to the amount needed to sustain one family on purchased foods for one month.

Ebb Tide of the Hawksbill

Owing to their localized tropical coastal distribution and their highly prized shell, hawksbill populations have been subjected to heavy exploitation for hundreds of years. "Among the several species of giant marine turtles that inhabit the tropical seas, it is the hawksbill. . . , source of the tortoise shell of commerce, that has probably experienced the longest and most sustained history of commercial exploitation" (Parsons, 1972:45). It is from the beautifully mottled, translucent shell that the hawksbill receives its fame and makes it a lucrative quarry. Easily worked and exquisite in pattern and color, tortoiseshell has long been a highly sought-after item of trade from tropical coastal areas. Hawksbills have been depleted or eradicated from much of their former pantropical range primarily because of the tortoiseshell trade. "Today, despite increased competition from plastics, the shell is in new demand on many markets, especially in industrializing Japan and in the new tourist centers along the shores of the Caribbean and other tropical seas" (Parsons, 1972:45). The world price and demand for tortoiseshell continue to climb as hawksbill populations continue to decline.

For many coastal peoples in the Caribbean the capture and sale of one hawksbill is often equivalent to one or two weeks' wages; that is, if jobs were even available. One female hawksbill (in 1979) can bring as much as $50 or $60 from the sale of its shell, meat, eggs, skin,[7] and calipee.[8] "So now the hawksbill has three prices on its head: one for its shell, one for its hide, and one for its calipee" (Carr, 1967:229). To this bounty list can be added the additional economic inducements of its eggs and meat frequently used to supply tourist-hotel restaurants, and small hawksbills that are stuffed and shellacked for hotel and airport curio shops.

Approximately 1,000 to 1,200 hawksbills are taken annually from eastern Nicaraguan waters, one of the last remaining hawksbill refuge areas. The shell is purchased by many local dealers, later to be sent on to larger buyers in Managua, where the shell is packed and crated for shipment via Corinto to Japan.

Although the taking of mature hawksbills for their shell and other byproducts is making considerable inroads on remnant populations, the greatest

---

[7] Salted fresh skins from hawksbill, loggerhead, and green turtles have been exported from Nicaragua to Europe where they are tanned and manufactured into leather articles.

[8] Calipee is the cartilaginous material obtained from boiling and breaking apart the turtle's carapace and plastron. Green turtle calipee is extremely valuable and serves as the basis for the famed green turtle soup. Hawksbill calipee, while not as superior as that from green turtles, nonetheless is often sold and substituted.

threat to hawksbill survival is from egg collection. Carr noted this more than 20 years ago when he wrote, ". . . egg hunting is probably the most serious factor in the depletion of hawksbill populations. . . . The eggs are universally appreciated, where obtainable, and are eaten either fresh or cured. Shelled eggs are dried and sometimes strung like beads to be smoked; while those taken from butchered females are salted and smoked in sausage skins or in their own oviducts" (1952:371).

The price on the hawksbill's head is so high, and other means of earning cash in the western Caribbean are so limited, that hawksbills are being subjected to year-round, almost continuous, exploitation by a variety of techniques. Hawksbills are caught by means of (1) turtle nets set over coral shoals to entangle hawksbills when they surface for air; (2) harpoons with detachable points and long lines used to capture hawksbills when they come to the surface; (3) hooprings and nets that are dropped from the surface over sleeping and feeding hawksbills below; (4) "bay nets" strung up on stakes in front of nesting beaches; (5) the turning of nesting females; and (6) the excavation of nests. In addition, the commercial pursuit of two other marine resources has added to the pressure on surviving hawksbill numbers: shrimping and lobstering. Shrimp boats frequently bring up suffocated hawksbills in their nets. In several areas of the Caribbean, skin and scuba divers are being used to catch lobsters in coral reef areas. The divers often are able to catch hawksbills and bring them to the surface. In the Miskito Cays area, for example, approximately 100 Miskito Indian and Creole divers are working off large lobster boats using scuba equipment. During their 2- to 3-week-long periods at sea, each diver averages at least one or two hawksbills, some obtaining many more. When the price of hawksbill shell went up to almost $20 per pound in 1978, the divers concentrated exclusively on securing *Eretmochelys* from the reefs.

The intensity of hawksbill exploitation has been determined mainly by commercial rather than subsistence factors. There is a close correlation between tortoiseshell market price and the degree of human pressure on *Eretmochelys* populations. Coincident with rising prices for shell (fig. 9) has been a steady increase in the numbers killed. For example, between 1969 and 1971, the local market price for shell in eastern Nicaragua went up 50 percent, which resulted in exploitation increases as high as 400 percent in one Miskito Indian village (Nietschmann, 1972:60). By 1978 the price had risen 600 percent.

Schmidt (1916:12) in referring to the depletion of hawksbill nesting grounds in the Danish West Indies, remarked that: "It is literally this species that pays the penalty every time turtle eggs are enjoyed as a delicacy. As hawksbill, on account of its 'tortoise shell,' is the most valuable of all turtles, a well-grown specimen often bringing a price of 100 francs ($20) or more, it would be difficult to imagine a more extravagant article of diet than turtle eggs, even though these are sold for a few centimes apiece."

During the height of the nesting activity in July of 1971 and 1972, two reconnaissances were made on offshore eastern Nicaraguan coral cay beaches.

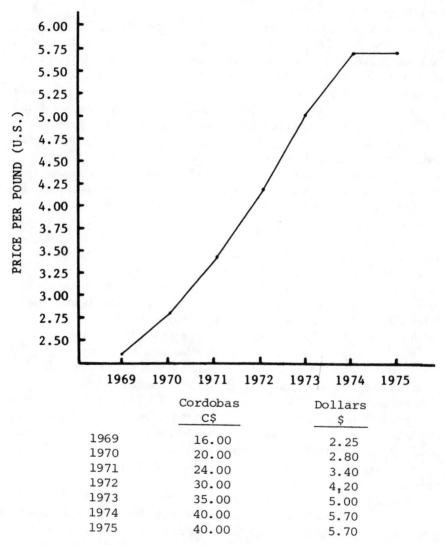

	Cordobas C$	Dollars $
1969	16.00	2.25
1970	20.00	2.80
1971	24.00	3.40
1972	30.00	4,20
1973	35.00	5.00
1974	40.00	5.70
1975	40.00	5.70

FIG. 9.   Recent increases in market price of hawksbill shell.

The first survey showed that approximately 95 percent of the recent nestings had been discovered and dug up by turtlemen. In 1972 a more extensive survey was conducted, which again indicated that more than 90 percent of the nests had been found and excavated. Of the remaining nests, natural predation would claim a high percentage of the hatchlings in their first few hours of life. The excavation of egg clutches and the decimation of mature hawksbills are outstripping this species' ability to survive much longer. One Miskito turtleman told me that "hawksbill don't die by themselves. They only die when a shark or man gets them."

Three events recently occurred that provide some encouragement in the face of an otherwise dismal survival outlook for hawksbill and other sea turtles. In June 1975 Archie Carr and I were invited to Nicaragua to meet with President Somoza and other government officials to discuss sea turtle conservation problems. Results from the National Geographic Society research project were presented along with similar data on green turtles. The commercial exploitation of green turtles for export markets was halted in early 1977. In November 1979 the new Nicaraguan government proposed establishing a National Park in the Miskito Cays area in order to protect hawksbills and green turtles. On October 28, 1975, the Costa Rican Congress passed a bill for the creation of the Tortuguero National Park largely as the result of the efforts of Carr, the Caribbean Conservation Corporation, and Costa Rican conservationists. The establishment of this park will protect the last remaining major green turtle nesting beach in the Caribbean and one that is also used frequently by hawksbill turtles, an even more endangered species than *Chelonia mydas.*

In small areas, scattered here and there in the Caribbean, the remaining hawksbills hang on. We know little about them as a species and almost nothing about their migrating behavior or role in the ecology of coral reef environments. Any SCUBA diver who has seen a hawksbill gliding over the reef edge, silhouetted against the deep blue of the dropoff, knows that when the hawksbill is gone, more will be lost than just another species from the reef.

REFERENCES

CARR, ARCHIE
1952. Handbook of turtles, xv + 542 pp., illus. Comstock Publishing Associates, Cornell University Press, Ithaca, New York.
1956. The windward road, xvi + 258 + viii pp., illus. Alfred A. Knopf, New York.
1967. So excellent a fishe: A natural history of sea turtles, x + 248 pp., illus. Natural History Press, New York.

CARR, ARCHIE (continued)
1969.   Sea turtle resources of the Caribbean and Gulf of Mexico.   IUCN Res. Bull., vol. 2, no. 10, pp. 74-83.

CARR, ARCHIE; HIRTH, HAROLD; and OGREN, LARRY
1966.   The ecology and migrations of sea turtles, 6: the hawksbill turtle in the Caribbean Sea.   Amer. Mus. Novitates, no. 2248, 29 pp.

CARR, ARCHIE, and STANCYK, STEPHEN
1975.   Observations on the ecology and survival outlook of the hawksbill turtle. Biol. Conserv., vol. 8, no. 3, pp. 161-172.

INTERNATIONAL UNION FOR THE CONSERVATION OF NATURE AND NATURAL RESOURCES (IUCN)
1973.   Convention on international trade in endangered species of wild fauna and flora.   IUCN Bull., vol. 4, no. 3, pp. 1-12.

NIETSCHMANN, BERNARD
1972.   Hunting and fishing focus among the Miskito Indians, eastern Nicaragua.   Human Ecol., vol. 1, pp. 41-67, illus.
1973.   Between land and water: The subsistence ecology of the Miskito Indians, xiv + 279 pp., illus.   Seminar Press, New York.
1974.   When the turtle collapses, the world ends.   Nat. Hist., vol. 83, pp. 34-43, illus.
1975.   Who will kill the last turtle?   Collected Papers on Vanishing Species and Societies, Nicaragua, 190 pp. Processed. (Includes "The Exploitation and Conservation of Hawksbill Sea Turtles," "The Predicament and Protections of Sea Turtles," and "Protecting Endangered and Depleted Fauna in Nicaragua." Spanish and English.)
1977.   Memorias de Arrecife Tortuga: Historia natural y económica de las tortugas en el Caribe de América Central, viii+258 pp., illus.   Colección Cultural, Banco de América, Managua, Nicaragua. (contributing editor; includes new and reprinted papers by Archie Carr, David D. Duncan, Peter Matthiessen, James J. Parsons, Brian Weiss, and others.)
1979a. Ecological change, inflation, and migration in the far western Caribbean, pp. 1-24, illus.   The Geographical Review, vol. 69, no. 1.
1979b. Caribbean edge: The coming of modern times to isolated people and wildlife, xv+280 pp., illus.   Bobbs-Merrill, New York.

PARSONS, JAMES J.
1972.   The hawksbill turtle and the tortoise shell trade.   Pp. 45-60 *in* "Études de Géographie Tropicale Offertes à Pierre Gourou."   Mouton, Paris, La Haye.

SCHMIDT, JOHS
1916.   Marking experiments with turtles in the Danish West Indies.   Medd. Komm. Havundersøgelser, Fiskeri ser., vol. 5, pp. 1-26.

BERNARD NIETSCHMANN

Natural History of Vertebrates on the Brazilian Islands of the Mid South Atlantic

Principal Investigator: Storrs L. Olson, National Museum of Natural History, Smithsonian Institution, Washington, D. C.

Grant Nos. 1105, 1409.   For study of the past and present vertebrate fauna, particularly birds, of Fernando de Noronha Island and for a study of the status of the living and fossil birds of Ilha da Trindade.

I. Zoology and Paleontology of the Terrestrial Vertebrates of Fernando de Noronha Island, South Atlantic Ocean

Because of the destruction of habitat and the introduction of exotic predators and grazing animals, terrestrial faunas now found on small oceanic islands are often considerably altered from those that existed before the arrival of man. For this reason I have conducted paleontological investigations on the islands of the mid South Atlantic Ocean in order to search for evidence of exterminated species, particularly of birds. On Ascension Island, I found remains of an extinct species of flightless rail (Olson, 1973) and also those of resident sea birds and a few vagrant land birds (Olson, 1977a). Extensive fossil deposits on St. Helena I found to contain remains of 6 species of extinct land birds and 3 new species of sea birds. At the same time, these revealed a nearly complete turnover of the sea-bird fauna of the island during the Pleistocene whereby subtropical petrels were largely replaced by tropical terns, boobies, and frigatebirds (Olson, 1973, 1975). Thus, I decided next to turn my attentions to Fernando de Noronha.

The archipelago of Fernando de Noronha lies 345 kilometers east of the easternmost point of Brazil (lat. 3° 50′ S., long. 32° 25′ W.) and consists of one main island and about 12 smaller islets, with a total area of 18.4 square kilometers. These islands are entirely volcanic in origin, are well vegetated, and have a mild climate. The archipelago was discovered in 1503 and has been inhabited for much of its subsequent history. It is presently a Federal Territory of Brazil and is administered by the Brazilian army. Roughly 1,200 people, both civilian and military, now live on Fernando de Noronha, and the Brazilian air force runs regularly scheduled flights to the island.

The earliest reference to the fauna of Fernando de Noronha is found in the account of the so-called fourth voyage of Amerigo Vespucci (Markham,

1894), who claimed to have visited the island in the year of its discovery, finding there "marine and land birds without number" and also "very large rats." No native rats are now found on Fernando de Noronha, and thus the possibility that an endemic rodent may have existed there at the time of the island's discovery is of considerable interest. Naturalists have visited Fernando de Noronha on a number of occasions, but almost always for very brief periods. In 1887, H. N. Ridley collected specimens on the island from August 14 to September 24, and his accounts of the botany and zoology have provided the groundwork for all subsequent biological studies there (Ridley, 1890a, 1890b).

Three species of land birds are native to Fernando de Noronha: a distinctive species of vireo *(Vireo gracilirostris),* an endemic subspecies of tyrannid flycatcher *(Elaenia spectabilis ridleyana),* and a subspecies of the eared dove *(Zenaida auriculata noronha)* first described from the island but later ascertained to occur in mainland Brazil as well. Sea birds known from the island include the magnificent frigatebird *(Fregata magnificens),* red-billed and white-tailed tropicbirds *(Phaethon aethereus* and *P. lepturus),* red-footed, brown, and masked boobies *(Sula sula, S. leucogaster,* and *S. dactylatra),* sooty tern *(Sterna fuscata),* brown noddies and black noddies *(Anous stolidus* and *A. tenuirostris),* and white terns *(Gygis alba).* No petrels (Procellariidae and Oceanitidae) have ever been reported from the island itself.

My primary interest in going to Fernando de Noronha was in searching for fossil deposits that might yield remains of Vespucci's rat, extinct land birds such as rails (Rallidae), and extirpated sea birds, particularly petrels. Also, I wished to determine the status of the existing land birds and to make observations on their habits, since little besides brief taxonomic descriptions has been published concerning these species.

In May 1973, authorization for a scientific expedition to Fernando de Noronha was granted by the Conselho Nacional de Pesquisas of Brazil. Funds were provided mainly by the National Geographic Society, with a small additional grant supplied by the International Council for Bird Preservation. I arrived on Fernando de Noronha on July 6, 1973, and remained until August 18, accompanied by O. A. Roppa and I. A. Cruz, who assisted in collecting specimens. Quarters were in quonset huts on the northern side of the island at Tres Paus, at the base of the distinctive phonolitic plug known as the Pico, the highest point on the island.

Attempts to find fossils were at first unsuccessful. Fernando de Noronha is comparatively level and there are no steep valleys with deep fossiliferous sediments like those found on St. Helena (Olson, 1975). Nor are there fumaroles or lava tunnels such as produced fossils on Ascension Island (Olson,

1973, 1976). A deep sea cave, the "Buraco de Captão Kidd" near Ponta da Pedra Alta, proved inaccessible, owing to the great waves rushing into its entrance. At last I discovered that the sandy area of Pleistocene dunes at the base of the Santo Antonio peninsula contained vertebrate fossils as well as those of terrestrial snails and land crabs. Fossils were usually found scattered on the surface of the dunes, but parts of skeletons were occasionally found in association. Many of the specimens are well mineralized, and these appear to have weathered out of a somewhat indurated layer of white nodules. This layer was exposed in position at a small sand-quarrying site near the road passing through the dunes. Only the shells of land snails were found in place in this exposed section. On the surface of the dunes, vertebrate fossils appeared to be most abundant where there were concentrations of the white nodules and snail shells. I made 12 collecting trips to the Santo Antonio site, spending most of the time gleaning fossils from the surface of the dunes, but also screening in areas where associated material was found.

The most frequently encountered fossils were those of a large rodent of the family Cricetidae, very different from the recent remains of the introduced rats *(Rattus),* which were also encountered on the dunes. This cricetid is almost certainly the rat mentioned by Vespucci. It is a new species, and possibly a new genus in the subfamily Sigmodontinae. The specimens are currently under study by Michael Carleton of the Smithsonian Institution.

Remains of a new species of rail (Rallidae) were also found, bringing the total known land-bird fauna to four species. Most of the elements of the skeleton, from several different individuals, are represented. This was a medium-size rail with the wings reduced, but to a lesser extent than in many flightless species. It does not appear to be particularly close morphologically to any of the species of rails from mainland Brazil. I have briefly alluded to this form elsewhere (Olson, 1977b), but it has yet to be formally described.

Well-mineralized bones of boobies and frigatebirds were collected fairly frequently. A single proximal end of a humerus of a frigatebird appears to belong to a small species the size of the lesser frigatebird *Fregata ariel,* which in the Atlantic now exists only at Ilha da Trindade, although subfossil remains of a frigatebird of this size have been found on St. Helena (Olson, 1975). The present record adds significantly to our information and raises a number of interesting questions about the distribution and relationships of the smaller forms of frigatebirds.

Resident species of Procellariiformes are not represented in the fossil material, yet some of the tropical species such as *Puffinus lherminieri, Oceanodroma castro,* or members of the *Pterodroma hasitata* group might be expected to have occurred on the island. The absence of these birds even from the fossil record at Fernando de Noronha may perhaps be attributed to the presence of two predators, the extinct rodent and the land crab *Gecarcinus lagostomus,* both of which could have made reproduction difficult or impossible for petrels that customarily nest in burrows or on the ground.

The three living species of land birds on the island proved to be very common. The vireo and flycatcher were most abundant in the remaining areas of forest at the eastern end of the island and around the base of Morro do Pico, but both were found in scrubby areas and in trees along roadsides and around dwellings. As during Ridley's visit, flycatchers were present but vireos were absent on Ilha Rata, the largest of the subsidiary islands.

The vireos appeared to feed almost exclusively on small insects gleaned from the underside of leaves, from which the birds would very frequently suspend themselves upside down to feed. They almost never took larger prey from trunks or limbs, or hawked insects from the air, as most other vireos do to varying extents. The long, slender bill and very long tail of the Noronha vireo may well be correlated with its seemingly rather specialized feeding habits. Although now usually regarded as a subspecies of the red-eyed vireo complex *(Vireo olivaceus),* the morphology of *Vireo gracilirostris* is so divergent that it must be recognized as a full species.

I found fossilized remains of the dove, indicating its long presence on the island. That the insular population has not differentiated from that of parts of northeastern Brazil is probably a reflection of fairly frequent influxes of new individuals from the mainland.

The populations of sea birds at Fernando de Noronha seem to be thriving better than elsewhere in the tropical South Atlantic. Exceptions are *Sula dactylatra* and *Sterna fuscata,* both of which need flat open areas, little of which is available on the predator-free offshore islets where these birds must now nest at Fernando de Noronha. Black noddies were the most abundant birds at the island. All the species of sea birds appeared to be breeding during our visit, although we could not confirm breeding in the frigatebird or in the decidedly rare red-billed tropicbird.

I encountered relatively few migrants: a tern *(Sterna* sp.), skua *(Catharacta* sp.), and whimbrel *(Numenius phaeopus)* have not been recorded previously from the island. Two specimens of whimbrel were collected—one of the North American race *(N. p. hudsonianus)* and the other of the European race *(N. p. phaeopus),* the first ever recorded for South America.

The most peculiar reptile on the island is the endemic worm-lizard *Amphisbaena ridleyi,* which on the slopes of Morro do Pico proved to be much more abundant than mainland populations of this genus usually are. Fossils of this species occurred in the dune deposits with the other vertebrate remains.

The endemic lizard *Mabuya maculata* was extremely common, and in the late afternoon more than 40 individuals catching the last rays of the evening sun could be seen on each utility pole along certain sections of road. Since Ridley's report in 1890, a toad *(Bufo paracnemis)*, the tegu lizard *(Tupinambis teguixin)*, and a caviomorph rodent *(Kerodon rupestris)* have been successfully introduced to the island.

On July 23 I used rotenone to collect fishes and marine invertebrates in a large tide pool at Saco de Atalaia. This pool yielded a wide variety of fishes and truly impressive numbers of moray eels. On the night of July 31 I collected needlefishes *(Platybelone)* and halfbeaks *(Hemiramphus)* with torches and dip-nets at Baio do Sueste. These collections are under study by various specialists. Among the more interesting fishes collected is an apparently new genus and species of sand stargazer of the family Dactyloscopidae (C. E. Dawson, pers. comm.).

II. AVIFAUNA OF ILHA DA TRINDADE, SOUTH ATLANTIC OCEAN

The exploration of Ilha da Trindade completed my investigations into the past and present birdlife of the tropical and subtropical islands of the South Atlantic. The site of this study is known in much of the literature as South Trinidad or Trindade Island. The former has resulted in confusion with the Caribbean island of Trinidad and the latter is almost invariably misspelled "Trinidade," an orthography that cannot be justified in either English or Portuguese. Therefore it is probably best to use the complete Portuguese designation "Ilha da Trindade" when there is any possibility of confusion.

Ilha da Trindade lies in the South Atlantic Ocean at a distance of 620 miles east of Vitória, Brazil, and 765 miles east-northeast of Rio de Janeiro. The neighboring islets of Martin Vas lie 26 miles eastward and are visible from the island. Ilha da Trindade has an area of 8 square kilometers and a maximum elevation of 600 meters. It is entirely volcanic in origin and quite steep and rugged throughout.

The only transportation to Trindade is by a Brazilian naval vessel that calls every 2 months to replenish supplies and transfer half the garrison of 40 naval personnel, who operate a small weather and communications station on the northern shore of the island. At 10 a.m. on December 10, 1975, I boarded the corvette *Bahiano* in Rio de Janeiro harbor. On the morning of December 12 I was still aboard the *Bahiano* and still in Rio harbor, because of engine trouble. All personnel and supplies were transferred to the research vessel *Almirante Saldanha*, which did eventually get under way after midday of the 13th. After 5 days at sea, we sighted Trindade in the moonlight at 2:30 a.m. of the 18th. A primitive landing was effected by means of a small barge, floated on oil drums, that was pulled through the surf from the island to the ship, and back, with several hundred yards of heavy cable. The ship's end of the cable was hauled by a winch, but that on the island was powered by 30 or so straining sailors, at least half of whom had extra incentive because their 4-month tour was up and they would soon be leaving the pure but austere island existence for the delights of Rio. I set foot on Trindade shortly after noon of December 18, 1975, and remained there until February 10, 1976, departing in the corvette *Caboclo* and arriving in Rio on the 13th.

Trindade once had extensive forest cover, but the trees experienced a die-off early in the 19th century. Murphy (1915) summarized what was then known of the history of this forest, noting the accounts of several travelers in the early 1800's who had remarked on the melancholy groves of dead trees then to be met with on the island. A number of far-fetched hypotheses to explain this seemingly total eradication on Trindade have been advanced, including destruction by volcanic gases, introduced goats, or a drastic decrease in rainfall.

The earlier visitors, puzzled by the stands of trees that appeared to have been killed simultaneously, seem to have overlooked the simplest and most satisfactory explanation for their demise—fire. Weathered pieces of wood from these trees may still be found in the higher parts of the island and I saw evidence of fire on many of them. Although it is possible that the wood may have been burned in grass fires after the trees had died and fallen to the ground, the specimens I examined rarely showed evidence of external charring but rather had a layer of dark, apparently fire-hardened wood beneath a weathered exterior. Fires set by man would explain the simultaneous death of mature trees. Destruction by volcanic gases could not have occurred, as there is no evidence of any recent volcanic activity on the island. The hypothesis that invokes a drastic decrease in rainfall does not hold when one considers that there has continued to be sufficient rainfall to perpetuate growths of hydrophilic tree ferns.

At my instigation, Dr. Richard Eyde of the Department of Botany, Smithsonian Institution, has delved extensively into the literature on, and the identity of, the "extinct" trees of Trindade. Previously there had been five different identifications published for these trees—all erroneous. Wood samples that I collected were identified by Eng. Calvino Mainieri, of the Laboratório de Anatomia e Identificação de Madeiras, São Paulo, as belonging to the genus *Colubrina*. As it turns out, the species *Colubrina glandulosa* var. *reitzii* is among the plants still occurring on Trindade. *Colubrina* has a propensity to colonize oceanic islands, though the mechanism of its dispersal is not apparent. Thus the trees of Trindade are not extinct. Evidently, after the original forest cover was destroyed, overgrazing by goats prevented the trees from regaining their former stature or extent.

Apart from fairly ubiquitous grasses and various trees, mostly exotic, that are found sparsely on the higher parts of the island, the principal native vegetation left on Trindade is tree-fern forest. Even this appears to have been reduced since the early part of the century, now being confined to two rather broad valleys on the southern side.

Goats are present in fair numbers. Feral cats are also met with on occasion and mice *(Mus)* are abundant. Trindade has somehow mercifully been spared invasion by rats *(Rattus),* probably because there are no beaches that would have been suited to careening a large vessel for scraping or repairs. One native organism that may have had an effect on the composition of the sea-bird fauna, the land crab *Gecarcinus lagostomus,* occurs in quantity in all parts of the island. These creatures, when properly prepared, are a delight to the human palate; so many are taken away alive in crates for home consumption by departing members of the garrison that large individuals are usually found only in the higher parts of the island and on the south side, which is reached solely by those persons inclined to traverse a vertiginous trail over the summit. Even small crabs become noticeably less abundant around the settlement in the week prior to the arrival of the supply ship.

Ornithological investigations of Trindade have usually been of short duration. In this century the island was visited briefly in 1905 by Nicoll (1906, 1909), and in 1901 and 1910 by Wilson (Wilson, 1904; Sharpe, 1904; Lowe and Kinnear, 1930). Murphy (1915), later to be regarded as the authority on Trindade, actually spent only one day in the waters around the island and was unable to go ashore. Preparators for the Museu Nacional do Rio de Janeiro spent 6 months on the island collecting various biological specimens in 1916, the ornithological results being published by Ribeiro (1919). The *Blossom* Expedition of the Cleveland Museum of Natural History visited Trindade from December 23, 1924, to January 26, 1925. No scientific report of this expedition was ever published, though some information may be gleaned from the popular writings of Simmons (1927) and Rockwell (1932, 1955). Finally, a small collection of birds was made in May 1950, again by members of the Museu Nacional, who were on the island for a week (Novaes, 1952). From these studies the avifauna was known to comprise eight or nine breeding species of sea birds, no land birds ever having been discovered. Subsequent to 1950 there has been no information on the birdlife of the island. Thus, in visiting Trindade I hoped to ascertain the present status of the sea birds and to search for fossils of exterminated species such as I found on Ascension, St. Helena, and Fernando de Noronha.

During my sojourn on Trindade I found that the populations of most species of sea birds had been greatly reduced in the 50 years since the *Blossom* visited the island. Unfortunately, I was not able to visit the islets of Martin Vas, the bird populations of which must be somewhat healthier, although I was told that these islets are used for target practice by the corvettes that service the Trindade garrison.

Trindade Petrel *(Pterodroma a. arminjoniana).*   This species is found in the Atlantic Ocean only at Trindade, and in the Indian Ocean only on Round Island, off Mauritius. What is alleged to be a slightly smaller race, *P. a. heraldica,* is found on a number of Pacific islands. It was encouraging to find this species present and fairly abundant on several of the high peaks of Trindade. Although the birds could be seen entering inaccessible holes and crevices in the cliffs, there was no indication of breeding in any of the 24 specimens I collected. Two of these appeared to be recently fledged juveniles, however. Stomach contents consisted entirely of remains of squid, with the exception of a small individual of the mackerel *Scomber japonicus.*

Frigatebirds *(Fregata).*   Both the greater and lesser frigatebirds *(F. minor* and *F. ariel)* are known from Trindade, the only place in the Atlantic where these otherwise Indo-Pacific species occur. Previously, I had found fossils of both a large and a small species on St. Helena (Olson, 1975) and assumed that they were probably the same two forms as represented at Trindade. However, because the bones of the smaller species from St. Helena were significantly stouter than in Indo-Pacific specimens of *F. ariel,* it seemed possible that the Atlantic populations might be specifically or subspecifically differentiated, something also suggested by the distinctive subadult plumage described for the Trindade birds (Lowe, 1924). Thus it became of considerable interest to learn more about these birds.

Unfortunately, the population of *F. ariel* at Trindade is now very small. I found this species only on a single, small steep islet at Ponta do Sul. Studies of birds in this area were limited; in order to reach this part of the island it was necessary to cross from sea level on one side, over the highest part of the island, to sea level on the other side. By wading and climbing over some of the connecting islets it was possible to reach the base of the islet on which the frigatebirds were breeding, but the vertical walls then encountered made it otherwise inaccessible and all observations of nesting birds had to be made with a telescope from an adjacent point of land several hundred meters away. On the west side of the islet I made out about 15 nests of *F. ariel.* There may have been a few more on the east side. These nests were situated on the bare rock or on clumps of vegetation on the steep sides of the islet. There were probably no more than 50 individuals of *F. ariel* at Trindade at the time of my visit, although I saw only one subadult bird, so it is possible that nonbreeding birds remain at sea.

Fregata minor, once considered the more abundant species at Trindade, evidently no longer breeds there. Occasional individuals were seen at various times, and when the green turtles began hatching, the birds became more regular, up to four being seen at one time. I presumed these to have come from Martin Vas, which must now be the only breeding outpost of this species in the Atlantic.

The juvenal plumage of the Trindade populations of *F. ariel* was not previously known. With a telescope I was able to examine a well-feathered juvenile on a nest at Ponta do Sul. This had the reddish head characteristic of the other populations of *F. ariel.* I obtained skeletons of two males of *F. ariel* on Trindade, but these do not appear to differ markedly from Indo-Pacific specimens. The taxonomic status of the South Atlantic populations of small frigatebirds, both living and fossil, thus remains equivocal.

Masked Booby *(Sula dactylatra).* Murphy (1936) overlooked Ribeiro's (1919) record of this species at Trindade. I examined these specimens, the only ones known for the island, at the Museu Nacional in Rio. Neither I, nor other collectors, encountered this species.

Red-footed Booby *(Sula sula).* Once very common on Trindade, this species has been reduced to two very small colonies of 10 to 12 and about 75, respectively, on the tops of two inaccessible peaks. There were nearly fledged young in both colonies. Despite the fact that Murphy (1936) repeatedly insists that this species must nest in trees, these birds were nesting flat on the ground.

Brown Noddy *(Anous stolidus).* This species was present in fair numbers but was not particularly abundant. I found birds nesting at Ponta do Sul and others no doubt nest on various cliffs and stacks on the inaccessible portions of the southern coast.

Black Noddy *(Anous minutus).* I did not see a single example of this species. The only records for the area consist of one seen but not collected by Nicoll at Martin Vas (1906; *contra* Murphy [1936] who erroneously reported this as a specimen record) and mention by Rockwell (1932) of what was probably this species nesting at Martin Vas, but again no specimens were collected. There is no evidence that *A. minutus* ever occurred at Trindade proper.

White Tern *(Gygis alba).* To judge from previous accounts, the population of these birds is now greatly diminished. I encountered only scattered pairs from time to time, the only numbers of any consequence being observed by telescope on the Monumento or Ninepin.

Sooty Tern *(Sterna fuscata).* This species nests on an annual cycle at Trindade and apparently the *Blossom* was the only previous expedition to have been on the island at a time coincident with its breeding. Although Rockwell (1932) mentioned that sooty terns were found only on one offshore islet, it was the most frequently observed bird during my stay. I found a colony of about 450 pairs on a flat, fairly easily accessible plateau on the eastern end of the island. Elsewhere on the island there were probably less than 1,000 pairs. There were a few tiny colonies in little grassy pockets on the cliff face of Pão de Açucar and somewhat larger colonies on the tops of tall isolated peaks near Cockscomb Point. I observed many over the Monumento, but at a distance too great to make any sort of estimate.

I collected specimens of the following four species of North American migrant shorebirds, all of which appear to be the first of their species recorded for the island, but none of which is unexpected: golden plover *(Pluvialis dominica),* black-bellied plover *(Pluvialis squatarola),* ruddy turnstone *(Arenaria interpres),* sanderling *(Calidris albus).*

The saffron finch *(Sicalis flaveola)* was introduced to Trindade in 1963, and there is a small population confined entirely to the houses and trees of the settlement. In the high, wilder parts of the island exist a few guinea hens *(Numida meleagris),* probably descendants of birds introduced more recently than those reported to have been released early in the 18th century.

To interject an encouraging note in the otherwise sad history of the depletion of the fauna of Trindade, I found the green turtle *(Chelonia mydas)* to be breeding plentifully. Females were laying throughout my stay and I found the first hatchlings on January 28. The turtles have no doubt benefited appreciably by the demise of the frigatebirds, which must have preyed heavily on the hatchlings. Land crabs still take a frightful toll. Turtles are completely protected at Trindade and the stricture against taking or molesting them was carefully observed by all members of the garrison.

In looking for fossils I located two likely deposits of wind-blown calcareous sand similar to those that yielded bones on Fernando de Noronha and St. Helena. Despite intensive searching, I found these to bear only the shells of land snails and the remains of land crabs.

Having gained some experience of Ilha da Trindade, I now consider that it is unlikely that any species of sea birds existed there in geologically recent time that have not already been recorded from the island. My observations further confirm those of other expeditions that tropicbirds *(Phaethon),* black noddies *(Anous minutus),* brown boobies *(Sula leucogaster),* and procellariiform birds other than *Pterodroma arminjoniana* are absent. The first three of these are cliff-nesting birds that have survived the introduction of predators and the habitat destruction on other islands of the South Atlantic and which could well be expected to have survived at Trindade had they ever existed there, as there is certainly no shortage of cliffs.

I believe that the presence of land crabs on Trindade may have prevented burrowing or ground-nesting petrels from colonizing the island. While boobies and even terns could defend their nestlings against the attacks of crabs, petrels leave their helpless young unattended for long periods, during which time they would certainly be consumed if the voracious *Gecarcinus* were present. It is of interest that, apart from the crevice-nesting storm petrel *Oceanodroma castro* on Ascension, and the cliff-nesting *Pterodroma arminjoniana* on Trindade, no procellariiform birds are ever known to have bred on Ascension, Fernando de Noronha, or Trindade. *Gecarcinus* is found on all of these islands, whereas it is absent from St. Helena, where at least 6 species of Procellariiformes once thrived (Olson, 1975).

In my opinion, it is highly unlikely that there was not an endemic species of rail (Rallidae) on Trindade in the past, as there was ample habitat and these birds successfully colonized all the other South Atlantic islands (Olson, 1973). That I was unable to find any fossil remains of such a bird may perhaps be attributed to my usual good fortune temporarily running out. The great abundance of land crabs on Trindade may also have reduced the chances of any rail carcasses surviving long enough to be preserved, although this did not prevent rail bones from being fossilized on Fernando de Noronha, where land crabs also occur.

REFERENCES

LOWE, PERCY R.
   1924.   Some notes on the Fregatidae.   Nov. Zool., vol. 21, pp. 299-313.
LOWE, PERCY R., and KINNEAR, NORMAN B.
   1930.   British antarctic *(Terra Nova)* expedition, 1910, Natural History Report.   Zoology, vol. 4, no. 5. Birds: pp. 103-193.
MARKHAM, CLEMENT R., trans. and ed.
   1894.   The letters of Amerigo Vespucci and other documents illustrative of his career.   Hakluyt Society, ser. 1, no. 90, 121 pp.
MURPHY, ROBERT CUSHMAN
   1915.   The bird life of Trinidad Islet.   Auk, vol. 32, pp. 332-348.
   1936.   Oceanic birds of South America, 2 vols.   American Museum of Natural History, New York.
NICOLL, MICHAEL J.
   1906.   On the birds collected and observed during the voyage of the *Valhalla,* R.Y.W., from November 1905 to May 1906.   Ibis, ser. 8, vol. 6, pp. 666-712.
   1909.   Three voyages of a naturalist, ed. 2, 246 pp.   Witherby & Co., London.

NOVAES. F. C.
  1952.   Resultados ornitológicos da "Expedição João Alberto" a Ilha da Trin-
           dade.   Rev. Brasil. Biol., vol. 12, no. 2, pp. 219-228.
OLSON, STORRS L.
  1973.   Evolution of the rails of the South Atlantic islands (Aves: Rallidae).
           Smithsonian Contr. Zool., no. 152, 53 pp.
  1975.   Paleornithology of St. Helena Island, South Atlantic Ocean.   Smith-
           sonian Contr. Paleobiol., no. 23, 49 pp.
  1977a.   Additional notes on subfossil bird remains from Ascension Island.   Ibis,
           vol. 119, pp. 37-43.
  1977b.   A synopsis of the fossil Rallidae.   Pp. 339-373 *in* "Rails of the World,"
           by S. D. Ripley.   David R. Godine, Boston.
RIBEIRO, A. DE MIRANDA
  1919.   A fauna vertebrada da Ilha da Trindade.   Arch. Mus. Nac. Rio de Jan-
           eiro, vol. 22, pp. 171-194.
RIDLEY, HENRY N.
  1890a.   Notes on the botany of Fernando Noronha.   Journ. Linn. Soc. London
           (Botany), vol. 22, pp. 1-95.
  1890b.   Notes on the zoology of Fernando Noronha.   Journ. Linn. Soc. London
           (Zoology), vol. 20, pp. 473-570.
ROCKWELL, R. H.
  1932.   Southward through the doldrums.   Nat. Hist., vol. 32, pp. 424-436.
  1955.   My way of becoming a hunter.   (Pp. 118-198 pertain to the *Blossom* Ex-
           pedition.)   W. W. Norton & Co., New York.
SHARPE, R. BOWDLER
  1904.   Report on the birds obtained by the National Antarctic Expedition at
           the Island of South Trinidad.   Ibis, ser. 8, vol. 4, pp. 214-217.
SIMMONS, GEORGE F.
  1927.   Sindbads of science: The narrative of a windjammer's voyage among is-
           lands of high adventure in the South Atlantic.   Nat. Geogr. Mag., vol.
           52, no. 1, pp. 1-75.
WILSON, E.
  1904.   The birds of the island of South Trinidad.   Ibis, ser. 8, vol. 4, pp. 208-
           213.

STORRS L. OLSON

Zoogeography of Selected Aquatic Insects in New Caledonia

Principal Investigator: William L. Peters, Florida A&M University, Tallahassee, Florida.

Grant No. 1099:   For a study of zoogeographical connections of selected insects in New Caledonia.

The study of continental drift and plate tectonics is important to both geologists and biologists. Geologists are interested in understanding the evolution and ever-changing nature of continents, while biologists, especially historical biogeographers, are interested in possible paths of dispersal of ancient plants and animals. Both geological and biological data are important in understanding the historical evolution of all continental areas.

For many years I and others have been interested in the possible paths of dispersal of an ancient group of aquatic insects called Ephemeroptera, or mayflies, in the Southern Hemisphere. Our interest turned to New Caledonia in 1965 when Prof. Dr. F. Starmühlner of the 1. Zoologischen Institutes der Universität Wien sent to us a collection of New Caledonian mayflies. The collection contained representatives of only one family of mayflies, Leptophlebiidae, and all the genera and species were unknown to science. Study of these mayflies indicated that they were related to other genera occurring in New Zealand, Australia, and South America, but not closely related to those of mainland Asia or New Guinea. As mayflies are sharply limited in dispersal, especially over vast areas of ocean (Edmunds, 1972), the question arose as to how these insects, and possibly other aquatic insects, could have invaded the island of New Caledonia.

Recent geological studies by Griffiths and Varne (1972) and Griffiths (1974) reconstructed the continental fragments of Gondwanaland in the southwestern Pacific. Prior to sea-floor spreading between the Campbell Plateau and Antarctica about 80 million years ago, Australia, Antarctica, Chatham Rise, Campbell Plateau, Lord Howe Rise, and Norfolk Ridge were all close together as one continental element. With the opening of the Tasman Sea about 80 million years ago and the start of the Alpine Fault about 50 million years ago, various continental fragments became isolated and drifted fur-

493

ther apart as time progressed. Based on these data, therefore, the island of New Caledonia is continental in origin.

If this geological hypothesis is correct then ancient ancestors of some plants and animals could have dispersed over land or across small areas of sea to the area that is now New Caledonia. Study of these ancient dispersals, often called palaeantarctic dispersal routes in the Southern Hemisphere, is based on the present geographical distribution and phylogeny of plants and animals. In many groups of plants and animals the present distributions can be explained only by various palaeantarctic dispersal routes. These routes are well illustrated by Edmunds (1972) for animals and by Raven and Axelrod (1974) for plants.

Most important animal data on palaeantarctic routes have been obtained from invertebrates, especially insects. Among the aquatic insects, excellent data have been reported by Brundin (1966) for Chironomidae, Illies (1969) for Plecoptera, Ross (personal communication) for Trichoptera, and Peters and Edmunds (1964, 1970) and Edmunds (1972, 1975) for Ephemeroptera.

In 1972, the Society made a grant available to me to collect and rear aquatic insects in New Caledonia for zoogeographical studies. The expedition included Dr. and Mrs. William L. Peters, their daughter Rae Ellen, Dr. and Mrs. George F. Edmunds, Jr., and Prof. William M. Beck, Jr. These members collected aquatic insects throughout New Caledonia from September 6 through November 15, 1972.

Results

During the expedition to New Caledonia large numbers of aquatic insects were collected in both the immature and adult stages. Many were reared from immatures to adults, especially Ephemeroptera and Chironomidae. After curation all insects were sent to various specialists throughout the world for study. In most cases taxonomic and phylogenetic studies had to be completed before zoogeographical studies could begin. At the writing of this report (1977) many studies are only partially completed, and it will be many years before all studies are completed. Listed below is progress made to date on some of the groups of aquatic insects.

1. Ephemeroptera—studied by W. L. and J. G. Peters, Florida A&M University, and G. F. Edmunds, Jr., University of Utah. Except for two adult specimens of *Pseudocloeon?*, all mayflies collected in New Caledonia were Leptophlebiidae. All genera and species are new to science and all are endemic

to New Caledonia. A series of taxonomic manuscripts has been prepared and will be published in the publications of the Office de la Recherche Scientifique et Technique Outre-Mer (ORSTOM) in Paris.

Phylogenetic studies indicate that these Leptophlebiidae in New Caledonia are most closely related to modern representatives in New Zealand. Evolution of the main Southern Hemisphere phyletic lines appears to have occurred while New Caledonia and New Zealand were connected or in close proximity to each other. Most of these phyletic lines also have more distantly related modern representatives in Australia, southern South America, Africa, Madagascar, Sri Lanka, and southern India. Results of the phylogenetic and zoogeographical studies will be published in ORSTOM publications.

2. Odonata—studied by M. A. Lieftinck, Rhenen, the Netherlands. All results based on our collections and collections of others have been published by Lieftinck (1975, 1976).

3. Trichoptera—studied by H. H. Ross, University of Georgia. At present, studies on the New Caledonian caddisflies are continuing. Ross (1974, 1975) has published results on the Helicopsychidae.

4. Plecoptera—no stoneflies were collected by the expedition in New Caledonia, and this order appears to be absent from the island.

5. Chironomidae—studied by W. M. Beck, Jr., Florida A&M University. At present, studies on the New Caledonian midges are continuing.

Acknowledgments

We extend our thanks to Dr. P. Cochereau, formerly of the Office de la Recherche Scientifique et Technique Outre-Mer, Nouméa, New Caledonia, for his friendship and valuable help during our collecting trip; and to Dr. M. Legand, director, ORSTOM, Nouméa, for the invitation to work at Centre ORSTOM in Nouméa. We especially thank M. Corbasson, director, Centre Technique Forestier Tropical, Nouméa, and F. Goy, director, Service des Eaux et Forêts, Nouméa, for their valuable help in field arrangements. Grateful acknowledgment is made also to the late Dr. G. Loison, program director (health), South Pacific Commission, Nouméa, for making many arrangements for us.

All the curation of the insects and most of the laboratory research on Ephemeroptera and Chironomidae were supported by various grants from the Cooperative State Research Service, United States Department of Agriculture (P.L. 89-106), to Florida A&M University.

REFERENCES

BRUNDIN, LARS
1966.   Transantarctic relationships and their significance as evidenced by the chironomid midges, with a monograph of the subfamilies Podonominae, Aphroteaeninae and austral Heptaginae.   Kongl. Svenska Vet.-akad. Handl., ser. 4, vol. 11, no. 1, pp. 1-472.

EDMUNDS, GEORGE F., JR.
1972.   Biogeography and evolution of Ephemeroptera.   Ann. Rev. Ent., vol. 17, pp. 21-42.
1975.   Phylogenetic biogeography of mayflies.   Ann. Missouri Bot. Gard., vol. 62, pp. 251-253.

GRIFFITHS, J. R.
1974.   Revised continental fit of Australia and Antarctica.   Nature, vol. 249, pp. 336-337.

GRIFFITHS, J. R., and VARNE, R.
1972.   Evolution of the Tasman Sea, Macquarie Ridge and Alpine Fault. Nature, Phys. Sci., vol. 235, pp. 83-86.

ILLIES, JOACHIM
1969.   Biogeography and ecology of Neotropical freshwater insects, especially those from running waters.   Pp. 685-708 *in* "Biogeography and Ecology in South America," vol. 2, Ernst Josef Fittkau et al., eds.   Dr. W. Junk, N.V., The Hague.

LIEFTINCK, MAURITS A.
1975.   The dragonflies (Odonata) of New Caledonia and the Loyalty Islands, pt. 1: Imagines.   Cah. ORSTOM, Sér. Hydrobiol., vol. 9, pp. 127-166.
1976.   *Idem,* pt. 2: Immature stages.   *Ibid.,* vol. 10, pp. 165-200.

PETERS, WILLIAM L., and EDMUNDS, GEORGE F., JR.
1964.   A revision of the generic classification of the Ethiopian Leptophlebiidae (Ephemeroptera).   Trans. Roy. Ent. Soc. London, vol. 116, pp. 225-253.
1970.   Revision of the generic classification of the Eastern Hemisphere Leptophlebiidae (Ephemeroptera).   Pacific Insects, vol. 12, pp. 157-240.

PETERS, WILLIAM L.; PETERS, JANICE G.; and EDMUNDS, GEORGE F., JR.
1978.   The Leptophlebiidae of New Caledonia (Ephemeroptera), Part 1, Introduction and Systematics.   Cah. ORSTOM, Sér. Hydrobiol., vol. 9, pp. 97-117.

RAVEN, PETER H., and AXELROD, DANIEL I.
1974.   Angiosperm biogeography and past continental movements.   Ann. Missouri Bot. Gard., vol. 61, pp. 539-673.

ROSS, HERBERT H.
1974.   Observations on the Helicopsychidae (Trichoptera) of New Caledonia. Pp. 1-3 *in* "Proceedings of the First International Symposium on Trichoptera."   Dr. W. Junk, N.V., The Hague.
1975.   A preliminary report on the Helicopsychidae (Trichoptera) of New Caledonia.   Cah. ORSTOM, Sér. Hydrobiol., vol. 9, pp. 67-80.

WILLIAM L. PETERS

Feeding Habits and Population Studies of Maine's Harbor and Gray Seals

Principal Investigator: David T. Richardson, Fisheries Research Station, Maine Department of Marine Resources, West Boothbay Harbor, Maine.

Grant No. 1125: To study feeding habits and population dynamics of Maine's harbor and gray seals.

Field studies of abundance, distribution, and habits of harbor seals (*Phoca vitulina*) and gray seals (*Halichoerus grypus*) in the vicinity of Acadia National Park, Maine, were conducted by me under contract with the National Park Service and the Maine Department of Marine Resources (formerly, Sea and Shore Fisheries) during the summers of 1971 and 1972 (Richardson, 1973). Lack of baseline population data and inadequate understanding of habits and historical abundance of seal species in Maine prompted study of these attractive members of the Acadia National Park fauna.

Continued study of Maine's seals during 1973 was made possible by the combined support of the National Geographic Society and the Maine Department of Marine Resources. Photocensusing studies during 1973 expanded to the entire Maine coast the population estimates for both seal species. Attempts were made to employ biotelemetry to track seals during their foraging hours so as to learn more of their feeding habits and pelagic behavior. I appreciate the assistance given by David Barnes during summer fieldwork and by the Department's warden pilot Donald McIntosh during photocensusing. Special acknowledgment is given to the late Dr. Leonard Carmichael whose love of the Maine coast and personal encouragement helped make this study possible.

Telemetry Studies

The first year of work proved necessary to investigate and attempt the use of capture techniques, of harnesses for sonic tag attachment to the seal, and of tracking equipment. No data pertinent to feeding behavior of seals were gained, owing to problems in capturing adult seals and in finding suitable attachment methods for sonic tags.

It is hoped that future study of feeding or foraging territories can be pursued (total area, greatest linear dimension, mean activity radius, distribution of activity radius) so that estimates may be made of qualitative and quantitative predation of finfish by seals. Telemetry may enable study of diving behavior, capabilities, and observations of feeding and behavioral interaction with other seals, wildlife, and man.

Photocensusing Studies

Aerial photography was used to estimate Maine's total population of seals and to gather preliminary data of haulout distribution of harbor seals during one season.

All aerial surveys employed the use of a light, single-engine high-wing plane flying at approximately 400 feet over coastal shoreline, small coastal islands, and half-tide ledges. All photographs were taken by hand holding a 35-millimeter SLR camera and using a 135-millimeter lens and appropriate polarizing or haze filters. All photos were taken with high-speed (ASA 160) Kodak Ektachrome film. All shots were taken at 1/500-second shutter speed. Developed transparencies were illuminated on a lenticular screen for counting with the aid, at times, of 6× binoculars.

As nearly as possible, time of tide, sea state, and illumination conditions most attractive for seals to sun and rest were chosen for aerial census and photography. Low-drain tides occurring in the late morning to early afternoon on days with maximum sunlight and calm wind and sea state were chosen.

Table 1 summarizes data obtained from all flights of all coastal sections from Kittery to Eastport, Maine. Water area is expressed in square nautical miles and is that area lying within the 12- and 60-foot depth contours—that area likely to be used by seals for foraging and hunting activity on high-tide hours.

Numbers of seals censused per section are expressed as total seals photographed and counted and as a percent of the total population count for the Maine coast. The density of seals is given as the number of seals per square nautical mile and as the number of seals per haulout. Also given for each section is the total number of haulout locations photographed and an expression of haulout density as the number of square nautical miles per haulout.

In all, approximately 6,000 seals were counted on 203 haulout sites on 7 census flights. Seal densities, calculated from water area lying within the 12- and 60-foot depth contours of each of 15 coastal sections, ranged from 1.35 to 20.94 seals per square nautical mile. Lowest densities occurred along the York County shore west of Cape Porpoise (1.35) and the northerly waters of Penob-

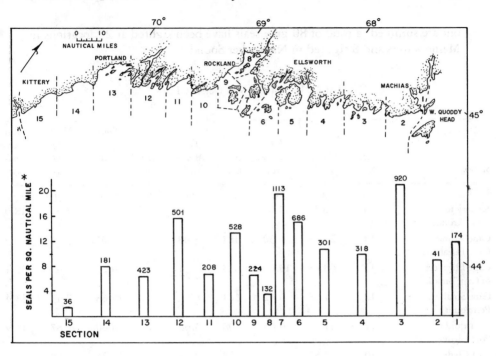

FIG. 1.   Graph showing density of seals by coastal sections.

scot Bay (3.35). Waters having greatest densities included Cape Small to Pemaquid (15.68), approaches to Penobscot and Jericho Bays (19.46), approaches to Blue Hill Bay (15.00), and waters east of Cape Split to Cutler (20.94). Maine's total water area bounded by the 12- and 60-foot depth contours is 522 square nautical miles. An average of one seal haulout every 2.58 square nautical miles supports 28.1 seals; or every lineal nautical mile from Kittery to West Quoddy Head supports about 36 seals.

A partial aerial census of Blue Hill and Frenchman Bays was taken on June 8, 1973, and compared with the *same area* coverage of 1971 and 1972. These data are shown in table 2.

A record of gray-seal sightings taken by boat census during this study and since 1965 by myself and others has been compiled. Sex and maturity of young gray seals are difficult to determine but have been recorded when possible. If values for the maximum number of gray seals ever sighted at each haulout are summed, a total of 80 gray seals have been sighted at 27 locations in Maine waters and 8 sighted in Nantucket Sound.

TABLE 1.   Maine Seal Density Data

Section	Sect. No.	Naut. mi.^{2}	Pct. Maine area	No. seals	Pct. Maine seals	No. haul-outs	Seals per naut. mi.^{2}	Naut. mi.^{2} per haul-out	Seals per haul-out
		A	B	C	D	E	C/A	A/E	C/E
Kittery to Cape Arundel	15	26.59	5.09	36	0.62	2	1.35	13.30	18.0
Cape Arundel to Cape Elizabeth	14	22.48	4.30	181	3.08	7	8.05	3.21	25.9
Cape Elizabeth to Cape Small	13	68.05	13.03	423	7.31	28	6.22	2.43	15.1
Cape Small to Pemaquid	12	31.96	6.12	501	8.66	15	15.68	2.13	33.4
Pemaquid to Port Clyde	11	31.53	6.03	208	3.60	11	6.60	2.87	18.9
Port Clyde to Owls Head plus offshore islands	10	39.83	7.62	528	9.13	10	13.26	3.98	52.8
West and Central Penobscot Bay	9	35.50	6.80	224	3.87	8	6.31	4.44	28.0
North Penobscot Bay	8	39.42	7.55	132	2.28	5	3.35	7.88	26.4
East Penobscot and West Jericho Bay	7	57.18	10.95	1113	19.25	33	19.46	1.73	33.7
Blue Hill Bay and approaches	6	45.72	8.75	686	11.86	30	15.00	1.52	22.9
Frenchman Bay and approaches	5	27.93	5.35	301	5.20	12	10.78	2.33	25.1
Schoodic Point to Cape Split	4	32.66	6.25	318	5.50	12	9.74	2.72	26.5
Cape Split to Cape Wash	3	43.93	8.41	920	15.91	23	20.94	1.91	40.0
Cape Wash to Lubec Channel	2	4.66	0.89	41	0.71	2	8.80	2.33	20.5
Eastport and Cobscook Bay	1	14.94	2.86	174	3.01	5	11.65	2.99	34.8
Σ/X		522.38		5786		203	10.47	2.58	28.1

The seasonal sightings of gray seals in Maine waters west to Penobscot Bay suggest a transient population of fewer than 100 individuals comprised mostly of subadults which have dispersed from breeding grounds in maritime waters.

The total population count of 5,786 seals shown in table 1 is derived by censusing the coast by sections between May 14 and August 23, 1973, and including census counts taken by the same methods during July 5 and 6, 1972, of sections 5, 6, and part of 4. Use of 1972 census data requires the assumption that the population in this area is unchanged for 1973. It is assumed also that no net exchange of seals among sections took place between census dates. The Kennebec and St. Croix Rivers and their tributaries were not covered by aerial census during this study. Table 2, comparing partial census coverage of Blue Hill and Frenchman Bays for three years, indicates an apparent increase in the seal population residing there. However, the increase in numbers of seals from 1971 to 1972 is thought to reflect, at least in part, acquisition of more thorough and experienced flight coverage and photography.

The approach taken here in estimating the abundance of Maine's seals is strictly intuitive. That is, census conditions were chosen as uniformly as possible to take advantage of opportunistic sunning by seals and favorable conditions for aerial photographic techniques. A thorough search pattern was flown of each coastal section and only seal haulouts utilized on that census date were photographed. It is unlikely that all seals in all sections were hauled out during the overflight. Moreover, some haulouts may have been missed. Some difficulty in counting individual seals at densely packed haulouts was encountered. In such cases a conservative count of clearly recognized individuals was made. I estimate that the census sampled at least 75 percent of the total population.

TABLE 2.   Three-year Comparison* of Blue Hill and
Frenchman Bay Seal Populations

Location	Maturity	1971		1972		1973
		June 15	*Sept. 30*	*May 23*	*July 5*	*June 8*
Blue Hill Bay	Adults	243	199	293	263	305
	Pups	—	—	52	—	94
Frenchman Bay	Adults	50	123	169	229	170
	Pups	—	—	9	—	40
	Total	293	322	523	492	609

*Comparison based on partial coverage of the Bay areas.

It is known, from studies in the Acadia National Park area (Richardson, unpublished notes), that seasonal changes in distribution occur within embayments. Also, daily changes in distribution of seals have been noted within rivers and embayments. Some net movement of seals to offshore ledges following whelping takes place during summer months. Thus the data shown in table 1 expressing density of seals by numbers of haulouts and expressing haulout density would be expected to change seasonally. Repeated sampling of coastal sectors in all seasons would make possible estimates of sampling error. It is felt that accurate counting is possible only with clear, nearly vertical aerial shots of seal ledges, especially when counting of pups and densely packed seals is encountered.

Recruitment data reported by Bigg (1969) for West Coast harbor seals and by Boulva (1971) for Sable Island harbor seals would suggest that Maine's post-whelping population of approximately 6,000 seals would recruit 20.4 percent or 1,224 pups (612 female and 612 male) each year. It is my hypothesis that Maine harbor-seal population is stable or nearly so. Yearly sampling of haulouts in all seasons might determine whether changes in the population are occurring that could only be detected in the long term.

REFERENCES

BIGG, M. A.
  1969.   The harbour seal in British Columbia.   Fish. Res. Board Canada Bull. 172, 33 pp.
BOULVA, J.
  1971.   Observations on a colony of whelping harbor seals, *Phoca vitulina concolor,* on Sable Island, Nova Scotia.   Journ. Fish. Res. Board Canada, vol. 28, pp. 755-759.
RICHARDSON, DAVID T.
  1973.   Distribution and abundance of harbor and gray seals in the Acadia Park area.   Final report, National Park Service and Maine Department of Marine Resources Contract 14-10-9-900-390, 59 pp.

DAVID T. RICHARDSON

Distribution and Biology of the Funnel Web-building Spider in a Lava-bed Area, South-central New Mexico

Principal Investigator: Susan Elise Riechert, University of Tennessee, Knoxville, Tennessee.

Grant No. 1090: For a niche analysis of the funnel web-building spider *Agelenopsis aperta* (Gertsch) in a lava-bed area in the Carrizozo Malpais, New Mexico.

Numerous agricultural reports on pest species discuss the potential of spiders to control certain insect populations. There is no consensus as to their effectiveness as predators (Bristowe, 1941; Vite, 1953; Kajak, 1965). Most of the work completed thus far in assessing the role of spiders in the invertebrate community has involved experimentation in the manipulation of spider densities in various test plots. The information gained from such experiments is limited (whether insect numbers are modified by change in spider density). It is my feeling that an understanding of spider population biology is necessary before the ecological significance of this important group can be learned.

Studies of vegetation patterning over the landscape have provided understanding of the behavior and interactions of plant populations in a community under varying conditions of environment and habitat. The mobility and secretive activities of most animals make them difficult subjects for studies of pattern. However, web-building spiders do lend themselves to such investigations. The detectability and relative permanence of spider webs permit study of the mechanisms underlying the distribution and characteristics of species populations. This report describes some of the factors affecting the local distribution of webs of the funnel spider, *Agelenopsis aperta* (Gertsch), in a Recent lava-flow area in south-central New Mexico.

Agelenopsis aperta is a member of the funnel web-building spider family Agelenidae (Araneae). The web consists of a flat sheet with an attached funnel extending into some feature of the surrounding habitat (figs. 1, 2). Occasionally a scaffolding is present. The sheet has no adhesive properties and serves merely as an extension of the spider's legs. *Agelenopsis* carries out much of its activity within a sheltered environment, coming out of the funnel only as long as required for securing prey and repairing the web.

503

FIG. 1.   Web and funnel of *Agelenopsis aperta* in depression.

The life cycle of *A. aperta* in south-central New Mexico is closely coupled with seasonal changes characteristic of the northern Chihuahuan desert at higher altitudes (fig. 4; Riechert, 1974b). Young emerge from the egg sac in August and September following the summer rains. Ground dispersal is accomplished between 1 and 2 weeks after emergence, at which time individual webs are built. Spiders overwinter as immatures or subadults and complete development the following spring; web-building activity stops in October and is not resumed until late February. Maturation and production of offspring occur during the hot, dry period between late May and early July. The first egg sacs may be laid in early June and additional eggs produced up to 6 weeks later. Few adults survive this long, however, since the majority are drowned in floods associated with summer rains beginning in July (fig. 4). The eggs require approximately 3 weeks for development, after which time spiderlings may emerge or stay within the egg sac, depending on outside environmental conditions.

For the most part then, *A. aperta* in New Mexico has an annual life cycle maintained by catastrophic flooding. Those few individuals surviving the floods do produce late eggs, resulting in some age-class overlap; this overlap is minimal.

Study Areas

Fieldwork was carried out on the Robert Shafer Ranch, Gallacher Cattle Corp., New Mexico, Lincoln County, T.6S., R.5E., S.34, alt. 5,400 feet.

Study areas were selected from a desert grassland habitat bordering the Carrizozo Malpais and from the lava bed itself (figs. 3, 5). The lava-bed study area offers a hot barren black substrate, marked by ropy corrugations, sink holes, and pressure ridges (fig. 3). Local concentrations of shrubs occur along

FIG. 2.   *Agelenopsis aperta* on sheet web.

the flow margin and where cracks and depressions have permitted collection of windblown soil and moisture. The grassland bordering the flow contains plant species contributions from both the flow and the surrounding rangeland and supports a more dense growth of vegetation than either of the other two habitats (fig. 3). This habitat is dominated by grasses which surround numerous depressions (straight sided, barren dirt holes, averaging 15-30 centimeters in depth and 1.4 square meters in area). The depressions probably are the result of outwash from underground aquifer tubes.

Field Methods

Periodically the location of all *A. aperta* webs was mapped in each study area. Habitat features (e.g., lava, bare ground, crevices, depressions, cow pats, shrubs, and grazed and ungrazed grasses were also mapped) (Riechert, Reeder, and Allen, 1973; Riechert, 1974b). In all, 222 individuals were captured and marked in 1971 and 1972. The exact locations of occupied webs were mapped and environmental characteristics of web sites were determined from line-intercept sampling techniques. Presence and height of plant species, their flowering status, depression depth, and the presence of various substrate features were recorded at 10-centimeter intervals. A second transect was sampled at a regular distance away from the web site and was arbitrarily defined as a nonweb transect.

The presence or absence of spiders at the web sites was determined by flushing them from their web funnels each morning between 0800 and 1000 MDST coinciding with maximum activity (Riechert and Tracy, 1975; Riechert, 1975). If a spider did not flush, the surrounding area was checked for a new web. When located, new webs were mapped and the occupants flushed to determine their marked status.

The energy balance of *A. aperta* within the local environments afforded by various web-site types (fig. 6) was determined by using an equation borrowed from heat-transfer physics after methods used by Porter (1967) and Gates and Porter (1969). All the components for the equation $Q_{abs} = \Sigma \sigma\ T_s^4 + h_c\ (t_s\text{-}t_a)$, where Q_{abs} is the amount of radiation absorbed by the animal surface, Σ is emissivity, σ is the Stefan-Boltzmann constant, T_s is the surface temperature of the spider, h_c is the convection coefficient, and T_a is air temperature, were determined either through physical measurements or calculations from known relationships (Riechert and Tracy, 1975).

The proportion of the potential prey community available to *Agelenopsis* and the influence of various web-site characteristics on prey availability were determined through the use of artificial sticky webs placed within various

FIG. 3. Aerial photo of Carrizozo Malpais study area. Note depressions on the grassland and shrub distribution on the lava bed.

microhabitats. The discrimination of *Agelenopsis* toward encountered prey was also assessed.

Results

Block-size analysis of variance (Greig-Smith, 1952) was used to examine the distribution of webs in the lava-flow study areas. The basic pattern observed for all samples of adult spiders consists of regularity at small quadrat sizes and aggregation within larger areas (fig. 7; Riechert et al., 1973; Riechert, 1974b). The regularity observed at small quadrat sizes appears to reflect a social pattern in that there is a mean spacing of webs, which is behaviorally regulated (Riechert et al., 1973; Riechert, 1974a,b). The regular spacing of webs noted for adult spiders is absent in immature individuals, and the size of the area maintained by older individuals is dependent on maturity and body size. This mean spacing is believed to function to ensure a food base of available prey and is presently being more closely examined.

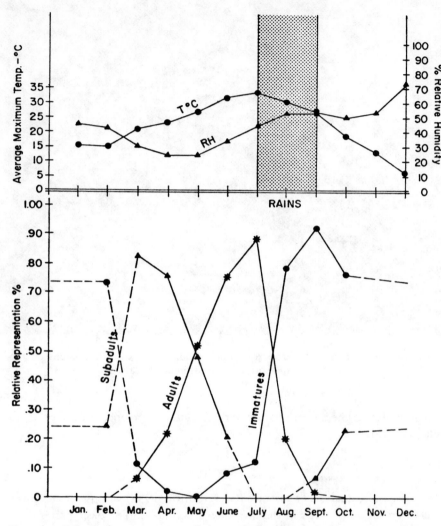

FIG. 4.   Relative representation of various age classes of *Agelenopsis* immatures,
   •; subadults, ▲; adults, *) with change in season and character of the
   macroenvironment.

The clumped distribution noted at larger block sizes (fig. 7) is, in part, a
result of the incomplete dispersal of individuals from the egg sac (reproductive
pattern: Riechert 1974a). To a greater extent it reflects the association of spiders with specific habitat features (vectorial pattern: Riechert et al., 1973;

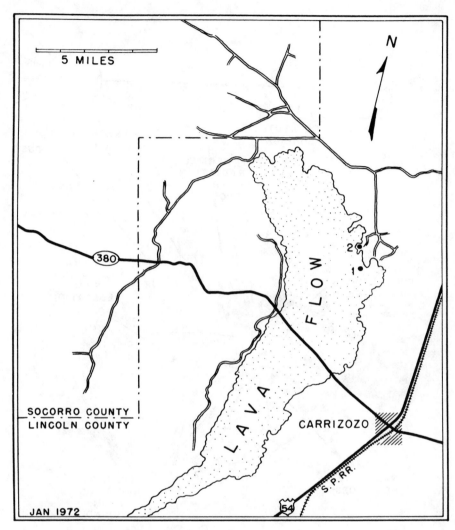

FIG. 5. Map of Carrizozo Malpais area showing study-plot locations: (1) Lava-bed study area; (2) desert-grassland study area.

Riechert, 1974b). The distribution of adult *A. aperta* is closely correlated with that of depressions on the desert-grassland habitat and shrubs on the lava bed (Riechert et al., 1973; Riechert 1974b). Spiders occupying the study areas in seasons other than the hot, dry period occurring in early summer demonstrate less specificity in location of their webs.

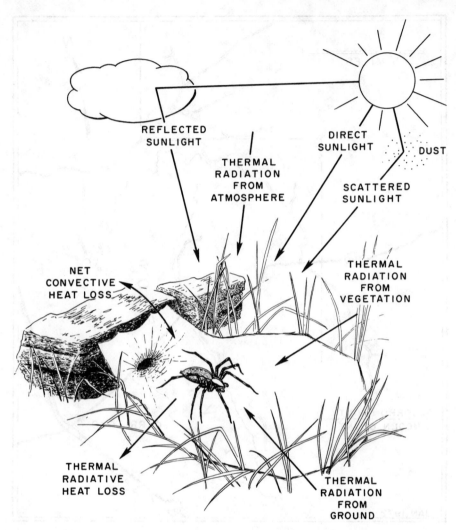

FIG. 6.   Energy exchange between the spider and its environment.

During the course of the study all marked spiders were observed to change the position and orientation of their webs at a given site, and most relocated, as many as seven times, elsewhere (Riechert, 1975). No difference was observed in the number of moves made between immature and adult spiders, although adults tended to move greater distances. A multiple discriminant analysis computed on the character of 634 web sites and associated "nonweb

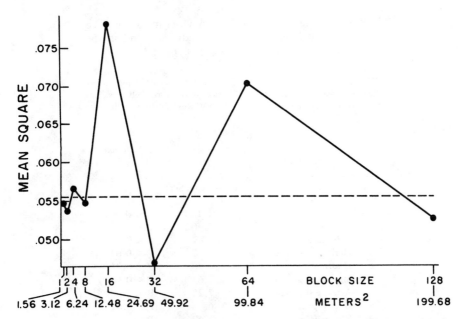

FIG. 7.   Example of adult *Agelenopsis* web pattern. Variance plotted against block
size; dotted line equals the mean.

sites" demonstrates that the microhabitat present at web sites differs from the
general microphysiography and vegetation of the study areas (fig. 8). Characters chosen by spiders in selecting web sites include shrubs, depressions, litter, and flowering plants (table 1). Web sites offering these features are
maintained significantly longer than others, and with successive moves spiders select sites of increasingly better quality.

A model of the effects of thermal environment and prey availability on the
reproductive success of spiders occupying various web-site types was developed (fig. 9; Riechert and Tracy, 1975). The estimated productivity for an excellent web site (grassland and depression with flowers) is 13 times that
determined for a poor site (lava surface). Model results suggest that more energy is to be obtained from selection of a favorable thermal environment (eight-
fold difference) than from a site offering greater numbers of prey (twofold
difference). The presence of flowers at web sites increases the probability of receiving an occasional high prey density, whereas litter and habitat features
providing shade (shrubs and depressions) allow increased spider activity
through limitation of body temperature.

TABLE 1. Variate Importance in Discriminating Web from Nonweb Sites in the Lava Study Area and in the Grassland Study Area

[Discriminant rank is based on the F test with characters arranged in order of usefulness in discriminating between web and nonweb sites. Significance levels represent the results of the Wilcoxon Rank Sum Test.]

	Discriminant rank	F	Significance level
	LAVA STUDY AREA—WEB SITE		
1	Litter	91.13	$P < 0.001$
2	Leaf litter	57.40	$P < 0.01$
3	*Fallugia paradoxa*	21.97	$P < 0.01$
4	Herbs (flowering)	13.47	$P < 0.01$
5	*Hilaria jamesii*	10.78	$P < 0.01$
6	Maximum shrub height	8.62	$P < 0.001$
7	Average shrub height	7.25	$P < 0.001$
8	Grazed grass	6.48	$P < 0.01$
9	*Rhus trilobata*	6.42	$P < 0.05$
10	*Muhlenbergia minutissima*	6.19	$P < 0.10$
11	Woody litter	5.81	$P < 0.01$
12	*Sapindus saponaria*	5.40	Not significant
13	Scats	5.24	Not significant
14	Ungrazed grass	4.98	$P < 0.01$
15	*Artemisia ludoviciana*	4.84	$P < 0.02$
16	*Cuscuta undecora*	4.16	Not significant
17	*Opuntia imbricata*	2.71	Not significant
18	Cow pats	2.65	Not significant
19	*Amaranthus reflexus*	2.64	Not significant
20	*Muhlenbergia porteri*	2.64	$P < 0.01$
21	*Tribulus* sp.	2.58	$P < 0.02$
22	*Oenothera flava*	1.96	Not significant
23	*Bouteloua gracilis*	1.79	Not significant
24	Malvaceae	1.72	Not significant
25	Average crevice depth	1.25	Not significant
26	*Eragrostis*	1.04	Not significant
27	*Juniperus monosperma*	1.01	Not significant
28	*Sida lepidota*	1.00	Not significant
29	Maximum crevice depth	.80	Not significant
30	Rabbit droppings	.68	Not significant
31	*Bouteloua curtipendula*	.66	$P < 0.10$
32	*Yucca baccata*	.62	Not significant
33	Crevices	.42	Not significant
34	*Artemisia dracunculoides*	.28	$P < 0.05$
35	*Sporobolus cryptandrus*	.23	Not significant

	Discriminant rank	F	Significance level
36	*Sphaerulea*	.14	Not significant
37	*Gutierrezia*	.09	Not significant

LAVA STUDY AREA—NONWEB SITE

1	Lava	45.75	$P < 0.001$
2	Bare ground	4.45	Not significant
3	*Portulaca retusa*	2.93	Not significant
4	*Panicum obtusum*	2.68	Not significant
5	*Bouteloua aristidoides*	1.17	Not significant
6	Shrub	.93	Not significant
7	*Erigonum tennellum*	.68	Not significant
8	*Berberis haematocarpa*	.09	Not significant

GRASSLAND STUDY AREA—WEB SITE

1	Depression	321.57	$P < 0.001$
2	Average depression depth	230.09	
3	Litter	90.46	$P < 0.001$
4	*Sida lepidota*	29.96	$P < 0.01$
5	*Oenothera flava*	10.66	$P < 0.001$
6	*Portulaca retusa*	9.89	$P < 0.01$
7	*Eragrostis pectinacea*	7.20	$P < 0.001$
8	*Gutierrezia*	3.65	$P < 0.05$
9	Herbs (flowering)	3.07	$P < 0.01$
10	Shrubs	2.93	Not significant
11	Bare ground	2.60	Not significant
12	*Salsola kaoli*	2.36	$P < 0.01$
13	*Rhus trilobata*	1.98	Not significant
14	*Yucca baccata*	1.86	Not significant

GRASSLAND STUDY AREA—NONWEB SITE

1	*Sporobolus flexuosus*	25.92	$P < 0.001$
2	Grazed grass	9.36	$P < 0.01$
3	Ungrazed grass	8.24	$P < 0.01$
4	*Panicum obtusum*	3.57	$P < 0.02$
5	*Bouteloua barbata*	1.87	Not significant
6	*Erigeron divergens*	1.25	$P < 0.90$
7	Cow pats	1.25	Not significant
8	*Hoffmanseggia* sp.	1.00	Not significant
9	*Hilaria jamesii*	.57	Not significant
10	*Thelosperma* sp.	.34	Not significant
11	*Bouteloua gracilis*	.33	Not significant
12	Woody litter	.23	Not significant

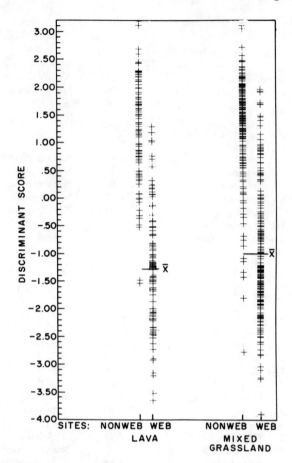

FIG. 8.   Discriminant scores of web versus nonweb sites on the desert-grassland and lava-bed study areas. Each + represents one sample transect. Web quality increases with decreasing discriminant score.

The results presented here demonstrate one aspect of spider biology that contributes to their success in most habitats, the capacity for maximization of food intake. Production of offspring clearly is more dependent on total food consumption than on the time required for development. Within limits, individuals receiving less food will still mature, but more slowly than those exhibiting greater prey consumption. Those individuals that select good web sites will receive larger quantities of food, and can then complete the life cycle prior to the advent of summer rains. Under these local catastrophic conditions production of the next generation is dependent on these individuals, and thus

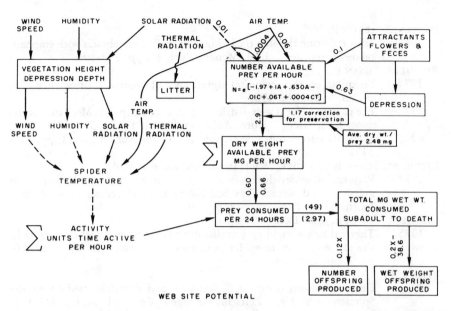

Fig. 9.   Diagram of the numerical relationship between web-site character and reproductive success. Prey-capture success averaged 60 percent of the available prey.
Ingestion efficiency determined for captives averaged 66 percent of the prey weight
captured. 2.97 is a conversion for dry weight to wet weight. Other numbers reflect
results of multiple and linear regressions.

the genotypes of individuals demonstrating greater habitat discrimination
will predominate.

REFERENCES

BRISTOWE, W. S.
     1941.   The comity of spiders II, 560 pp.   Ray Society, London.
GATES, DAVID M., and PORTER, WARREN P.
     1969.   Thermodynamic equilibria of animals with environment.   Ecol.
               Monogr., vol. 39, pp. 245-270.
GREIG-SMITH, P.
     1952.   The use of random and contiguous quadrats in the study of the structure
               of plant communities.   Ann. Bot., new ser., vol. 16, pp. 293-316.
KAJAK, A.
     1965.   An analysis of food relations between the spiders *Araneus cornutus* Clerck
               and *Araneus quadratus* Clerck and their prey in meadows.   Ekol. Polska,
               ser. A., vol. 13, no. 32, pp. 717-764.

PORTER, WARREN P.
1967.   Solar radiation through the living body wall of vertebrates with emphasis on desert reptiles.   Ecol. Monogr., vol. 37, pp. 273-296.

RIECHERT, SUSAN E.
1974a.   Thoughts on the ecological significance of spiders.   BioScience, vol. 24, no. 6, pp. 352-356.
1974b.   The pattern of local web distribution in a desert spider: Mechanisms and seasonal variation.   Journ. Anim. Ecol., vol. 43, no. 3, pp. 733-745.
1975.   Web-site selection in a desert spider.   Oikos, vol. 26, no. 3, pp. 311-315.

RIECHERT, SUSAN E.; REEDER, WILLIAM G.; and ALLEN, T. A.
1973.   Patterns of spider distribution (*Agelenopsis aperta* (Gertsch)) in desert grassland and Recent lava bed habitats, south-central New Mexico. Journ. Anim. Ecol., vol. 42, pp. 19-35.

RIECHERT, SUSAN E., and TRACY, C. R.
1975.   Thermal balance and prey availability: Bases for a model relating web-site characteristics to spider reproductive success.   Ecology, vol. 56, no. 2, pp. 265-284.

VITE, J. P.
1953.   Untersuchungen über die ökologische und forstliche Bedeutung der Spinnen im Walde.   Zeitschr. für angew. Ent., vol. 34, pp. 313-334.

SUSAN E. RIECHERT

Ichthyological Exploration of the Rapids of the Lower Congo River

Principal Investigator: Tyson R. Roberts, California Academy of Sciences, San Francisco, California.

Grant No. 1107: For an ichthyological survey of the Congo River's lower rapids.

The most extensive and perhaps the oldest rapids in any major tropical lowland river occur in the lower Congo River. The Congo ichthyofauna is second in richness and diversity only to that of the Amazon, with the species often characteristic of particular habitats, but clear evidence that the rapids might harbor an endemic fauna of highly specialized fishes did not come until 1958. In that year Belgian ichthyologist Max Poll described *Caecomastacembelus brichardi,* the first known blind mastacembelid spiny eel (Poll, 1958). The following year he published a general account of the rapids habitats and the fishes thus far found in them (Poll, 1959), based entirely upon collections and observations made near Kinshasa, at the beginning of the rapids.

In 1963 Pierre Brichard, the Belgian exporter of Congo aquarium fishes who discovered *Caecomastacembelus,* guided me to the rapids and showed me how to collect the blind eels. We also got two new genera of bagrid catfishes, *Rheoglanis* described by Poll (1966) and *Zaireichthys* by myself (Roberts, 1968), and I began to plan the ichthyological exploration that was to take place 10 years later with support from the National Geographic Society. On June 23, 1973, Donald Stewart and I set out by Land-Rover from Kinshasa, the capital city of the Republic of Zaïre (formerly Belgian Congo), to begin 3 months of fieldwork in the lower Congo. Our principal objective was to obtain fish collections and ecological information from the most extreme rapids habitats at as many localities as possible along the mainstream of the Congo River between Kinshasa and Matadi. Stewart, a graduate student from the University of Michigan, had done fieldwork on African fresh-water fishes in Zambia, but this was his first look at the Congo River and its fishes. Our enthusiasm at the outset was tempered by anxiety about the difficulties that might lie ahead. We were concerned about whether we would be able to gain access to the rapids habitats and find places where collecting would be successful. Our Land-Rover held up well, despite travel over excessively rough roads

517

and occasionally open country, and with strenuous hikes of up to 10 kilometers and help from local guides we found sites where we could collect with rotenone at nine different localities well spaced between Kinshasa and Matadi. Perhaps the most impressive rapids to be found in the Congo Basin are those at Inga, one of the last localities where we sampled. Here the most extensive rapids in the lower Congo River continue unbroken for 10-12 kilometers; at high water the river is 3 or 4 kilometers wide, but when we were there, at low water, it was confined to a channel less than 1 kilometer wide. The low water channel is narrowest where it passes to the left bank of the "coude (elbow) de Inga" and the main course of the river abruptly makes a 120° turn from southeast to due west. The resulting cataracts leap awesomely and throw spray high into the air. Extensive collections were obtained at this locality. By the middle of August, when collecting conditions were no longer suitable because of the seasonal rise in water level, we had obtained over 7,000 specimens belonging to 129 species, accompanied by limnological and other ecological observations. Of these 129 no fewer than 66 were highly specialized rapids fishes, 34 of them apparently endemic (restricted) to the rapids of the lower Congo River, and 19 of them undescribed.

These specimens have been deposited in the fish collection of the Museum of Comparative Zoology at Harvard University, and a comprehensive report, accompanied by photographs of the rapids habitats and many of the fishes, appeared in the *Bulletin of the Museum of Comparative Zoology* (Roberts and Stewart, 1976). We recognized two distinct ecological categories of highly specialized rapids fishes: (1) strongly rheophilic or current-loving species and (2) hyporheic or intrusive species, which evidently avoid light as well as strong current by delving into the interstices offered by jumbled rockpiles, and perhaps in some instances by burrowing into loose rubble or mud. The most consistent evolutionary modification in both categories is reduction (but most not complete loss) of the eyes. Of the 66 specialized rapids fishes, 26 are microphthalmic (with small or minute eyes superficial in position), 5 cryptophthalmic (eyes reduced in size and partially or completely covered by skin and other tissues), and only one species anophthalmic (totally without eyes). In one case we found that a cryptophthalmic blind form (*Caecomastacembelus brichardi*) apparently is able to hybridize with a microphthalmic offspring. Almost all previously known fresh-water blind fishes have been taken from cave habitats. A talk on the evolution of eye reduction in rapids fishes was presented by us at the annual meeting of the American Society of Ichthyologists and Herpetologists held in Virginia in 1975. Other adaptations of the rapids fishes, including methods of feeding and reproduction, and modifications of body form, fins, mouth, teeth, and coloration, are discussed in our paper published by the Museum of Comparative Zoology.

The most general conclusion from our study is the significant extent to which evolution in the rapids has contributed to the diversity of fishes in the Congo and other African rivers, most importantly in the evolution of many cichlids and catfishes and of such mormyrid genera as the elephant-beaked *Campylomormyrus,* and the apparent preadaptation of rapids-inhabiting cichlids such as *Lamprologus* (and *Steatocranus?*) to evolution in the rocky habitats of Lake Tanganyika, the predominantly cichlid fauna of which is the most diverse lacustrine ichthyofauna in the world.

REFERENCES

POLL, MAX
    1958.   Description d' un poison aveugle nouveau du Congo Belge, appartenant à la famille des Mastacembelidae.   Rev. Zool. Bot. Afr., vol. 57, no. 3-4, pp. 388-392.
    1959.   Recherches sur la faune ichthyologique de la région du Stanley Pool. Ann. Mus. Roy. Congo Belge, ser. oct., zool., vol. 71, pp. 75-174, illus.
    1966.   Genre et espèce nouveau de Bagridae du fleuve Congo en région de Léopoldville.   Rev. Zool. Afr., vol. 74, no. 3-4, pp. 425-428.
ROBERTS, TYSON R.
    1968.   *Rheoglanis dendrophorus* and *Zaireichthys zonatus,* bagrid catfishes from the lower rapids of the Congo River.   Ichthyologica (the Aquarium Journ.), July-Dec. 1967, pp. 119-131.
ROBERTS, TYSON R., and STEWART, DONALD J.
    1976.   An ecological and systematic survey of fishes in the rapids of the Lower Zaïre or Congo River.   Bull. Mus. Comp. Zool., vol. 147, no. 6, pp. 239-317, illus.

TYSON R. ROBERTS

Ethnobotany of the Kwanyama Ovambos, South West Africa, 1973

Principal Investigator: Robert J. Rodin,[1] California Polytechnic State University, San Louis Obispo, California.

Grant No. 1113:   To study the ethnobotany of the Kwanyama-speaking Africans in Ovamboland, South West Africa.

Can you imagine a vast stoneless tropical plain, without mountains or valleys or permanent streams, dotted with trees and interspersed with thousands of individual farms? That roughly describes the native homeland of 345,000 Ovambos who are permanent residents on the northern border of South West Africa (see map, fig. 1) and who are scattered throughout South West Africa—their numbers, including those in the homeland, estimated to be 395,000, of whom about 40,000 are migrant laborers away from the homeland on labor contracts. This vast area of some 16,500 square miles of territory, of which about 2,500 square miles is occupied by the Kwanyama-speaking people, is covered by sand washed in from the overflowing of the Kunene River to the north. Flooding is common in most rainy seasons. The water drains into the Etosha Pan to the south, where it eventually evaporates. The rains bring life-saving water to humans and livestock, although sometimes there are serious droughts. During the rainy season shallow waterways called *oshanas* carry off most of the water and bring several species of fishes down from the Kunene. In or on the borders of the *oshanas* grow a number of aquatic plants, and as the water recedes the *oshanas* are covered by grasses that provide good grazing for some months after the rainy season is over. There is no permanent water supply, but a high water table permits shallow wells to be dug by men for use in the dry season between May and December. A few deeper wells with windmills have been dug by the government in recent years, especially in slightly elevated areas not near *oshanas.* A new canal from Ruacana Falls carries water a distance of over 108 miles southeast, irrigating land along its entire length and providing water for the administrative community of Oshakati, a town with houses for the 1,000 Europeans and Africans working there, for Ongwediva, site of the new government boarding high school and teacher-training college, and for Ondangwa, the old administrative center for

---

[1] Dr. Robert J. Rodin died June 27, 1978, at San Luis Obispo, California.

521

FIG. 1.   Map of Ovamboland, South West Africa. Kwanyama area is where this project was conducted. South West Africa is slated to become Namibia in the immediate future.

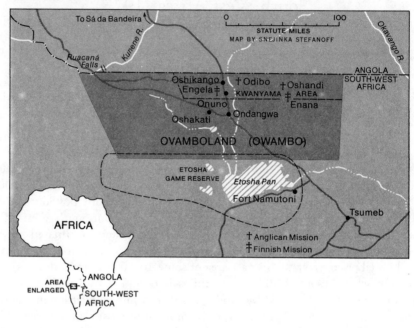

GEOGRAPHICAL NOTES (1975) TO THE MAP OF OVAMBOLAND (OWAMBO)

Oshakati (also called Owambo by the Afrikaans-speaking people) is a modern "town" with segregated modern brick houses, for whites and blacks, has about 1,000 blacks and whites and is the new administrative center of Ovamboland. It has modern grocery stores, hardware and building supplies stores, a Coca Cola plant, a sawmill and furniture factory, several gas pumps (but no good garage yet for repairs), a new 500-bed hospital, an FM radio station, water purification plant, etc.

Ondangwa, the old administrative center, has a few hundred inhabitants and houses, some government offices, including the magistrate's office, education offices for Ovamboland, and a post office. The old Native Commissioner's residence and office of 25 years ago is abandoned and falling apart.

Oshikango (at the border) contains a customs office, with several houses being built for Customs Police, and possibly for the Bantu Investment Corporation helping to set Ovambos up in businesses and providing wholesale outlets. There are two white customs' police families, a few single men (white), and some black customs officials. The post office has six or eight black employees (no whites).

this territory. Plans are under way to pump the water some 40 miles north of Ondangwa to Oshikango, where a small community is being developed at the border.

Many changes have taken place since my first visit to Oshikango, 25 years ago, when I worked with the late Dr. Edwin M. Loeb, anthropologist from the University of California at Berkeley. As a graduate student I assisted Dr. Loeb in his search for "magic" plants used in Ovambo culture (Loeb, 1955a, b, c, 1962; Loeb, Koch, and Loeb, 1956). Evidence of change now includes such physical signs as the presence of roads, cars, trucks, bicycles, women

---

GEOGRAPHICAL NOTES—continued

Odibo has been on restricted staff for a number of years because Anglican priests, especially from the United States of America, have urged the natives to ask for independence. There were no doctors, only two British nurses, a British teacher, a couple to manage property, and one or two single maintenance men. All were after the time of this expedition ordered evacuated after a strike in Ovamboland. I am convinced they had nothing to do with it, but the Afrikaans-speaking people want to get rid of English influence and the teaching of English in schools, so the natives will not be able to communicate with anyone except South Africans. It has an accredited high school, and large church.

Oshandi has a school (elementary), and a T.B. hospital. Drugs for patients are paid for by the government. One single English nurse who has been living there alone was recently sent back to England.

Engela has a large Finnish station, with hospital, several nurses, doctors, schools through high school, a large well-attended church and a seminary. The teaching personnel is mostly European, with some Africans. They were not, as far as we know, affected by the recent strike. All teaching in schools is in Afrikaans.

Enana I did not visit this time because the roads were too poor for the 2-wheel-drive vehicle I had. It formerly was a small hospital with one Finnish nurse. It has a church with a native pastor (all churches are supplied with native pastors only).

Roads: The road to Oshakati is excellent, modern and paved. The road to Ruacana Falls is good but unpaved; it parallels the new canal taking water from the Kunene. The road from Ondangwa to Oshikango, well built but as yet unpaved, is supposed to be paved this year (1975) because of the heavy traffic in produce and manufactured products now traveling between Angola and South West Africa. A very poor road parallels the border westward from Oshikango. A reasonably good road running for 104 kilometers eastward is being steadily extended all the way to the Okovango area, but has not yet been paved.

with attractive dresses, and portable radios, as well as great increases in the numbers of schools, hospitals, and stores.

The Kraal

In order to examine the life style in the Kwanyama area of Ovamboland, where the Kwanyama Ovambos represent approximately 80,000 out of a total population of 345,000 in Ovamboland (fig. 1), let us first look at patterns of the Ovambo family. The Ovambos, unlike many other Bantu people in southern Africa, have never lived in villages. Their individual family dwelling units, called kraals (fig. 2), consist of a series of round huts for sleeping, cooking, storing food, and tools and are surrounded by a palisaded fence. Outside is their own garden of from a few to 20 acres, often with a fence of thorn bushes around it to keep out cattle and goats. In pagan families where the kraal owner had several wives, the kraals are much more complex. In these are a maze of passageways, palisade fences that separate sleeping huts for the husband and each wife, as well as areas for cooking, making beer, storage of grain (fig. 4), a stamping place for milling grain, and a sitting place for conversation with visitors. Outside the kraal, but nearby, is a shallow well protected by a hedge of cut thorn bushes.

Headmen traditionally had, and at present have, bigger kraals with more wives and more servants than other members of the tribe. Among the servants are frequently one or two Bushmen. In 25 years most of the kraal organization has become much more simplified (see figs. 2-4 for comparison of today's kraal with those common in 1947). The simplified kraal is a reflection of the fact that today most kraals contain monogamous families. In 1973 I visited approximately 100 kraals and usually asked how many wives there were. I never did find a kraal where polygyny was practiced. From my aerial observations I know that in some of the more remote areas the kraals still occasionally have the complexity needed for polygynous families. I noted there were no passageways inside the monogamous kraals but often short screens opposite the hut doors (fig. 2). When I asked the owners why there was a screen, they said it was to give privacy when people are inside. A few of the storage huts for foods and tools, I noted, now have doors with padlocks. Ovambos are exceptionally honest, though, and none of our equipment was ever disturbed, even in unlocked buildings.

Every kraal has a sitting place (olupale) with logs from special species of trees about three sides of the fire. These seats were made from Burkea africanus (omutundungu), Lonchocarpus capassa (omupanda), or Colophospermum mopane (omufyati).

FIG. 2.   Aerial view of an Ovambo kraal, with surrounding garden, cattle and goat
enclosures, and a well in the field in the foreground.

    In the days of the kings, or chiefs as they are sometimes referred to, every
kraal had a sacred fire which was never allowed to go out, unless the kraal
owner died. All fires for headmen were started from the king's fire, and in
turn all persons under one headman started their fires from his. Green trees of
Colophospermum mopane (omufyati) were always used for these fires because they
smoulder slowly for days, but never flame up. It was the first wife's responsibility to maintain this fire, which was kept in her sleeping area. Other fires for
cooking, lighting, or keeping warm were started from the sacred fire, but it
was never used for any purpose except to start fires. In Loeb's time the 8 headmen in the Kwanyama area were pagan and polygynous, and all maintained
sacred fires. Today only one old headman is polygynous because all the younger ones are Christians. My informant told me that sacred fires are no longer
maintained. One factor in the loss of this custom is the availability of inexpen-
sive matches. Also, the divine nature of the king as the source of fire has lost
its meaning in their pagan rituals because they have not had a king since
1917. The increasing number of Christians has likewise been a factor in the
loss of this and similar rituals.

The stamping place in the kraal is the place where the mortar and pestle are kept and where grain is ground into meal. Millet *(Pennisetum americanum,* or *omahangu)* is their chief staple and the grain is ground daily for porridge. Kaffir corn or milo maize *(Sorghum caffrorum,* or *oshilyavala)* or millet is also malted by germination, then dried and pounded in preparation for making their beer. Many other things such as nuts for oil, both for cooking and for cosmetics, and dried herbs for body powders, are ground here.

Because there are no stones in Ovamboland, the mortar and pestle are made of hard wood, the mortar always being made of the harder wood. The mortar is called locally the "stamping block" in English, which has been derived from the Afrikaans "stampblok." The mortar is usually made from the heartwood of Rhodesian ash *(Burkea africana,* or *omutundungu),* or sometimes from leadwood *(Combretum imberbe,* or *umukuku).* The pestle is made from mopane *(Colophospermum mopane,* or *omufyati).* Dirt is brought in from termite hills nearby, moistened, and compacted around the mortar, which is sometimes half imbedded in the ground. Sometimes it is not imbedded; so it can be moved to a shady or cooler place. A special broom is used to keep the ground clean, so that meal that spills on it can be easily picked up. It is made from either bundles of split fan-palm leaves *(Hyphaene ventricosa,* or *omulunga)* or a grass *(Aristida junciformis,* or *omushoke).*

The cattle enclosure and a smaller enclosure for goats are usually attached to the outer edge of the kraal, or are close by, formed by stacking large branches that have been cut from different species of *Acacia* or other thorny trees or shrubs. A few extra branches are placed across the enclosure opening at night to keep the cattle in and intruders out.

The Headman

Although the king is gone, the tribal structure for political organization and maintenance of law and order has remained basically unchanged at the primary level. The most important political figures in Ovamboland are the headmen. They have absolute control over the land within their districts *(omikunda).* There are 8 headmen among the Kwanyamas, each governing his own district. This is not a hereditary position. Although a new headman's name is nominated or proposed by the people, the confirmation or appointment is by the cabinet of the Ovambo Legislative Assembly. This is an all-Ovambo body. Ownership of all land is ultimately in the hands of the headman. When a man dies, his land reverts to the headman, who then redistributes it, usually to someone in his matriclan. The person receiving the land pays for it, usually a few head of cattle or a specified amount of money. Within each district a head-

FIG. 3.   Hut construction, using mopane (*Colophospermum mopane*) poles for the framework, and bark of the same tree to tie the poles. This species is termite resistant.

FIG. 4.   View within a kraal showing two large granaries under one roof, and some of the palisaded fencing. Granaries hold millet (*Pennisetum americanum*).

man appoints a number of sub-headmen to administer a ward or subdistrict of about 10 kraals each. Some headmen have as few as 11 sub-headmen, but the largest area has 74.

The headman not only is the administrator of his area but also the lowest man in the judicatory system, and therefore sits as a judge. If both people involved in a dispute are not satisfied with his decision, they appeal to the next judicatory, called the *omalenga oovene vomikunda,* composed of seven sub-headmen, one from each district. The next judicatory is composed of the seven headmen. One further appeal may be made to the magistrate, a European in Ondangwa, serving all of Ovamboland. Severe crimes, such as homicides, which occur infrequently, are taken to the magistrate directly. At least theoretically they may be appealed through the courts of South West Africa to the Supreme Court.

Occupations of Men

The Ovambos have a cattle-hoe culture. Traditionally, the men, or more particularly the boys, have been responsible for herding the cattle and goats. Cattle were rarely killed, and then only for very special feasts such as the celebration of a wedding. Wealth was measured by the number of cattle a man possessed. The Ovambos appear to have learned hunting from the Bushmen, with whom they have always had good trading relations. The Bushmen probably even taught them how to make arrow poison. Hunting wild antelope gave them fresh meat to supplement the proteins of their diet. Hunting was good in Ovamboland in 1947, but wild animals are nearly extinct in that whole area today. That source of meat in their diet has largely been replaced today by goat meat. In different areas there are merchants who kill one or two goats a day, hang up the carcasses in the open air, and sell meat directly from the carcass. Boys herd cattle and goats together. Goats, which are now much more numerous than they were in 1947, do considerable damage to the vegetation, especially to certain shrubs and young mopane trees, *Colophospermum mopane,* on which the goats graze heavily at the end of the dry season when there is very little food available for them.

Men are also responsible for carving wooden objects, including beer mugs, milk pails, and utensils of wood, for preparation of skins for leather, for building new huts (fig. 3), for building and repairing fences and granaries, for digging water holes, and for making blacksmithing tools and utensils from native iron obtained in Angola. With the advent of cheap iron tools from South Africa in the numerous small stores, blacksmithing has become a dying art. I encountered one man, Gabriel Hidengwa, living 12 kilometers south of

FIG. 5.   Bellows for the blacksmith's forge, made nearly 40 years earlier, are demonstrated by Gabriel Hidengwa. The bellows, made of *omuuva (Pterocarpus angolensis),* are partly buried in the ground and the kiln-baked clay funnel keeps the heat of the burning charcoal in the forge from burning the bellows.

Oshikango (fig. 5), who became a blacksmith over 40 years ago. He said he learned his trade by working a few years for a Portuguese man. He had never heard of special initiation rites, long apprenticeships, special songs, special drinks for the smith, nor had he ever heard of mixing blood with a master smith, as mentioned in Loeb (1962). He showed me some wooden bellows *(omupepo)* he had made 40 years ago from the Dolf tree *(Pterocarpus angolensis,* or *omuuva);* covered with hides of springhare *(Pedetes cafer),* they were used to force air into the forge where charcoal heats the iron. He uses the forge occasionally but has largely given it up to carve wooden cups. I took a series of photographs of the wood carving and the burning on of the designs (fig. 6), an art that may be lost in this generation, for instead of using the traditional wooden cups for drinking their beer, the Ovambos usually use glass, quartsize Mason canning jars.

I tried diligently to find native curers. My informant said there was only one in the whole area. He said that people do not go to witch doctors any more because they do not always recover. They liked the medicine at the mission

FIG. 6.   Gabriel Hidengwa demonstrates how designs are burned on wooden cups used for drinking beer. These cups are carved from *omboo (Commiphora africana).*

hospitals, or more recently at the new government hospital at Oshakati. At one time I was supposed to meet an herbalist, but we only met his daughter. This man is not the type described by Loeb, but rather cures various ills such as stomach ache, headache, and diarrhea with herb teas, poultices, and plant extracts. There is now apparently no magic as practiced a generation ago.

There were only two professions in earlier times, according to Loeb (1962): blacksmithing and being a doctor, or more properly a witch doctor. Four grades of practitioners were recognized in this latter category, not all of whom were men. The first was the herbalist, a category that included midwives, female diagnosticians, and male homosexuals who practiced medicine. The second level of doctor cured by sacrifice, exorcism, and detection of witches. The third was the witch doctor, with special magical powers, a specialist in exposing thieves and finding lost articles. The fourth and highest grade was the doctor-teacher, who trained and initiated all lower grades of doctors. He was a maker of amulets and was considered the supreme authority on matters of religion, medicine, rites, and ceremonies.

Loeb (1962) claimed that occupations such as butchering, tailoring, and wood carving were not of professional rank. There have been many technological changes since Loeb's time and today there is no longer any special distinction or initiation into any profession or occupation. I have attempted with the assistance of several Ovambos to list the occupations now in existence. These reflect the many new skills involved in the rapid transition to a modern technological society.

OCCUPATIONS AMONG KWANYAMAS IN OVAMBOLAND

Storekeeper: *omulandifi,* including those who sell beer
Any repairman: *omupangeli* (one who repairs)
   Bicycle repairman: *omupangeli weembashikela*
   Auto and truck mechanic: *omupangeli womahauto*
   Electrical repairman: *omupangeli womalusheno*
   Mender of buckets and pans: *omupangeli womavela*
   Radio repairman: *omupangeli weeradio*
   Stove and lamp repairman: *omupangeli weelamba*
   Repairer of watches and clocks: *omupangeli weevili*
Woodcarver: *omuhongi* (teacher) *womaholo*
Barber: *omukululi*
Blacksmith: *omuhanbuidi*
Brickmaker (of cement and sand): *omufolomi*
Brickmason: *omufolomi*
Carpenter: *kalupindelu* (an adapted word), *omupangeli*
Plumber: *omulongi* (worker) *wominino* (with pipes)
Road repairman: *omulongi* (worker) *womoitauwa*
Heavy equipment operator: *omukombi womoitauwa*
Teacher: *omuhongi* (teacher) *wofikola* (of school)
Nurse: *omuhakuli*
Seamstress: *omuhondji* (one who makes clothes)
Basket maker: *omutungi* (one who makes) *woimbale* (baskets)
Potter: *omuhongi* (teacher) *woitoo*
Washer of clothes: *omukoshi woikutu* (*oikutu* are clothes)
Ironer of clothes: *omukanquli woikutu*
Office worker: *ovalongi vomeembelewa*
   in a post office: *omunapoosa* (*opoosa* is post office)
   typist: *omushangi wokomashina, omutopatopi*
   clerk: *hamushanga*
Butcher (mostly of goats): *omulandifi wombelela* (*ombelela* is meat)
Manager of a cafe (seller of cooked meat from an iron pot): *omushingifi*
   omulandifi wombelela
Baker (of small loaves of bread): *omuteleki weemboloto*
Fisherman: *omkwati weeshi* (*eeshi* is fish)
Grain farmer (who sells extra grain): *omulandifi woilya*
Transportation serviceman (in pickup truck): *omututi woshipota*
Fence repairman (along the border, employed by the South African police):
   omulongi wodalate (*omulongi* is a worker)

OCCUPATIONS AMONG KWANYAMAS IN OVAMBOLAND—continued

Police (as those working for the Customs Office at the border): *omupolifi*
Miner (in Tsumeb): *omulongi womomina* (worker in mines)
Interpreter: *omutoloki*
Doctor and person in related professions:
    Midwife: *omudalifi* (deliver babies, especially out away from hospitals)
    Homosexual doctor: *eshenge* (my informant said there were still a few
        around)
    Herbalist: *ondudu onganga*
    Person in highest class of witch doctors: *omupuliki* (none of these remain)
Seller of thatch: *omulandifi womwiidi*
Seller of kraal materials (i.e., poles, usually mopane): *omulandifi woiti*
Radio announcer: *ovaleshinghundana voradiyo*
Minister or priest:
    Lutheran: *ovafita-ongalo, ovahongi*
    Anglican: *ovapilisteli ovahongi*
    Roman Catholic: *pata* (singular), *oopata* (plural)
    Dutch Reformed: *ovahongi vongeleka*
Musician (especially 1-stringed instrument): *ovashiki*
Servant (as in kraals of headmen): *omupiya* (singular), *vonxumba ompia
    ovapiya* (plural)
Slave (once captured in war, no longer found): *omupika* (singular),
    ovapika (plural)

Slaves and servants were common under Ovambo kings. Slaves were con-
quered in warfare, and Lebselter (1934) believed most servants in his day were
former slaves. Servants today are given food, clothing, and protection. They
can leave their master, usually a headman or sub-headman, at any time, but
rarely do. Now the cost of land and food requires money or cattle and they lack
capital or initiative to begin a new life. I became acquainted with a Bushman
who was the servant of a headman and was his musician. He came to my place
several times and played his one-stringed instrument and sang. It was a very
simple instrument called *okambulumbumbua,* constructed of a bow with one
string pulled taut with a dried gourd as a sounding resonance box on the back
side. The instrument is played by hitting the string with a small twig and the
musician can make about 3 different tones, with many variations of rhythm.

Occupations of Women

In this cattle-hoe culture it is the women who till, plant, weed, and har-
vest the garden. The principal staple crop has always been millet, *Pennisetum
americanum (omahangu),* with considerable kaffir corn *Sorghum caffrorum (oshilyavala),* and other cultivated crops such as gourds *(Lagenaria siceraria)* of at

least 4 distinctive types, squash and melons *(Citrulus lanatum* and *Acanthosi-cyos naudinianus),* black-eyed beans (or peas) *(Vigna sinensis),* peanuts *(Arachis hypogaea),* ground nuts *(Voandzeia subterranea),* sweet potatoes *(Ipomoea bata-tas),* and others. A short-handled hoe is the only tool I observed for prepara-tion of soil and weeding. Considerable change is taking place now that it has become a predominantly monogamous society. Under polygyny the husband had several wives to do all the agricultural work. Now that at least 90 percent of the population is Christian, by my estimate, and very few polygynous fam-ilies remain, there is too much work for one wife. Men who never touched the soil in previous generations now till the soil with a steel-bladed plow pulled by a pair of cows or bulls, and so one could say they are in transition to a plow culture. On rare occasions near the missions south of the Kwanyama area, I have seen the cooperative use of a tractor. Now during the tropical rainy sea-son when weeds, including many grasses, come up abundantly, a man and wife are often seen weeding their field together with hoes. It appears that be-cause of Christianity some basic cultural changes have taken place, in this case giving women less drudgery in the fields.

Women are gatherers of wild fruits, some of which are eaten raw and some of which may be dried and stored for use in the dry season. Some are fermented and made into wine, but I did not find this to be common except for marula wine, since the Kwanyama Ovambos prefer beer. Some also ferment either fresh or dried fruits to make a fermented fruit brandy *(olambika).* Many species of wild fruits are fermented and distilled in this manner. I observed one wom-an distilling the beverage in a smoke-filled hut. She had filled a clay jar with wild persimmons *(Diospyros mespiliformis),* with the seeds still in the fruit. She said it had taken 5 days to ferment the fruit. Then she suspended the jar of fer-mented fruit over a fire, covering it with a special clay lid, which had been baked in a kiln. The lid had on one side a hole into which a $^3/_4$-inch iron pipe about $3\,^1/_2$ feet long was fitted. The pipe and the lid were sealed onto the jar of fruit by some puttylike wet clay. For a condenser on the pipe they had a hollowed-out log about 2 feet long through which the pipe passed. She poured about two buckets of water into this hollow log. The water was changed for cold water with each new batch of fruit. At the end of the pipe, a string was dropped into an old wine or whiskey bottle, into which the strong, clear alco-holic distillate drained. I was told that they recovered about $^1/_5$ gallon of bev-erage from about 2 gallons of fermented fruit in the large jar. My informant told me he did not drink it because it was very strong alcohol.

One of the wild fruits gathered by women is the marula *(Sclerocarya afri-cana,* or *omwoongo).* The fruit is eaten raw and has a pleasant taste. It is in the same family as the mango but is smaller and has usually a somewhat tart but

Fɪɢ. 7.   Women making marula wine under a marula tree *(Sclerocarya caffra)*. This
          is the chief beverage drunk during the month of the marula.

sweet flavor. The fruit has an irregular shape about 2 inches across with a
leathery outer skin, a soft pulp, and a hard inner stone covering 2 or 3 seeds.
The women from several kraals gather under one of the very large trees about
the time the golden-colored fruit is ripe and falling to the ground. They come
to squeeze juice from the fruits, and it is a joyful time as they sit and talk while
they work. In order to puncture the leathery skin of the fruit each woman has a
small tool, usually a sharpened cow or antelope horn and usually held in the
left hand. After the fruit wall is ruptured, the fruit, held in the right hand, is
squeezed and the juice is put in a small bowl, woven of palm fibers (fig. 7),
that is 6 or 8 inches across and holds 2 or 3 cups of liquid. It is tightly woven

FIG. 8.   Removing the outer fibrous husk from the seeds of the fan palm *(Hyphaena
ventricosa)*. The outer part is edible raw, but sometimes is fermented to make wine,
or fermented and distilled to make brandy *(olambika)*. The very hard inner part is
vegetable ivory and was once carved into buttons and ornaments.

and has no mastic to make it watertight. When her small bowl is nearly filled
with juice, she carefully pours it into a large earthenware jar in the center of
the circle. The earthenware jars in Ovamboland are all similar, without glaze
or design, and are of rather poor quality, because the quality of clay is poor in
that area.

_Natural yeasts from previous batches of wine are present in the large clay
jar, so that fermentation begins immediately. Some of the beverage may be
drunk that evening before much fermentation has taken place. Even the next
day the alcoholic content is not too high, and in the month of the marula so
much marula wine is drunk that it perhaps only rarely develops a high alco-
holic content. It is a pleasant, slightly sweet, and rather refreshing beverage.

Marula wine is also significant to Ovambo culture because during this
month there is a moratorium on all crime in Ovamboland, and it is strictly
honored.

No one steals, and no man brings charges if his neighbor's cow accidentally breaks into a field and destroys some of his crops. Furthermore, no court

sessions are held and no one is arrested. This ancient tradition is still followed by the majority, regardless of their religious traditions.

Not only is the marula fruit eaten, but the pips are kept in other jars, taken home, and spread out to dry. Later the stony layer is broken open by hitting it with a stick, about 18 inches long and $1\frac{1}{2}$ inches wide, against an upturned ax blade. The seeds inside may be eaten raw or cooked with various foods, including gravies with roasted chickens, which I have eaten and found to be quite delicious. The marula nuts may also be stamped for their oil.

Other fruits gathered by women include *Berchemia discolor (omuve)*, which taste like dates and dry easily in the sun. The fan palm *Hyphaene ventricosa (omulunga)*, has a spherical fruit, $1\frac{1}{2}$-2 inches in diameter, with a thin fibrous layer that is eaten, although the fibers must be spit out (fig. 8).

Several subspecies of *Ximenia (oshipeke)*, whose fruit flavor closely resembles the acid of plums in temperate regions, and several species of wild persimmons *(Diospyros)* are sweet and edible, including *omukokofi, omuvandi, oshimumu,* and *omudine*. Of the wild figs, *Ficus sycomorus (omukwiyu)* is the favorite and is eaten raw or dried. Most of the above fruits may be made into fermented beverages. Among the few fruits eaten raw and not preserved or cooked are *Strychnos pungens (omupwaka)* and *Strychnos cocculoides (omuuni)*.

Women are responsible for brewing the beer that is an integral part of their diet, a time-consuming daily occupation. Long before Europeans entered this area the Ovambos already were malting their grains for this process to produce a refreshing, generally low-alcoholic-content beer. The grain is germinated, ground, and dried in the sun. A small portion of the malted grain is taken for their daily batch. Next morning the beer pot will have effervescent foam on the top, and the beer will be ready. It does not have good keeping qualities and is usually drunk that day. If kept too long it often turns to vinegar by bacterial action. Sometimes today the beer shops add some brown sugar to increase the alcoholic content.

A large number of annual herbs that come up as weeds in the cultivated fields are gathered by women as pot herbs (spinach), which they boil in water. The flowers of *Aloe zebrina (ekundu)* are boiled and eaten in a like manner. Any extra pot herbs or cooked *Aloe* flowers may be flattened into cakes about 6 inches in diameter and dried in the sun, or dried slowly over a charcoal fire to form dried "cabbages" *(omavanda)*, which are kept until the dry season when no greens are available. They are then soaked in water, boiled, and eaten with a little salt. Not previously mentioned in the literature, these greens contain important minerals and vitamins in the diet of the Ovambos for other seasons, contributing to their continuing good health.

All food in the kraal is prepared by the women, either by the wife of the kraal owner, or by his daughters, if they are old enough. Almost daily the women pound millet *(Pennisetum americanum,* or *omahangu)* in their wooden mortar and pestle, for their staple porridge, and preparation of other cooked foods such as black-eyed, or Ovambo beans, *Vigna sinensis (omakunde),* ground nuts, *Voandzeia subterranea (eefukwa),* and several gourds and squash. They also eat whole cooked kaffir corn or milo maize *(Sorghum caffrorum* var. *ondongas,* or *oshilyavala).* Very little maize *(Zea mays)* is grown in Ovamboland.

Women are the weavers of all household baskets, except the large granaries for storing the bulk of their crops, which are woven by men. Women gather the leaves of the fan palm and after drying them, they dye some of them if necessary before soaking the fibers and weaving the baskets. The most common dye is from the bark of *Berchemia discolor (omuve),* which makes a deep brown color. To obtain orange they use the fruit of the same tree, called *eembe.* Baskets, each of a special size and shape, are made for holding grain, flour, seeds, beverages, and other objects found in the kraals. In the eastern part of Ovamboland no palms are found growing, and it is necessary for women to walk sometimes more than 50 kilometers to gather leaves for baskets. The thatching grass has been gathered by women and today they still cut much of it. I saw a few kraals where they sold bundles of it. They were asking the Africans about 20 cents (South African rands), which was about 28 cents USA per bundle. It takes 16 to 20 bundles to re-cover a small sleeping hut and perhaps twice that number of bundles for a larger hut.

There are a few herbalists who still practice the art of curing people with all kinds of plants. As one walks through the kraals in many parts of the country, it becomes evident that women in the kraals have considerable knowledge of many medicinal plants for common ailments such as wounds, sores, headaches, stomach aches, earaches, diarrhea, fevers, skin disorders, and others. In every area visited women were willing to bring me their special herbs with formulae for curing specific ills. In one area about 107 kilometers east of Oshikango such a large number of people, including a few men, brought in herbs at one time that they became impatient as I tried to record all the data possible about the uses of each species, through my informant, Roland Kalitu.

Kinship

The Kwanyama people have a combination of matrilineal clans and neolocal residence, with a few cases of avuncular residence, where a young married man lives with his uncle who had married his mother's sister. Clan exogamy is strongly enforced and clans remain as units for the regulation of inheritance. This has been true with all Bantu people in South West Africa, and since, at death, the land reverts to the headman of a district for redistribution, the chief inherited wealth is their cattle, or sometimes some money. True relatives are only those linked lineally through the mother and her clan. Thus a man's cattle will be inherited by his younger brother and then by his wife's sister's son in the next generation. A man may distribute a few of his own cattle to his own son in his lifetime, although in Sckär's (1916) time that was prohibited. If a woman has any personal wealth, it goes not to her son, but to her brother or to her sister's son. Sckär gathered a list of 17 clans. Loeb (1962) listed in 1948 a total of 29 clans for his work, but Bruwer (1961) found that there are only 20 clans and that some of the earlier names used by Loeb were interchangeable or synonymous.

In order to have continuity to the matrilineal system, the boys usually live part of their lives with their maternal uncle, from whom they will inherit cattle. The boys often are responsible for herding their uncle's cattle, rather than cattle owned by their father. During his early youth the eldest son often resides permanently for long periods of time in the maternal uncle's kraal. The uncle then becomes his teacher.

According to Loeb (1962) in 1948 the Christians attempted to change the inheritance to a patrilineal pattern, following the Old Testament. The young Christians were in favor of it, but the old tribesmen spoke against it. The latter argued that the cattle were property of the clan through the woman. It was feared that if a son were to inherit the cattle he might kill his father. They also argued that the matrilineal system was established in the days of the kings so there was no reason to change. Such a system would destroy the matriclan system, since the two are incompatible.

Dr. Johan S. Malan, anthropologist for the State Museum at Windhoek and a collaborator with our expedition, suggested that I see if there was any break in the matrilineal inheritance pattern. In perhaps 100 kraals I visited I asked key questions pertaining to inheritance. According to Dr. Malan (pers. convers., February 1973; also see 1974) there has been a break with the matrilineal descent pattern among Hereros in two distinct steps. First when a couple is married they move to a new local residence separated by a considerable distance from the kraal of the mother's brother. The father has tried, because of the separation, to have his own children care for his own cattle, so that they can inherit them. But he has not established full authority and children lack discipline. Mothers are never responsible for discipline. When a man dies, his nephews have come to claim the cattle as their rightful inheritance, and there is a serious conflict.

A second phase of development among Hereros is when a father eventually gets full control of his sons. He takes material care of them, establishes some taboos, perhaps over foodstuffs, if they are pagan. The patrilineal religious control, through the taboos, leads to a double descent, because while there is patrilineal group control, matrilineal cattle control still exists.

Ultimately a full change to a patrilineal society does in some areas take place, but only with the breakdown of the matrilineal clans. In such a changed society cattle as well as group control then are under the father, and the cattle are passed from father to sons. In these situations the son is never living near his matriclan uncle and has no close relationship to him.

Some Herero people I have observed are quite nomadic and may lack permanent residences. Because they are widely scattered in relatively poor grazing country there is little possibility of residence close to the mother's brother in many cases. This is quite different from the sedentary type of society among the Ovambos. Hereros also differ from the Ovambos in having essentially a stateless society without the centralized authority of a paramount chief or headmen.

The following information has been furnished directly by Dr. Malan:

This decentralized political system is associated with double descent, but it may be noted that five generations ago the Hereros still had a traditional hereditary chieftainship, after the shift to double descent and statelessness occurred (also see Malan, 1973).

According to my observations, the Ovambos are engaged in a similar transitional process from matrilineality to double descent though in a much earlier stage than the Herero, who by now practice full-fledged double descent. The crucial concept in this regard seems to be the changing mode of residence. It stands to reason that once there is a major breach away from the rule of matrilocal or avunculocal residence, the matrilineal local groupings are geographically dispersed and consequently lose much of their corporateness. Functions of active social and political control, religious care, and daily material maintenance cannot be performed if kinsmen are not members of the same household or kraal.

As a result of the neolocal residence, which is an intermediary step towards patrilocal residence, the matriclan in Ovamboland is gradually losing many of its functions: Religious ties between matri-kinsmen are weakened as they no longer live together permanently. The rapid fading of matrilineally inherited sacred fires also accounts for this phenomenon.

The dispersion of matrilineage by the adoption of the new rule of residence resulted also in the discarding of hereditary leadership positions according to matrilineal descent. Not only the Kwanyama but also the Kwambi and Mbalantu tribes in Ovamboland have already lost their tradition of chieftainships, or kings, and are now stateless or segmentary societies under the control of a number of nonhereditary headmen. The cruelty of the last chiefs of these tribes is therefore a secondary aspect that cannot be offered as a reason why the tradition of matrilineal royal clans has been allowed to disappear completely. This does not happen in societies with a stable rule of descent—rather the unpopular chief is replaced by someone else in the royal family.

Among the remaining Ovambo tribes the traditional status and image of matrilineal chiefs are also crumbling away.

The only function still performed strongly by the dispersed matrilineages is property control and the inheritance of moveable wealth. In order to safeguard their economic interests, young men often reside temporarily with their matrilineal uncles although less frequently after marriage when they erect their own kraals elsewhere. As a result, the uncle is largely committed to his own sons for the care of his livestock. Although some sons still respect the rule of matrilineal inheritance they are confronted with the nephew who comes from elsewhere to take charge of his uncle's estate. The sons of the deceased frequently hide a number of the cattle on faraway cattle posts, and some of them even bury their father's money to hide it from the rightful heir.

From the above it is clear that the Ovambo can no longer be regarded as a purely matrilineal people although no clear-cut patrilineal descent groups have emanated as yet, the evidence of a major break away from matrilineality is present in many spheres of social life. One may therefore conclude that a process of social evolution is basically responsible for the change and that the influence of the Christian faith and western civilization are secondary aspects further accelerating the pace.

My own observations are that the matrilineal system is still very strong among the Kwanyamas. I found many young men in the kraals of their matrilineal uncle. In all the many kraals I visited, matrilineal inheritance patterns are still the only pattern followed. I believe this has been because of their sedentary society and because they have been relatively isolated from outside influence, except missions, and they have not followed the missionaries' earlier advice to change to a patrilineal system.

The Future of the Kwanyama People

There have been many changes in the cultural pattern in a relatively few years. Part of these changes are due to the impact of Christian missions on the culture, and part are the influences of the South African Government which is responsible for administering the area. Five different departments are now completely administered by Africans and gradually more responsibility is given to Ovambos as they are trained for administration. The government has made considerable effort in recent years to prepare these people for self administration, at least within their homeland area, by developing Legislative Councils and providing improved judicial systems with means of appeals; and the government has spent millions of rands on modern hospitals, schools, roads, irrigation systems, and services such as post offices, radio stations, and transportation. The government has made genuine efforts to improve the quality of life for the people. Some of this investment undoubtedly they hope to recover by new markets for South African manufactured products. Although the tribe will be affected by new technology in the future, they will probably remain essentially an agricultural and pastoral society.

In the Oshikango Post Office, run efficiently entirely by Ovambos, there is a tremendous C.O.D. mail-order business for clothing. The postmaster said they take in over 7,000 rands some days on such purchases (about USA $9,800 at that time), mostly for such items as clothes and radios. All these pressures on the culture have not yet changed the basic structure of the kraal, the diet, or of some other aspects. However, if everybody decides to start building brick houses, if purified water systems are developed throughout the land, if flush toilets become a part of every household, we will see even more drastic cultural changes. The use of plants is still quite what it was for generations, with the major exception of magic, as studied by Dr. Loeb (1962). There is a much less significant use of the plants once used in pagan ceremonies and rituals; this has been diminished almost to the point of extinction. It would be tragic to the health of these people if they replaced their millet and Kaffir corn with maize, because the latter lacks important amino acids essential to human health. Their diet is far more balanced, I believe, than was previously realized, because of plants they dry for other seasons than the rainy season, both fruits and pot herbs. Also they eat more fish, including some they dry, and more goat meat. Some canned meats are now bought in stores.

Although Ovamboland may have a potential for exporting some agricultural products, there is no surplus at this time. I did not observe any chemical fertilizers in use. Portions of their gardens are usually planted on old cattle enclosures, utilizing the manure which has fallen in that area as their only fertilizer. Frequent floods of the Kunene River undoubtedly help the soil fertility. In their culture cattle are so important as a symbol of wealth that there is great reluctance to sell any of their stock. Ovambos, in spite of the presence of banks, have not yet come to the place where money from cattle sales is held in esteem equivalent to wealth in cattle. A quarantine bars exporting cattle from this area because of a lung disease and occasional outbreaks of hoof and mouth disease. The Bantu Investment Corporation of the government, which has helped finance some stores for Ovambos, has plans to build a meat canning factory in Ovamboland, and it is possible in the future that beef grown in Ovamboland will be canned there. There is at present a surplus of goats, which in part are considered wealth, but not to the degree of cattle, and some goats are slaughtered and sold raw, or cooked. This surplus should be reduced and utilized partly as a protein food by the Africans living there, and partly in the interests of good ecology.

The details of plant uses which are not given fully here will be more completely discussed in the book on this subject which is under preparation.

Acknowledgments

As botanist of the University of California African Expedition, 1947-48, I wish to acknowledge the assistance of its director the late Dr. Charles L. Camp; the late Dr. Edwin M. Loeb, anthropologist; his wife, Ella Marie Loeb; and the late Wendell Phillips, who raised the funds for that expedition. In 1947, I met Dr. N. J. van Warmelo, later to become the chief ethnologist, Bantu Administration, Pretoria, and have been encouraged by him in recent years to complete this ethobotanical study.

Acknowledgment is gratefully made for assistance from the South African and South West African governments for plant collecting permits and permits to enter areas rarely seen by foreigners. The late Dr. Johann Gildenhuys, director of medical services, Ovamboland, in 1973 prepared the way and was most interested in the diets, medicines, and poisons used by the Africans, as related to their health problems. Mr. Wilhelm Giess, the State Herbarium, Windhoek, and the staff of the South African National Herbarium, Pretoria, under its former director, Dr. M.L.E. Codd, kindly identified about 400 plant collection numbers. Duplicates have been distributed to the State Herbarium, Windhoek; South African National Herbarium, Pretoria; Missouri Botanical Gardens, St. Louis, Missouri; the State Herbarium, Munich, Germany; Kew Herbarium, England; the Herbarium, University of California, Berkeley; Robert F. Hoover Herbarium, California Polytechnic State University, San Luis Obispo, California; and a partial set to Harvard Botanical Museum, Cambridge, Massachusetts.

Dr. Johan S. Malan, anthropologist, State Museum, Windhoek, was a collaborator on this expedition and kindly made physical preparations. He assisted us in Ovamboland, and gave much needed help in understanding the culture. Another collaborator was W. Zimmerman of the Native Language Bureau, Department of Education, Windhoek. He and Gabriel Taapopi, a Kwanyama Ovambo in the same office, were most helpful with the linguistic aspects of the Kwanyama names. Roland Kalitu, Oshikango, Ovamboland, was my chief informant in the field. Elva Bain Rodin, the author's wife, was technical assistant for the expedition. Her typing of over 3,200 herbarium labels, taking care of correspondence, and managing camp are gratefully acknowledged.

The 1973 expedition would not have been possible without a faculty research grant from the National Geographic Society, which supported travel and field expenses, and a 6-month sabbatical leave from the California Polytechnic State University, San Luis Obispo, California.

REFERENCES

BRUWER, J. P.
1961.   The Kuanyama of South West Africa, a preliminary study.   Unpublished Ms.
LEBSELTER, V.
1934.   Eigeborenenkulturen in Südwest- und Süd-Afrika, vol. 2, Leipzig.
LOEB, EDWIN M.
1955a.   Kuanyama Ambo magic. Part 1, Kuanyama witchcraft.   Journ. Amer. Folklore, vol. 68, pp. 35-50.
1955b.   Kuanyama Ambo magic. Part 2, Kuanyama doctors.   Journ. Amer. Folklore, vol. 68, pp. 153-168.
1955c.   Kuanyama Ambo magic. Part 3, Kuanyama magicians; Part 4, Kraal moving magic; Part 5, Sacred animals and omens.   Journ. Amer. Folklore, vol. 68, pp. 291-311.
1962.   In feudal Africa.   Intern. Journ. Amer. Linguistics, vol. 28, pp. i-xxi + 1-383.
LOEB, EDWIN M.; KOCH, C.; and LOEB, ELLA-MARIE
1956.   Kuanyama Ambo magic. Part 6, Medicinal, cosmetical, and charm flora and fauna.   Journ. Amer. Folklore, vol. 69, pp. 147-174.
MALAN, JOHAN S.
1973.   Double descent among the Himba of South West Africa.   Cimbebasia, ser. B, vol. 2, pp. 81-112.
1974.   The Herero-speaking peoples of Kaokoland.   Cimbebasia, ser. B, vol. 2, pp. 113-129.
SCKÄR, K.
1916.   Oukuanjama in Ovamboland.   Unpublished manuscript.
RODIN, ROBERT J.
1981.   The ethnobotany of the Kwanyama-speaking Ovambos, Namibia. Missouri Botanical Gardens, St. Louis, Missouri.

ROBERT J. RODIN

Psilotum in Japan: Classical Culture, Mutants, and Wild Populations

Principal Investigator: Albert S. Rouffa, University of Illinois, Chicago, Illinois.

Grant No. 1081:   To collect mutant varieties of the primitive vascular plant *Psilotum nudum;* to search out and study the possibility of morphological and/or chromosomal races in the wild populations of *P. nudum;* and to determine the past history of the horticulture of this plant in Japan.

I was extremely fortunate in having as my co-leaders in this study Kaname Kato, Satoru Kurata, Kenichi Iwata, and Yasuji Fukuda, all of Japan. The Japanese *Psilotum* Association and the Japanese Fern Society also were most helpful and contributed to the success of my investigation.

In the fall of 1967 I received from Longwood Gardens a number of living varieties of *Psilotum nudum.* Most of the plants were derived from the collections made by Dr. John L. Creech during a horticultural plant-collecting visit to Japan in 1957 for the U. S. Department of Agriculture's New Plant Section. One of the plants proved to be distinctly different in that it had none of the tiny leaves associated with the typical *Psilotum nudum,* nor did it appear to have any vestiges of such leaves. Subsequent growth of the plant showed that the branching was often uneven. Furthermore, the spore cases (synangia), which are typically produced adaxially to specialized leaves along the sides of the upper part of the branches in the usual *Psilotum,* were produced apparently at the ultimate tips of the various sized branches. Eventually this was reported in the literature (Rouffa, 1971). At that time I had no idea about the origin of this leafless *Psilotum*—whether it was a garden selection or a wild variant collected for cultivation.

My visit to Japan was essentially organized by Mr. K. Kato, a Tokyo horticulturist, who arranged with Mr. K. Iwata, of Ise, the president of the Japanese *Psilotum* Association, to visit a number of greenhouse-grown *Psilotum* collections, and with the late Dr. S. Kurata of Tokyo University for members of the Japanese Fern Society to accompany me on field trips. I was ably accompanied by Dr. Y. Fukuda, Chiba University, who acted as a companion botanist and interpreter during the *Psilotum* Association visits.

The results of the study in Japan were discussed in the two papers which emanated from the trip (Rouffa, 1973, 1978). The leafless *Psilotum* was found to be derived from a wild plant collected perhaps two centuries ago in what is now Wakayama Prefecture. A book in Japanese published by the *Psilotum* Association subsequently was translated into English after my return. This provided valuable information on the horticultural history of this plant; however, this has not as yet been published. I photographed representative illustrations from the rare Japanese *Psilotum* books published in the 1830s which depicted the leafless variant and indicated its origin. A number of variants were purchased from or donated by the *Psilotum* Association members. Some of these varieties had leaves, but produced synangia only at the tips of the branches rather than from specialized leaves. Furthermore, wild plants were collected and preserved which bore terminal synangia. The chromosomal situation has yet to be elucidated since the fall season was too late to obtain synangia in the right stages of meiosis. However, synangia with mature spores were collected and preserved for future size analysis and correlation with chromosomal ploidy.

The 1978 paper resulting from this study is a synthesis of new concepts derived from a comparative study of typical and aberrant variants. A fresh outlook has been provided for the phylogeny of this enigmatic group of plants, and a new hypothesis has been proposed for the evolution of the synangium. The sociological context of *Psilotum* horticulture during the later years of the Tokugawa Shoguns needs more complete study before publication.

REFERENCES

ROUFFA, ALBERT S.
  1971.   An appendageless *Psilotum*. Introduction to aerial shoot morphology. American Fern Journ., vol. 61, pp. 75-86.
  1973.   Natural origin of the appendageless *Psilotum*.   American Fern Journ., vol. 63, pp. 145-146.
  1978.   On phenotypic expression, morphogenetic pattern and synangium evolution in *Psilotum*.   American Journ. Bot., vol. 65, pp. 692-713.

ALBERT S. ROUFFA

The Hirundo-Young Archeological Project— Results and Prospects

Principal Investigator: David Sanger, University of Maine, Orono, Maine.

Grant Nos. 1066,   For an interdisciplinary archeological study at the Hirundo
1217, 1447.   site, Maine.

The Hirundo site was discovered and the project initiated in 1971. The project had three goals: (1) To establish the first interior cultural chronology in Maine; (2) to gather data on the habitation sites of the Indians responsible for the Moorehead burial tradition cemeteries; and (3) to juxtapose the cultural record with the paleoenvironmental record in the area.

The Hirundo site, located on Pushaw Stream in Alton, central Maine, was found by W. Winter and brought to the attention of Robert G. MacKay, who tested the site in 1971. The University of Maine excavation team recovered a wide range of artifacts, particularly chipped and ground stone implements attributable to what Ritchie (1965) has called the Laurentian Tradition. Because of the evident potential of the site, a grant proposal for the year 1972 was prepared by Sanger and sent to the National Geographic Society for consideration.

The 1972 field season was a 6-week excavation supervised by MacKay. Involvement by Ronald B. Davis and his students resulted in a detailed botanical map of the site and the acquisition of a sediment core from Holland Pond located approximately 9.6 kilometers away. Excavation continued on a limited scale during the fall, while further coring took place in Mud Pond during the winter. Results to date appeared in *Man in the Northeast* (Sanger and MacKay, 1973).

The next major excavation was made in 1974, under a second grant from the National Geographic Society. Activity centered on the upstream portion of the site (Area A), although efforts were made to determine the full extent of the site. Soils analysis indicated levels of phosphorus that varied from section to section. A second radiocarbon sample was submitted to the Smithsonian Institution and a date of about 4400 B.P. received. The date matched an earlier assay from a sample close by. Sanger and MacKay directed fieldwork. This work was reported in *Arctic Anthropology* (Sanger, 1975, p. 65).

By 1975 the combined testing and excavation of the previous seasons had indicated the need to acquire statistically valid samples. At the same time

547

plans were made for a test of the site directly across the river from Hirundo—
the Young site. Grants from the National Geographic Society, the University
of Maine Faculty Research Fund, and the Hazel Smith bequest to the university allowed us to field a crew of 25 for 6 weeks. During this period new categories of artifacts were gathered and old categories expanded significantly. A
thorough test of the Young site revealed a fine Susquehanna-related component sandwiched between Laurentian and later levels.

A review of the research through 1975 was presented at a symposium
sponsored by the New York Academy of Sciences in 1976. The paper (Sanger
et al., 1977) presented general comments on regional geology, a review of pa-
leovegetation, and the early prehistory of the region up to around 3500 B.P. A
discussion of the significance of the project concluded the report. During
1976 the Young site joined Hirundo on the National Register of Historic
Places.

In 1976 fieldwork was limited to a few test squares, but in 1977 a grant
from the Maine Historic Preservation Commission, combined with support
from the University of Maine and the Hazel Smith fund, enabled us to work
for an additional 11 weeks in the field. Christopher Borstel, a graduate student at UMO, directed operations for 7 weeks at the Young site. Robert
MacKay then supervised a crew of 9 at Hirundo for another 4 weeks. At both
sites the emphasis was on deposits containing preserved faunal remains. The
Susquehanna collection from the Young site was increased significantly while
at Hirundo an early historic component was located for the first time.

To date about 300 square meters at Hirundo (fig. 1) and 56 square meters
at the Young site have been excavated.

Those of us involved with the project have many people and institutions
to thank, from the granting agencies and foundations (National Geographic
Society; Maine Historic Preservation Commission; the Smithsonian Institution Radiocarbon Lab; University of Maine, Orono; and the Hazel Smith
fund) to the landowners, J. Oliver Larouche and K. Young, and the many colleagues and students who have worked with us since 1971.

The Ecosystems

The Hirundo and Young sites are located on Pushaw Stream about 5 kilometers below the outlet of Pushaw Lake. The area is dominated by low-lying,
poorly drained bog land. Although most of Pushaw Stream is slow moving,
the stream for several hundred meters in front of the site is quickwater, running over bedrock outcrops. The sites are approximately 36 meters above sea
level.

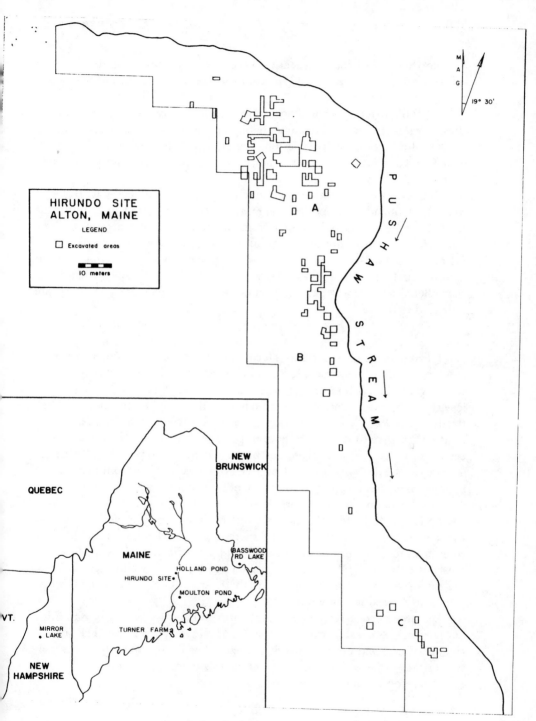

Fig. 1. Map of Hirundo site showing areas of excavation.

Northern hardwoods (such as beech, maple, birch, and elm) and softwoods (especially spruce and fir) dominate the local forests. The bogs are of the sphagnum-heath type.

It is not currently known how long the rapids have been in front of the sites, but it is reasonable to assume that it has been a substantial portion of the 12,000 plus years since deglaciation. It is clear that the bogs were once much larger, and a study to determine the chronology of the metamorphosis from lake to bog is in process.

Regional paleovegetational regimes have been determined by R. B. Davis from the Holland Pond pollen diagram, which is presented in a simplified fashion in table 1. The pollen zones from Holland Pond are generally synchronous with diagrams from nearby Moulton Pond as well as Mirror Lake, New Hampshire, and Basswood Road Pond, New Brunswick, all lying between approximately lat. 44° and 45° N. (Sanger et al., 1977, p. 461). Changes in the pollen data generally parallel cultural shifts of some magnitude. These are indicated in figure 2.

The Sites

Hirundo site, on the right (south) bank of Pushaw Stream, lies a little above average summer water level and is periodically inundated by high water. Lower terrain behind the site acts as a safety valve for all but highest water levels. Young site, protected by a bedrock sill, is higher and has not been flooded since 1971 when the stream has been observed on a regular basis. The positions relative to the stream have important implications for the nature of the deposits. As a result, there is a better record of the past 3,500 years at Young. Both sites were covered by trees when excavations commenced and neither has been subjected to plowing or other major man-made disturbances.

The Hirundo site is the larger, stretching for about 250 meters, while Young is approximately 75 meters long. Both sites vary in width; the Hirundo site approaches 40 meters and more in places. Hirundo is divided into three areas for reference purposes. Area A, the upstream end, is the most intensively excavated. The relatively narrow Area B is also well tested. Area C, the extensive downstream portion, is the least explored area, although test pits clearly reveal its potential.

Features are relatively rare at both sites and consist largely of pits filled with fircracked rocks. Feature 3 at the Young site is an exception. The quantities of charcoal and broken bifaces lead excavator Borstel to suspect a cremation burial pit. A series of radiocarbon dates suggest an age of around 3500 B.P. No recognizable house features are present at either site.

Zone	Holland Pond pollen diagram interpretation	Cultural Unit and assemblage	Radiocarbon years ago
III b	Increasing spruce	CERAMIC	-0
		(unnumbered Assemblages)	-1,000
			-2,000
		(unnumbered Assemblages)	-3,000
III a	Northern hardwoods	SUSQUEHANNA (Assemblages 3)	
	Hemlock	LAURENTIAN (Assemblage 2)	-4,000
			-5,000
II b	Hemlock-birch Western pine- Northern hardwoods	MIDDLE ARCHAIC (Assemblage 1)	-6,000
			-7,000
II a	Uncertain	EARLY ARCHAIC	-8,000
			-9,000
			-10,000
		PALEO-INDIAN	-11,000
I	Tundra		-12,000
			-13,000
	Deglaciation		-14,000

Fig. 2.   Relationship of vegetation and cultural units at Hirundo-Young locality.

Although the soils at Hirundo generally range in pH a few tenths either side of 5.0, an area excavated in 1977 has pH values close to 7.0, with high phosphorus levels. Mammal, bird, and fish bones are present. At the Young site there are also pockets of preserved bone. The reasons for this differential preservation are not well understood, and an exhaustive program of physical and chemical soils testing is in progress.

The earliest component is called Assemblage 1. It consists of a few bifaces located beneath Assemblage 2. On the basis of similarities with radiocarbon

FIG. 3. Bifaces of Assemblage 1 (left) and chipped points of Assemblage 2, from Hirundo.

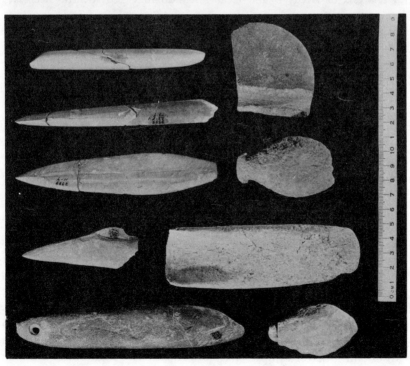

Fig. 4. Ground stone artifacts of Assemblage 2 (left) and chipped points and drills of Assemblage 3, from Hirundo.

dated artifacts in southern New England (Sanger and Bourque, n.d.), Assemblage 1 should be around 7,000 years old (fig. 2). To date it is found only at Hirundo.

Assemblage 2 is a large collection made up of chipped side-notched bifaces and ground stone tools such as plummets, slate points, gouges, celts, and various abrasive stones. Two radiocarbon dates of about 4400 B.P. may apply to the Assemblage, although some observers suggest the dates are too recent. Assemblage 2 is very close in general form to the Vergennes phase of the Laurentian Tradition (Ritchie, 1965). This Assemblage is best represented in Area A of Hirundo, but it is found also at the Young site (fig. 3).

Assemblage 3 is related to the Susquehanna Tradition best known farther to the south. Although it is at both sites, it is best seen at the Young site. It is probably about 3,500 years old (fig. 4).

In addition to the three assemblages there are at least four and possibly others that have yet to be clearly defined. The difficulty is that archeology in Maine has concentrated on the early portion of the record, essentially Assemblages 1-3, whereas the period between 3500 and 2000 B.P. is poorly known. Careful analysis of Areas B and C at Hirundo may provide the necessary details.

Until the 1977 excavations, any account of subsistence activities at the Hirundo-Young locality remained largely inferential. With the addition of faunal remains the hypothesis that the sites served as summer fishing stations can be checked.

Analysis and Publications

The analysis is progressing at several levels. Attempts to understand the depositional history of the sites are proceeding through chemical and mechanical analysis of the soils. Flotation samples are being examined for organic and inorganic remains. Artifact analysis is largely completed.

In the area of regional environmental studies we have a report on the genesis of the local bogs and the final report on the Holland Pond pollen diagram.

The support given the project by the Maine Historic Preservation Commission, administering National Register funds, will extend for a second year (1978–79), primarily for analysis. The proposal plans limited fieldwork, concentrating instead on analysis leading to major publications. The plans for publication currently call for description and analysis of the first 3,500 years (from 7000 to 3500 B.P.) in a report to be readied for publication in 1980. In time proposals will be prepared for renewed fieldwork in Area C at Hirundo in order to obtain a better sample of later occupations. At the same time an attempt will be made to obtain a detailed understanding of the history of bog development and man's adaptation to the changing local ecosystems. Following this research a second major report on the last 3,500 years will be prepared for publication. Finally, the results of the paleoecological research and the implications for man will be published, bringing the Hirundo-Young project to a close.

Conclusions

Our initial goals, as stated in the introduction, are being met with varying degrees of success. The first step in the archeology of any region is the matter of a cultural chronology. Although it is by no means complete, we do have the beginning of a 7,000-year local sequence, the first in interior Maine.

The question of the Moorehead burial tradition cemeteries and the habitation sites is far more complex than anticipated a few years ago. We are now having to face the possibility of not one, but two, or even more, related major cultural traditions between 5000 and 3500 B.P. in parts of the Northeast.

To date, the paleoenvironmental record is largely derived from the pollen analytic data. These indicate remarkable correspondences in time between major floral shifts and cultural changes. The correspondences are indicated in figure 2, and a case can be made for a certain degree of causality.

One of the frustrations of modern archeology is that it moves so slowly. The expectations of science go far beyond the statements considered adequate a decade ago. The Hirundo-Young project has been experimental to the extent that several disciplines have been involved in a systematic way to help solve certain cultural problems. At this time we know of no other situation quite like Hirundo-Young in Maine and perhaps even northern New England. It is our firm intention to develop it to the best of our collective abilities.

REFERENCES

RITCHIE, WILLIAM A.
    1965.   The archaeology of the State of New York, xii + 357 pp., illus. Natural History Press, Garden City, New York.
SANGER, DAVID
    1975.   Culture change as an adaptive process in the Maine-Maritimes region. Arctic Anthrop., vol. 12, no. 2, pp. 60-75.

SANGER, DAVID; DAVIS, RONALD B.; MACKAY, ROBERT G.; and BORNS, HAROLD
			W., JR.
	1977.	The Hirundo Archaeological Project—an interdisciplinary approach to
			central Maine prehistory.	Pp. 457-471 *in* "Amerinds and Their Paleo-
			environments in Northeast North America," W. Newman and B. Sal-
			wen, eds.	Ann. New York Acad. Sci., vol. 288, illus.
SANGER, DAVID, and MACKAY, ROBERT G.
	1973.	The Hirundo Archaeological Project—preliminary report.	Pp. 21-29
			in "Man in the Northeast," vol. 6, illus.

DAVID SANGER

Survey of Pottery Sites in Karamoja District, Uganda

Principal Investigator: Hamo Sassoon, Fort Jesus Museum, Mombasa, Kenya.

Grant No. 1057:   For an archeological survey and excavation in Karamoja District, northeast Uganda.

The purpose of this survey was to find and record occurrences of a distinctive assemblage of pottery types, characterized by one that has already been described by Wilson, using the term "grooved pottery" (Wilson, 1970). My attention was first drawn to grooved pottery in April 1970 by John Wilson of Moroto, Karamoja. It is usually a pale brick-red color with a sandy body, which makes it rather friable and brittle. The only pot profile I was able to reconstruct (from sherds gathered at Ngolipok) lacked the base, but it shows a pear-shaped pot about 30 centimeters high with an inturned rim. The widest part of the pot is at the shoulder and it becomes narrower toward the base. The exterior is decorated with closely spaced horizontal grooves from the rim downward. The grooving is so remarkably deep and precise that it suggests the use of a potter's wheel. Bases of grooved pots in Mr. Wilson's collection showed that the grooved pattern ended with diminishing concentric circles. Wheel-thrown pottery is not known to have been made anywhere in East or Central Africa before the arrival of the Europeans, with the possible exception of the East African coast. If the very regular grooving was made with a comb, it is difficult to see how the base could have received its concentric grooves. So the method of manufacture remains a mystery.

Fragments of grooved pottery are often found scattered on the surface around the bases of the inselbergs, which are a feature of the landscape in Karamoja. Other types of pottery with finely rouletted and incised decoration are frequently found with it. The southwestern limit of the grooved pottery area is, in my experience, in the region of Napak (Akisim), lat. 02° 07' N., long. 34° 13' E. This impressive group of hills is on the border between Karamoja and Teso Districts. I have found grooved pottery also in Gemu-Gofa District, southern Ethiopia, at the prehistoric site on the east side of the Omo River, which is some 400 kilometers northeast of Napak. Wilson indicates that it is found also in western Kenya in the Uasin Gishu. The high quality of the craftsmanship and the wide distribution of this grooved pottery and its associated forms suggest that it may represent an important phase in the history of the peoples who lived in the lands that form the junction between Uganda, Kenya, and Ethiopia. What period this pottery represents is not known because it has not yet been studied in a stratified deposit.

The survey, which was carried out in June 1972, was no more than a token of the work originally planned. The political and security situation in Uganda at that time was not conducive to fieldwork. The survey began in Kidepo National Park, in the northeastern corner of Uganda, and finished 150 kilometers to the southeast in Moroto. The Nangeya Hills and the National Park were surprisingly unproductive. The first site found was at Sidok (lat. 03° 16′ N., long. 34° 15′ E.). The village and school had been deserted 5 months earlier because of a particularly murderous armed raid carried out by warriors, said to be Turkana from Kenya. A grooved pottery site was located at the base of a hill just beside the village; the pottery was associated with other distinctive types (see fig. 1). A large number of pieces of what were obviously the same two pots showed that the site would probably repay excavation. Further survey is needed in the hills around Sidok.

On the north side of Koten Hill (lat. 03° 04′ N., long. 34° 26′ E.) a surface scatter of sherds of grooved pottery was found, together with obsidian flakes. Koten is now deserted, but it is known as the traditional home of the eastern section of the Jie people; this tradition probably represents nothing more remote in time than the 17th century. Certainly the Jie nowadays make only a coarse type of pottery with rouletted decoration. They make no claims to be the makers of the grooved pottery.

At Jimos, 6 kilometers north of Kotido (approx. lat. 03° 04′ N., long. 34° 08′ E.) there is a long, low mound about 10 meters high and stretching for some 200 meters. It was under cultivation at the time of my visit. Grooved pottery found in the farmland suggests that the mound is an occupation deposit. This feature is a Jie rain priest's mound, and permission to excavate would have to be sought with tact.

Near Jimos there is an inselberg called Lomilo (exact location not recorded); around the base of this hill there are some clearly defined stone circles, some of which are small enough to be granary bases. Others are 2 or 3 meters in diameter, with some of the stones standing vertically up to 1 meter high. It is not known whether these circles are the remains of domestic housing or of religious shrines, though the latter seems more probable. Throughout the area of these stone circles there are occasional surface occurrences of grooved pottery.

The last site examined is probably the one that would yield most information if it were to be excavated. The site extends around a small hill referred to on the 1:50,000 survey sheet as Ngolipok. The position of the hill is approxi-

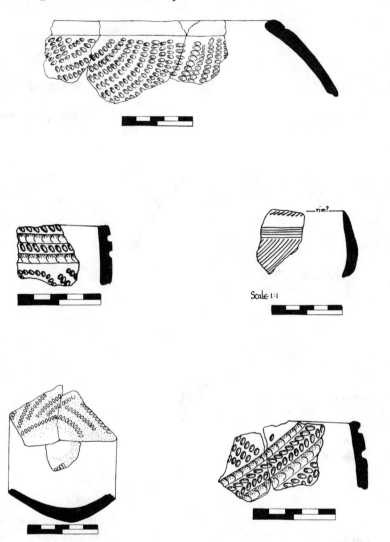

FIG. 1.   Pottery from Sidok.

mately lat. 02° 47′ N., long 34° 27′ E., and the pottery occurs at the base of the hill (fig. 2).

An important aspect of grooved pottery is the very wide area in which it can be found. This immediately calls to mind another distinctive type of African pottery, known as Urewe (or dimple-based) ware. Urewe ware is known to

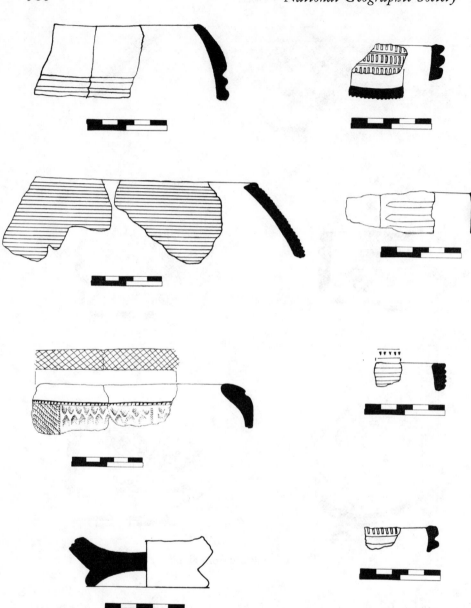

FIG. 2.   Pottery from Ngolipok.

occur in Rwanda, in central Tanzania, around Lake Victoria, and even as far east as the Shimba Hills, just inland from Mombasa, which gives it a much greater area of distribution than that known for grooved pottery. Urewe ware is often very finely potted, and the decoration is meticulously carried out. One of the characteristic decorative motifs of this ware is a pattern of deeply incised parallel grooves, often forming semicircles, and occasionally concentric circle designs (Leakey et al., 1948). Urewe ware dates usually fall within the first four centuries of the first millennium A.D. (Soper, 1971). The wide distribution of grooved pottery and its generic similarity to Urewe ware with its grooved decoration suggest (if one may hazard a double guess) that grooved pottery may be a descendant of Urewe ware, in which case it eventually may be found to belong to the end of the first millennium A.D.

Since grooved pottery is a very limiting term for an assemblage which, although characterized by grooved pots, also includes other notable forms of decoration, it is proposed that this assemblage should be given a location name. The two main locations so far recognized in Uganda are Sidok and Ngolipok. The latter site offers better excavation prospects, and it is therefore proposed that the pottery assemblage here briefly described should be called Ngolipok ware.

All the material collected during the survey here reported has been left with the Department of Antiquities in Kampala. The material was not available for study at the time when this report was written.

REFERENCES

LEAKEY, MARY D.; OWEN, W. E.; and LEAKEY, LOUIS S. B.
    1948.   Dimple-based pottery from central Kavirondo, Kenya Colony.   Coryndon Mem. Mus. Occ. Pap., no. 2, 43 pp., illus.
SOPER, E. C.
    1971.   Early Iron Age pottery types from East Africa: Comparative analysis. Azania, vol. 6, pp. 39-52, illus.
WILSON, JOHN G.
    1970.   Preliminary observation on the Oropom people of Karamoja.   Uganda Journ., vol. 34, no. 2, pp. 125-145 (esp. pp. 138-139), illus.

HAMO SASSOON

The Verapaz Archeological Project:
The 1972-1973 Field Seasons

Principal Investigator: Robert J. Sharer, The University Museum, University of Pennsylvania, Philadelphia, Pennsylvania.

Grant Nos. 1068, 1184, 1264. For an archeological investigation in the Northern Maya Highlands (Salamá Valley), Baja Verapaz, Guatemala.

The Verapaz Archeological Project began operations in the Salamá Valley, Baja Verapaz, on the southern edge of the Northern Maya Highlands, in June 1972 under the sponsorship of the National Geographic Society, the Wenner-Gren Foundation, and the Southern California Academy of Science, and with the aid of several private donations. The 1973 excavations were conducted with the continued support of the National Geographic Society.

From its inception, the project was directed by Dr. Robert J. Sharer of the University Museum of the University of Pennsylvania. The field operations were conducted by David W. Sedat. Field laboratory procedures were carried out by Mrs. Rebecca Sedat. During both field seasons the following individuals assisted in various phases of the fieldwork: Mrs. Mary Clapp (1972), Mr. and Mrs. Willard Seitel (1972, 1973; site survey and mapping), and Edward M. Schortman (1972, 1973; excavation, site survey and mapping, ecological survey.)

Permission to excavate was extended by the director of the Institute of Anthropology and History, Lic. Luis Lujan M. Security guards for the project, two permanent military police, were provided by the Minister of Defense. The support of the Tikal Association, through its president Mrs. Laura de García Prendes, was received throughout all phases of the work, especially in the financial assistance for the erection of several important monuments in the town plaza of San Jerónimo, Baja Verapaz. The success of the project is due in large part to the continued cooperation of the local municipal authorities, as well as many citizens.

The headquarters for the project continue to be located in the town of San Jerónimo, Baja Verapaz, in the eastern section of the Salamá Valley, where the bulk of the sites studied are located. The comfortable facilities and the congenial climate afforded by this location not only allowed for ease of access and excavation of the many sites in the area but also continue to provide an estab-

563

lished base for the project and the completion of the analysis of artifacts and for the writing of the work accomplished to date (see Sharer and Sedat, 1973, and Sedat and Sharer, 1973).

Goals

The research objectives of the Verapaz Project were predicated upon the strategic location of the Salamá Valley, the virtual lack of research in the area, and several interesting insights gained from the brief preliminary field seasons of 1970 and 1971. In brief, the Salamá Valley, at an altitude of 1,000 meters, is a lush and fertile topographic unit transitional between the higher and more dissected highlands to the south (the Southern Maya Highlands), and the humid, jungle lowlands of the north (the Maya Lowlands). Prior to the work of this project little was known of the prehistory of this intermediate region, the Northern Maya Highlands. In spite of the lack of adequate knowledge of this area, it was generally believed that the more ancient cultures of the Southern Maya Highlands had little or no direct influence in the occupation of the jungled lowlands and the subsequent evolution of the Classic Maya civilization (Adams, 1972). In 1971, however, excavations at Sakajut (Sedat and Sharer, 1972), 50 kilometers to the north of the Salamá Valley, suggested substantial populations for the Northern Maya Highlands during the period of time that the earliest known populations in the Lowlands were becoming established. Furthermore, the location in the Salamá Valley of an apparently Preclassic monument and the several large Preclassic sites in the area reinforced the suspicion that the Salamá Valley and adjacent areas were important centers of early populations, populations with longstanding relations toward the south and a great stimulus to the emerging civilizations to the north.

Thus, the research objectives of the project were to test the hypothesis of early populations in the Northern Maya Highlands; to determine their chronology, to elucidate their structure, ecological adaptation, and evolution, and to investigate their interrelations with both the south and the north.

Methodology

Sites located in the Salamá Valley were first named according to the local place name, or according to some prominent local feature. Later a comprehensive grid system was developed for the valley, with sites and structures within sites receiving their corresponding designations. As sites were recorded, they were preliminarily mapped with Brunton and tape, and surface collected. The major site of the valley, El Portón, was more rigorously mapped with transit and rod. The site survey report for the valley was written up by Mrs. Lurene Seitel and preliminary site maps drawn by Willard Seitel based on data collected by both the Seitels and Edward M. Schortman.

The recording of excavations was done according to a system patterned after that used at Tikal and Chalchuapa, with the first two letters standing for the code for the site name, with subsequent numbers and symbols recording operation, suboperation, section, and lot and, later, the catalogue number. All standards and symbols for excavational drawing followed those established for the Tikal and Chalchuapa projects. Field notes were kept on day-to-day procedures. Actual digging was done by local workers, trained on the job, using picks and shovels for the removal of overburden and finer tools for more critical deposits. All artifacts were field segregated according to lot and later processed in the laboratory.

Laboratory procedures involved the cleaning and numbering of every artifact, including sherds, repair work on damaged whole vessels, cataloguing of every artifact except pottery sherds and scrap obsidian flakes, and, later, photography and scale drawing of each artifact. All artifacts so processed are in the custody of the Institute of Anthropology and History, although stored in San Jerónimo.

The pottery sherds recovered during the course of the 1972 excavations, after being washed and numbered, were classified by the type-variety method (Smith, Willey, and Gifford, 1960), currently favored by many scholars of Maya ceramics. Later, the 1973 material, after being processed, was sorted separately according to the same type-variety system. The two seasons' sherds were then combined to form one chronological scheme. This chronological scheme has undergone exhaustive internal checking and formulation, but it should be noted that in the absence of valley-wide stratigraphic consistency, the chronology is one based in large part on typological analysis and external comparisons, and so represents only a relative scale by which to judge the evolution of society in the Salamá Valley. At this date the entire Preclassic sequence, from about 1200 B.C. to A.D. 200 is typed and quantified, lacking only the completion of the descriptive and comparative studies.

The 1973 ecological survey by Edward M. Schortman was the beginning effort to study the various forms of microenvironments and their relation to ancient occupation. This study has already offered numerous insights into the ancient pattern of land usage and settlement location, and with its completion will be a major portion of the final report.

Other analyses of the recovered archeological material include the preliminary classification of about two-thirds of the recovered obsidian artifacts, the submission of radiocarbon samples for the dating of various ceramic and architectural complexes, the preservation and identification of recovered human and animal bones, and mineralogical analysis of selected jade samples.

The 1972 Season (June to December)

EL PORTÓN

The major operation of 1972 was centered at the very large and centrally located site of El Portón, which covers one-half square kilometer and is composed of 13 recognized mounds, 2 being over 14 meters high. The 6 excavation operations carried out were controlled by 60 excavation sections and segregated by the definition of 369 provenience lots. Also undertaken were 5 surface operations. The highlights of this preliminary exploratory work (considering the largeness of the site only a small fraction could be investigated) were: the recovery of a 60-vessel Late Preclassic cache in front of the largest structure (J7-2), including two intact effigy incense burners; excavation of Monument 1 and related monuments; recovery of jade workshop debris and various cached jade objects, including one effigy weighing 12.5 pounds; and delineation of a Late Preclassic shrine and other structures. El Portón is considered to be the dominant Preclassic site in the valley, witnessing the achievement of a unique variant of Highland valley civilization.

LOS MANGALES

The excavation of this site was undertaken as a salvage operation because of its impending destruction for agricultural purposes. The survey indicated that this small hamlet-size site seemed to have been inhabited at an early date, i.e., prior to the Late Preclassic. The 5 operations undertaken comprised 7 excavational units and 42 lots. The interesting feature of this site was that it had been used from Middle Preclassic times as a necropolis. Included in the explored bulk of the mound were some 17 discrete burials representing probably over 40 individdiduals. One burial was accompanied by more than 10 apparently sacrificed individuals, but unfortunately this very early and important burial had been anciently disturbed or looted. The most important single item recovered was Monument 16, a small, rustically but intricately inscribed stone that was serving as a lintel for a Middle Preclassic (900-400 B.C.) tomb. This fact, along with other evidence, reinforces the hypothesis that early developments found in the Salamá Valley later became integral parts of Maya civilization.

SAN JUAN

The site of San Juan was also excavated in a desire to record the very inter-esting features revealed by illicit looting operations. The 2 operations under-taken comprised 19 excavational units and 39 lots. This work revealed complex adobe-brick construction of the substructure and temple walls of what might have been a Late Classic center. More work is needed at this badly damaged site to explain the unique and evolved architectural features encountered.

SIBABAJ

The one exploratory operation at this site, consisting of only one lot, was an attempt to date the very complex inscribed boulder encountered there. This excavation was placed at the base of the boulder on the front side, but because of very shallow deposits all around this feature only one lot was removed. The analysis of the material seems to indicate that the designs inscribed on the stone represent a very early form of a writing or notational system comparable to that on the important Los Mangales monument.

SITE SURVEY

During the 1972 season 17 sites were identified, including the 2 pre-viously known sites of El Portón and Pachalum. These sites were located in an area of about 40 square kilometers of the eastern portion of the Salamá Valley, in the vicinity of San Jerónimo, and ranged in size from small occupation groups to the very large Late Classic site of El Cacao (over 1 square kilometer). The survey located some 120 distinct man-made features (structures, terraces, platforms) and was invaluable, as it pinpointed, through surface collection, the sites most likely to yield evidence of early habitation.

Another important aspect of the site survey was its recognition of several sites in the process of being looted to supply the antiquities market. Several tombs being illegally excavated were taken over by the project and recorded, with the recovery of many valuable artifacts and much information. With the cooperation of local and governmental authorities the toll exacted by looters on the archeological sites of this valley was gradually lessened. At present it can happily be said that this local pillage of the past has been reduced.

LABORATORY OPERATIONS

The 1972 excavation season yielded some 1,110 catalogued artifacts including 201 whole or restorable vessels. The mending of many of these ves-sels, especially the 60-vessel ceremonial cache, was a lengthy and painstaking operation. With the vessels repaired, scale drawings were made and photographs taken.

Among the artifacts processed were several fine pieces of jade, including a complete necklace of large spherical beads, a small jade mosaic mask in Classic Maya style, and the 12.5-pound effigy of poor quality jade. Also catalogued were many pieces of jade in the various stages of manufacture. The quantity of jade recovered during testing operations strongly indicates that the valley served as an important manufacturing area and conduit for the passage of jade trading routes from the source area, 30 kilometers to the south, to the Maya lowlands. Furthermore, the recovery of jade debris for manufacturing, ranging from partially worked chunks to jade dust, reinforces this preliminary conclusion.

As part of the general correlative effort, information pertaining to some 30 monuments was compiled. The time period represented by this collection of monuments extends from the Late Middle Preclassic (ca. 600 B.C.) to the Late Postclassic. Five monuments still retain vestiges of ancient notational systems, all pertaining to the Preclassic period. Recording of these involved photography, drawing, and the making of latex molds.

The 1973 Season (June to December)

LAS TUNAS

The refinement of the 1972 working hypothesis following the 1972 season called for the careful excavation of a Middle Preclassic center to test several theories regarding the evolution of civilization in the valley. The site of Las Tunas was selected because not only was it well preserved and favorably located according to the topography of the valley, but also surface collection indicated mostly Middle Preclassic occupation, or earlier. Consequently, 3 operations were undertaken that involved 9 excavation units and a total of 70 lots. Complex architecture consisting of adobe platforms and staircases with intriguing stair-side molding was uncovered. The ceramic sample indicated exclusively Middle Preclassic occupation for the structures, but Early Preclassic material was also recovered from the fill of the structures. Depending on the confirmation of carbon-14 dates for the various levels of the construction the site of Las Tunas is presently believed to contain the best-preserved and earliest revealed construction in the northern Maya highland area.

EL TRAPICHITO

The site of El Trapichito, on the north side of the valley in a setting analogous to the site of Los Mangales already mentioned, was test excavated, in 3 operations with 9 excavations and 17 lots, to determine if it pertained to the Preclassic era. The site proved to be Classic in date, and, once all its units were recognized and mapped, it was shown to be another major Classic center of over one-half a kilometer square. Several anciently looted Classic burials were recovered prior to closing-down operations at this site in favor of expanding the Las Tunas operations.

LAS IMPRESIONES

Testing excavations were conducted at this site following the finding, in a nearby municipal sewer trench, of in situ Early Preclassic remains. The single operation undertaken included 5 excavation units containing 32 lots. Early Preclassic material was confirmed for the site, but apparently the only major in situ deposit was taken out by the sewer trench.

EL MOLINO

When looters broke into two mounds at this site, efforts were taken to reveal the interior of the mound before the material would be lost. The 3 operations, with 4 units and 5 lots taken, revealed several anciently looted multiple-burial tombs belonging to the Early Classic period, a period previously represented inadequately in our material. Several fine jades were found, overlooked by the ancient looters, including one representing a rattlesnake in profile. The anciently looted burials at this site strengthened the observed pattern of ancient looting of tombs and burials, probably either for the recovery of precious jades or for the acquisition of articles for ancestor worship. Indeed, one of the elaborately prepared tombs at El Molino was completely vacant except for some pottery vessels and a large painted seashell where the cranium should have been located. One corbeled vaulted Late Classic tomb was also recorded.

SITE SURVEY PROGRAM

A reevaluation of the sites discovered to date, plus 3 additional new sites, necessitated the implementation of a comprehensive grid system with which to retain more adequate control over the sites and their structures. In this way the cumbersome place-name nomenclature for site recording could be deemphasized, avoiding many inherent problems. Several sites recorded in 1972 were clear of growth in 1973, meaning that more exact mapping procedures could be employed. These operations revealed new groups for several sites and some previously unnoticed structures within studied sites. It also became apparent that several sites previously thought of as discrete units were actually parts of a greater complex. Consequently, the total number of sites was revised to 18, containing 145 features. This total, of course, represents only the recognizable sites for the Salamá Valley proper and does not take into consideration several major sites in the mountains directly above the valley.

ECOLOGICAL SURVEY

The definition of the various ecological subregions within the valley is a necessary step in the process of unraveling the ancient pattern of land utilization and resource distribution. Significantly, it was noted that the greater concentration of sites is in the eastern, better-watered section of the valley, rather than in the drier, western end. Apparently, Preclassic sites are located more favorably to the routes of access toward the south and east, rather than to the western outlet of the Salamá River that leads to the Petén lowlands. But by the Late Classic a large center had been established at the western outlet of the valley leading to the lowlands, probably better to control the trade routes to that region. More study is needed to determine the ancient routes of communication both north and south, but it has become apparent that long-held views regarding the manner of Maya overland travel must be seriously reexamined. For example, the Middle Preclassic site of Sakajut in the Alta Verapaz (north of the Salamá Valley) was reached probably more conveniently via trails over the intervening mountains than through paths following routes of natural drainage. Furthermore, Preclassic sites were located in 1972 by a survey following the Chixoy River (to which the Salamá River is a tributary), not within the valley, where customarily they would have been expected, but along the ridgetops above the valley, again suggesting that at least as early as the Middle Preclassic communication between areas followed diverse and complex patterns.

For the Salamá Valley itself, preliminary correlation of data indicates that during the Preclassic period the valley was probably densely forested in the eastern and southern sections, with scrubby growth in the drier western and northern portions. The mountainsides around the valley probably were pine-forested more extensively than today. Only a few kilometers to the east of the valley highland rainforests prevailed, as today. Identification of recovered animal bones indicate the existence of a tropical forest fauna, including such major species as tapir and jaguar. It is apparent that the closely spaced, varied ecological zones afforded the ancient inhabitants a great diversity in resource acquisition opportunities. Other resources such as jade and obsidian were close enough for steady importation in volume, thus encouraging the establishment of the valley as an important center for the redistribution of these commodities to the north and east. The sociopolitical implications of these data, along with the excavated material, will be one major focus of the final report.

LABORATORY OPERATIONS

Throughout 1973 material from the investigations continued to be processed. By the end of the year a total of 1,325 artifacts had been catalogued for both seasons. These artifacts include not only the jade and figurine pieces, but also stone tools, grinding stones, obsidian artifacts, etc. Some 25 additional vessels were added to the total of complete or reconstructable vessels recovered. It is estimated that 98 percent of the two seasons' material is catalogued, drawn, photographed, and studied, but further work will still need to be done as the writing of the final report progresses. This will be facilitated by the material still being available for study at the project headquarters.

The total number of Preclassic pottery sherds typed and named ranges over the 10,000 mark. The Classic period sherds have been preliminarily sorted and are probably of equal number to the Preclassic sample.

The obsidian artifacts and debris studied so far show a strong percentage of cortex (outside weathered portion of the original nodule), indicating that raw material was brought into the valley for later manufacturing procedures.

Preliminary Conclusions

It is now quite clear that the Preclassic adaptive strategy in the Maya area was more variable and widespread than previously suspected. The research completed to date in the Salamá Valley reveals that this early adaptive strategy included the exploitation of highland valley zones, probably through a combined agricultural and hunting subsistence pattern. The evidence from the Salamá Valley indicates that the earliest local combined agricultural-hunting subsistence system was maintained in a low-density, dispersed-settlement pattern. This strategy may have fostered an increase in game reserves (especially in fallow milpa fields) that led to an intensification of this mixed subsistence base (cf. Lowe, 1971, pp. 228-229).

Since the earliest known populations in the Salamá Valley and elsewhere in the Maya area (including both the south coast and the northern lowlands) all reflect a rather complex ceramic inventory, it seems obvious that none of these peoples represent the roots of Maya society. Rather, we must still postulate a previous time-span (Early Preclassic, ca. 2000-1200 B.C.) during which the basic elements of sedentarism began to expand into the diverse regions of the Maya area. Indeed, the initial populations in the Salamá Valley may have originated in the lower Motagua Valley, in a pattern analogous to the better documented early Pacific coast developments (see, for instance, Coe and Flannery, 1967). In addition, the presence of early and distinctive pottery in the Salamá Valley (Ekla Sub-Complex) might be another clue to previously suspected South American catalytic factors in Mesoamerican development (Green and Lowe, 1967, pp. 53-79).

When succeeding events in the Salamá Valley are contrasted to other Mesoamerican areas (Oaxaca, Valley of Mexico, and so forth), it is apparent that the local population enjoyed a rather independent and unique cultural development. Most obviously, while other areas underwent, during the Middle Preclassic, a vigorous period of either Olmec influence or control, there is no evidence of similar processes occurring in the Salamá Valley. Instead, sedentary society in the Salamá Valley develops ever more complex systems, culminating in the aggregate society of the Late Preclassic that we term Highland Valley Civilization, without known Olmec influence. In contrast to south coastal areas, such as Izapa, Abaj Takalik, and Chalchuapa, where early Olmec ceramics and sculptural-style monuments were combined with local traditions to produce regional Late Preclassic civilizations, the development of a local sculptural and notational system in the Salamá Valley can be traced without Olmec or any other external antecedents. We conclude from this, therefore, that it is not advisable to postulate a single region or tradition for deriving the origins of Maya civilization, since unilinear theories fail to consider diverse and independent developments such as the Salamá Valley.

For the Maya at least, one crucial indicator of this process is the development of writing and calendrical systems. From the evidence elsewhere (Gulf Coast, Oaxaca, South Coast, Kaminaljuyu, and so forth) we postulate a series of codeveloping regional centers of civilization, many with incipient writing systems, within southern Mesoamerica by the Middle Preclassic. The local social milieu in each of these regions including the Salamá Valley both required and encouraged diverse forms of notation to record predictable celestial and ritual events. Ultimately elements of these early writing systems became standardized to form the basis of the particular system we recognize as Classic Maya. Seen in light of this origin and development, the various components of the Classic Maya calendrical and writing system (bar and dot numerals, place notation, head-varient numerals, 260 and 365 day counts, and so forth) may be reflections of this diverse ancestry.

In addition to the presence of early forms of writing and calendrical systems in the Salamá Valley, the completed research has also revealed evidence of many other prototypes of later Classic Maya civilization. Present during the Middle Preclassic are domestic and ritual structures arranged around plazas and exhibiting complex architectural features, burial mounds with prepared stonelined tombs, and patterns of ritual activity that are all distinctively Maya at a time some 500 to 1,000 years before the Classic period.

To conclude, we wish to emphasize the diverse origins of Maya civilization and the crucial role of regional centers, such as the Salamá Valley and other highland populations, in this process of development. We feel that the development of Maya civilization cannot be satisfactorally explained by reliance upon simplistic models stressing one origin area, or even the interaction between two rather arbitrary environmental zones ("highlands versus lowlands"). The origins of Maya civilization will be revealed only by further refinement in both the research objectives and the interpretive models used by archeologists.

REFERENCES

ADAMS, RICHARD E. W.
  1972.   Maya Highland prehistory: New data and implications.   Contr. Univ. California Archaeol. Res. Fac., no. 16, pp. 1-21.
COE, MICHAEL D., and FLANNERY, KENT V.
  1967.   Early cultures and human ecology in south coastal Guatemala.   Smithsonian Contr. Anthrop., vol. 3, 136 pp., illus.
GREEN, D. F., and LOWE, GARETH W.
  1967.   Altamira and Padre Piedra: Early Preclassic sites in Chiapas, Mexico.   Pap. New World Archaeol. Found., no. 14, 133 pp.
LOWE, GARETH W.
  1971.   The civilizational consequences of varying degrees of agricultural and ceramic dependency within the basic ecosystems of Mesoamerica.   Contr. Univ. California Archaeol. Res. Fac., no. 11, pp. 212-248.
SEDAT, DAVID W., and SHARER, ROBERT J.
  1972.   Archaeological investigations in the Northern Maya Highlands: New data on the Maya Preclassic.   Contr. Univ. California Archaeol. Res. Fac., no. 16, pp. 23-35.
  1973.   Preclassic populations and writing systems in the Salamá Valley, Guatemala.   Paper presented at 72d annual meeting of American Anthropological Association, New Orleans.
SHARER, ROBERT J., and SEDAT, DAVID W.
  1973.   Monument 1, El Portón, Guatemala and the development of Maya calendrical and writing systems.   Contr. Univ. California Archaeol. Res. Fac., no. 18, pp. 177-194.
SMITH, ROBERT E.; WILLEY, GORDON, R.; and GIFFORD, JAMES C.
  1960.   The type-variety concept as a basis for the analysis of Maya pottery.   Amer. Antiq., vol. 25, pp. 330-340.

ROBERT J. SHARER
DAVID W. SEDAT

Archeological Study of Monte Alto, Guatemala, and Preclassic Cultures on the Pacific Coast, 1972-77

Principal Investigator: Edwin M. Shook, Antigua, Guatemala.

Grant No. 1115:   For an archeological study in Guatemala.

Monte Alto Progress, 1972

During 1972 the analysis of the ceramic material from Monte Alto was carried on by Edwin M. Shook in his laboratory in Antigua, Guatemala. The work was a continuation of that initiated in 1970-71 and consisted of sorting, typing, counting, photographing, and illustrating the great mass of sherds from the previous excavations. For the analysis he was fortunate to have from time to time the generous help of the Reverend Carlton Sage; voluntary photographic assistance was ably provided by Charles Withers. Antonio Oliveros, from the Museo Nacional de Guatemala, was hired to do the ceramic illustrations. Also during this time Gene Paull was able to carry out in the laboratory a study of the stone artifacts and to write up a resumé for the final Monte Alto report.

The ceramic analysis was interrupted in July when it was deemed urgent to carry out salvage archeology at La Blanca, a very important Middle Preclassic site on the south coast of Guatemala which was in the process of being destroyed by road construction. Shook's fervent pleas to get other parties interested in the salvage activity met with little response, thus making it necessary for him to undertake the work himself. The remaining months were spent at La Blanca, again with the voluntary assistance of the Reverend Sage, collecting ceramic samples from the mounds being bulldozed out of existence, and conducting, where possible, controlled stratigraphic tests. By the end of the year the job was completed, with the La Blanca material sorted and stored in the Shook laboratory for future study.

Monte Alto Progress, 1975

Work on the Monte Alto ceramic analysis, under the direction of Shook, was resumed vigorously in January 1975 with the return of Marion P. Hatch from Berkeley where, since the fall of 1971, she had been completing her

Ph.D. at the University of California. Also, valuable temporary assistance was received from a young Colorado student, Sally King, who worked in the Antigua laboratory from January through March.

In previous years we had completed the descriptions of the pottery vessels from the 50 caches excavated at Monte Alto. These vessels have been drawn by Antonio Oliveros and photographed by Shook. We had also completed the preliminary analysis of the pottery lots from some 40 (out of a total of 82) test trenches from the excavations of 1969-70, and had set up a tentative classification of the Monte Alto pottery types. Numbering some 60 types in all, they ranged from Middle Preclassic to Early Classic in style, with one small Late Classic deposit. The material included what were undoubtedly locally produced wares, as well as identifiable trade wares.

In January the preliminary analysis was resumed, beginning with Lot M-40. By the end of the month we had completed Lots 38-49, and 55-59. Our system was to have Hatch do the initial sorting, to be then checked by Shook, thus supplying two independent observations of the same material. After this, the types were counted according to the number of sherds per stratigraphic level, and were recorded by Sally King on charts giving the total content of each excavation. Shook then selected the sherds to be saved and those to be discarded.

In February Jamie Donaldson, a student from The Evergreen State College, Washington, joined the lab crew as a volunteer. She was doing a research project on Guatemala archeology to fulfill the requirements of her sophomore spring semester, and chose to investigate the Monte Alto Project as her subject.

Most of the month of February was spent on Lot 67, a very large amount of ceramic material. By the end of March, we had completed Lots 67-82. By April 18 we had done Lots 16-37, which finished the preliminary analysis of all the Monte Alto pottery, some 127,000 sherds. Sally King left the lab in March to return to her studies in the United States.

Having completed Phase I of the ceramic analysis, we began Phase II, the final classification of the Monte Alto pottery types. By this time, being much better acquainted with the material than when starting on the preliminary analysis, we were aware that we had in some cases lumped types that were different, and in other instances divided similar types that really belonged together. To begin the new task, we had to again sort the pottery, which up to that point had been separated according to lot number and stratigraphic level; it was now necessary to divide the sherds according to the type number assigned to them in our preliminary classification. By May the re-sorting was done and we were launched into Phase II.

Before proceeding with our final classification of the ceramic types at Monte Alto, it was deemed necessary to draw up a scheme that would guarantee consistency in mapping out degrees of relationship between the pottery types. We investigated the Type-Variety method of classification (Smith, Willey, and Gifford, 1960; Sharer and Gifford, 1970), currently in favor among New World ceramicists. Although we felt it advisable to maintain a certain uniformity with the other typological systems in use, we found we could not apply the Type-Variety method without some modification, the main problem being that we utilize vessel form as an important diagnostic tool and Type-Varietists do not. Nevertheless, we attempted to devise a hierarchical scheme which can be plugged into the Type-Variety taxonomic framework should there be the desire to do so.

Because the archeology of the Pacific Coast of Guatemala is not yet well understood or defined, it is not possible at this time to identify the higher levels in the hierarchical scheme of analysis such as ceramic "spheres" or "complexes" (Sharer and Gifford, 1970, p. 459). At present our highest level is the "ware," a broad category held together in our scheme on the basis of texture and composition of the paste, color, and general surface appearance of the pottery. We then divide the ware into one or more types, which are identified by variations in surface treatment (e.g., slip, burnishing). Each type consists of basic vessel forms which are characteristic of the type (e.g., comales, bowls, tecomates, jars). Each vessel form category can then be further divided according to the style of decoration (e.g., plain, incised, modeled). Lastly, finer details are noted, such as minor variations in rim form or in decoration. The hierarchical scheme is thus conceptualized as follows:

Ware (characteristic paste, temper, color)
   Type (characteristic surface treatment, forms)
      Vessel form
         Decoration
            Variations in shape/decoration

Work progressed steadily during May as we began testing our scheme. During this time, Jamie Donaldson completed her semester project, but had become sufficiently interested in the lab work to decide against returning to the United States. In June the lab research was interrupted for a short period by unforeseen events. By July, however, work had been resumed and was proceeding normally. The remaining months of the year witnessed no further incident, and the analysis not only progressed smoothly but seemed to gain momentum as it went. The hierarchical scheme held up under the test of the endless details of the ceramic analysis and facilitated the recognition of the more important relationships between the pottery types.

During the course of the year's investigation, several important and interesting facts have come to light. The first of these is the recognition of an early pottery group which is present at Monte Alto but which precedes the main occupation of the site. The sherds show up in mixed fill of the later occupations; no pure lots of the earlier pottery were uncovered by the excavations. A brief trip to La Blanca to secure samples of the early pottery types indicates that the Monte Alto group is related to it. Similar material is also present at the nearby site of El Balsamo. The presence of white rim black ware suggests the term "Olmecoid" for this early pottery group.

A second interesting point is that we have been able to map out the chronological evolution of certain pottery types in several of our ceramic groups. One of these is a brown bowl with ticked decoration on the rim which is familiar as a cache bowl at Monte Alto. It can now be recognized that it evolves into a buff "flower pot" characteristic of the Arenal Phase at Kaminaljuyu.

By coincidence, a Middle Preclassic grave or cache lot of whole vessels was discovered recently near Parramos, Department of Chimaltenango, and brought to the Antigua laboratory. The group of 32 vessels contained mainly Sacatepequez white paste white ware, a diagnostic type of the Providencia-Sacatepequez Phase at Kaminaljuyu. Within the lot was a brown bowl with ticked edge of the Monte Alto cache bowl type, thus confirming that this particular type is at the earlier end of the sequence at Monte Alto.

There had been little hope that any of the large heads at Monte Alto could be dated. The excavations had indicated that only one head rested in its original location, but was found to have a scant amount of sherd material in the fill beneath it. However, now recognizing the finer details in the chronological development of a few of the vessel forms, it begins to be apparent that this head can be linked to the Arenal Phase (Late Preclassic).

Shook originally surmised that, according to the pottery, the site of Monte Alto had a moderate to heavy occupation in Middle Preclassic times, which reached its height during the Late Preclassic period. Occupation continued into the beginning of the Early Classic, after which the site was abandoned. This observation has not been altered by the ceramic evidence. The fact that there are indisputable indications of Teotihuacán presence at the nearby site of Río Seco suggests that this may have been a factor causing the cessation of activity at Monte Alto. No Teotihuacán-style refuse has ever been uncovered at Monte Alto. One small section of the site was reoccupied in the Late Classic period.

Monte Alto Progress, 1977

Work in the Shook Laboratory, Antigua, Guatemala, continued through 1977 under the direction of Shook, with Hatch assisting in the ceramic analysis, and Donaldson as ceramic illustrator. The major objective of the year, the completion of the Monte Alto ceramic analysis, was accomplished.

In addition to the work on the Monte Alto ceramics, several other projects were carried out during the year. From January to March the staff participated in the Abaj Takalik archeological investigations under the direction of Dr. John A. Graham, University of California, Berkeley. Shook was project advisor, making the initial arrangements for the work to be carried out, then visiting the site to help plan excavations and advise on the analysis of the ceramics and sculpture. Hatch and Donaldson spent full time at the site, with Hatch in charge of the ceramic analysis and Donaldson as camp manager and ceramic assistant.

While the above was in progress, Shook was also advisor to the El Balsamo Project, another archeological study on the south coast, conducted by C. William Clewlow, University of California, Los Angeles. The work at this site continued until April.

The site of El Balsamo had been of considerable interest to our analysis of Monte Alto. Shook had discovered, examined, and mapped the site in 1969 and had made a representative sherd collection from the principal mound, which the Finca owner was bulldozing. We had analyzed the sample in the laboratory during 1976, because of its obvious relationships with the Monte Alto ceramics, and recognized the sherds as pertaining to the Middle Preclassic period, many of the same types being present at Monte Alto but mixed with sherds of later date. The El Balsamo assortment had made it possible for us to identify and separate the equivalent material from the later types at Monte Alto. For this reason we had completed and written the El Balsamo study with the intention of incorporating it as a part of the Monte Alto ceramic report (see Shook and Hatch, 1978).

At the end of the field season, in April, it became apparent to Dr. Clewlow that our preliminary analysis of the El Balsamo ceramics would greatly facilitate the study of the materials from his excavations, which were being taken up to the University of California at Los Angeles. At his request, therefore, we extracted the El Balsamo analysis from the larger Monte Alto report, and prepared it for publication in the *Journal of New World Archæology*.

Early in June, Shook made arrangements to record and photograph an important but almost inaccessible Olmec painting on a rock cliff in the Amatitlan area, and Dr. Clewlow sent a group of students to assist in this work. The task was completed in a week and the report was assembled at UCLA for publication in the *Journal of New World Archæology* (see Shook and Heizer, 1976). Meanwhile, Donaldson worked on the illustrations of the Monte Alto ceramics for the report, and Hatch devoted July to September advising and helping a Berkeley graduate student with the preliminary analysis of the ceramics from the Abaj Takalik excavations. This work was completed by mid-September, and the Berkeley student agreed to take over the Abaj Takalik ceramic analysis in 1978 as his dissertation subject.

On September 1 Shook, who had spent the summer in Mexico and the United States, returned and resumed the Monte Alto ceramic analysis. By October all the classification and description of the materials of the Preclassic period (the main period of occupation) was complete. However, the identification of the small number of Classic types remained elusive. Although it could be recognized that occupation at Monte Alto ceased early in Early Classic times, and that there had been a small Late Classic village on one portion of the site, we were unable to determine the exact chronological placement and development of the Early Classic wares and styles. The solution to this problem, we decided, was to find an area on the south coast with substantial occupation during the Classic period, and use it as a basis of comparison with Monte Alto.

It was clear that the best region for such a comparative study would be the area of Tiquisate. Fortunately, in 1947 Shook had made extensive test pits in this area, with excellent stratigraphic control. The material had been deposited in the National Museum of Guatemala awaiting further study, and was available. With permission from the Museum Director, the collection was removed to the Shook Laboratory where the pottery was sorted and typed. With this background knowledge, we were then able to understand and interpret with more accuracy the cultural sequence at Monte Alto.

Upon completion of the Monte Alto report we plan a subsequent but less comprehensive one on the ceramics of the Tiquisate region. Because it is one of the few areas on the south coast with substantial Early Classic occupation, it has important implications for the prehistory of the south coast in general. Questions immediately come to mind, such as, where does the Early Classic population at Tiquisate come from? Why were most sites abandoned on the south coast during the Early Classic? The Teotihuacán style can be recognized at Tiquisate as a strong intrusive element but of short duration in the upper levels of the Early Classic Period. What is the nature of this intrusion? Is the identification of a "Middle Classic" period valid for south coast chronology?

It is clear that the long occupation sequence at Monte Alto comes to an end just prior to the intrusion of Teotihuacán influence in the Tiquisate area and at Río Seco (a site located closer to Monte Alto than Tiquisate.) The final Early Classic phase of occupation at Monte Alto is characterized by a new vigor in introduced forms and wares, but of quality that is inferior to the Preclassic technology. In other words, the period before abandonment is not marked by a decline in activity, only a degradation of style and technology. We do not yet understand this final phase at the site.

The initial hopes in undertaking investigations at Monte Alto, i.e., to find evidence of a "Pre-Olmec" population, were not realized. However, we believe the study has value in establishing a more complete and needed chronological yardstick for the ceramic phases and trade relationships on the south coast of Guatemala. The occupation at Monte Alto, present from Early Preclassic times to the beginning of Early Classic, was at its peak during the latter phases of the Preclassic and it is probable that the large stone heads date from this time. However, a great deal of study remains needed for the Early and Middle Preclassic periods on the south coast, a project we anticipate and are also preparing to carry out upon completion of the Monte Alto report in 1978.

REFERENCES

SHARER, ROBERT J., and GIFFORD, JAMES C.
  1970.   Preclassic ceramics from Chalchuapa, El Salvador, and their relationships with the Maya lowlands.   American Antiquity, vol. 35, pp. 441-462.
SHOOK, EDWIN M., and HATCH, MARION P.
  1978.   The ruins of El Balsamo.   Journ. New World Archaeol., vol. 3, no. 1, pp. 1-38.
SHOOK, EDWIN M., and HEIZER, ROBERT F.
  1976.   An Olmec sculpture from the south (Pacific) coast of Guatemala. Journ. New World Archaeol., vol. 1, no. 3 (January), 8 pp.
SMITH, R. E.; WILLEY, G. R.; and, GIFFORD, J. C.
  1960.   The type-variety concept as a basis for the analysis of Maya pottery. American Antiquity, vol. 25, pp. 330-340.

EDWIN M. SHOOK
MARION P. HATCH

Social Behavior of Brown Bears
at McNeil River, Alaska

Principal Investigator: Allen W. Stokes, Utah State University, Logan, Utah.

Grant Nos. 1072,   To study the social behavior of Alaska brown bears *(Ursus*
1194.   *arctos).*

This is a study of brown-bear *(Ursus arctos* L.) behavior at McNeil River State Game Sanctuary located on the Alaska Peninsula about 100 kilometers northeast of Katmai National Monument. We studied the behavioral strategies bears used to make efficient use of salmon, a food resource limited in time and space because of its concentration at McNeil River Falls. We were interested in seeing how sex, age, reproductive state of the mother, and group size affected rank; and how fishing success was related to social rank, ability to fish at preferred locations, fishing skill, and salmon abundance.

Bears would normally gain little from social cooperation. They have no predators other than man, and a single bear can bring down the largest of prey without assistance. Selection has favored an essentially solitary existence presumably to exploit more efficiently a homogeneous food supply. Bear concentrations may occur, however, where a favored food source is limited either in time or space. At McNeil River Sanctuary brown bears concentrate on a portion of the river approximately 20 meters wide by 100 meters long to exploit salmon made vulnerable as they move upstream through a series of flat rocks and boulders in the river. As many as 35 different bears have been seen at the falls at one time, and 85 individuals have visited the area at least once during the 6-week-long salmon run (Rausch, 1958). This suggests salmon constitute an important component of the bears' diet and that competition may be relatively severe.

Methods

We observed bears from a bank above the falls, usually between 0600 and 2200, a total of 380 hours for the years 1972 and 1973. We recorded for each bear its time spent at the falls, specifics of its fishing efforts, and the time and form of its interactions with other bears. We could identify bears by sex and approximate age, by presence of ear tags placed on known-age bears, urination patterns, size, and presence of young. We could identify individuals by the above characteristics in addition to distinguishing scars, color, size and number of young, and their behavior while fishing and in relation to other bears. In the study of actual fishing techniques and how these varied with age and between individuals we observed 16 bears regularly in 1972 and 14 of the same 16 in 1973. They ranged in age from 3 to 22 years.

We measured salmon abundance by counting the number of times a fish broke the surface of a pool below the falls in a 2-minute period each half hour. The daily average of these counts provided an index of salmon abundance. This index compared closely with the fishing success of bears. Specific fishing techniques were recorded on movie camera for later analysis.

Results

Bears seen in 1971-1973 are listed in table 1 by sex and age. Salmon reached the falls the first week of July. Onset of fishing began somewhat later, July 25, 13, and 8 for 1971 to 1973, respectively. High water levels and scarcity of salmon affected the extent of lag between arrival of salmon and onset in fishing. The annual buildup and decline of bears is shown in figure 1. Factors leading to a drop in fishing were a sudden rise in water level, ripening of berries, and a drop in salmon numbers.

At least 54 percent of the bears had been seen the previous year, and these were the first to reappear in the following year; 47 percent of bears seen stayed for at least half the season; but 9 percent were seen for only 5 days or less.

To determine social status of individuals we recorded the outcome of decisive encounters in which one bear clearly dominated or was subordinate to the other (table 2). There was a clear-cut straight-line hierarchy among the large

TABLE 1. Population Composition of McNeil River Brown Bears, 1971 to 1973

				Numbers of bears seen				
Year	Males 4.5 yr.+	Single females 4.5 yr.+	Females with young	Cubs	Yearlings	Subadults (2.5 to 3.5 yrs.)	Unclassed (125 kg+)	Total
1971	14	11	12	14	6	13	6	76
1972	18	14	9	9	9	3	4	66
1973	21	16	5	6	3	10	5	66
Mean	17.7	13.7	8.7	9.7	6.0	8.7	5.0	69.5
Percent	26	20	12	14	9	12	7	100

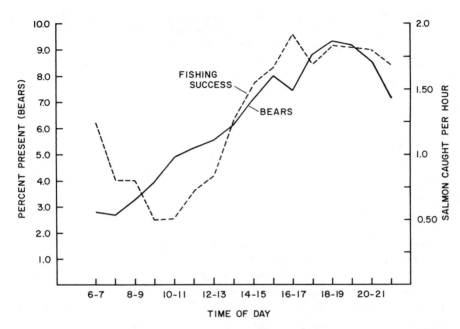

FIG. 1.   Seasonal abundance of brown bears at McNeil Falls, 1972 and 1973. Days
are numbered consecutively from the date bears began fishing each year.

males. Females with young dominated all but the large males. Relationships
within and between large females and small males and females were flexible.
At any one time high status depended upon which bear was first to arrive at a
fishing location and was inverse to how long and how successfully a bear had
been fishing. Subadults were so low in status that they largely avoided other
bears.

Bears were most active in afternoon and evening, the hours when fishing
success was also highest (fig. 2). In general, bears of highest status, old males
and females with cubs, fished most actively during these same hours. Other
bears tended to fish at less productive times of day. But even bears of low status succeeded in getting some fish. Thus subadults, which rarely could fish at
good fishing locations, were able to catch or scavenge the equivalent of 0.8
fish per hour, and supplement this food with the abundant but probably less
nutritious plant foods. Even in 1972 when there were few salmon the subadult
bears seemed sleek and fat.

During encounters between bears we recognized several forms of agonistic
behavior: high- and low-intensity threat charge, contact involving striking at
the rival, approach, and avoidance. The forms of these behaviors have been de-

TABLE 2.   The Fraction of Decisive Encounters Won by Individuals
of Different Sex and Age Groups at McNeil Falls, 1972 and 1973
(Data Presented Here Are for Interclass Encounters)

Classification	Fraction of encounters won	
	1972	1973
Large males	0.91	0.97
Females w/young	0.82	0.84
Single females	0.63	0.55
Small males	0.15	0.42
Small females	0.30	0.27
Subadults	0.00	0.02

scribed in detail elsewhere (Egbert and Stokes, 1976). Threat, charges, and contact aggression were the most dramatic and conspicuous forms of encounters. But the most common agonistic interaction was a simple avoidance of a bear already at a fishing location, or withdrawal upon approach of another. Bears were extremely aware of the arrival of a superior individual and would often withdraw when the other was still 20-40 meters away.

Subadults generally avoided other bears and so were involved in few high-intensity encounters. The same was true for large males but for another reason. Lower-ranking males were quick to depart upon the mere arrival of an adult male at the falls. And the presence of four adult males at once was enough to force all others to leave without contest. So the only high-intensity encounters large males had was when they met bears of nearly similar rank.

Females with young usually avoided large males and with good reason, for adult males will kill cubs. We recorded one incident at McNeil Falls, and there are numerous records in Yellowstone National Park (Craighead and Craighead, 1971). Still, when these females were fishing, they often threatened, charged, and even slashed at these adult males.

Small males were the least aggressive of any group excluding subadults (table 2). Those high-intensity interactions they had were almost entirely initiated by larger bears. The fact that these small males were mostly 4 to 8 years old and not yet fully mature sexually may have accounted for their relative lack of aggressiveness.

We had expected there would be fewer encounters as the season progressed. In neither year did this occur. Nevertheless the intensity of encounters did decline with season as did the distance at which bears would tolerate another. By the end of the season all but the large males and females with

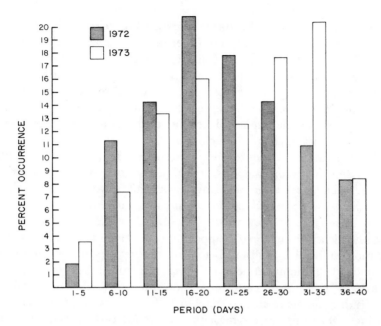

FIG. 2.   Changes in numbers of bears and fishing success with time of day, McNeil
Falls, 1972-73. Cubs and yearlings are excluded.

young would tolerate each other within two meters while fishing or passing
each other. As the season progressed bears seemed more interested in fishing
than interacting and merely used low-intensity threats as means of maintaining their fishing position.

Many of the above changes in frequency and intensity of interactions
could be attributed to the greater familiarity of bears as the summer advanced.
But salmon abundance also influenced encounters. In 1973, when salmon and
fishing success were high, there were only half as many agonistic encounters as
in 1972 when fishing success was half that of 1973. Another consequence of
the drop in fishing success at days 31-35 in 1973 was a decline in play and rise
in aggression. In the next five days fishing success rose again, accompanied by
drop in aggression and rise in play.

Fishing for salmon by bears involved three steps: orientation, approach,
and capture. Some bears sat along the river's edge; others stood in water,
sometimes belly-deep; and still others walked along in shallow water until
sighting a fish. On detecting a fish the bear would move toward it in a slow
run (lope); put its head under water; or plunge from rock ledge or bank directly into the water. Actual capture was with forepaws or mouth or both. We
called each separate combination of the above three steps in actual capture of a

fish a technique. In general younger bears used more techniques than older bears. We thought bears might use fewer techniques over the weeks as they learned the most efficient way to fish, but this was not so. Three techniques were used in about half of all attempts both years (table 3). Bears changed technique after a mean of 1.4 attempts. The varied topography of the falls, changes in salmon abundance and water level, and a bear's frequent change in location seemed mainly responsible for the steady use of many techniques and the high frequency of change in technique.

The three most frequent techniques were also the most efficient (table 3). The standing-plunging-forepaws technique seemed relatively inefficient. However, many of the attempts using this technique were half-hearted, made when fishing was poor, and did not require much time or energy.

The abundance of salmon in 1973 resulted in a correspondingly higher capture efficiency. Bears in 1973 apparently could afford to wait for salmon to be in more vulnerable positions before attempting capture. Fishing success, measured in fish caught per hour of fishing, rose from 1.5 per hour in 1972 to 2.8 in 1973, reflecting the greater salmon abundance. Hence, an individual bear's fishing success related to these main factors: its social rank and corresponding right to fish at the most productive locations; specific technique, which was often matched to the location; hours spent fishing; and salmon abundance.

Discussion

Normally solitary brown bears quickly adjusted to the crowded conditions associated with fishing at McNeil Falls. Many brown bears have been visiting McNeil Falls since their first summer of life and so have experienced the crowded conditions previously; they appeared to quickly establish their position vis a vis others. The most remarkable changes in social behavior occurred among adolescents and subadult bears; adults neither were as wary at the onset of fishing nor did they habituate to the same extent as younger animals. Some bears visited the falls for only a brief period and then evidently moved on. They may have found the competition and proximity of so many bears intolerable, or they may have been unable to catch enough salmon to warrant staying, a result of being excluded from choice fishing spots or a simple lack of fishing skill.

A second factor that governed tolerance between brown bears was salmon abundance. Bears were much less aggressive as salmon numbers rose. Not only did salmon become easier to catch as the season progressed but also very successful bears discarded fish that others could scavenge. A drop in salmon

TABLE 3. Efficiency and Relative Use of Three Most Frequent Fishing Techniques

Technique	Use*		Efficiency**	
	1972	1973	1972	1973
Standing-plunging-forepaws mouth	23	20	35	55
Standing-plunging-forepaws	19	8	9	11
Standing-mouth	10	18	25	44
Number of attempts	781	1178		
Salmon index			21	99

*Percent of all attempts.   **Fish caught per 100 attempts.

abundance resulted in an immediate increase in intolerance. Since salmon generally increased in numbers for at least the first half of each fishing season, it is likely that competition and the resulting intolerance among the bears waned as a result of this increase in salmon.

Brown bears also adjusted to crowding by sorting themselves out by time and location. Dominant bears fished at times when salmon were moving through the falls in greatest numbers. Lower-ranking bears could still do well by fishing longer hours at less lucrative sites. Dominant animals could claim the best fishing locations, but subordinates have great flexibility in the manner in which they attain fish: by using poorer locations, scavenging scraps, or locating dead fish on the river bottom.

Recent comparative studies on the social behavior of some species of Canidae indicate that solitary forms have a smaller, less complex array of close-contact visual social signals than the gregarious species (Kleiman, 1967; Fox, 1970). The results suggest that social species have evolved communication repertoires to minimize aggression among group members by the substitution of ritualized behavior for actual fighting. Brown bears seem to fit this pattern in that being solitary they do not have a wide assortment of visual signals in comparison to other carnivores. Kleiman and Eisenberg (1973), however, have questioned the presumed relationship between a species' social organization and complexity and quantity of close-contact social signals. They suggest that information value of signals may be as important or more so than complexity or number, and that the context of an interaction may carry considerable information as well.

Brown bears use a great variety of fishing techniques that allow them to fish effectively over a range of conditions, from shallow rivulets to waist-deep rapids. The occasionally high degree of competition we observed for fishing sites and fish suggests that salmon are an extremely important source of food for coastal brown bears. Salmon, along with the mosaic of abundant foods of the Alaska coasts, may explain why coastal bears are the largest of all brown-bear subspecies.

Acknowledgments

We thank the Alaska Department of Fish and Game for providing field facilities, transportation, and supplying data on McNeil River brown bears. Special thanks go to James B. Faro for his major role in immobilizing and tagging bears and for giving generously of his wealth of knowledge of McNeil River brown bears. It was through the enthusiasm and dedication of Derek Stonorov that this study was made possible.

Our research was supported by the Alaska Department of Fish and Game; Boone and Crockett Club; Bureau of Sport Fisheries and Wildlife; Carnegie Museum, Allegheny Foundation Fund for Studies in Animal Behavior; the National Geographic Society; and the National Park Service.

REFERENCES

CRAIGHEAD, JOHN J., and CRAIGHEAD, FRANK C., JR.
    1967.   Management of bears in Yellowstone National Park.   Environ. Res. Inst. and Montana Coop. Wildlife Res. Unit Rpt., 113 pp.
EGBERT, ALLAN L., and STOKES, ALLEN W.
    1976.   The social behavior of brown bears *(Ursus arctos)* on an Alaskan salmon stream.   *In* "Bears—Their Biology and Management," M. R. Pelton, J. W. Leutler, and G. E. Folk, eds., I.U.C.N. Publ., new ser., no. 40. Morges.
FOX, M. W.
    1970.   The anatomy of aggression and its ritualization in Canidae: A developmental and comparative study.   Behaviour, vol. 35, pp. 242-258.
KLEIMAN, D. G.
    1967.   Some aspects of social behavior in the Canidae.   Amer. Zool., vol. 7, pp. 365-372.
KLEIMAN, D. G., and EISENBERG, JOHN F.
    1973.   Comparisons of canid and felid social systems from an evolutionary perspective.   Animal Behav., vol. 21, pp. 637-659.
RAUSCH, R. A.
    1958.   Alaska brown bear studies.   Alaska Fed. Aid Wildlife Rest. Project W-3-R-13.

ALLEN W. STOKES
ALLAN L. EGBERT
MICHAEL H. LUQUE

Pollination Studies in Australian Terrestrial Orchids

Principal Investigator: Warren P. Stoutamire, University of Akron, Akron, Ohio.

Grant Nos. 1096, 1233. To determine the function of anomalous flower forms in Australian terrestrial orchids.

Fieldwork in southern Australia during the September-December months of 1972 and 1973 was planned to determine the function of anomalous floral characters in the terrestrial orchid species. Many native terrestrials exhibit bright colors and often pronounced odors characteristic of orchid species elsewhere, but some species in the genera *Chiloglottis, Drakaea, Caladenia, Arthrochilus,* and *Cryptostylis* are both dull in color and odorless to the human observer. Most of the species in question also produce large glandlike protuberances on the labellum, column, or sepals. These thickened tissues were found to be highly attractive to male hymenopterans, which often were sexually excited by the flowers. The sexual attraction of insects to orchid flowers resulting in pollination has been termed pseudocopulation and is documented for the Australian species of *Cryptostylis* (Coleman, 1927-1930). Field observations indicate that pseudocopulation is operative also in other genera, and examples are described here. Wasps locate flowers by odor, finding concealed flowers without difficulty. The odors function as sexual attractants (sex pheromones) and are specific for the orchid species producing them. Each orchid attracted only one wasp species at a given locality. Additional details have been presented elsewhere (Stoutamire, 1974, 1975). All wasps visiting flowers of the above genera belong to the family Tiphiidae, subfamily Thynninae, with the exception of *Cryptostylis* wasps, which are Ichneumonidae.

Observations

Chiloglottis gunnii (fig. 8) exhibits the pseudocopulation mechanism. It is geographically widespread, ranging from New South Wales through Victoria to Tasmania. Geographic races differ in peduncle length, flower color, and positon of labellum glands. Flowers of the race occurring on Mount Roland, Tasmania, were visited only by an *Eirone* wasp species in 1972 and 1973. This is not, however, the only wasp visitor to the various *Chiloglottis gunnii* races. When flowers of several races were used as bait I found that the *Eirone* visited only the Mount Roland race, while two morphologically differentiated races in Mount Field National Park, Tasmania, and another race in the Snowy Range of New South Wales each attracted different wasps. The two races of *Chiloglottis gunnii* in Mount Field flower concurrently with another species, *C. cornuta*. The latter was not observed to attract any insect and appears to be self-pollinating. Self-pollination occurs also in species of the Australian orchid genera *Thelymitra* and *Calochilus*. Although *Chiloglottis cornuta* has well-developed glands on the labellum these appear to be nonfunctional. The glands of *Chiloglottis gunnii* races are active sites for pheromone production. When glands are clipped from the flowers and dropped on the forest floor wasps find the structures and investigate them with apparent excitement.

The three biological entities flowering within feet of one another at Mount Field are reproductively isolated, one apparently by self-pollination and the other two by selective attraction of different wasps. The latter two fall within the taxonomic-morphological concept of *Chiloglottis gunnii*. The complex of races included in *C. gunnii* have considerable morphological unity, and the complex is distinct from other *Chiloglottis* species. It consists of several morphologically distinguishable geographic races, which are in some cases partially sympatric and which appear to rely on different thynnid wasps for pollination. The races probably will require taxonomic recognition when the complex is better understood.

A pair of *Chiloglottis* species, *C. formicifera* (fig. 7) and *C. trapeziformis* (fig. 9), occur in the vicinity of Sydney. Flowers are superficially similar but differ in gland configuration. Two different thynnid wasps (*Neozeleboria* spp.) respond to the pheromones of the orchids. It cannot yet be assumed that these wasps are the pollinators of the respective orchids throughout their ranges, in view of the *Chiloglottis gunnii* observations. Pollinators may be replaced geographically and only field observation will determine if this is the case. The lip appendages of *C. formicifera* are superficially antlike and the specific epithet refers to this resemblance. The glands also resemble the wingless female thynnid wasps chemically and physically, and it is the wasps that respond, not ants.

It is difficult to relate orchid flower characters to the mimicked female wasp, which is usually unknown. Female thynnids, which are the chemical and/or physical models for orchid flowers, are rarely captured because they are usually found by males before the human observer chances upon them. Male wasps locate the wingless, pheromone-producing females and carry them off, and the mating pairs feed on local flowers, especially nectar-producing species of *Leptospermum, Eucalyptus,* and *Vertecordia.* The pairs can be collected, but one has difficulty in assigning a collection to a known orchid pollinator. The wasp males differ by minor characters, and there is uncertainty in identifying a mating pair as a pollinator of a particular orchid species. One is sure that one has an orchid pollinator only when the insect is collected on the orchid, and such collections are always of single males.

I have observed females of only two orchid pollinators. The *Thynnoides* wasp that pollinates *Caladenia dilatata* (fig. 2) in the Mount Lofty area of South Australia was observed mating on *Leptospermum* (tea tree) in an area where orchid flowers were being used as bait. The wasp was the only common species in the area, and mating males appeared identical to the unmated males attracted to the *Caladenia* flowers. The female wasp bears little resemblance to the flower. The maroon labellum tip and similarly colored labellum glands may act as visual cues to the approaching male wasp, but there is little physical resemblance beyond this, at least to the human observer. The chemical similarity is obvious to the wasp, however.

A greater physical resemblance between female wasps and orchid flowers occurs in the western Australian *Drakaea elastica* (fig. 13). The flowers were used as bait in an area where male *Zaspilothinnus* wasps were cruising in numbers and actively visiting the bait flowers. Unusual activity in the grass several feet from the observation site involved a group of four male wasps and one female for which they were competing. The competition prevented her being carried away. The female was released and was observed to crawl up a grass stem, make her way to a leaf tip, and hang in a position similar to that of a *Drakaea elastica* labellum, approximately the same height above the ground as that of an orchid flower. Her rear legs were rubbed several times over the tip of the abdomen and then over the abdomen surface, presumably releasing or spreading pheromone material. She was soon located and removed by a searching male. The color, position, and general resemblance of this wasp to the flowers of *Drakaea elastica* were striking. Here was obvious physical and chemical mimicry.

Drakaea glyptodon (fig. 12) is pollinated by a related *Zaspilothynnus* wasp, in a manner similar to that in *D. elastica*. The female wasp has not been observed, but I predict that general dimensions and color will be similar to those of the orchid labellum.

The *Caladenia* species of southeastern and southwestern Australia are a large and diverse group, some being brightly colored, fragrant, and adapted to insect visitors searching for food. *Caladenia patersonii* occurs in several forms across the southern states, the largest being *C. patersonii* var. *longicauda* of Western Australia, the flowers often measuring more than 9 inches between sepal tips. This large and relatively common spider orchid attracts a variety of flies and bees to the flowers, which have an odor suggesting fermentation. *Caladenia lobata,* the butterfly orchid of the Stirling Mountain region, tends to flower later than *C. patersonii* although the flowering periods overlap slightly. *Caladenia lobata* is a pseudocopulation orchid visited by *Thynnoides* wasps, and one might expect that pseudocopulation and food-promising mechanisms are

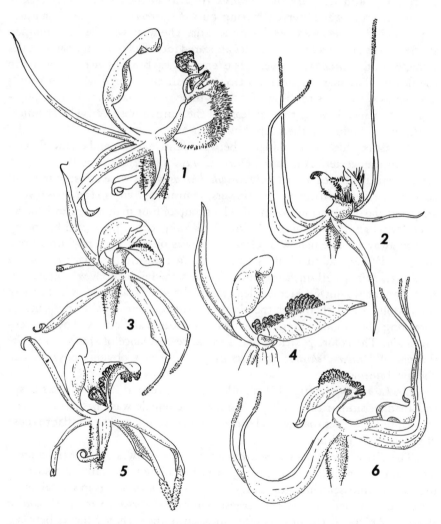

FIGS. 1-6.   Floral details of Australian terrestrial orchids, illustrating the glands that attract wasps of the family Tiphiidae: 1, *Caladenia barbarossa*, X 3; 2, *C. dilatata*, X 3; 3, *C. doutchae*, X 3; 4, *C. cairnseana*, X 3; 5, *C. roei*, X 3; 6, *C. multiclavia*, X 2.5.

mutually exclusive. In one area west of the Stirling Range, I found a population that included late-flowering *C. patersonii*, fresh flowers of *C. lobata*, and

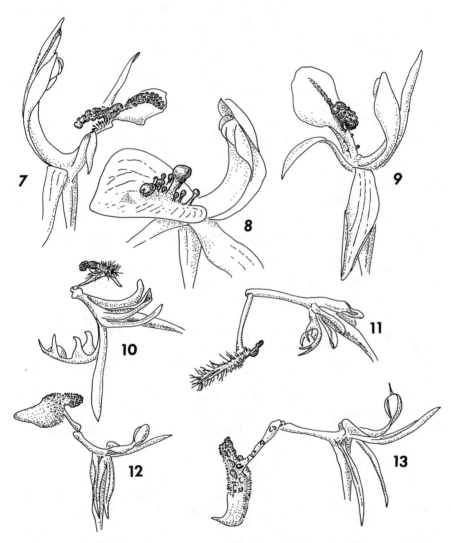

FIGS. 7-13. Floral details of Australian terrestrial orchids, illustrating glands that attract wasps of the family Tiphiidae: 7, *Chiloglottis formicifera*, X 2; 8, *C. gunnii*, X 2.5; 9, *C. trapeziformis*, X 2; 10, *Arthrochilus irritabilis*, X 4; 11, *A. hunteana*, X 4; 12, *Drakaea glyptodon*, X 2.5; 13, *D. elastica*, X 2.5.

what appeared to be a hybrid swarm involving the two species. The intermediates recombined the white color and pronounced odor of *C. patersonii* with
the wide-fringed, dark-tipped labellum of *C. lobata*. Different species utilizing differing attracting strategies can produce hybrids if the pollinator responds to both strategies: male thynnid wasps are nectar feeders as well as
seekers after female sexual attractants. The male wasps may occasionally visit
C. patersonii flowers in search of food and *C. lobata* flowers in search of females.
In this example there are strong restrictions on such promiscuous behavior,
however. *Caladenia lobata* is later flowering and geographically more localized
than the earlier flowering widespread *C. patersonii*. These factors will function
in maintenance of species integrity.

A parallel situation may exist between races of the polymorphic *Caladenia
patersonii* in eastern and western Australia and the equally widespread *C. dilatata*. The *dilatata* × *patersonii* cross has been reported, and I have seen flowers
that are morphologically intermediate in bush areas where the species flower
concurrently. Differences in flowering time cannot be invoked as a breeding
barrier between these species. In the absence of other information the pseudocopulation and food-promising specializations appear to be the obvious isolating factors.

Caladenia roei (fig. 5) and *C. doutchae* (fig. 3) are a pair of concurrently
flowering species of western Australia with green to maroon flowers on thin,
flexible stems. Their colonies are local, and species were not observed together
although they occupy the same general geographic area. They are visited by
different thynnid wasps of undetermined genus. When the two orchid species
are used as bait at a test site the appropriate wasp visits the flower simulating
its female and does not visit the other orchid species. Chemical signals appear
to isolate effectively these two morphologically similar orchids.

Caladenia multiclavia (fig. 6) is a remarkable western Australian species in
which the horizontal labellum, delicately balanced above the flower, rocks
and trembles with air movements. The insectlike appearance is enhanced by
this movement. I encountered the appropriate combination of weather, wasp,
and flowering populations only once during the 1973 season and was able to
collect the thynnid wasp several times on bait flowers. The *Tachynomia* wasp
approaches the decoy, alights, and is tilted forward into the cup-shaped floral
reproductive structures. Pollen masses are attached to the wasp thorax in the
process.

Arthrochilus huntiana (fig. 11) is a member of a small genus of Australian
orchids with mobile labellums bearing insectlike decoys. The decoys may be
above (fig. 10), in front of, or below the reproductive structures in different

species, but all are hinged so that they swing into the column. The *huntiana* labellum, below and to the front of the anther-stigma, bears two anterior glands and a fringed bodylike extension. It attracts a small thynnid in Victoria which attempts to fly away with the bait. In so doing it swings into the column and removes pollen. Rotherham (1967) illustrated the process.

Conclusions

The field observations suggest the presence of biologically differentiated races in *Chiloglottis gunnii,* the races being isolated in part by differences in pheromones. Each wasp species appears to be strongly attracted to a particular orchid race and not to others. In transporting bait flowers to sites where *Chiloglottis* orchids are not known to grow the wasps are still very specific as to the race of orchid which they visit. The complex of biological races of *Chiloglottis gunnii* is an example of a species which may be in the process of differentiating into separate reproductive entities.

Well-differentiated biological races may still hybridize occasionally. This appears to be the case in the putative hybrids *Caladenia dilatata* × *patersonii* and *C. lobata* × *patersonii.* The intermediates appear to have little biological potential since the species have maintained their integrity over extensive geographic areas.

The complex systems of labellum glands physically resemble female thynnid wasps in such species as *Drakaea elastica, Chiloglottis formicifera,* and *Caladenia cairnseana* (fig. 4) but bear less resemblance to insects in *Caladenia dilatata, C. lobata,* and the *C. roei-doutchae* pair, although the statement must be hedged by admission that I do not know the appearance of females of the wasps concerned. The wasps' initial attraction is pheromonal, and only on close approach could physical resemblance play a role, while humans distinguish the entities entirely by sight—we cannot sense the pheromones.

The origins and differentiation of pheromone systems in Australian terrestrial orchids have not yet been investigated. European *Ophrys* orchids producing pheromones are currently being investigated (Kullenberg and Bergström, 1974). *Ophrys* species (tribe Orchideae) are distantly related to the Australian species reported here (tribe Neottieae), and the pseudocopulation syndrome probably has evolved at least twice. The Australian orchid species attract wasps of the families Tiphiidae and Ichneumonidae, while European *Ophrys* are pollinated by hymenopterans belonging to other groups. Pseudocopulation involving sex pheromone-like attractants is not known in any other group of plants. Factors predisposing orchids for this mechanism are unknown.

REFERENCES

COLEMAN, E.
   1927.   Pollination of the orchid *Cryptostylis leptochila*.   Victoria Nat., vol. 44,
           pp. 20-22.
   1928.   Pollination of *Cryptostylis leptochila*.   Victoria Nat., vol. 44, pp. 333-
           340.
   1929.   Pollination of *Cryptostylis subulata* (labill.) Rchb. f.   Victoria Nat., vol.
           46, pp. 62-66.
   1930.   Pollination of *Cryptostylis erecta* R. Br.   Victoria Nat., vol. 46, pp. 236-
           238.
KULLENBERG, B., and BERGSTRÖM, G.
   1974.   The pollination of *Ophrys* orchids.   Pp. 253-258 *in* "Chemistry in Bo-
           tanical Classification." Proceedings of the 25th Nobel Symposium,
           1973.
ROTHERHAM, E. R.
   1967.   Pollination of *Spiculaea huntiana* (F. Muell.) Schltr.   Orchadian, vol. 2,
           no. 9, p. 120.
STOUTAMIRE, WARREN P.
   1974.   Australian terrestrial orchids, thynnid wasps, and pseudocopulation.
           Bull. Amer. Orchid Soc., vol. 43, no. 1, pp. 13-18.
   1975.   Pseudocopulation in Australian terrestrial orchids.   Bull. Amer. Or-
           chid Soc., vol. 44, no. 3, pp. 226-233.

WARREN P. STOUTAMIRE

Ichthyological Expedition to Lord Howe Island

Principal Investigator: Frank H. Talbot, The Australian Museum, Sydney, Australia.[1]

Grant No. 1121:   To survey the fishes of Lord Howe Island.

Lord Howe Island, lying at 31°33'S. in the Tasman Sea, possesses the southernmost coral reef and associated lagoon in the world. Some 630 kilometers off the east coast of Australia (fig. 1), the island's coral reef community is of particular interest to biologists because of its geographic position. While considerable recent work has been completed on the fishes of eastern Australia, the last compilation of fishes for Lord Howe Island was done at the beginning of this century (Waite, 1904).

In February 1973 a team of ichthyologists including G. R. Allen, D. F. Hoese, J. R. Paxton, B. C. Russell, F. H. Talbot, and G. P. Whitley of the Australian Museum, B. Goldman of Macquarie University, J. E. Randall of the B. P. Bishop Museum in Honolulu, and W. A. Starck with his research vessel *El Torito* spent a month at Lord Howe collecting fishes. The expedition was financed by a grant from the National Geographic Society and had as its aim the collection of as many species as possible from Lord Howe.

The fish fauna of Lord Howe has long been of interest. The first inshore fishes were collected by the crew of H.M.S. *Herald* in 1853 and the first Australian Museum fish collecting team went to Lord Howe in 1887. Ogilby (1889) published his list of Lord Howe Island fishes, numbering 80 species, primarily as a result of that trip. Later museum collecting by Waite and McCulloch enabled Waite (1904) to increase the total to 180 species in his catalogue of Lord Howe Island fishes. Irregular collecting had increased the known fish fauna to 208 species by the end of 1972.

Most of the previous fishes had been taken by hook and line, shallow seinings, and beach strandings. The 1973 team utilized modern collecting methods, including aqualungs, the ichthyocide rotenone, explosives, quinaldine anaesthetic, and a variety of nets and spears. Especially valuable was the participation of Dr. Starck and the *El Torito*. This 65-foot shallow draft research vessel is equipped with a 2-man wet submarine, 2 decompression chambers, and a 21-foot auxiliary launch, as well as a laboratory, library, and photographic facilities.

---

[1] Present address: Macquarie University, North Ryde, Australia.

The size and varied expertise of the collecting team allowed us to identify almost all of the fishes in the field. Armed with a list of the previously record- ed species, we were able to keep an up-to-date tally of all species collected as the expedition progressed. Most of the group had extensive experience with coral-reef fishes and the high level of new species records resulted from the spearing of unrecorded species, particularly in the later stages of the trip. The bright colors of many coral-reef fishes allow identification by an experienced diver without actually capturing specimens, much as is done in bird watch- ing. A small proportion of our new records are based on these unquestioned sight records only.

The expedition was an unqualified success, more than doubling the known species of Lord Howe Island fishes from 208 to 448. Over 6,000 speci- mens belonging to 77 families and 295 species were collected during the month-long expedition. In addition to providing a basic study collection of Lord Howe Island fishes, the specimens will be utilized in future taxonomic studies involving South Pacific fishes. The bulk of the study collection is reg- istered in The Australian Museum and the Bishop Museum while duplicates of common species have been sent to a number of other institutions.

While the coral reef and lagoon are well developed, the fish fauna is de- pauperate when compared to that of the Great Barrier Reef. Museum work on the southern end of the reef indicates that more than 800 fish species occur in the Capricorn Group, almost twice the number found at Lord Howe.

The majority of Lord Howe species are widely distributed in the tropical areas of the Indian and/or West Pacific oceans. A significant proportion of the fauna is also found in the temperate regions of New Zealand and/or Australia, while a few of the fishes are distributed among the subtropical Pacific islands of Easter, Rapa, and Pitcairn. Thus the Lord Howe Island fish fauna is made up of a number of different zoogeographic components, with the tropical ones dominant. The four dominant fish families at Lord Howe—Labridae (47 spe- cies), Pomacentridae (26 species), Gobiidae (23 species), and Chaetodontidae (22 species)—are also among the most speciose families on the Great Barrier Reef and most species at Lord Howe also occur in eastern Australian waters.

Briggs (1974) considered Lord Howe Island a distinct zoogeographic province that included Norfolk Island and Middleton Reef, primarily on the basis of Waite's (1916) data indicating 22 percent endemic shore fish species. We have greatly reduced that number to less than 4 percent, and consider Lord Howe a part of the transition zone between tropical and temperate east- ern Australia.

In addition to the collections made on Lord Howe Island, individual members of the party continued with research projects begun in other areas of

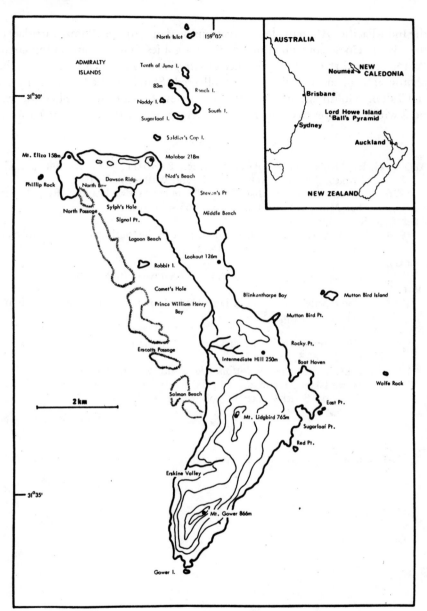

FIG. 1. Map showing Lord Howe Island and its location off east coast of Australia.

the Indo-Pacific. Allen made observations on damselfishes (Pomacentridae) of the island, Hoese continued his studies on gobies living in branching coral, Paxton studied the bioluminescence of *Parapriacanthus unwini,* Randall took photographs of most of the species collected, Starck studied shark behavior and Talbot, Goldman, and Russell ran a series of quantitative collecting stations with explosives to compare with different areas of the Great Barrier Reef.

REFERENCES

ALLEN, G. R.; HOESE, D. F.; PAXTON, J. R.; RANDALL, J. E.; RUSSELL, B. C.; STARCK, W. A.; TALBOT, F. H.; and WHITLEY, G. P.
    1976.   An annotated checklist of the fishes of Lord Howe Island.   Rec. Australian Mus., vol. 30, no. 15, pp. 365-454, illus.
ALLEN, G. R., and PAXTON, J. R.
    1974.   Lord Howe Island, a tropical outpost in the south Pacific.   Aust. Nat. Hist., vol. 18, no. 2, pp. 50-55.
BRIGGS, J. C.
    1974.   Marine zoogeography, 475 pp.   McGraw-Hill, New York.
OGILBY, J. D.
    1889.   The reptiles and fishes of Lord Howe Island.   Australian Mus. Mem., vol. 2, no. 9, pp. 51-74.
WAITE, E. R.
    1904.   Catalogue of the fishes of Lord Howe Island.   Rec. Australian Mus., vol. 5, no. 3, pp. 87-230.
    1916.   A list of the fishes of Norfolk Island and indication of their range to Lord Howe Island, Kermadec Islands, Australia and New Zealand.   Trans. Roy. Soc. South Australia, vol. 40, pp. 452-458.

JOHN R. PAXTON[2]

[2] Department of Ichthyology, The Australian Museum, Sydney, Australia.

Settlement-Pattern Survey at Becan, Campeche, Mexico

Principal Investigator: Prentice M. Thomas, Jr., Institute for New World Research, New Orleans, Louisiana.

Grant Nos. 1041, 1150. In support of a study of prehistoric settlement patterns at the Maya site of Becan, Campeche, Mexico.

By the end of 1973 two field seasons had been completed at the ancient Maya site of Becan in the Río Bec region of the Yucatán Peninsula under my directorship and financed through grants from the National Geographic Society. Numerous individuals participated in the project either in the field or in the laboratory, but I extend special thanks to the following: Steve Ahler, Robert Newman, and Mary Jane Thomas, who oversaw the test excavations and are responsible for the full completion of that portion of the project; Howard Earnest, who undertook the tedious position of project ceramist and provided the chronological information for the completion of the settlement-pattern survey; and finally, Susan Kluge and Michael Blackwell, who drafted the maps.

The site of Becan is located roughly in the center of the Yucatán Peninsula in a region today heavily marked by the remains of ancient occupation; housemounds and agricultural terracing are densely and widely distributed in this presently sparsely inhabited area. In dealing with these remains, we employed several archeological research techniques, including mapping, surface collection, and a program of test excavations. Each procedure yielded different, yet complementary, evidence on the nature of ancient settlement.

Background

Becan is one of the principal sites of the Río Bec area, an archeological region of the central Yucatán Peninsula distinguished architecturally by the presence of twin- or tri-towered masonry temples. The vegetation in this area is transitional between the dry scrub forest of northern Yucatán and the high rain forest of the Petén region to the south. For purposes of agriculture and settlement, there are two types of terrain. First, the areas highly favored for agriculture and settlement throughout the history of Becan are the well-drained elevated areas covered today by a high forest canopy. Second, there are poorly drained seasonal swamps, or bajos, which are covered with a low impenetrable forest of small trees and shrubs. These swampy areas were shunned as areas of settlement in prehistoric times as they are today. In general, the area around Becan is well watered during the May-to-December rainy season with rainfall averaging 125 centimeters per year (Vogeler, 1970). Surface streams and cenotes are absent in this region. Instead, the water is trapped in shallow clay-lined basins called aguadas (Vogeler, 1974), and settlement, both ancient and modern, tended to cluster in the vicinity of these water sources. Although the aguadas usually retain water throughout the year, the present inhabitants have experienced two droughts since 1972, the most recent leaving Aguada Carmelita at Becan completely dry.

Serious archeological research began in the Río Bec region when, in 1912, Robert Merwin set out on horseback from Chetumal, Quintana Roo, to explore areas to the west. Mapping and describing a number of ruins, Merwin discovered the now famous ruins of Río Bec Groups A-F (Merwin, 1913).

After Merwin's exploratory investigations, the Río Bec region went largely unnoticed until the early 1930's, at which time the Carnegie Institution of Washington supported four successive reconnaissance missions into the area. Under the direction of Karl Ruppert and John Denison, these explorations encompassed a substantial portion of the Río Bec region; included among their many discoveries were the enormous ruins of Becan.

These two thrusts into the Río Bec zone constituted the only archeological work of note conducted in the area until 1969. In that year E. Wyllys Andrews IV directed a Tulane University–National Geographic Society expedition designed to investigate the ruins of Becan. Although his unfortunate death subsequently terminated the project prior to completion, Andrews was responsible for directing the first excavations of any type in the Río Bec region. As a result of his project, a complete ceramic sequence for the area was developed; moreover, excavations of an exploratory nature conducted in various locations around Becan provided valuable information on architectural form. In particular, extensive excavations were conducted in one major pyramid temple complex, Structure IV in the central ceremonial precinct. However, prior to the inauguration of the 1972 National Geographic Society settlement-pattern survey at Becan, no systematic attempt had been made to examine small nonceremonial structures in the sustaining area of the center. The goal of our project was to fill this information gap.

Site Description

The site of Becan is a medium-sized ceremonial center with a central precinct covering over 2 hectares. The major structures, including pyramidal and palace-type structures, a ball court, and range-type structures, have been described by Ruppert and Denison (1943) and Potter (1977). A most interesting feature of the site is the large ditch, 1,890 meters in circumference, which completely encircles the central ceremonial district. This dry ditch and interior rampart rank with the greatest of all Mesoamerican defensive fortifications, and the Early Classic date of construction places it as perhaps the earliest (Webster, 1976). Although the elite surely lived within the confines of the defensive fortification, virtually no remains of the smaller domestic structures, so typical of the Classic Maya, are to be found in the ceremonial zone. Rather, the houses of the supportive population are densely distributed outside the ceremonial precinct.

Consequently, our investigations of settlement patterns were devoted almost exclusively to the remains lying in the peripheries of the center.

Project Objectives

The primary objective of our settlement-pattern survey was to present as accurate and complete a picture as possible of the settlement system at Becan as it existed in each of the archeological phases. In such a study the types of information sought refer in part to the form, size, and spacing of structures, but attention is focused also on other factors closely related to settlement, such as water supply and agricultural techniques, factors that bear a direct relation to the size and density of the population. The project was designed to obtain data pertinent to the distribution of occupational structures in the peripheries of Becan and, more importantly, to delineate population trends evident in the development and decline of the site. In addition, we sought to secure information as to the relative size of the sustaining area of Becan and the relationship between that major center and smaller ceremonial centers such as Xpuhil and Chicanna, located nearby. Thus, the project consists of two parts: (1) mapping and surveying of residential remains in the peripheries of Becan and (2) test excavation of a sample of mounds and subsequent dating of their construction and occupation.

Mapping

The mapping program was designed to provide a total picture of all presently remaining artificial surface features. A grid system was established with each grid section 500 meters square. Using the telescopic alidade and plane table, two-man surveying crews plotted a total of 1,912 mounds during the two field seasons, 665 of which are the remains of dwellings.

Remains were mapped in all directions from the center of Becan, with coverage extending a distance of about 3 kilometers west of the central ceremonial precinct. North of Becan the dense forest remains uncleared, and only a small area was covered by the site map. To the east the ruins of Xpuhil lie approximately 7 kilometers distant from Becan, and areas between these two centers that have been cleared for cultivation are covered by the maps. A second center, Chicanna, lies about 2 kilometers southwest of Becan, and mapping operations were extended to that center as well.

Surface Survey and Test Excavation

The second part of the project was devoted to surface collection and test excavation. Chronological control for the reconstruction of prehistoric settlement patterns at Becan is based upon the ceramic analysis of materials obtained from house-mound collections. Under usual conditions the dense vegetation cover in the Maya lowlands makes surface collection all but impossible. But in the areas burned by the local agriculturalists surface survey is quite feasible prior to the onset of the rainy season, and our efforts were concentrated toward collection at the appropriate time. Surface collections were made on as many structures as time and vegetation conditions would allow. Materials were recovered from some 1,000 mounds, and, of this total, 734 collections yielded datable ceramics. It was assumed that the presence of materials assignable to a particular phase indicates activity during that phase. Of the 734 mounds dated by surface collection, 362 are presumed to be the remains of houses (fig. 1), while the remainder represent nondomiciliary constructions such as terraces, outbuildings, etc.

In addition to the surface survey, 60 mounds were excavated, usually by means of a 2- by-2-meter test pit located either on the summit of the structure or on an adjacent plaza. The test excavation program was designed to provide chronological data on the construction and occupation of the various mounds. The enormous number of house-mounds at Becan precluded the possibility of total excavation or even the placing of a test pit in each mound, and so only a portion of the total could be excavated. In selecting mounds for excavation a stratified random sampling technique was employed. Utilizing an arbitrary type system based on size, surface configuration, and surface composition of the mounds, we selected a sample by randomly choosing a representative of each structure type from within each 500-meter-square grid section. This

Fig. 1.   Large house-mound 1.5 kilometers southeast of the ceremonial district.

sampling schedule was rigorously followed during the first several weeks of excavation, but as time drew to a close we began concentrating our efforts on house structures, thereby reducing the sampled number of extremely small nondomiciliary mounds.

Results and Conclusions

In general, our settlement-pattern survey, including mapping, test excavations, and surface collections, yielded data indicating a wide variation in structure type and, presumably, function. The different varieties of mounds are described below with additional discussion of their probable function.

Almost 300 artificial ridges (fig. 2) have been located and mapped within the sustaining area of Becan. In appearance they are linear mounds or ridges varying in height from only a few centimeters up to 2 meters. They range from a meter to over 5 meters in width. The ridges vary in composition from limestone pebbles and earth to large unshaped limestone chunks (some appearing to comprise crude basal retaining walls) to unmodified chert nodules. No ridges have been located within the confines of the defensive ditch or the bajo areas. Although some of the ridges skirt or run down to the edge

FIG. 2.   Artificial ridge in recently burned milpa. Note large retaining stone at lower left.

of the bajos, they always terminate at that point. These artificial ridges comprise a system of agricultural terracing (Thomas, 1974a, b); generally paralleling the contours of the terrain, most are located on gentle slopes. There are some ridges, however, that do not seem to be terraces; some run up-hill directly perpendicular to the contours, while others wind across flat ridge tops, around, between, and frequently joining house platforms.

A total of eight artificial ridges were selected for excavation. Analysis of the ceramic remains obtained from these excavations and from surface collections made on other ridges indicates that the practice of constructing artificial ridges and terraces at Becan began and ended during the Late Classic Period. This elaborate system adds to the growing evidence for the adoption of intensive agricultural techniques during the Late Classic Period (A.D. 600-900) in portions of the Maya lowlands. In the case of non-Terrace ridges, excavations showed them to be constructed no differently than the terraces. It is assumed, therefore, that the entire system of artificial ridges was designed to inhibit soil erosion while maintaining proper drainage into selected areas (bajos). Additionally, several of the ridges are suitable to have served as walkways between fields or as field dividers, although evidence to this effect is not conclusive.

FIG. 3. Small nondomiciliary mound of limestone pebbles and cobbles.

Another variation discovered during the course of mapping was the large number of mounds composed predominantly of unmodified chert nodules. After two seasons of mapping, close to 200 chert mounds have been plotted at Becan, with definite patterns discernible with regard to their distribution around the site. With very few exceptions, they cluster near the edges of bajos where chert nodules occur naturally and could have been gathered during the dry season. To the ancient Maya the local chert was a valuable natural resource from which a wide range of utilitarian implements were fashioned. Although the actual function of these mounds is open to question, they appear to represent stockpiles of chert accumulated during the Late Classic Period.

There is an unbroken continuum of mound sizes documented by the survey. Although the larger of these were obviously the remains of house structures, there are many mounds much too small to have served as dwellings (some no more than a meter in diameter). The question then arises as to the origin and function of these small nondomiciliary mounds. It seems clear that at least a certain percentage of the smaller of these mounds is the result of natural processes such as erosion and weathering of the limestone bedrock, or perhaps, root action and disturbances created by the periodic upheaval of large trees. The majority of the small mounds, however, are obviously the product of human activity (fig. 3). Examination of the test excavation profiles shows that most concentrations of stone are deliberate and not the result of the disintegration of underlying bedrock. In other excavations traces of walls or obvious patterns of stone concentration were observed; and the excavations yielded large quantities of cultural remains. Granted, then, that the majority of these small nondomiciliary mounds are the direct result of human activity, the question remains as to the nature of that activity. In his classic study of modern Maya houses, Wauchope (1938) discusses a variety of structures that may be appurtenant to the living quarters. With the exception of several forms that could have emerged only in the postcontact period, we may assume that these outbuildings of the present-day mirror the function of those in the pre-Columbian context. These associated outbuildings may include the following: kitchen; storehouse; sweatbath; beehive shelter; shelter for washbowl and wash trough; family shrine; tannery; corn bin; oven. In addition to actual structures, many small mounds may be the result of localized activity such as the aforementioned chert stockpiling, stone knapping, or simply the piling of stones in the course of agricultural clearing. Although origin and function cannot be stated absolutely, there was evidenced during the settlement-pattern survey a large number of small artificial mounds that are not the remains of dwellings but the result of a variety of human activities.

Of the total 1,912 structures mapped to date at Becan, 665 are the remains of presumed house structures. From these 665 mounds the occupational dates of 364 have been derived on the basis of ceramics recovered from surface collections. In addition, 38 of the 60 test excavations were located in house structures (fig. 4). On the basis of this information, it is possible to reconstruct the patterns of prehistoric settlement at Becan.

Becan was first occupied sometime prior to 250 B.C. during the Middle Pre-Classic Period (Acachen Phase). Materials dating to this initial period of occupation are quite sparse. Beyond the fact that the population was extremely small, little can be said concerning this phase. During the subsequent Late Pre-Classic Pakluum Phase (250 B.C.–A.D. 250), however, the population increased significantly. At this time people were occupying the central ceremonial precinct of Becan as well as all the well-drained habitable areas covered by our survey. The population at Becan steadily increased from this period through the Late Classic Bejuco Phase, at which time an explosion in construction occurred. Analysis of surface collections reveals that over 75 percent of all house-mounds in the survey area show evidence of Bejuco activity. Further excavations have determined that the vast majority of houses in the sustaining area of Becan were either constructed or occupied during this phase. In addition to the extensive population growth evidenced by the explosion in house construction, excavations within the central zone of the Becan docu-

FIG. 4.   Typical profile of house-mound excavation. Note the three construction
stages with plaster floors.

ment a contemporaneous surge in architectural activity (Potter, 1977). The
Late Classic Bejuco Phase also witnessed the final developmental stage of
agricultural terracing, and the tremendous growth in population during this
period was accompanied by a shift to intensive agriculture. Likewise, the accumulation of chert nodules from nearby bajo areas reached its climax during
the Bejuco Phase. Clearly, the Late Classic Period is outstanding as the period
of peak population density at Becan.

      In contrast, the following Terminal Classic Chintok Phase evidenced a
significant decrease in construction activity. The percentage of house-mounds
either occupied or constructed during this time drops to approximately the
same level as that seen during the Early Classic Period. Although the sheer
quantity of construction greatly diminishes, many of those house structures
that were erected during the Chintok Phase are quite impressive in terms of
size and quality of workmanship. The practice of constructing agricultural
terraces and the accumulating of chert nodules, however, were discontinued
at this time. Beginning with the succeeding Xcocom Phase, all major construction had come to a halt. In the ceremonial precinct, the remaining popu-
lace set up residence in many of the temples and palaces still standing. In
addition a very small number of Xcocom houses has been identified, sparsely

distributed throughout the survey in the peripheries of the center. By this time the population was a mere shadow of its former size, and even this did not last long, for within several hundred years the area was completely abandoned.

In conclusion, the settlement pattern survey at Becan has provided answers to a number of questions regarding prehistoric occupation of this site. The mapping program revealed Becan to be a Maya center much like those in other regions with a central ceremonial precinct consisting of large temple/pyramid structures, palaces, ball courts, etc., surrounded by a dispersed settlement of small residences. Typically, these residential units consist of groups of two or more structures set about a central plaza. However, at Becan this typical plaza grouping did not occur with the frequency found at sites such as Tikal in the Petén. Additionally, the houses or house groups are not situated according to any systematic plan, and streets and alleyways are not apparent. Rather, the structures are situated seemingly at random on well-drained terrain.

Although typical of many Maya centers, Becan exhibits several variances. First, the defensive fortification, the huge ditch completely encircling the ceremonial precinct, is somewhat atypical for a classic Maya center. Second, the system of artificial ridges and agricultural terraces is unknown in the Petén; likewise, it has not been reported to the north. Third, the concentrations of chert nodules into mounds are apparently an atypical feature, although Gann (1911) reported chert mounds in Belize. It has been suggested here that these mounds represent stockpiling activities of a natural resource used in the manufacture of utilitarian implements. Fourth, numerous small mounds, clearly nonresidential in nature, were discovered and are believed to be the remains of outbuildings or the loci of various activities.

The study of the house-mounds through surface survey and test excavation has provided a picture of population growth and decline at Becan. From the initial settlement in the Middle Pre-Classic Period the population reached its maximum peak during the Late Classic Bejuco Phase; then began a massive decline during the Terminal Classic, ultimately resulting in total abandonment of the site.

REFERENCES

GANN, THOMAS W. F.
    1911.   Explorations carried on in British Honduras during 1908-1909.   Liverpool Univ. Ann. Archaeol. and Anthrop., vol. 7, pp. 28-42.

MERWIN, ROBERT E.
1913.   The ruins of the southern part of the peninsula of Yucatán with special reference to its place in the Maya area.   Unpublished Ph.D. thesis, Harvard University.
POTTER, DAVID F.
1977.   Maya architecture of the central Yucatan Peninsula, Mexico.   Middle Amer. Res. Inst. Tulane Univ. Publ. 44.
RUPPERT, KARL, and DENISON, JOHN H., JR.
1943.   Archaeological reconnaissance in Campeche, Quintana Roo, and Peten. Carnegie Inst. Washington Publ. 543, 156 pp.
THOMAS, PRENTICE M., JR.
1974a.   Prehistoric settlement at Becan: A preliminary report.   Middle Amer. Res. Inst. Tulane Univ. Publ. 31, pp. 139-146.
1974b.   Classic Maya terracing and artificial ridges at Becan, Campeche, Mexico. Paper presented at 39th annual meeting, Society for American Archaeology, Washington, D. C.
VOGELER, INGOLF
1970.   Frontier settlements in southeastern Campeche.   National Geographic Society–Tulane University Becan Project, mimeo report for 1970.
1974.   The cultural ecological setting of southeastern Campeche.   Middle Amer. Res. Inst. Tulane Univ. Publ. 31 pp. 110-112.
WAUCHOPE, ROBERT
1938.   Modern Maya houses: A study of their archaeological significance. Carnegie Inst. Washington Publ. 502, 181 pp.
WEBSTER, DAVID L.
1976.   Defensive earthworks at Becan, Campeche, Mexico: Implications for Maya warfare.   Middle Amer. Res. Inst. Tulane Univ. Publ. 41.

PRENTICE M. THOMAS, JR.

The Capture and Study of Two Coelacanths off the Comoro Islands, 1972

Principal Investigator: Keith Stewart Thomson, Yale University, New Haven, Connecticut.

Grant No. 1046: For research on the coelacanth *(Latimeria chalumnae* Smith).

Although fossil coelacanth fishes *(Latimeria chalumnae* Smith) had been known since the early 19th century, it was not until the discovery of a living representative of the group on the South African coast in December 1938 that both popular and scientific interest began to be concentrated upon these remarkable fishes. The reason is twofold. Coelacanths had long been thought to have become extinct at the end of the Cretaceous, when the widespread extinctions of terrestrial and aquatic organisms removed from the face of the earth dinosaurs, pterosaurs, pelsiosaurs, and many groups of invertebrates and even plants. But by 1938 it was also clear to paleozoologists that coelacanths had been very close relatives of fishes (usually known as lobe-finned fishes), from which the first land vertebrates evolved in the Devonian. In a sense, then, the coelacanths, like the living lungfishes of Africa, Australia, and South Africa, were discovered to be the "cousins" of the lineages that gave rise eventually to man. How exciting that a living lobe-finned fish should be discovered.

The interest of the scientific world was not matched by obvious willingness of the living species *Latimeria chalumnae* to be studied. Despite the best efforts of the late Professor J.L.B. Smith of South Africa, no further specimens were found until 1952, when a second specimen was caught by a native fisherman off the Comoro Islands in the western Indian Ocean. Since 1952 perhaps some 80 more specimens have been caught, all from the Comores, and until about 1965 all were studied at the Museum d'Histoire Naturelle in Paris.

Given the relatively undeveloped conditions of the Comores, and particularly the primitive state of the local fisheries, it is perhaps not surprising that the best that had been possible in the study of coelacanths up to 1966 was the dissection of formalin-preserved specimens, with one single and notable occasion when a specimen was kept alive long enough to be observed in an "aquarium" jury-rigged from a submerged dinghy. Until this occasion there had even been dispute over the natural coloration of the fish.

By 1966 interest was becoming focused upon other aspects of coelacanth biology than its formal anatomy. Not only was functional morphology an active area of research, but many questions of comparative biochemistry having to do with the origins of vertebrate metabolic and regulatory systems began to require data from such close relatives of the tetrapod line as the lungfish and coelacanths. In 1966, in an attempt to increase the base of information, a specimen of Latimeria was shipped fresh-frozen from the Comores to the laboratory of the author at Yale University. The result in scientific information was astounding. Apart from major discoveries in the biomechanics of the head and limbs, it was discovered that coelacanths had a nitrogen metabolism and a pattern of osmotic regulation almost identical to that of sharks, rather than that of the other bony fishes with which comparison had usually been made. Further attempts to ship frozen specimens to other laboratories confirmed both the potential interest in the fish and the difficulties of working with fish in this way.

In 1969 the British Royal Society and French Museum d'Histoire Naturelle sponsored an expedition to the western Indian Ocean to attempt trial fishing for coelacanths in a large area north of the Comoro Islands. The National Academy of Sciences was invited to send a representative, and the author had this honor. Unfortunately, the effort was a failure in that no coelacanth was caught; however, a great deal of basic information was obtained, including confirmation of the fact that all the components of the Comoroan deep-slope fish fauna were indeed present at the other islands. Fishing techniques were evaluated and hope rose that an all-out effort, preferably concentrated upon the Comores, would yield the desired result: capture of a live specimen, its retention live in a holding tank for observation, and preferably its filming prior to preparation of specific tissues for laboratory study around the world.

Committees were established in the three national organizations to plan both what to do and what would be done with the data and tissues obtained. In a sense it was like planning for the most effective distribution and study of the moon-rock samples. Finally, in late 1971 plans for a three-nation expedition were completed. The National Geographic Society graciously consented to fund the American contribution to this expedition and sent to the Comores Dr. Michael Lagios (a physician studying lower vertebrate endocrine systems, at that time serving at the Armed Forces Institute of Pathology); Dr. Robert Griffith (a comparative fish biologist and physiologist in my laboratory); and Mr. Edward Goldstein (a graduate student in ecology at Yale University).

The French and British contingents arrived at the Comores first and started to set up a laboratory in facilities made available by the Comoroan authorities. There were the usual delays in receiving materials and gear. The personnel arrived on the island of Grande Comore on January 1, 1972, and on

January 4, before they were even properly set up, news came that a specimen had been caught on the neighboring island of Anjouan. Professor J. Anthony from France and Dr. R. Forster of Britain set off by chartered plane but arrived just after the specimen died. The fish, however, was a large and ripe female, the first such ever captured. In her body were found 19 large eggs, each about the size of a grapefruit. Yet the puzzle was that although they were completely unprotected by shell membranes, there were no shell-forming glands in the oviduct (as is now well known). This discovery eventually set off a debate in the literature as to whether coelacanths are oviparous or ovoviviparous (Anthony and Millot, 1972; Griffith and Thomson, 1973). The puzzle was eventually solved by the discovery in a specimen preserved at the American Museum of Natural History in New York of five developed embryos, each about 10 centimeters long. Thus the fish is ovoviviparous.

This discovery on January 4, 1972, and the subsequent study of reproduction in the coelacanth is typical of the sort of major advance that had been hoped for in knowledge of this important fish. But the real prize, the capture and study of a living specimen, was not so easily obtained.

Analysis of the previous catch statistics had established that a significant majority of captures by the native fishermen of the Comores had been in the months of January through March, at night, off Grande Comore and in depths of 100 to 800 meters. The expedition, therefore, stuck to its plan of attempting to work from Grande Comore. But it was not easy. This is a stormy season of the year, when many local fishermen have their boats hauled out of the water for safety. That they catch coelacanths at all seems to be a side-result of fishing for two other fishes, the "roudi" (*Promethichthys*) and the "nyessa" (*Ruvettus*). Furthermore, since the local fishermen can catch market fish within the reef complex, they hesitate to venture beyond the reef to fish the deep-slope waters. Each fisherman works from a dug-out "piroque" and fishes a single vertical long line with one hook baited with a chunk of any fish. The "sinker" is a lump of coral tied with a slip knot.

After two months of attempting to work from small boats, it became clear to the expedition that the only shore-based operation likely to succeed would be that of the local fisherman. Therefore, efforts were redoubled to persuade the fishermen to venture out at night. The traditional reward of $200 to a successful village was reinforced by radio announcements. After considerable difficulty in negotiating with various parties, the fishermen of several villages increased their nightly fishing effort on behalf of the expedition. The rewards for this finally came.

On March 22, 1972, when the major part of the expedition was being wound up, news came to Drs. Locket and Griffith that a fish had been caught and brought into the nearby village of Iconi. The successful fisherman, Madi Youssouf Kaar, had caught his fish at about 165 meters, using a tuna bait. The catch occurred at about 2:00 a.m. As he had caught two other specimens, he knew the significance of his prize and got it to shore alive (a lengthy process, taking several hours). The fish was observed in good condition by torchlight and then, as dawn rose, motion-picture records were made. It was possible to make the first accurate observations of the swimming patterns and fin movements of the fish, which indeed props itself up from the bottom using the paired fins. Unfortunately, by the time it was light enough to make useful films, the fish was too moribund for intracranial movements to be recorded.

Soon after daylight the fish was sacrificed, and almost a whole day was occupied in making careful tissue preparations in the laboratory for the many workers who had requested that particular tissues be prepared according to different precise protocols. The success of this project can be measured by the output of research from the many laboratories around the world that received such samples—work that still continues.

With the capture and study of these two specimens and the results that came from them, the expedition has to be counted a marvelous success. In addition, it is possible to use the experience of the study to make some recommendations for any future research on coelacanths. The extent to which it will be possible to follow up this work will depend on political climates in the Comoro Islands and upon levels of funding, preferably again through international cooperation.

It is obvious from all available experience that it is better to rely upon the local fishermen, suitably encouraged to risk their gear at night, than to try to reproduce their techniques. The fishermen, however, have to tow their catch a long way back to shore very slowly and this mitigates against survival of the fish. The ideal result would be the capture of a specimen that could be kept in controlled aquarium conditions at a shore base. It is necessary, therefore, to cut down the time between capture and delivery. Given the fact that it may take a man several hours to "play" the fish to the boat, and that it is a long time before it reaches shore, the fact that coelacanths typically survive several hours more when finally beached gives great hope for keeping one alive.

One possible scheme is that motor launches should patrol the fishing areas at night. The fisherman, if he thinks he has a coelacanth, and most know it by the "feel," should be instructed not to exhaust it by hauling it to the boat but should first summon a launch by flare or radio. The launch should be equipped with a portable tank capable of maintaining high pressure and low temperature. The fish should then be hauled up as rapidly as possible (there are no gas-filled organs) and immediately transferred to the chamber for return to the ambient conditions of the depth at which it was taken. During this time the launch can be returning to base, where similar and larger facilities should be available. Eventually the fish should be brought very slowly to surface conditions. In fact, variations of this scheme could be tried, but also the stress of capture and beaching can be greatly reduced.

Alternatively, study of the fish ought to be carried out in situ from submersible craft, but for this the costs are very great. Yet the returns would be immense, particularly in the study of ecology, behavior, and possibly even reproduction.

Almost everything that has been discovered about the biology of the living coelacanth *Latimeria chalumnae* has been strongly at odds with our preconceived notions of what "it ought to be." The 1972 expedition, financed in part by the National Geographic Society, has helped answer many important questions about this fish and, of course, it has posed even more questions. The bibliography that follows is an excellent measure of the diverse and manifold results achieved so far.

REFERENCES

ANTHONY, J., and MILLOT, J.
  1972.   Première capture d'une femelle de Coelacanthe en état de maturité sexuelle.   Comptes Rend. Acad. Sci., Paris, vol. D224, pp. 1925-1926.
BONAVENTURA, J.; GILLEN, R. G.; and RIGGS, A.
  1974.   The haemoglobin of the crossopterygian fish, *Latimeria chalumnae* (Smith)—Subunit structure and oxygen equilibria.   Arch. Biochem. Biophys., vol. 163, pp. 728-734.
CHAUVET, J. P., and ACHER, R.
  1972.   Isolation of coelacanth *(Latimeria chalumnae)* myoglobin.   F.E.D.S. Letters, vol. 28, pp. 16-18.
CHAVIN, W.
  1972.   Thyroid of the coelacanth *Latimeria chalumnae.*   Nature, London, vol. 239, pp. 340-341.
CIMINO, M. C., and BAHR, G. F.
  1973.   Nuclear DNA content and chromatin ultrastructure of the coelacanth *Latimeria.*   Journ. Cell Biol., vol. 59, p. 55a.
COLE, D. F.
  1973.   Intraocular fluid composition in the Coelacanth, *Latimeria chalumnae.*   Exp. Eye Res., vol. 16, pp. 389-395.
DARTNELL, H.J.A.
  1972.   Visual pigment of the coelacanth.   Nature, London, vol. 239, pp. 341-342.
DEVYS, M.; THIERRY, A.; BARVIER, M.; and JANOT, M-M.
  1972.   Premières observations sur les lipides de l'ovocyte du coelacanths *(Latimeria chalumnae).*   Comptes Rend. Acad. Sci., Paris, vol. D275, p. 2085.

FORSTER, G. R.
  1974.   The ecology of *Latimeria chalumnae* Smith: Results of field studies from
           Grande Comore.   Proc. Roy. Soc. London, vol. B186, pp. 291-296.
GOLDSTEIN, L.; HUXLEY-DEWITT, S.; and FORSTER, R. P.
  1973.   Activities of ornithineurea cycle enzymes and of bimethylamine oxidase
           in the coelacanth *Latimeria chalumnae*.   Comp. Biochem. Physiol., vol.
           44B, pp. 337-362.
GRIFFITH, R. W.
  1973.   A live coelacanth in the Comore Islands.   Discovery, vol. 9, no. 1, pp.
           27-33.
GRIFFITH, R. W., and THOMSON, K. S.
  1973.   Observations on a dying coelacanth.   Amer. Zool., vol. 12, p. 730.
  1973.   *Latimeria chalumnae* reproduction and conservation.   Nature, London,
           vol. 242, pp. 617-618.
GRIFFITH, R. W.; UMMINGER, B. L.; GRANT, B. F.; PANG, P.K.T.; and
           PICKFORD, G. E.
  1974.   Serum composition of the coelacanth, *Latimeria chalumnae* Smith.
           Journ. Exp. Zool., vol. 187, pp. 87-102.
GRODZINSKI, Z.
  1972.   The yolk of *Latimeria chalumnae* Smith.   Folia Histochem., vol. 10, pp.
           11-18.
HAMOIR, G. A.; PIRONT, A.; GERDAY, CH.; and DANDO, P. R.
  1973.   Muscle proteins of the coelacanth *Latimeria chalumnae* Smith.   Journ.
           Mar. Biol. Assoc., U.K., vol. 53, pp. 763-784.
HUGHES, G. M.
  1972.   Aspects of the respiration of *Latimeria chalumnae*.   Proc. Internat.
           Union Physiol. Sci., Sydney, vol. 21, no. 28 (August), p. 136.
  1972.   Gills of a living coelacanth *Latimeria chalumnae*.   Separatum Experien-
           tia, vol. 28, pp. 1401-1402.
HUGHES, G. M., and ITAZAWA, Y.
  1972.   The effect of temperature on the respiratory function of coelacanth
           blood.   Separatum Experientia, vol. 28, p. 1247.
IMAKE, H., and CHAVIN, W.
  1973.   Ultrastructure of integumental melanophors in the coelacanth.   Amer.
           Zool., vol. 13, p. 521.
KOLB, E., and HARRIS, J. I.
  1972.   Purification and properties of glycolytic-cycle enzymes from coelacanth
           muscles.   Biochem. Journ., vol. 130, p. 26.
LAGIOS, M. D.
  1972.   Evidence for a hypothalmous-hypophysial portal vascular system in the
           coelacanth *Latimeria chalumnae*.   Gen. Comp. Endocr., vol. 18, pp.
           73-82.
  1974.   Granular epithelioid (Juxtaglomerular) cell and renovascular morphol-
           ogy of the coelacanth, *Latimeria chalumnae* Smith (Crossopterygii) com-
           pared with that of other fishes.   Gen. Comp. Endocr., vol. 22, pp.
           296-307.

LOCKET, A.
1972.   Learning from an anachronistic fish.   New Scientist, vol. 54, pp. 427-428.
LOCKET, N. A.
1973a.   Possible discontinuous retinal rod outer segment formation in *Latimeria chalumnae*.   Nature, London, vol. 244, pp. 308-309.
1973b.   Retinal structure in *Latimeria chalumnae*.   Phil. Trans. Roy. Soc., London, vol. B266, pp. 493-521.
1974.   The choridoidal tapetum lucidum of *Latimeria chalumnae*.   Proc. Roy. Soc., London, B186, pp. 281-290.
LOCKET, N. A., and GRIFFITH, R. W.
1972.   Observations on a living coelacanth.   Nature, London, vol. 237, p. 175.
MCCOSKER, J. E., and LAGIOS, M. D.
1979.   The biology and physiology of the living coelacanth.   Occ. Pap. Calif. Acad. Sci., vol. 134, pp. 1-175.
MILLOT, J., and ANTHONY, J.
1972.   La glande post-anale de *Latimeria*.   Ann. Sci. Nat., vol. 14, pp. 305-317.
1973.   L'appareil excréteur de *Latimeria chalumnae* Smith (Poisson Coelacanthide).   Ann. Sci. Nat., vol. 15, pp. 293-328. La position ventrale du rein de *Latimeria chalumnae* (Poisson coelacanthidé).   Comptes Rend. Acad. Sci., Paris, vol. D276, p. 2171.
1974.   Les oeufs du coelacanthe.   Science et Nature, no. 121, pp. 3-5.
MILLS, G. L., and TAYLAUR, C. E.
1973.   The distribution and composition of serum lipoproteins in the coelacanth *(Latimeria)*.   Comp. Biochem. Physiol., vol. B44, pp. 1235-1241.
NISHIMURA, H., and OGAWA, M.
1973.   The renin-angiotensin system in fishes.   Amer. Zool., vol. 13, pp. 823-838.
NISHIMURA, H.; OGURA, M.; and SAWYER, W. H.
1973.   Renin-angiotensin system in primitive bony fishes and a holocephalian.   Amer. Journ. Physiol., vol. 224, pp. 950-956.
ROBINEAU, M. D.
1973.   Signification fonctionelle de l'articulation intracrânienne chez *Latimeria chalumnae* (Poisson crossopterygien Coelacanthidé).   Comptes Rend. Acad. Sci., Paris, vol. D277, pp. 1341-1343.
ROBINEAU, M. D., and ANTHONY, J.
1973.   Biomécanique du crâne de *Latimeria chalumnae* (Poisson, Crossopterygien, Coelacanthidé).   Comptes Rend. Acad. Sci., Paris, vol. D276, p. 1305.
SMITH, M. M.; HOBDELL, M. H.; and MILLER, W.
1972.   The structure of the scales of *Latimeria chalumnae*.   Journ. Zool., London, vol. 167, pp. 501-509.
THOMSON, K. S.
1973.   Secrets of the coelacanth.   Natural History, New York, vol. 82, pp. 58-65.

THOMSON, K. S.—continued
   1973.   New observations on the coelacanth fish, *Latimeria chalumnae.*
           Copeia, no. 4, pp. 813-814.
THOMSON, K. S.; GALL, J. G.; and COGGINS, L. W.
   1973.   Nuclear DNA contents of coelacanth erythrocytes.   Nature, London,
           vol. 241, p. 126.
TIPPETT, I., and TEESDALE, P.
   1973.   Limited blood group tests on samples from two coelacanths *(Latimeria
           chalumnae).*   Vox. Sang., vol. 24, pp. 175-178.
WEBER, N. E.; BOL, J. R.; JOHANSEN, K.; and WOOD, S. C.
   1973.   Physiocochemical properties of the haemoglobin of the coelacanth *Lati-
           meria chalumnae.*   Arch. Biochem. Biophys., vol. 154, pp. 96-105.
WOOD, S. C.; JOHANSEN, K.; and WEBER, R. E.
   1972.   Haemoglobin of the coelacanth.   Nature, London, vol. 239, pp. 283-
           285.

                                        KEITH STEWART THOMSON

Russian Influence on Aleut Ecology, Culture, and Physical Anthropology

Principal Investigator: Christy G. Turner II, Arizona State University, Tempe, Arizona.

Grant Nos. 1043,   In support of grantee's Eastern Aleutian Anthropology
1181.   Project, 1972 and 1973.

As elsewhere in the world following European contact, the number of Aleuts rapidly declined after Russian discovery of Alaska in 1741. Contact by the early fur-seeking Russians, and Americans after 1867, also brought changes in Aleutian culture, health, physical anthropology, environment, and ecology. Few of the many possible kinds of changes are documented in historical written accounts; particularly lacking are those changes affecting the archipelago's ecology and Aleut physical anthropology. There is considerable need to develop historic period information by means other than written records. One way is through archeological excavation, which can also provide data on the prehistoric Aleutian condition, a baseline against which historic and modern conditions can be compared for qualitative and quantitative changes.

I chose to study in the eastern Aleutian's Krenitzin Islands, particularly at the abandoned old village of Chulka on Akun Island and its descendent 100-person village on adjacent Akutan Island, as well as at other Akun sites on a brief basis, after preliminary surface surveys and test excavations in 1970 and 1971 revealed Akun sites (especially Chulka) had deep middens rich in historic and prehistoric artifacts, food refuse, and good potential for assessing the effects of Russian and American contact. Chulka was slowly abandoned after 1879 when its inhabitants founded Akutan Village on the north shore of nearby Akutan Harbor (fig. 1). There are no pure-blooded Aleuts any more in Akutan. All are variously admixed to some degree with Russian, American, Eskimo, Indian, and possibly even Negro genes. Our diachronic dental studies suggest that much of the admixture occurred before the present century, that is, in the Russian period from 1741 to 1867, and early in the American period after the United States purchased Alaska from Russia (Turner et al., 1978). Our archeological findings correspond with the physical anthropological findings—namely, much of Aleut culture had been modified or affected a great deal before 1867 (Turner and Turner, 1974; Turner, 1975).

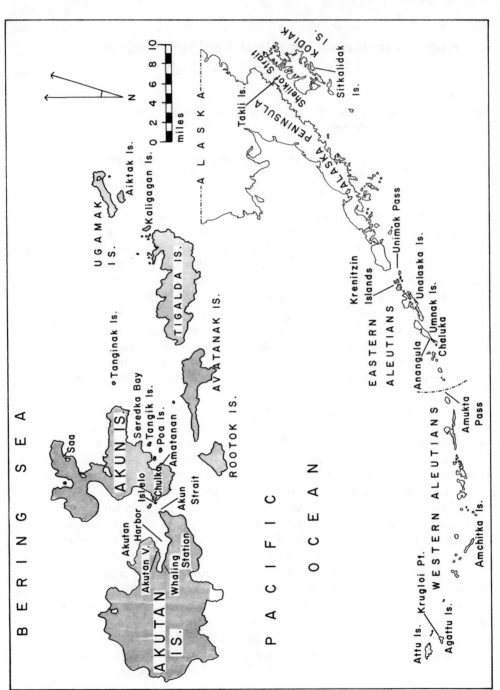

Fig. 1.   Krenitzin Islands, Aleutian Archipelago, Alaska.

With permission for scientific study from all required United States and Alaskan government agencies and the Akutan village council, including Luke Shelikof, village chief, the summer fieldwork was carried out by the following:

1970. Christy G. Turner II and William Tcheripanof. Site survey and test excavations around Akutan Harbor and on western Akun Island. Most time was spent in Akutan Village, at Siskena at the mouth of Akutan Harbor, and on Chulka, overlooking Akun Strait. Excavations were conducted at Siskena and Chulka. Dental impressions, Aleut genealogies, island place names, and other ethnographic data were gathered in Akutan Village.

1971. Christy G. Turner II, Jacqueline A. Turner, and William Tcheripanof. Additional site survey of western Akun Island. Continued testing at Chulka and on offshore Islelo islet. Dental impressions and genealogies added in Akutan.

1972. Christy G. Turner II, Jacqueline A. Turner, Edward F. Harris, Karen Harris, William Tcheripanof. Continued surveying of Akun Strait district and excavations at Chulka and Islelo islet. Additional genealogies and ethnographic data collected in Akutan.

1973. Christy G. Turner II and Gerald Bair. Survey and testing along the north and east coasts of Akun Island. Intensive testing at the northeast site called Saa where much prehistoric wood had been preserved by reason of unusual ground-water conditions.

During these years, and continuing to the present, various laboratory analyses have been conducted on the collections. Most of these have been carried out at Arizona State University: Radiocarbon dating, Dr. Robert Stuckenrath, Smithsonian Radiation Biology Laboratory; soil and ash samples, Dr. Robert Merrill; obsidian hydration, Dr. Leslie B. Davis, Montana State University; sea-mammal identification, Dr. Robert B. Chiasson, University of Arizona; avifauna remains, Dr. David A. Yesner, University of Maine; sea-mammal pathologies, Dr. George Bjotvedt; dog remains, Christy G. Turner II and Stanley Howard; human osteology, Paul Mamula, Charles Utermohle, and Christy G. Turner II; human dentition, Jeffrey C. Long, Christy G. Turner II; stone and bone artifacts, Christy G. Turner II, Jacqueline A. Turner, and Ellen Riche; living faunal inventory, Linda Richards; additional dental impressions (1952, 1973), Dr. William S. Laughlin, Dr. Andrew Poole, and Susan Beman; laboratory cataloguing and inventorying, Jacqueline A. Turner; artifact analyses, (Mrs.) Kathryn Holland, Betty Schmucker, Michael Boyce, and Cindy Hausel; pollen analyses, Kathryn Holland; obsidian sourcing, John P. Cook.

A considerable amount of descriptive and analytical findings of the Akun and Akutan research has already been published or prepared for limited distribution. Interested readers should refer to the cited works in the bibliography for more details and documentation of the main conclusions listed in this short report.

Principal Findings, Prehistoric (Baseline)

The prehistoric comparative baseline obtained from 1970 to 1973 by means of test excavations, surface-site survey, and natural historical study of Akun Island, and its marine and terrestrial animal, plant, and geographical features, indicates that the early Aleutian orthodox priest I. Veniaminof's estimate of 500 prehistoric Akun inhabitants was probably close to correct. Our surveys turned up four village sites, two additional villages or very large camps, and eight small seasonal hunting or fishing camps. Altogether, these indicate at least 500 inhabitants (Turner et al., 1974).

Aleut occupation of Akun Island, and the use of the Akun Strait district, began more than 3,800 years ago according to carbon-14 dates obtained from charcoal samples of middens and occupation horizons on now nearly severed Islelo islet (Turner and Turner, 1974).

Before A.D. 800 Islelo was more or less abandoned, with settlement shifting to 150-meter-distant Chulka (fig. 2). The move may relate with the breakdown of the above-water link between Islelo and Akun, which today is present only for less than one hour at lowest tide.

Also prior to A.D. 800 ground slate tools, mainly ulus, were introduced to Chulka, but apparently nowhere else on Akun. The slate presumably was carried by Eskimo traders from the slate-rich areas of Kodiak Island and/or Alaska Peninsula. The prehistoric dogs found at Chulka (the first and only ones known prehistorically for all the Aleutians) may have been introduced along with the slate tools (there is a chance that both the dogs and ground slate tools were obtained by Aleut raiding parties originating from Chulka).

Aleut head form was changing by this time from long to broad (cranial index >79.9), because a broad-headed Aleut skeleton was found at Chulka in association with ground slate artifacts, other more typically Aleut artifacts, and a carbon-14 date of A.D. 780. This old Chulka female has the distinction of being the most ancient broad-headed Aleut skull discovered to date.

Aside from what appear to be minor Pacific Eskimo trade or interaction influences, Chulka and the other sites tested on Akun and Akutan, including Saa, Amatanan, Siskena, Islelo, and others, are completely like other Aleut sites in their cultural content and maritime orientation (Turner and Turner, 1974). However, unlike prehistoric sites farther west in the Aleutian Chain,

---

FIG. 2. View westward showing Chulka (left), Islelo (right), Akun Strait, and Akutan Island in background. The flooding tide isolates Islelo from the younger Chulka upon which tent and old fox-trapper cabin stand. Within memory of living Akutan Aleuts, Chulka had a sandy beach out to the end of the present gravel bar. The beach is all gone today, and Chulka itself is washing away into the sea.

Akun's middens did not contain the expected number of sea-otter bones. This strongly suggests that these animals were rare in the Akun district because of the very long and very intensive Aleut use of these far eastern Aleutian Islands. As far as we can determine, the habitat conditions for sea otters are as good as, if not better than, those that occur on islands where remnant sea-otter populations exist.

The prehistoric ecology of Akun Island suggests that a large proportion of food was obtained from seasonal sources like migrating whales, fur seals, various birds, and some fishes, which concentrated in and around the Krenitzin Islands owing to the intense upwelling here from the shallow sea bottom that nourishes the planktonic food-chain base. Resident animals, such as sea-urchins and harbor seals, were also gathered and hunted in large numbers. At Chulka alone, we estimate that 16,000 sea-urchins a year were gathered from at least A.D. 800. This number seems large enough to warrant the conclusion that the sea-urchin population was controlled by Aleuts alone without the aid of the urchin-eating sea otter (Turner, 1976). We see no evidence for any conservation practices or selectivity of species. Akun Aleuts ate just about everything available.

Principal Findings, Historic (Archeological)

Occupation refuse of the Russian and American periods at Chulka suggests that various trade items like steel needles, brass containers, glassware, and iron scrap were acquired and used in various ways that replaced native stone, bone, horn, wood, and skin types—all materials splendidly developed and utilized several thousands of years before contact. Many kinds of stone and bone tools, such as fishhooks, knives, needles, and stone lamps, were made less frequently or abandoned altogether (Turner, 1975). New cultural practices were introduced like steam-bathing, which used wastefully the more critical or rare resources. Prior to Russian contact driftwood was mainly reserved for constructional or fabricational deployment. After, it was also consumed as fuel to generate steam for bathing. For the most part then, contact appears to have initiated a wide number of disadvantageous changes that resulted on the whole in a higher expenditure of energy by the Aleuts to gain the

---

FIG. 3.   View southward showing the Saa locality. Tent is located at level of prehistoric occupation, which today is lower than the level to which driftwood is tossed in heavy storms. For Saa to have been occupied it must have had more fronting beach and protective offshore kelp or a higher elevation in the past. Low thick clouds of figures 2 and 3 are characteristic of Aleutian summers.

same ends, namely reproduction and eating. Ethnographically, there is no evidence that the Aleuts were any happier after contact than they were before.

Two seemingly very significant changes that we feel came about were a disruption of the seasonally sensitive Aleut birth cycle and a severe reduction in summer whale and other migratory sea-mammal hunting (Turner et al., 1974). The Russian practice of taking the able-bodied Aleut males away for the summer months, and up to two years, to hunt the coveted sea otters for their valuable pelts, reduced the number of conceptions in early summer—the optimal time for Aleut conception relative to time of birth when winter resources have not been used up and nutrition for pregnant females is still acceptable. Taking the Aleut males away not only had a limiting effect on the conception rate during the early summer, it also clearly reduced the amount of sea-mammal meat, blubber, and fabricational bone, skin, and gut that would be normally procured during the summer hunting period. Note also that the summer months are the best sea-faring months in a region well known for its stormy weather and hazardous boating conditions most of the year. Thus, some births were occurring too late in the winter to have good chances for infant survival, and the winter stockpiles of meat and blubber were probably much smaller after the arrival of and take-over by the fur-seeking Russians. By 1890 American fur-trading posts stocking flour and other foodstuffs were becoming the source of much winter food for the remnant Aleut population. These commodities did not come cheap.

Throughout the historic period population size declined on Akun, as elsewhere throughout the Aleutians and Alaska, until the island was completely abandoned by 1907. By that date all the Krenitzin Islands except Akutan were also abandoned, and Akutan retained only the one small village that exists today in Akutan Harbor. The early rapid decline of the Aleut population is certainly attributable to Russian brutality, disease introduction, and resulting starvation in some instances. We believe that we have also identified that ecological disturbances occurred with the arrival of the Russians and these disturbances are still in effect today.

One disturbance we feel to be worthy of much more attention by earth scientists is the possibility that, with the extinction of the Aleuts on many of the previously long and intensively occupied islands, coastal erosion has occurred as a consequence of the sea urchins no longer being controlled by Aleut predation where the Aleuts had previously eliminated the sea otter also. The coastal erosion results when these marine invertebrate grazers increase in number and attack intensively the nearshore kelp forests for food. The live kelp stands in the summer dampen the shore-damaging storm-generated waves, and in winter the windrows of dead kelp upon the shore assist in holding the beaches in place (figs. 2, 3).

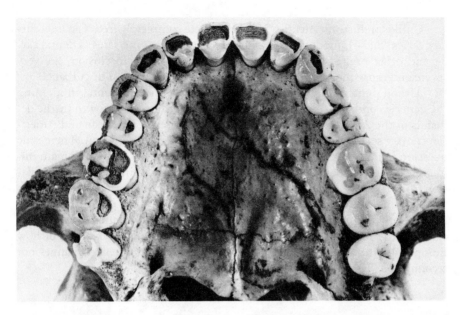

F<small>IG</small>. 4. Heavily worn but noncarious tooth crowns of A.D. 780 Neo-Aleut elderly female from Chulka. Morphology of the teeth shows her (and all other Aleuts) to be more like Eskimos than like Indians and more like Chinese, Japanese, and Mongols than like Indonesians, Ainu, or other Pacific peoples. With admixture living Aleut tooth morphology has changed to become more like that known for Europeans and American whites.

Principal Findings, Modern

Compared with the technology that can be recognized from prehistoric levels, modern living Akutan Aleuts have abandoned nearly all the precontact ways. They have adopted new ways of hunting (with guns instead of with spears and arrows), fishing (with metal hooks and plastic line instead of bone hooks and grass twine), preparing and storing food (canned and dry goods versus sun or wind-dried fish, sea-mammal or bird meat), house types (above-ground frame structures instead of underground sod-covered dwellings), and many, many other cultural elements including religious ones. In general, modern Aleut culture is rural American in type and quality. Drinking is a serious problem. Other than the obvious value of medical technology, there are few other aspects of industrial culture that appear to be much better in the Aleutians than those they replaced. Starvation may no longer be the dread possibility that it must have been in many prehistoric winters, but food stockpiles are still very costly and extremely rare in all the homes we have visited.

Unlike prehistoric Aleuts whose teeth were completely free of enamel surface caries (fig. 4), modern Akutan Aleuts suffer very high rates of dental caries and other oral disorders. Some of these, such as malocclusion, are very severe and cause more than simple cosmetic or psychological disturbances.

Although natural selection may have been very instrumental in molding the genetic configuration of the prehistoric Aleutian population to fit the demands of the Aleutian environment, a few centuries of European and American contact seem to have disrupted thousands of years of selection. There is no question in our minds that the contact has disrupted the cultural domain immensely. We are convinced that the ecology of the archipelago, if extrapolation from Akun is proper, has also been heavily impacted.

In sum, we feel that earth scientists should consider prehistoric conditions before judging the nature of an area long occupied by aboriginal populations. If the Aleutian case has general utility, we should take note of how European culture has brought about human and environmental changes not recognizable by synchronic or short-term analysis.

REFERENCES

BJOTVEDT, GEORGE, and TURNER, CHRISTY G., II
    1976.   Tooth trauma and feeding behavior in prehistoric Aleutian sea otters. Veterinary Medicine/Small Animal Clinician, vol. 71, no. 1 (June), pp. 831-833.
    1977.   Mandibular lesions of prehistoric Aleutian sea mammals. Journ. Wildl. Diseases, vol. 13, pp. 360-365.
TURNER, CHRISTY G., II
    1972.   Preliminary report of archaeological survey and test excavation in the eastern Aleutian Islands, Alaska. Arctic Anthrop., vol. 9, no. 2, pp. 32-35.
    1974.   The use of prehistory for direct comparative baselines in the study of Aleut microevolution. Pp. 205-215 *in* "International Conference on the Prehistory and Paleoecology of Western North American Arctic and Subarctic," S. Raymond and P. Schlerdermann, eds. University of Calgary, Alberta.
    1974.   Report on 1973 anthropological fieldwork on Akun Island, Alaska, 22 pp., illus., mimeo. (Limited circulation.)
    ———.   Evidence of Russian contact in the Krenitzin Islands, eastern Aleutians, Alaska, 35 pp. (MS., awaiting publ.)
    1976.   The Aleuts of Akun Island. Alaska Journ., vol. 6, no. 1, pp. 25-31.
TURNER, CHRISTY G., II, and HOWARD, STANLEY
    ———.   Akun prehistoric dogs. (In preparation.)
TURNER, CHRISTY G., II; LAUGHLIN, WILLIAMS S.; BEMAN, SUSAN; and POOLE, ANDREW
    ———.   Dental microevolution in Aleuts of Akutan Village, Alaska, 21 pp. (MS., awaiting publ.)

TURNER, CHRISTY G., II; MAMULA, PAUL; and UTERMOHLE, CHARLES
———. Aspects of physical anthropology of Akun skeletal remains. (In preparation.)
TURNER, CHRISTY G., II; RICHARDS, LINDA R.; and TURNER, JACQUELINE A.
1974. The relation of Aleut population size to seasonality of marine fauna. Paper presented at XLI International Congress of Americanists, Mexico City, September 2-7.
TURNER, CHRISTY G., II, and RICHE, ELLEN
———. Inter-site analysis of Akun tools with suggestions about ecological relationships. (In preparation.)
TURNER, CHRISTY G., II, and TURNER, JACQUELINE A.
1973. Report of the 1972 evolutionary anthropology field investigations on Akun and Akutan Islands, eastern Aleutians, Alaska, 7 pp., mimeo. (Limited circulation.)
1974. Progress report on evolutionary anthropological study of Akun Strait district, eastern Aleutians, Alaska, 1970-71. Anthrop. Pap. Univ. Alaska, vol. 16, no. 1, pp. 27-57.
TURNER, CHRISTY G., II, and YESNER, DAVID A.
———. The prehistoric avifauna of Akun Island, Alaska, and some possible changes following Russian contact. (In preparation.)

CHRISTY G. TURNER II

Radio Telemetry Analysis of Habitat Utilization by the Santa Rosa Mountain Desert Bighorn Sheep

Principal Investigator: Jack C. Turner, Sam Houston State University, Huntsville, Texas.

Grant No. 1106:   For study of the environmental and physiological biology of the desert bighorn sheep.

The desert bighorn sheep (*Ovis canadensis cremnobates*) is a distinct ecological race of the northern Rocky Mountain bighorn species (Manville, 1980). Populations of this ecotype occur in remote, arid, precipitous regions of the desert in the southwestern United States. Although generally concluded to be the smallest of the North American native wild sheep, it is considered to be the noblest and most elusive of all North American big game species. Despite the coveted revering by sportsmen and conservationists, the desert bighorn has sustained a chronic population depletion commensurate with an acute loss of habitat over the last hundred years (Buechner, 1960). Nowhere is this reduction more dramatic than in the Colorado desert of southern California where the desert bighorn has enjoyed legislative protection since 1873. The century-long protection has seemingly afforded them few benefits, as many populations have dwindled beyond reproductive resiliency, resulting in local extinctions. Once healthy populations have been reduced to drastically low numbers (Weaver, 1972).

One of the common denominators in the demise of these populations has been human encroachment and a subsequent loss of habitat. Only recently has the importance of habitat protection been recognized as being the equal of, if not greater, than that of species protection.

The recent environmental awareness attitudes have provoked an exodus of people from urban to more remote regions. The deserts of southern California, once thought to be barren, uninhabitable and hostile wasteland, have provided a focus for the immigrant urbanites. Unfortunately, this has occurred at the expense of the state's wilderness habitat, and more directly, at the cost of much of the state's wildlife.

The desert bighorn sheep is the largest endemic species inhabiting North American deserts. Consequently, their habitat demands are correspondingly large and uniquely specific. This study investigated the habitat utilization, seasonal distribution and movements of bighorn sheep in relation to critical habitat and habitat quality, and to document changes in these parameters with increased encroachment and habitat usurpation within the Santa Rosa Mountains. This mountain range, on its northern limits, abuts the growing metropolis of Palm Springs, California, a city which has annexed major portions of bighorn habitat into its sphere of influence.

Twenty free-ranging desert bighorn sheep (*O.c. cremnobates*) were immobilized on the east slopes of the Santa Rosa Mountains, Riverside County, California (116° 25′ N., 33° 39′ W.; see Turner, 1980, for complete description of the study area). Bighorn sheep were located and immobilized from a helicopter with a scope-mounted CO_2 Cap-Chur rifle. Immobilization was effected with 5 milligrams etorphine hydrochloride (M99) and drug reversal achieved with 10 milligrams diprenorphine (M50-50) (see Turner and Payson, 1980, for techniques of immobilization and prophylaxis). Ten bighorn sheep (6 females, 4 males) were outfitted with long-range radio telemetry collars. Additionally, 10 bighorn sheep were furnished with numbered blue vinyl neck collars, attached in such a manner as not to impede the animal's normal behavior or to develop unusual abrasion of the neck or chest area. Many of the bighorn sheep within the population were observed with sufficient frequency as to be individually identifiable and, therefore, increase the total number of "marked" individuals observed.

The collared bighorn sheep were monitored on foot and from fixed and rotary-wing aircraft with radio-tracking equipment on a weekly schedule during the first year of study, monthly during the second year of study, and during seasonal movements and the summer during the third year. Presently, bighorn sheep are surveyed once during the winter season and intermittently during the summer months (May-September).

The classical concept of home range (Calhoun, 1963; Jewell, 1966) is not directly applicable to the desert bighorn sheep, owing to the bighorn's multiple home-range character. The home ranges of individual animals vary according to age, sex, season, and weather. Moreover, seasonal home ranges may not be contiguous, but connected by seasonally utilized corridors.

Patriarchal groups, consisting only of rams of age greater than 3 years, showed summer home ranges with a radius of 5-19 kilometers. Winter home ranges did not exceed 8 kilometers and were remote from summer home ranges. The increased size of the summer home ranges relates to the summer reproductive season and to the rams attending the several water holes to locate breedable ewes. Movement between seasonal home ranges occurred along distinct corridors to which they remain loyal (86 percent fidelity, 7-year average). These corridors appear to be ancestral, and are considered critical for maintenance of herd and, possibly, population integrity.

FIG. 1. Three desert bighorn sheep *(Ovis canadensis cremnobates)*, two mature rams (left) and a pregnant ewe (right), near a water hole in the Santa Rosa Mountains, Riverside County, California.

Matriarchal bands, consisting of all-age ewes and rams to 3 years of age, show significantly (P<0.05) smaller home ranges during both winter and summer seasons. Summer home-range patterns have a radius of 0.7-3 kilometers with permanent sources of water at their focus. Winter home ranges have a radius of 1.5-7 kilometers, often with the summer home range included within the periphery. The importance of water during the summer is evidenced by its central position within the summer home range. However, bighorn sheep are not dependent upon water during the balance of the year (Turner and Weaver, 1980). Water holes are not of central importance within the winter home range. The dependence of desert bighorn sheep upon water during the dry summer drought period justifies the inclusion of the summer home range as critical habitat.

Individual animals within ewe and ram groups showed 100 percent home-range fidelity to both summer and winter home ranges over a 7-year period. Home-range fidelity averaged 89 percent for 210 individuals within the same 7-year period. Immigration was less than 2 percent.

FIG. 2. A yearling desert bighorn sheep *(Ovis canadensis cremnobates)* ram.

Lambing areas were select pieces of habitat—generally not included within the seasonal home range of the barren ewes, juvenile rams, or bachelor ram herds—where lambs were born annually in consecutive years. These sites were consistently observed in extremely precipitous, secluded areas with ready access to escape cover (Turner and Hanson, 1980). The essentiality of these ancestral sites is suggested by the 93 percent fidelity of pregnant ewes to a given lambing site and an 82 percent fidelity of the ewes born on the lambing site.

The desert bighorn sheep is not characterized by a seasonal, vertical migration pattern. Typically, desert bighorn sheep are found at an average elevation of 961 meters (275-1,525 meters). The crest of the Santa Rosa Mountains is in excess of 2,470 meters. Seasonal drift away from summer concentrations around water holes occurs laterally along the mountain block. Vertical movement within the elevational optimum can occur during the onset of the spring growing season, when bighorn sheep follow newly sprouting vegetation up from lower elevations. However, increased vegetation shows greater dependency upon erratic precipitation patterns and local edaphic effects than strict altitudinal stratification. Vertical migration to the crest of the Santa Rosa Mountains appears to be impeded by a lack of suitable precipitous rocky habitat in concert with forage competition with mule deer *(Odocoileus hemionus)*.

The mode of habitat utilization by desert bighorn sheep reflects patterns acquired from birth, enforced ontogenetically, and perpetuated ancestrally. The particular habitat and routines to which desert bighorn adhere are inflexible, not only because of centuries of success-sanctioned behavior, but due to the evolution of habitat requirement specifically and to the, comparatively, contemporary inavailability of adequate habitat in which to move.

Acknowledgments

The research reported herein was completed through affiliation with the following organizations: California State Department of Fish and Game, Desert Bighorn Council, Living Desert Reserve Association, Palm Springs Atajo Corporation, Philip L. Boyd-Deep Canyon Desert Research Center, Society for the Conservation of Bighorn Sheep, University of California, University of Wyoming, and the Valley Clinical Laboratory.

The following persons assisted in the collection of field and laboratory data: Mr. J. Bedwell, Mr. M. Blackwell, Mr. B. Blong, Mr. D. Brown, Mr. T. Brown, Mr. J. DeForge, Ms. K. Dils, Ms. D. Foster, Lt. J. Harris, Ms. L. Hensley, Mr. E. Hunt, Dr. C. Jenner, Mr. D. Landells, Ms. A. Long, Dr. W. Mayhew, Ms. M. Merritt, Mr. R. Murphy, Ms. K. Sausman, Dr. H. Salk, Mr. L. Tevis, Mr. R. Thompson, Ms. G. Thompson, Dr. I. P. Ting, Ms. D. Turner, Dr. M. Wiliamson, and Mr. R. Worley.

REFERENCES

BUECHNER, H. K.
    1960. The bighorn sheep in the United States, its past, present and future. Wildl. Monogr. No. 4, The Wildlife Society.
CALHOUN, J. B.
    1963. The social use of space. Pp. 2-185 *in* "Physiological Mammalogy," vol. 1, W. Mayer and R. Van Gelder, eds. Academic Press, New York.
IKEDA, M., and TURNER, J. C.
    ———. Grit ingestion by Nelson's bighorn sheep, *Ovis canadensis nelsoni,* in southern California. Calif. Fish and Game. (In press.)
JEWELL, P. A.
    1966. The concept of home range in mammals. Symp. Zool. Soc. London., vol. 18, pp. 85-109.

MANVILLE, R. H.
    1980.   The origin and relationships of American wild sheep.   Pp. 1-6 *in* "The
             Desert Bighorn Sheep, Its Life History, Ecology and Management," 307
             pp., G. Monson and L. Sumner, eds.   University of Arizona Press,
             Arizona.
TURNER, J. C.
    1972.   Deep Canyon watch for desert bighorn.   Westways, March, pp. 53-56.
    1972.   Desert Bighorns.   Carnation Magazine, Fall, pp. 17-22.
    1977.   Cemental annulations as an age criterion in North American sheep.
             Journ. Wildl. Man., vol. 41, pp. 211-217.
    1978.   Chlorinated hydrocarbon residues in perianal fat of desert bighorn sheep.
             Bull. Environ. Contam. Toxicol., vol. 19, pp. 23-31.
    1978.   Transplacental movement of organochloride residues in desert bighorn
             sheep.   Bull. Environ. Contam. Toxicol., vol. 21, pp. 116-124.
    1979.   Seasonal changes in the fatty acid composition of desert bighorn sheep
             bone marrow.   Comp. Biochem. Physiol., vol. 62A, pp. 599-604.
    1979.   Osmotic fragility of the red blood cells of dehydrated desert bighorn
             sheep.   Comp. Biochem. Physiol., vol. 64A, pp. 167-175.
    _____. Water Economy of the Desert Bighorn Sheep.   Wildl. Monogr., The
             Wildlife Society.   (In press.)
TURNER, J. C., and HANSON, C. G.
    1980.   Reproduction.   Pp. 145-151 *in* "The Desert Bighorn Sheep, Its Life
             History, Ecology and Management," 307 pp., G. Monson and L. Sum-
             ner, eds.   University of Arizona Press, Arizona.
TURNER, J. C., and PAYSON, J. B.
    _____. The occurrence of selected infectious diseases in the desert bighorn sheep
             (*Ovis canadensis cremnobates*) herds of the Santa Rosa Mountains, Califor-
             nia.   Calif. Fish and Game.   (In press.)
    _____. Antibody prevalence against selected infectious disease agents in desert
             bighorn sheep (*Ovis canadensis cremnobates*) herds of the Santa Rosa Moun-
             tains, California.   Journ. Wildl. Dis.   (In press.)
TURNER, J. C., and WEAVER, R. A.
    1980.   Water.   Pp. 100-112 *in* "The Desert Bighorn Sheep, Its Life History,
             Ecology and Management," 507 pp.   G. Monson and L. Summer, eds.
             University of Arizona Press.
WEAVER, R. A.
    1972.   Conclusion of the bighorn investigation in California.   Desert Bighorn
             Council Trans., vol. 16, pp. 56-65.

JACK C. TURNER

Behavior of the African False Vampire Bat
(*Cardioderma cor*)

Principal Investigator: Terry A. Vaughan, Northern Arizona University, Flagstaff, Arizona.

Grant No. 1118:   For a study of the social, foraging, and roosting behavior in a false vampire bat.

Although common in parts of East Africa and well represented in many museums, the false vampire bat has a life history that is poorly known. This bat and the yellow-winged bat *(Lavia frons)* are the only African members of the family Megadermatidae. The remaining three species in the family occur in southern Asia, the Malayan region, the northern half of Australia, and the Philippine Islands, and these are carnivorous. Members of this family are large for microchiropterans, having huge ears, nose leaves, and broad wings.

The major objective of this study was an understanding of the nocturnal behavior of *Cardioderma* throughout the year. The feeding strategy, nocturnal time budget, vocalizations, and territorial behavior were of special interest. Some information on the reproductive cycle and on seasonal movements was assembled. A complete report on that research has been published (Vaughan, 1976).

Methods

This study was basically an observational one. Between early June 1973 and mid-July 1974, 140 nights were devoted partially or completely to observing *Cardioderma*. (Because the study was done in June and July of both 1973 and 1974, when these months are referred to the year is given.) At night individuals were kept under observation as long as possible, durations of flights and other activities were timed with a stopwatch, and schedules of nocturnal activity were recorded. In most months several entire nights during moonlight were devoted to observing *Cardioderma*. Bats were observed at night with a Javelin night-viewing device equipped with a 135-millimeter f. 1.8 lens. This device is manufactured by Apollo Lasers of Los Angeles, California. Adequate illumination was provided on overcast or moonless nights by a candle in a tin can some 15 meters from the bats. Vocalizations of *Cardio-*

derma were studied on occasion with an ultrasonic receiver manufactured by Holgates of Totton, Southhampton, England. Bats were captured in mist nets and bat traps (Tuttle, 1974) and were marked by notching the ears. Using the night viewer, I could recognize individuals at distances of at least 8 meters. Some areas occupied by marked individuals were mapped and distances between regularly used perches were measured. Food habits were determined by observing bats capturing prey and by collecting discarded fragments of prey beneath well-used perches.

Thomas J. O'Shea assisted me during nocturnal observation periods for part of the study.

Study Area

Observations of *Cardioderma* were made in the vicinity of Bushwhacker's Safari Camp, 17 kilometers east and 10.5 kilometers north of Kibwezi, in southern Kenya, at about lat. 2° S. The camp is beside the Athi River at an elevation of 940 meters and is largely surrounded by gently rolling terrain supporting deciduous woodland. In some places the four common local species of *Commiphora* trees are interspersed with the taller *Acacia tortilis, Melia volkensii,* and *Delonix elata* to form more or less open woodland with a brushy understory. Especially conspicuous are the baobab trees *(Adansonia digitata);* these are the largest trees of the area and give a distinctive and picturesque appearance to the landscape. Important shrubs are *Combretum exalatum, Grewia villosa,* and *Premna resinosa;* these are usually 2 to 3 meters high. Although these and other brushy species form nearly impenetrable thickets locally, over most of the area shrubs have a patchy distribution and are interspersed with openings grown to low forbs and grasses. Along the Athi River, and at intervals where dry washes interrupt the woodland, are linear stands of *Newtonia hildebrandtii, Salix* sp., *Acacia elatior,* and *Tamarindus indica.* These trees remain green for most of the year, and some *A. elatior* reach heights of about 16 meters. The area is inhabited by members of the Kamba tribe, who in scattered places have cleared the vegetation from a few acres and have planted corn.

Seasonal changes in vegetative productivity have an important effect on the animals of the study area and are dependent on patterns of precipitation. The annual precipitation in the period from 1969 through 1973 averaged 474 millimeters. There are two rainy seasons, one in March and April and the other in October and November; during these times some 81 percent of the annual precipitation is received. Temperatures are moderate throughout the year, ranging from highs of 32°C. at midday in January and February to lows of 12°C. during nights in July and August.

Daytime Roosts

I examined carefully five cavities in baobabs that were occupied by groups of *Cardioderma*. Each was spacious; two were approximately 2.2 meters high and 1.8 meters wide; two were at least 4 meters high and 3 meters wide; and one was some 2 meters wide and no less than 2 meters high. The two colonies that I studied were in cavities with openings roughly 0.45 meter wide and 1.60 meters high; the base of one opening was 4.3 meters above the ground and the base of the other was at ground level. The entrances to four of the cavities were unobstructed, but one entrance was partly screened by branches of the evergreen shrub *Maerua kirkii*.

The bats hung pendant from the ceilings of the cavities and maintained a spacing such that individuals were not in contact with each other. Bats in daytime roosts were extremely wary and easily disturbed. No other kind of bat was ever found roosting with *Cardioderma*.

Population Changes

The numbers of bats in roosts followed a bimodal annual pattern. From a total of 26 individuals on June 19, 1973, when I first counted bats at Baobab I, the population dropped to 5 bats on July 10 and remained low until November. In mid-November the numbers rose sharply to a peak of 81 bats in early December and declined precipitously in late December. I have few accurate counts from early January through March, but my impression was that numbers of bats in the roosts did not fluctuate widely in this period. Careful counts at Baobab I through April and May 1974 demonstrated a sharp drop in numbers of bats in early May, immediately followed by an abrupt rise in the population.

Audible Vocalizations

Cardioderma emits several types of calls audible to man. The most frequently used vocalization is the "song," which consists of a series of four to nine (usually six) high-intensity pulses with a fundamental frequency close to 12 kHz. Each pulse has the quality of the sharp, metallic chip given by some passerine birds as they forage. The pulses of the song are emitted in a rapid, staccato series that lasts about one second. Typically the perching bat revolves its body almost constantly and the songs are given in a variety of directions throughout 360°.

The frequency with which the song was given changed markedly with the seasons. From late March through July and part of August the song was given regularly by foraging *Cardioderma;* but beginning in mid-August, and continuing through October, the song was given progressively less frequently. During the night of October 9, 1973, for example, songs were given by one *Cardioderma* at the rate of only one every 4.8 minutes, whereas the rate in July was one every 11 seconds. During November and December the song was seldom used. In January it was given at an extremely low rate (roughly one song each 12.4 minutes for a bat observed early in the month), and the rate picked up in February. The annual cycle seems to involve no singing during the short rains, regular singing during the long rains and through the early part of the long dry season, and singing at a low rate in the long dry season and in the short dry season. Each brief pulse of the flight call has a liquid quality seemingly caused by a rise in frequency from the beginning to the end of the pulse (at roughly 12 kHz). The flight call is far more variable than the song and includes three to ten or more individual pulses given at rates of about one or two per second. These calls are quite loud; my impression is that they can be heard farther than the song. The flight call is given most often when a bat takes flight but is occasionally interspersed with the song or given by a perching bat that is not singing. Infrequently the flight call is given prior to the emergence of a bat from a roost. Perhaps this is a long-range location call, serving to apprise the bats of one another's locations and directions of flight.

Rarely a single note is given. This note is at the same frequency as the other vocalizations, resembles a single pulse of the flight call, and is given by a flying bat in the daytime roost.

Emergence

Bats emerged from the roost roughly one-half hour after sunset, flew low, usually within 2 meters of the ground, and usually followed trails maintained by bushbuck *(Tragelaphus scriptus)* and water buck *(Kobus ellipsiprymnus).* Dispersal from the roost to foraging areas involved a series of short flights interrupted by periods when the bats perched in low vegetation. In April 1974 the first perching place of one bat was only 8 meters from the roost; another bat perched first about 35 meters from the roost. Observations made at distances of 0.5 to 1.0 kilometer from Roost I indicated that each bat approached its foraging area by a series of short flights interrupted by perching. One marked female habitually took at least 30 minutes to reach her foraging area approximately 0.5 kilometer from the roost.

Feeding Strategy and Food

Compared to most bats, *Cardioderma* forages in a remarkably sedentary fashion; as it hangs from the low branch of a tree or bush the bat listens for ground-dwelling prey, occasionally swoops to the ground to capture food, and returns to the perch to eat it. This bat usually perches on horizontal or downward-arching twigs sheltered above by interlacing branches of *Acacia senegal* or *A. mellifera,* each of which has twigs armed with wicked, recurved thorns. I observed *Cardioderma* perching 0.3 to 3.5 meters above the ground.

Cardioderma perches most commonly in situations where the overhead canopy of vegetation has limited the density of grasses and low-growing forbs below. Conditions in these places are suitable for foraging: the soil is either leaf-covered or has detritus that when displaced by the movement of large invertebrates produces sounds detectable by the bat; there are few obstructions that impede a downward-swooping bat; and the density of ground-dwelling beetles and centipedes is sufficiently high all year round to reward this bat's style of foraging.

Foraging areas were small. Only four areas could be accurately measured. Two areas measured in late August were 1.01 and 0.55 hectares; each belonged to an adult male. The former area, judged from rough measurements made of a number of foraging areas, was unusually large. Two areas measured in mid-April were 0.11 and 0.10 hectare; these belonged to an adult female and an individual of unknown sex and age, respectively.

The foraging behavior of *Cardioderma* is highly stereotyped. The bat hangs by its hind feet from a branch with the wings loosely folded and the head slightly elevated so that the ears are at an angle of some 30° above the horizontal. The bat revolves its body, and its ears "scan" the area beneath the perch. *Cardioderma* can revolve nearly 360° without shifting the position of its feet; the body revolves almost 180° in one direction, returns to the relaxed position, and revolves 180° in the opposite direction. The legs cross each other during part of each revolution. During these revolutions the angle of the ears is such that they can "sweep" a circular area with a radius at least equal to the height of the bat above the ground. When perched 2 meters above the ground, then, a bat scans a circular area some 4 meters in diameter and 13 square meters in area. My judgment of the area the bat scrutinizes is based on many observations of a bat flying from its perch to the ground to capture prey. Flights were nearly always directed at an angle of 45° or less from the vertical. During times of most intense foraging, *Cardioderma* makes one revolution and surveys all this area every 5 to 8 seconds. The ears are moved in unison, and when a bat's attention is attracted by a sound it aims its head and ears directly toward the source. The speed and extent of the revolutions diminish as a bat's stomach becomes full.

The swoop to pick up prey is swift. The wings beat rapidly as the bat leaves its perch, and the bat accelerates quickly as it slants downward to the ground. The broad wings are spread fully to break the speed just before the bat reaches the ground, the prey is snatched up, and in a burst of rapid wing beats the bat returns directly to the perch. The bat alights by performing a rapid half roll and swinging its feet upward; this same style of alighting is used by phyllostomatid and rhinolophid bats. Characteristically, the prey is picked up so quickly that there is little sign of the bat having touched the ground. Even on one occasion when I saw a *Cardioderma* capture a centipede about 80 milli- meters long the bat remained on the ground for only a fraction of a second. Much of the economy of this style of foraging must depend on the bat's ability to choose from a vast array of nocturnal sounds—including insect calls, rus- tling vegetation, and the delicate footfalls of genets *(Genetta tigrina)* and ger- bils *(Tatera* spp.)—those sounds made by suitable invertebrate prey.

The extent to which *Cardioderma* depends on terrestrial or flying prey de- pends upon the dramatic seasonal changes in the degree to which the ground is covered by vegetation and in the abundance of insects. Especially during the May to October dry season, insect density is low and much bare ground is ex- posed owing to the destruction of dead vegetation by termites. In these dry times, in at least partial compensation for low densities of prey, more bare ground where *Cardioderma* can forage profitably becomes available. This bat feeds virtually exclusively on terrestrial prey in these dry periods and low perches are used. But when the rains come much of the surface of the ground soon becomes covered by forbs and grasses and the areas affording ground for- aging for *Cardioderma* are greatly reduced. *Cardioderma* responds to this re- striction by doing an unusual amount of aerial foraging.

Cardioderma feeds primarily on large, terrestrial arthropods. Beetles of the families Scarabeidae, Tenebrionidae, and Carabidae are especially important; centipedes are taken regularly and scorpions at least occasionally. Chrysome- lid beetles are of importance in the wet seasons. Orthopterans, mostly katy- dids (Tettigoniidae), and large moths (Sphingidae) are major foods during brief periods in the wet seasons.

Time Budgets

Although *Cardioderma* utilizes the same basic foraging style throughout the year, seasonal changes in the nocturnal time budget are pronounced.

These changes are associated with dry-season wet-season shifts in rainfall and with changes in vegetation and insect availability.

Several seasonal differences in the use of time during foraging by *Cardio-derma* are especially well marked. Bats tend to perch for short intervals in the dry season and for longer times in the wet seasons, and more flights per hour are made in the dry seasons. Also, flights average over twice as long in the dry season as in the wet season. As an example, post-midnight flights averaged 24.4 meters on a dry-season night (July 20, 1973) as compared to 9.4 meters on a wet-season night (April 10, 1974). These means are significantly differ-ent ($t = 2.40$, $P < .02$). In terms of time spent on the wing per night, foraging schedules differ seasonally. A total of 11 minutes 48 seconds was spent in flight by a *Cardioderma* from 2000 to 0500 on July 19-20, 1973, whereas on October 12 the estimated total minimum flight time during these hours was 27 minutes. In mid-April, in the midst of the April-May rains, records from parts of three nights indicated that between 2000 and 0500 each of two bats probably spent an average of some 5 minutes in flight each night. Because of the high energy demands of takeoffs and landings, the 27 minutes of frequent, brief flights in October must have expended far more than five times the ener-gy required by the 5 minutes of flight in April. All seasons considered, the average duration of a flight was but 5 seconds.

Discussion

Of central importance in the lives of many tropical animals is the pattern of alternating wet and dry seasons. Wet seasons are times of plenty and both food and cover are typically abundant. In the dry seasons, however, food is of-ten scarce, cover is reduced, and there is a high adaptive premium on foraging efficiency.

Cardioderma is a "pure pursuer" (a term used by MacArthur and Levins, 1964). During the bleakest parts of the long dry season its survival must de-pend on the specialized feeding strategy that includes: (1) a search image for large, vulnerable prey; (2) stereotyped search behavior allowing meticulous scanning for terrestrial prey from a vantage point; (3) exclusive use of a pre-viously established foraging area and short flights between familiar perches; (4) the capture of slow-moving, terrestrial prey by brief flights without erratic pursuit; (5) consumption of prey while perching. Of key importance in opti-mizing energy gains/unit of time is the high energy yield/food item, the dras-tic reduction of time spent on costly activities (parsimonious use of flight), and low expenditures of energy for time-consuming activities (searching for prey from a vantage point). The balance between the expenditure and the income of energy in the long dry season must be precarious, and selection for tight adherence to this unusual foraging strategy must be intense.

Possibly the foraging style of *Cardioderma* evolved under selective pressures for an alternative means of securing food during stressful East African dry seasons. A "novel" type of foraging, involving meticulous nocturnal scanning of the ground for prey, was perhaps highly adaptive in dry periods when ground-dwelling arthropods were made vulnerable by the denuding of the ground by termites and when aerial insect activity was low. If shifts in climatic patterns tended toward the long dry seasons and short wet seasons that are typical today of parts of East Africa where *Cardioderma* occurs, the use of terrestrial prey might have been the key to survival. Of interest in connection with these speculations is the skill of *Cardioderma* in making aerial captures in the wet seasons and its total dependence on terrestrial prey during dry seasons.

Viewed against the bimodal pattern of annual rainfall, the unimodal pattern of frequency of singing is unusual because it is not associated consistently with rainfall or food abundance. Perhaps the seasonal pattern of singing is related to the seasonal establishment of an exclusive foraging area. During the March-May rains, when food is abundant and foraging does not occupy all of the night, time and energy are invested in the establishment and maintenance of an exclusive foraging area and singing reaches its annual peak. The perches within a bat's area at this time are usually around its periphery, suggesting the use of the perches both for feeding and for vocal establishment of the boundaries of the area. The area established during these times of plenty seemingly has survival value later, chiefly from August into October, when the time and energy to establish an exclusive area could not be spared. At this time singing dwindles and nearly ceases. Defense of the sparse resources under conditions of low densities of bats is probably no longer of advantage energetically. Abandonment of the defense of an exclusive area by birds when such behavior is economically unfeasible is discussed by Brown (1964). In the November-December wet season and during the brief and not entirely dry interval between these rains and those from March to May, the advantage in the maintenance of exclusive areas is reduced and in these times *Cardioderma* sings infrequently. Singing may thus be used chiefly for a once-a-year establishment of exclusive foraging areas for the stressful May-October dry season.

REFERENCES

BROWN, JERRAM L.
    1964.   The evolution of diversity in avian terrestrial systems.   Wilson Bull.,
            vol. 76, pp. 160-169.

MACARTHUR, ROBERT H., and LEVINS, RICHARD
   1964.   Competition, habitat selection, and character displacement in a patchy
            environment.   Proc. Nat. Acad. Sci., vol. 51, pp. 1207-1210.
TUTTLE, M. D.
   1974.   An improved trap for bats.   Journ. Mamm., vol. 55, pp. 475-477.
VAUGHAN, TERRY A.
   1976.   Nocturnal behavior of the African false vampire bat *(Cardioderma
            cor)*.   Journ. Mamm., vol. 57, no. 2, pp. 227-248; illus.

TERRY A. VAUGHAN

Phenological Relationships of Batesian Mimics, Their Models, and Insectivorous Birds in an Illinois Sand Area

Principal Investigator: Gilbert P. Waldbauer, University of Illinois, Urbana, Illinois.

Grant No. 1053:   To study the phenology of stinging Hymenoptera, their mimics, and insectivorous birds.

The most widely known type of mimicry is Batesian mimicry, named for and first described in 1862 by its discoverer, the famous English naturalist Henry W. Bates. Batesian mimics are edible animals which have little or no active defense against predators, but often escape attack because they have evolved a superficial resemblance to species which are toxic, venomous, or otherwise protected against predation. Batesian mimicry occurs all over the world, and is especially frequent among insects as an escape from insectivorous birds. In North America one of the best known examples is the close resemblance of the edible viceroy butterfly to the toxic monarch butterfly (Brower et al., 1968; Brower, 1969). Wasps and bees—protected by their venomous stings—also serve as models which are mimicked by various kinds of flies, beetles, moths, and other insects. Some flies of the family Syrphidae, for example, are almost uncanny mimics of the physical appearance and behavior of wasps or bees (Rettenmeyer, 1970).

Numerous instances of Batesian mimicry have been documented, and laboratory studies have shown that predators do learn to avoid toxic or venomous prey, and that they are usually deceived by mimics of such prey. However, we actually know very little about the ecological and phenological relationships of models, Batesian mimics, and predators, although unfounded assumptions are frequent in the literature. For example, it is commonly assumed that mimics gain no protection unless they occur in the same place and at the same time as the models, and that the predators will not learn to avoid the models unless the models outnumber the mimics.

Waldbauer and Sheldon (1971) examined the intricacies of the phenological relationships of mimics, models, and predators in a moist forest at the University of Illinois' Robert Allerton Park near Monticello, Illinois. They found that specialized mimics of wasps and bees are present almost exclusively in spring and early summer. The models for these mimetic flies, however, are scarce at that time, although they are abundant in late summer and early fall. These findings are obviously contrary to the assumption that models and mimics must occur at the same time and that models must outnumber mimics.

This seeming paradox is resolved if we consider the role of the insectivorous birds which exert the selection pressure that maintains the mimetic resemblance and that brought about its evolution in the first place.

Waldbauer and Sheldon (1971) were the first to point out that the phenology of a mimetic species is affected not only by the seasonal history of its models, but also by the seasonal history of relevant predators. They proposed that the mimics in question fly in spring and early summer to avoid a hazardous period in midsummer when there are large numbers of young birds which have left the nest but have not yet learned to avoid wasps and bees. Spring and early summer are far safer because the great majority of birds out of the nest then are adults which learned to avoid wasps and bees in a previous summer.

This raises the problem of whether or not birds can remember the appearance of stinging insects over the winter. Experimental evidence (Mostler, 1935; Rothschild, 1964) shows that some birds continue to reject both wasps and their mimics from $6\frac{1}{2}$ to $14\frac{1}{2}$ months after their last experience with a wasp. Furthermore, most of our insectivorous birds migrate to the tropics for the winter, and it is likely that the avoidance of wasps and bees is reinforced there by experiences with similar stinging insects.

The study reported here was made as a further test of the hypothesis proposed by Waldbauer and Sheldon (1971). The site of the study was Sand Ridge State Forest (formerly known as Mason State Forest) which is in an extensive sand area east of the Illinois River near Havana, Illinois. The surveys were made in collaboration with James G. Sternburg and Chris T. Maier of the Department of Entomology, University of Illinois.

Because of the sandy soil, the forest association at Sand Ridge is much more xerophytic than either the upland or bottomland forest at Allerton Park. The upland forest of Allerton is characterized by white oak, black oak, and red elm; the bottomland forest by silver maple, sycamore, and hackberry. At Sand Ridge the characteristic trees are blackjack oak, black oak, and red hickory; a cactus (*Opuntia compressa* Macbr.) is abundant in open places.

Two-hour surveys were made at about weekly intervals from May 9 to October 3 on sunny mornings, when wasps, bees, and their mimics are most abundant at flowers. Using an insect net we attempted to collect all models and mimics seen on blossoms or elsewhere along a standard route which ran mostly through forest and forest edge. All common plants in blossom were sampled unless we knew from previous experience that a plant is not visited by either models or mimics.

At Allerton Park Waldbauer and Sheldon (1971) found four mimetic complexes, one with bumblebees as the models and the others with three different types of wasps as the models. We found the same complexes at Sand Ridge plus a fifth which has a fourth type of wasp as the model. Although the same complexes were involved, the profound ecological differences between Sand Ridge and Allerton Park were reflected by major differences in the species composition of both the model and mimic components of these complexes in the two areas. Many species occurred in only one of the areas, and those that occurred in both were usually scarce in one and common in the other.

Data on when young insectivorous birds leave the nest are not available for Sand Ridge, although there is a list of the breeding birds (Bjorklund and Deters, 1972). Since Allerton and Sand Ridge are at almost the same latitude and only about 75 miles apart, and since they differ little with respect to the bird species which breed in the forest, we have assumed that the distribution of fledging times reported by Waldbauer and Sheldon (1971) for Allerton is a reasonable approximation of the situation at Sand Ridge.

Despite the differences in species composition of the mimetic complexes, the phenological relationships of models and mimics and, almost certainly, insectivorous birds are very similar at Allerton and Sand Ridge. In general, mimics were abundant at Sand Ridge from late May to the first week in July but had almost disappeared by the middle of July. Their models (female wasps or bees), on the other hand, were generally relatively scarce until late July and did not become really abundant until August and September. This is best illustrated by the bumblebee complex. Bumblebee mimics were abundant until the end of June and present in declining numbers until the middle of July, but bumblebees were relatively scarce until the end of July, although they were the most abundant of all models in August and September.

One of our most interesting findings at Sand Ridge involves a wasp-mimicking fly of the family Conopidae, *Physoconops brachrhynchus* (Macq.), which is on the wing in midsummer rather than earlier when it would presumably avoid young birds that have not yet learned to shun its models. This may well be the exception which proves the rule, since it is likely that this species, in order to locate suitable hosts for its parasitic offspring, must fly at a time when it does not gain maximum protection from its mimicry. Conopid females insert their eggs into the bodies of adult insects, usually stinging Hymenoptera. Unfortunately, the hosts of *P. brachyrhynchus* are not known, although another member of the same genus parasitizes solitary bees, and several Old World species of a closely related genus are known to parasitize solitary bees and wasps as well as social wasps and bumblebees. Bees and wasps—especially social species—are generally most abundant in August and September.

Our findings at Sand Ridge State Forest support the hypothesis proposed by Waldbauer and Sheldon (1971). Mimics of bees and wasps do not necessarily fly when their models are most abundant, but may occur in spring and early summer when their models are relatively scarce. The mimics thus gain an adaptive advantage by avoiding most newly fledged birds which have not yet learned to avoid wasps and bees.

REFERENCES

BJORKLUND, RICHARD G., and DETERS, J. R.
   1972.   An annotated checklist of the birds of Mason State Forest.   Proc. Peoria Acad. Sci., vol. 5, pp. 20-24.
BROWER, LINCOLN P.
   1969.   Ecological chemistry.   Sci. Amer., vol. 220, no. 2, pp. 22-24, illus.
BROWER, LINCOLN P.; REYERSON, WILLIAM N.; COPPINGER, LORNA L.; and GLAZIER, SUSAN C.
   1968.   Ecological chemistry and the palatability spectrum.   Science, vol. 161, pp. 1349-1351, illus.
MOSTLER, G.
   1935.   Beobachtungen zur Frage der Wespenmimikry.   Zeitschr. Morphol. Oekol. Tiere, vol. 29, pp. 381-454.
RETTENMEYER, CARL W.
   1970.   Insect mimicry.   Ann. Rev. Ent., vol. 15, pp. 43-74.
ROTHSCHILD, M.
   1964.   An extension of Dr. Lincoln Brower's theory on bird predation and food specificity, together with some observations on bird memory in relation to aposematic colour patterns.   Entomologist, 1964, pp. 73-78.
WALDBAUER, GILBERT P., and SHELDON, J. K.
   1971.   Phenological relationships of some aculeate Hymenoptera, their dipteran mimics, and insectivorous birds.   Evolution, vol. 25, pp. 371-382.
WALDBAUER, G. P.; STERNBURG, J. G.; and MAIER, C. T.
   1977.   Phenological relationships of wasps, bumblebees, their mimics, and insectivorous birds in an Illinois sand area.   Ecology, vol. 58, no. 3 (late spring), 1977, pp. 583-591, illus.

GILBERT P. WALDBAUER

Comparative Population Ecology of Pierid Butterflies

Principal Investigator: Ward B. Watt, Stanford University, Stanford, California.

Grant No. 1089:   To study population ecology of pierid butterflies.

More than a century has passed since Darwin and Wallace published their first insights into the process of evolutionary change in living things. In that time biologists have gathered much varied evidence for the occurrence of evolution by natural selection and have begun to understand how the laws and mechanisms of inheritance interact with natural selection in wild populations (e.g., see Mayr, 1963; Lewontin, 1974). Indeed, our own origins as a species have been increasingly well fitted into a context of evolutionary understanding (e.g., Dobzhansky, 1962). Nevertheless, we remain ignorant of many crucial aspects of the evolutionary process. In particular, we know little of the "ground rules" by which the game of evolutionary adaptation is played from day to day or year to year in the wild. Can we make any generalization as to why certain inherited variants are favored by natural selection, while others are not? If alternative adaptations to some environmental stress are possible, why is this one favored and not that? Present understanding of this area of short-term evolutionary mechanisms is minimal. Yet, such understanding is essential to a more comprehensive, and generally predictive, evolutionary theory of biology. Nor is such understanding for its own sake, important as this may be, the only meaning of such work. Many problems of forest or range management, control of environmental pollution damage, and so forth can be effectively dealt with only when a more causal and predictive understanding of adaptive change in animal and plant populations is on hand.

Careful selection of a "test system" for study is needed if we wish to be able to examine all important aspects of adaptive change in a wild population. The creatures to be studied should be readily observable in the wild, so that forces of natural selection acting on them can be identified (and, eventually, measured). They should display much variation within and among their populations, since we must be able to study the interaction of selective pressures with many alternative inherited states of adaptation. Also, they should be amenable to culture and experimental study in the laboratory, so that we can understand the chemical, physiological, or behavioral mechanisms by which inherited variations change their bearers' success in the face of natural selection. For some time now I and my coworkers have been studying adaptation in butterflies of the family Pieridae, especially the genera *Colias* and *Pieris* (the "sulfurs" and the "whites"). These insects admirably meet all the above criteria for a suitable "evolutionary test system." Of course, the study of short-term evolution in these insects, as perforce in any other test system, has at first yielded knowledge most pertinent to the test system itself. But we believe that energetic followup of initial results will lead to the successful posing and answering of more general questions once the test system is itself better understood.

That part of our work supported by the National Geographic Society in 1972 was concerned with discovering the ecological "ground rules" applicable to a series of pierid populations in the Rocky Mountains of Colorado. Here several species of *Colias* and *Pieris* butterflies occupy habitats ranging from lowland valleys to mountain ridges well above timberline. This array of habitats, and of species of differing relationships inhabiting them, is an ideal "outdoor laboratory" for our comparative fieldwork. In the summer of 1972 we were concerned with:

(a) the patterns of nectar food resource use by adult *Colias;*
(b) the numbers and migration behaviors of a population of the usually alpine species *Colias meadii,* which we found occurring below as well as above timberline;
(c) the reproductive "strategy" of adult *Colias;* and
(d) the numbers and dispersal behavior of the related *Pieris napi* in a mountain-stream drainage.

We now turn to descriptions of our results and, where possible, some discussion of the directions in which they are presently leading us.

Nectar Resource Use by Colias Butterflies

We began by wishing to know the content of the nectar that is the sole adult food of *Colias.* This was essential "context" information for the interpretation of studies of food-processing adaptations in *Colias,* then being planned. In the course of field studies on numbers and dispersal of *Colias* (see below), we could easily record their preferences for different flowers as nectar sources. These preferences might be thought to be related to flowering plant distributions in the habitat. We could test this by doing our work in the study plots of Langenheim (1962), who published detailed information on plant distributions in the Colorado montane and alpine grasslands inhabited by *Colias alexandra* and *Colias meadii,* respectively. To test relations between *Colias*'s nectar preferences and the nectar content itself, we sampled nectars of all available flowering-plant species in the montane and alpine grasslands, using microsyringes fitted with fine-bore needles. The samples were then chemically analyzed for water content, identity and quantity of dissolved sugars, and identity of amino acids, a nitrogen source that had just been found to be widespread in flower nectars (Baker and Baker, personal communication and 1973). Finally, we photographed all prominent flowers in both "visible" and ultraviolet light. Insects see the ultraviolet component of sunlight, which we cannot, and we were aware that many flowers in the communities we studied display patterns in the ultraviolet range (Eisner et al., 1969). Thus we wished to test the possibility that flowers preferred by *Colias* might be attracting these pollinating insects by ultraviolet and/or "visible" color patterns.

The results we obtained were striking and in some ways unexpected. Plant abundance, or evenness of distribution, appeared to have no bearing on our butterflies' preferences for nectar sources. For example, in studying *Colias alexandra* of the montane grassland, we found four of its five most favored nectar sources to be distributed in very localized clumps and to show very low total numbers in the grassland, while the fifth (the blue flax, *Linum lewisii*) was abundant throughout and was, indeed, the second most evenly distributed flower in the community. However, data analysis showed clearly that nectars preferred by *Colias,* whether in montane or alpine habitats, are dilute, i.e., they have a high water content, and contain mostly sugars of simple chemical structure: glucose and fructose. These nectars contain also a variety of simple amino acids, which provide nitrogen nutrition useful to the insects' reproduction. On the other hand, flowers avoided by *Colias,* but avidly visited by larger pollinators such as bumblebees, hawkmoths, or even hummingbirds, have much more concentrated nectars, which also contain more complicated sugars, such as sucrose or raffinose. Finally, we found that the dilute-nectar flowers, visited by *Colias* and a variety of other small insect pollinators, have converged in evolution on the common display of a bull's-eye-like target pattern in the ultraviolet, frequently reinforced in the visible. Thus, they signal their common offering of dilute nectars to a "pool" of insect species that favor such food.

We were able to interpret the nectar content preferences of all these pollinating animals in terms of their temperature relations to their environment. Our *Colias* butterflies are active at high body temperatures (35-39°C.), similar to our own body temperature or 37°. However, they do not use internal physiological energy to maintain temperature as we do, but instead absorb solar energy by orienting to sunlight (Watt, 1968). The other small insects (flies, other small butterflies, etc.) that use the same dilute nectars appear to have similar strategies for maintaining high body temperature with the use of sunlight, rather than their own energy reserves. They thus are well served by nectars of low-energy yield, especially since their small size makes them more vulnerable to water loss and places them more in need of the water in dilute nectar. By contrast, the animals using concentrated nectars all maintain their own body temperatures in the same high range, by muscular effort (bumble-bees, hawkmoths; see Heinrich, 1974) or by other physiological means (hum-mingbirds). This, in turn, produces a need for much more concentrated energy supply in their food. Thus, the alternative thermoregulatory strategies used by pollinators impose different nutritional requirements on them and, in turn, open up opportunities for flowering plants to specialize in attracting one or another class of pollinators.

Further details of this work can be found in our published report of it (Watt et al., 1974). Follow-up work has taken two directions. On the one hand, we have begun to study the relative effectiveness of our insects as pollen carriers and how this affects the evolutionary relationships among those plant species that are sharing the same "pool" of low-energy-demand pollinators. On the other hand, armed with knowledge of the chemical composition of *Colias*'s nectar food, we have begun to study natural genetic variation in the biochemical machinery with which *Colias* processes that food.

Structure of an Ecologically Interesting Colias meadii *Population*

The term "population structure" is commonly used to refer to a group of population characteristics (including the size of the population, its composi-tion by age and sex, and its dispersal patterns) which strongly influence the ecology and the evolutionary genetics of populations of any organism. In sum-mer 1972 we undertook to study the structure of a population of *Colias meadii* on the side of a mountain, the Mesa Seco, in the northern end of Colorado's San Juan Range. This species is, as noted above, usually at home in the alpine tundra, above timberline. The Mesa Seco location was of interest, because there, as in a few other Colorado situations known to us, there is continuity between alpine tundra and montane grassland, and *Colias meadii* is found as much as a thousand feet *below* timberline, as well as above it. In such a place, the same species might be encountering very different extremes of natural se-lection. To evaluate the effects of selection on this population, it was necessary first to know: What numbers are present along the elevation gradient? How far up or down does an individual move during its lifetime? Are we dealing with a series of effectively separate small populations at different elevations, or with one huge population spanning the whole ecological and geographical range, or with some intermediate condition?

To attack these questions, we employed the "mark-release-recapture" techniques commonly used in the study of insect populations. *Colias* were captured, given individual numbers with permanent ink (in such a way that their behavior, susceptibility to predators, etc., were not affected), and released where they were caught. In repeated sampling of the population, the numbers of animals recaptured, the places of their initial capture and later recapture, and so forth can be used to calculate, preferably with the aid of a computer, the average numbers' lifespan, and migration distances of the insects in the population as a whole.

We found, in fact, that our *Colias meadii* move considerable distances up or down their steep mountainside habitat: so much so that nearly the entire elevation gradient is to be effectively considered as *one population.* Within this population several thousand insects each year move, during the month to 6 weeks of adult flight, among a diversity of ecological conditions at different levels on the mountainside. At least a few *Colias* each generation emerge from their pupal cases at one extreme of the elevation gradient and come to their ends only after reaching the other extreme.

The evolutionary results of this interaction between habitat-based patterns of natural selection and the extensive cross-habitat dispersal of the insects are likely to be far from simple. Indeed, results that we (W. Watt and D. Beaufait, unpublished results) and our colleague George Johnson of Washington University (Johnson, 1975) have obtained already suggest that for some characteristics, the patterns of natural variation in this *Colias* population are quite different in different parts of the elevation gradient, in spite of dispersal, while other characteristics may be quite uniform throughout. Clearly, we are just beginning to scratch the surface of the possibilities for biological insight that this and similar populations offer.

The analysis of which the foregoing is a summary has been complex and time-consuming. Indeed, it has taken on full interpretability only in comparison to much other data on *Colias* population structure. The analysis of all this material has only recently been completed, and so the further details of the Mesa Seco work and other related *Colias* population studies will be found in a large paper (Watt et al., 1977). The results of this work are indispensable for our programs of studying the genetic variation in *Colias* populations, as the preceding paragraph suggests. More and diverse understandings of evolutionary genetics will surely be built on this foundation in the coming years.

Reproductive Strategy of Adult Colias

A major aspect of population structure analysis, distinct enough to be considered by itself, is so-called "reproductive strategy": how does the animals' reproductive physiology respond to environmental stress? do the animals mate more than once in their lifetimes? Do they reproduce and disperse simultaneously, or reproduce only after a distinct dispersal period? Do they reproduce continuously, as a female might lay many single eggs interspersed with other activities, or in large batches, as a female might lay a few large egg clusters at widely spaced intervals? Such alternative "strategies" may evolve in response to various environmental selective pressures, and may then in turn influence later evolution of the populations displaying them. Here, we have combined field observations of *Colias's* courtship, mating, and egg-laying behavior with laboratory physiological work. This work, begun in summer 1972, is still in progress, but tentative conclusions on some aspects are already apparent:

  (a) Favorable temperature conditions and adequate adult food (see above) are essential for development of *Colias's* full reproductive potential, though a female may be able to lay one or two dozen eggs (out of many hundreds potential) on stored reserves without feeding as an adult.
  (b) Courtship occurs throughout the flight season, and individuals frequently mate more than once. Even very old individuals may court and mate; thus, nearly every adult succeeds in reproducing to some extent.
  (c) These insects reproduce as they disperse. Courtship behavior of "immigrant" male insects in new surroundings is normal and successful. Females lay one egg at a time, lay as many as several hundred eggs over their life spans, and continue to lay eggs until they are totally enfeebled.

Work is now going forward concerning the cues used by females in picking egg-laying sites, the efficiency of various ways of searching for suitable egg-laying sites, and so forth. Not only may this work prove essential for understanding basic evolutionary processes with these insects as an informing example, but considerable light may be shed on possibilities for agricultural control of pest insects through such work.

Population Structure of Pieris *Butterflies*

We carried out this work in collaboration with our colleague Dr. Frances S. Chew, now of Tufts University. Our purposes were, first, simply to compare the population structure of *Pieris* to our results on several species of *Colias,* its close relative. Second, Dr. Chew was interested in *Pieris's* movements in relation to this insect's use of series of related plants as larval food—for example, do adults move far enough that any given female has the opportunity to lay eggs on any of the alternative food plants? A final motivation was this: *Pieris* appears on first inspection to be an extremely weak flier, with "fluttery" wing strokes and very slow flight. We were interested to know whether the insect's fragile appearance really carries over into its dispersal behavior, or whether it moves farther than a casual look would suggest.

We studied the *Pieris* populations of the Copper Creek drainage, a "hanging valley" near the montane grassland study site we used in the *Colias* nectar work. Because the analysis of our *Colias* population structure data was itself so time-consuming, we have not yet completed analysis of the *Pieris* data. But one thing at least seems already clear—*Pieris*'s weak appearance belies its actual capacity for dispersal. Several individuals (out of one or two thousand) in each season studied have been observed to move distances of 3 kilometers or more up and down the Copper Creek Valley, sometimes within only a few days, while many more move shorter but still appreciable distances.

REFERENCES

BAKER, HERBERT G., and BAKER, IRENE
   1973.   Amino-acids in nectar and their evolutionary significance.   Nature, vol. 241, pp. 543-545.
DOBZHANSKY, THEODOSIUS
   1962.   Mankind evolving, 381 pp., illus.   Yale University Press, New Haven.
EISNER, THOMAS R.; SILBERGLIED, R. E.; ANESHANSLEY, D.; CARREL, J. E.; and HOWLAND, H. C.
   1969.   Ultraviolet video-viewing: The television camera as an insect eye. Science, vol. 166, pp. 1172-1174.
HEINRICH, BERND
   1974.   Thermoregulation by endothermic insects.   Science, vol. 185, pp. 747-756, illus.
JOHNSON, GEORGE B.
   1975.   Enzyme polymorphism and adaptation.   Stadler Symp. Genet., vol. 7, pp. 91-111.
LANGENHEIM, JEAN H.
   1962.   Vegetation and environmental patterns in the Crested Butte Area, Gunnison Co., Colorado.   Ecol. Monogr., vol. 32, pp. 249-285.
LEWONTIN, RICHARD C.
   1974.   The genetic basis of evolutionary change, 346 pp.   Columbia University Press, New York.
MAYR, ERNST
   1963.   Animal species and evolution, 797 pp.   Belknap Press (Harvard), Cambridge, Massachusetts.
WATT, WARD B.
   1968.   Adaptive significance of pigment polymorphisms in *Colias* butterflies, I: Variation of melanin pigment in relation to thermoregulation.   Evolution, vol. 22, pp. 437-458.
WATT, WARD B.; CHEW, FRANCES S.; SNYDER, L.R.G.; WATT, A. G.; and ROTHSCHILD, D. E.
   1977.   Population structure of pierid butterflies, I: Numbers and movements of some montane *Colias* species.   Oecologia, vol. 27, pp. 1-22.

National Geographic Society

WATT, WARD B.; HOCH, P. C.; and MILLS, S. G.
    1974.   Nectar resource use by *Colias* butterflies: Chemical and visual aspects.
        Oecologia, vol. 14, pp. 353-374.

WARD B. WATT

Biotic Communities of Hanging Gardens
in Southeastern Utah

Principal Investigators: Stanley L. Welsh, Brigham Young University, Provo, Utah, and Catherine A. Toft, University of California, Davis, California.

Grant No. 1109:   To study the hanging gardens of the Colorado Plateau.

The generalized outline of this presentation of hanging gardens in southeastern and southern Utah and northern Arizona is necessary to provide a basis for comparison of the many garden types, and for an understanding of the plant species in each of them and their phytogeographical relationships. More specific studies have been carried out in selected gardens near the confluence of the San Juan and Colorado canyons along Lake Powell, and in Arches and Canyonlands National Parks. This paper will provide a reference base for those studies.

The aspect of the low elevation lands in southeastern Utah is controlled by the color of the geological formations and alluvial deposits that are not obscured by the thin cover of vegetation. The region is arid, receiving only a few inches of precipitation during critical growing periods, or sometimes none at all. It is, in fact, a region where drought is normal, where periods between droughts are broken by intervals of precipitation of commonly much shorter duration than the drought intervals. The plants which grow in the region are adapted to the climate. In general, they are those that can withstand long periods of dessication under high temperatures, or those that can escape the extremes of temperature and drought condition by retreating into resistant propagules or by growing where water is more or less abundant.

Green vegetation is characteristic of mesophytic communities of plants that occur in canyon bottoms where conditions for growth are more moderate, and where water is available on a more or less continuous basis. This thin green line along the margins of streams and drainages does not extend much beyond the source of the water, stopping abruptly where drought becomes controlling. Smaller mesophytic communities with typical green aspect are known around the relatively small number of springs which occur in this vast region.

This paper is concerned, not with these riparian communities, but with the peculiar assemblages of biota which occur in wet habitats that occupy alcoves and grottos along sandstone cliffs in the great canyon system of the middle section of the Colorado River and some of its tributaries. These sites are additional exceptions, moist discontinuities, in an arid land where the only other truly green assemblages are those noted above. Because there is a tendency for these communities to cling to cliff faces, or to tumble cascade-like down slope, they have long been termed "hanging gardens." Both positionally and vegetationally, the gardens differ from the surrounding arid lands and from the riparian habitats of stream and river courses, although the gardens tend to be transitional outward with the former and downward with the latter.

Water, always at a premium in desert lands, is available in the gardens on a continuous, long-term basis for both plants and animals. The abundance of moisture allows for a substantially different climatic regimen to prevail in the gardens than in the desertic habitats only a short distance away. Additionally, the position of the gardens in alcoves or along cliff faces allows for further tempering of the environmental parameters within them; cliffs and alcoves offer protection in terms of obstructing the movement of drying winds and in decreasing the amount of light by shading the gardens for some portion of the day. Where alcoves are well developed there is a "house effect" wherein the sandstone acts as a great curved wall and the vegetation closes a portion of the other open wall. And, some gardens never receive direct sunlight, being in shade continually. As a result of protection received, the hanging gardens are buffered from the major factors which limit the growth of mesophytic communities in the arid lands about them.

Both people and animals have been attracted to hanging gardens throughout the existence of these spots of greenery on buff to red-colored sandstone. The first people to visit the gardens were Indians who inhabited the region for centuries prior to the advent of civilization as it is now known. The alcoves provided drinking water and cooling shade, and there the Indians stopped for refreshment, as indicated by shard and chert chippings both in and adjacent to some of the gardens.

While it is without a doubt that some of the hanging gardens were visited by many Caucasians prior to 1869, perhaps the earliest and best account of some of these intriguing sites is that of John Wesley Powell, who in his book *Canyons of the Colorado* (1895) published a diary of his 1869 trip through the canyons of the Green and Colorado rivers.

By late July 1869, Powell had entered a stretch of the canyon country which he named after the glenlike alcoves that marked the sandstone walls in some reaches of the canyon. His entry for August 3, 1969, includes a description of one of the glens—

Sometimes the rocks are overhanging; in other curves curious narrow glens are found. Through these we climb, by a narrow stairway, perhaps several hundred feet, to where a spring bursts out from under an overhanging cliff and where cottonwoods and willows stand, while along the curves of the brooklet oaks grow, and other rich vegetation is seen, in marked contrast to the general appearance of naked rock. We call these Oak Glens.

In the 1890's, Alice Eastwood (1896) collected plants from the moist garden-clad alcoves in the vicinity of Bluff, San Juan County, Utah. It seems probable that she was the first botanist of consequence to visit and to appreciate the uniqueness of this habitat type. She collected extensively in the gardens at Bluff, and stated that this habitat is "a boreal oasis in the midst of a Sonoran desert." Gregory (1938), in speaking of the canyons of the San Juan and of Butler Wash, noted that "the spring line at the base of the bare Bluff sandstone is marked by a bank of green vegetation formed by plant species that seem out of place in the present scheme of distribution."

Descriptions of some of the alcove gardens have been provided subsequently. Harrison et al. (1964) noted the tendency of stratification of plants in complex gardens in Arches National Monument, and Welsh and Moore (1968) described the transition in plants along an increasing moisture gradient from the dry habitats surrounding gardens to the moist areas within them. These latter observations concerned gardens in Natural Bridges National Monument and point to the variability of gardens, both in species composition and in organization.

It is the object of this study to describe and categorize the hanging gardens in southeastern Utah, using as classic examples those that occur along Glen Canyon near its confluence with the San Juan arm of Lake Powell. It is also of importance that the factors which control the unique features of gardens be discussed. Comparisons with other similar habitat types in other portions of the region and of the various geological formations in which they are found will be made as necessary. This will enable future workers to extrapolate from data presented herein. Additionally, several of the gardens included in this study are endangered by the rising waters of Lake Powell. Indeed, some of them are completely inundated and the information about them would have been lost forever had it not been for this study. And, now is the time when industrial development of the vast arid lands of southern Utah and portions of adjacent states will allow impacts on the remaining gardens at a level unknown in previous history. This vegetative type simulates the broad-leaved forests of the eastern United States, and might show symptoms of effluent damage before the native vegetation of adjacent xeric communities.

Geomorphology

Hanging gardens are intimately associated with the system of canyon development which has dominated the geomorphological processes in the Colorado drainage basin. Erosion of the stratified sedimentary rocks and the concurrent entrenchment of the river system into those strata have exposed the water-bearing sandstones. Cliffs form from the resistant sandstones and stand wall-like in stepwise fashion from the depths of the inner gorge to the margin of the canyon some distance away.

Due to a particular sequence of sedimentary strata, specifically that which consists of layers of sandstone alternating with formations of mudstone, siltstone, or shale, the canyon system as it now exists gains its character. Sandstone is more resistant to weathering processes than are the latter types of rock, and because of this, the sandstone cliffs are important in determination of shape and other features of canyons. Control of the retreat of sandstone cliffs is exerted by the softer formations which underlie them and by the presence of faults, joints, or bedding planes within the sandstones.

Hanging gardens are associated with sandstone formations, especially with those massive sandstones having impervious bedding planes or impervious strata beneath them. Water percolating through the porous sandstone contacts the impervious stratum, accumulates, and finally flows laterally along the impermeable member until the margin is surpassed or until the edge of the member is exposed along a sandstone cliff. When the latter case occurs, a drip- or spring-line is produced along which the hanging gardens are developed.

The development of a garden along a perched water table, as described above, tends to exert geomorphological control over alcove development and subsequent retreat of segments of the canyon wall. Undercutting along the bedding plane is hastened by the softening action of water and the dissolution of cementing materials. Further, growth of plants on the surface of the rock hastens the deterioration both by mechanical and chemical means. Roots and root hairs penetrate the surface, taking advantage of cracks and irregularities in the surface. Mild acids are produced which interact with cementing materials. The sandstone is weakened by the combination of factors described above and exfoliates in thin layers which fall free or which are pulled away from the cliff when attached plant assemblages become too heavy and overcome the support offered by the cliff face. Continuation of this dynamic process and a general weakening of the sandstone in moist sites results in larger slabs of rock falling free. Finally this results in the production of alcoves and grottos which sometimes bear a secondary sequence of alcoves within them.

Main Garden-Bearing Strata

Hanging gardens occur in sandstone formations or in sandstone members of a series of formations which range in age from Permian to Cretaceous as shown in the following tabulation:

Geologic Age	Strata	Region
Cretaceous	Wahweap	Kaiparowits
	Straight Cliffs	Kaiparowits
Jurassic	Entrada (various members)	Arches
		Kaiparowits
		Lake Powell
	Navajo	Bluff
		Canyonlands
		Lake Powell
Triassic	Navajo	Lake Powell
	Kayenta	Lake Powell
Permian	White Rim	Canyonlands
	Cedar Mesa	Natural Bridges

The extent and type of garden development varies from one formation to another, depending on the nature of the sandstone, its bedding planes and joint systems, and on the nature of the water which issues from it.

Wahweap Formation.   The Wahweap formation is composed of a thick sequence of mudstone and siltstone strata interbedded with sandstone lenses of varying thickness. Water-bearing members within the formation are few, and even these are seldom very productive. Exceptions occur at Four Mile Spring in the upper part of the formation on Four Mile Bench, and at other sites in Wahweap and Paradise (head of Last Chance) canyons on the western portion of the Kaiparowits Plateau. Few of these are definitely seep lines along hung water tables, and most of them cannot be classified as hanging gardens. Slight alcove development at Nipple Spring, near the north end of Nipple Bench, supports a small hanging garden. The sandstone lens associated with this latter spring is thin, and possibly this factor alone does not allow for formation of large alcoves. Those that are formed are produced in the shale or mudstone members below the more resistant sandstone. Water draining from the Wahweap is potable, but it is apparently heavily mineralized.

Straight Cliffs Formation.   Sandstone aquifers of varying thickness occur within the Straight Cliffs formation, especially in the drainages of Warm and

Last Chance creeks north of their junctures with Lake Powell. Alcoves in the sandstone strata are poorly formed, or they are lacking altogether. Water from the porous stone tends to weaken the underlying shaly layers and the overhanging edge of sandrock simulates alcove margins of better developed grottos. Quality of the water is poor, as indicated by encrustations of salts containing both sulphates and chlorides. Diversity of species in gardens on the Straight Cliffs aquifers is low, with only a few salt-tolerant species being common to them.

Entrada Formation. The Entrada formation consists of a complex sequence of strata which change in facies and in members from location to location in southeastern Utah. Mudstone, siltstone, and shaly members do not bear hanging gardens, and it is with the sandstones that this report is concerned. Bedded to cross-bedded sandstone members occur in various portions of the region and hanging gardens are to be found in both types of rock. However, gardens are best developed in the cross-bedded cliff-forming sandstones. For example, the gardens in Arches National Park are almost exclusively in massive sands of the Entrada. Smaller, less complex gardens are present along the bedded Escalante member of the Entrada in the Warm-Last Chance creeks vicinity on the north side of Lake Powell. Other gardens occur rarely in the Gunsight Butte member to the east of Wahweap in the Rock Creek vicinity. These latter gardens have been inundated by the waters of Lake Powell. The Cannonville member (situated between the Gunsight Butte and the Escalante member) and the Henrieville member (situated above the Escalante member or where that member is missing, directly on the Cannonville member) either lack hanging gardens or they are yet to be discovered.

The cross-bedded, massive sandstone members tend to produce gardens with attendant alcove formation and very complex assemblages of plants. Water quality in the gardens in Arches is potable, and evidently it is lacking in quantities of soluble salts. The quality of water in the massive sands of the Gunsight Butte member is not known, nor is it likely ever to be known.

Garden development in the bedded members is not so complex, and the gardens form in stepwise fashion down slope from the aquifers. Water quality in the Escalante member is saline, as indicated by salt encrustations along seep margins. Diversity of plant species apparently is limited, at least in part, by intolerance of some species to saline soils and water. Gardens of this type occur in Warm and Last Chance canyons along the arms of Lake Powell and northward.

Navajo Sandstone. There are numerous bedding planes in the massive cross-bedded matrix of the Navajo Sandstone. The bedding planes consist of more finely textured and more consistently cemented materials. Because of these characteristics, the bedding planes are impervious to the percolation of water, except where they are fractured by minor faults or by systems of joints. Where bedding planes bearing water are exposed, as along a cliff face, the moist surface provides the possibility for the growth of plants. Alcoves are formed by exfoliation of the stone along the bedding planes, both above and below. The alcoves can be of small to very large size, depending mainly on the size of the supply of water and on the thickness of the sandstone, especially that thickness above the bedding plane. Thus, the Navajo Sandstone, which tends to bear large quantities of water of high quality, satisfies all the conditions necessary for development of complex assemblages of plants in alcoves or grottos. Furthermore, the formation is situated atop the dense and more or less impermeable Kayenta Sandstone, which allows development of huge alcoves that can extend from the base to the top of the Navajo Sandstone. Taken together, these facts, along with the very large areal extent of the Navajo, combine to set this sandstone apart as the singly most important producer of alcoves and hanging gardens.

Kayenta Sandstone. The Kayenta Sandstone is bedded, very hard, and almost or quite impervious. Water penetrating to the surface of the Kayenta flows along it to the margin of the overlying formation. There the water flows down over the steplike surface typical of the margin of the Kayenta. The vegetative assemblage that develops there is seldom hanging, but rather it forms terrace gardens with plants that represent both hanging gardens and riparian habitats along streams in the region. Only rarely do alcoves form in the Kayenta, and these are almost always very small. Possibly because the Kayenta is so impermeable, the massive, cliff-forming Wingate Sandstone formation, which is capable of forming both arches and alcoves, is apparently almost completely lacking in even modest garden development. However, an exception exists in the huge alcove at Trail Canyon at Island-in-the-Sky in Canyonlands National Park. The alcove in the Wingate at that location is of monumental size, and while not strictly a hanging garden, it does support some characteristic hanging-garden plants.

White Rim Formation. The White Rim is a member of the Cutler group of formations, as is the Cedar Mesa, discussed below. The White Rim formation is important as an aquifer where it is exposed along the tributaries of the Green and Colorado rivers west and south of the Island-in-the-Sky portion of Canyonlands National Park. The formation is seldom more than a few tens of feet thick, and garden formation takes place along the contact with impervious strata of the Organ Rock member of the Cutler, which lies below it. Gardens are small, and species diversity is low. Most complex of the gardens in the White Rim are formed at the box ends of re-entries where structural considerations allow the existence of deeper, more consistently shaded alcoves of the Straight Cliffs type. The water quality is apparently poor, as indicated by accumulations of salts.

Cedar Mesa Sandstone.   Bedding planes in the massive, varicolored Cedar Mesa Sandstone are both numerous and thick. The lens-shaped bedding planes are of a type that would cause the formation of complex alcoves. The water supply in this formation, however, does not seem to be large, and few of the exposed planes are moist. Therefore, the gardens are limited both in size and in complexity. Water quality is not high, as judged from accumulations of sulphate and other salts in some of the seep areas. Hanging gardens are best developed in large nick-points in the re-entry tributaries of the White Canyon and Grand Gulch systems. Even at best, the gardens are less complex than those that occur in the massive Entrada and Navajo sandstones which the Cedar Mesa simulates.

Types of Gardens and Alcoves

Observations of numerous gardens in the several formations listed above indicate sequential patterns of development which lead to complexities in the plant communities and in the alcoves they inhabit. The processes are dynamic, and depend on the nature and size of both pervious and impervious rock strata, and on the amount and quality of water issuing from the rock, on the relationship of the moistened surface to the remainder of the canyon wall, and to the proximity to drainage channels both above and below the stratum. Additionally, such features as elevation and latitude seem to exert influence on the complexity and to some extent on the type of garden formed. The processes leading to alcove and concurrent garden formation can be terminated at any stage by the change of any of the components. Ultimate breakdown of the evolutionary sequence leads to a cyclic renewal as the margin of the formation is removed by erosion. Retreat of the canyon walls then exposes other moist bedding planes and the processes of garden and alcove formation begin again.

Apparently there are three main types of garden development. The first is the familiar alcove type that is formed in massive, usually cross-bedded sandstones. The second type is also formed in massive sandstones, but the alcove formation and probably the control of water supply is due to jointing that results in a window-blind type with a flat face-wall and a vaulted archlike alcove. The third type is associated with bedded sandstones such as the Kayenta, which ordinarily do not form cliffs with large vertical extent. In some places two or more of the types combine to form exceedingly compound gardens.

Although in attempting to categorize the various types of hanging gardens one runs the risk of oversimplification and also of disregarding the dynamic nature of the evolutionary sequence, it seems reasonable and necessary to arrange hanging gardens into a system of classification.

ALCOVE-TYPE GARDENS

Within the alcove developmental sequence there seem to be five reasonably well-defined stages. These are arranged in order from the most simple to the most complex or, ultimately, to the senescent climax that terminates garden formation.

Type I: Simple Dripline. The most elementary type of hanging garden is that which occurs on a nearly vertical rock face along the moist, exposed margin of a bedding plane. The number of bedding planes is sometimes greater than one, but the plants are of the same type regardless of the number of planes. The plants grow attached to the rock face; they are "clingers" and have roots that penetrate into minor crevices and other irregularities. Competition is low, because few species of vascular plants grow on these sites. Small plants grow appressed to the cliff surface, but larger ones tend to sag and finally to become pendulous, swinging free from the stone face. The diversity of species is very low, and individual plants are often widely spaced. The Type I gardens vary in size from small patches to elongate strips of great length along the sandstone walls.

Type II: Simple Alcove. The main difference between this kind of garden and the preceding Type I garden is the degree of alcove development. The face of the cliff has been undercut by erosion and a protective hanging wall (or roof wall) is developed to a greater or lesser degree. The moist surface is thus afforded more protection from dessication due to direct rays of the sun. The face-wall (or back-wall) of the alcove is rounded along both the vertical and horizontal axes. A foot-wall (or floor) is lacking and there is no place for the accumulation of colluvial detritus that falls from the alcove.

There are several modifications of Type II gardens which are referable here. Where the dripline, along which garden and alcove formation takes place, is elongate, a more or less uniform groove is formed by erosion, and a linear strip of vegetation results. When the sandstone is not uniform in hardness, then alcoves develop along the grooved Type II garden, and this leads to a row of minor alcoves along a single dripline. Gardens of the simple alcove type are ordinarily larger and they are more diverse floristically than are Type I gardens.

Type III: Classic Alcove. The alcoves of Type III gardens are well developed, with a sloping to nearly horizontal hanging wall and arched to flat face-wall. The foot-wall is sloping at an angle less than the angle of repose, and is covered by a vegetated colluvial slope. Driplines are exposed along the face-wall and/or buried beneath the colluvial slope. Clinging plants of Type I and II gardens occupy the face-wall, and in some cases the hanging wall as well. Vegetation on the colluvial slope consists of some of the clingers, and many additional plants that are rare or unknown in Type I or II gardens. The sloping foot-wall bears both species unique to hanging gardens and others that are merely fortuitous there, especially those that encroach from either the neighboring desertic shrubland or from the riparian habitats of the canyon bottoms. Diversity of species in the classic alcove type is great.

Type IV: Alcove-Plunge Basin.   Either there is a tendency for alcoves to form at nick-points, or else there is a tendency for alcoves to encroach on drainages from the plateau surfaces. In either event, the most complex gardens are those at nick-points where water pours from drainages over pour-points where it plunges to the sandstone at the base of the cliffs in front of Type III gardens. The sandstone is eroded by the falling water and eventually a plunge basin is formed. Alluvium in the water and other sandy detritus from the cliffs and garden accumulate in the sandstone basin. Falling water expends much of its energy when it strikes the basin, and when it leaves the basin it flows in a broad sheet that is incapable of carrying away the entire load of sediment. Thus, the lower margin of the plunge basin becomes a region of accumulation of silts and sands. In time this accumulation tends to form a dam which is occupied by other plants.

Thus, another mesophytic component, that of a vegetated margin of the plunge basin, is added to this garden type. The plunge basins are dry between storms in some gardens, but in others they are supplied by excess water produced from the driplines in the associated alcoves. This allows for a hydrophytic element and for the extension of the mesophytic community downstream to where it becomes indistinguishable from the riparian habitat.

Community development in Type IV gardens is more complex than in any other type. Diversity of species is great, even though size of Type IV gardens can vary from small to very large. For example, Step Garden in Driftwood Canyon has a vertical development of only about 20 feet, while that of Pool Garden in Reflection Canyon has a height of about 400 feet. The number of driplines in both Type III and IV gardens varies from one to many, and foot-wall detrital slopes vary from narrow and steep to very wide and only moderately angled. Compound gardens with alcoves within the main alcove are of Type III or IV origin, although some of them have lost the plunge basins by piracy of the next nick-point along the drainage below them.

Type V: Decadent Alcove. As alcoves continue to enlarge by loss of detrital colluvium, the angle of the colluvial slope lessens and becomes stable. The tendency for the weight of the wet vegetative slope to slip or slide from the foot-wall in early Type III gardens becomes less as the distance from the outer edge of the garden to the back of the face-wall increases. In very old alcoves (in terms of evolutionary sequence) the hanging wall is almost flat, vaulting of the arch is very low, and stability of the sandstone is lessened. In these cases there is a tendency for a huge slab of rock to break from the hanging wall. The slab falls onto the colluvial slope, burying it and effectively sealing the aquifer from further invasion by plant propagules. A few shrubs that are capable of surviving on little water and in low light persist in some Type V alcoves, but the evolution of the alcove as a garden type effectively ceases.

Dry alcoves of Type II and III mark the sandstone walls of canyons throughout the region. Some still contain thin moist lines, while others have evident dry bedding planes. It seems probable that these alcoves represent stages in garden and alcove development that were terminated in midevolution when the water supply was exhausted.

WINDOW-BLIND-TYPE GARDENS

Gardens of the window-blind type are those where the alcove breaks to a joint which results in the formation of a flat face-wall, and where water that results in garden formation is derived from along the fractures of the joint system. In some of the gardens of this type, such as the weeping walls in Zion National Park, the source of water is from above, and the entire face-wall is wet, providing a surface for clinging plants that are characteristic of driplines along face-walls in alcove-type gardens. In other gardens, the water source is at or near ground level, and the gardens are more characteristic of riparian habitats, although selected plants of the hanging garden type occur in some of them.

TERRACE-TYPE GARDENS

Aquifers consisting of bedded sandstones do not allow for development of classic alcoves. Rather, the gardens conform to the stepwise shape of the margin of the formation. Gardens of this terrace type occur in the Escalante member of the Entrada, and in the Kayenta. A huge garden of the terrace type is situated below a large Type V alcove at Death Camas garden in the first meander eastward along the San Juan arm of Lake Powell. Development is less complex than in the Alcove types, but diversity tends to be great due to incidence of both riparian and hanging garden plants.

Plant Communities

Plant communities in the various types of hanging gardens differ in composition and in kinds of species, not only along an apparent north-south climatic gradient and along an elevational gradient, but also from one garden to another in the same vicinity. Despite the variation, and the apparent disjunctions in patterns of distribution, it is possible to describe a generalized garden that will serve as a standard for comparison, and that will represent the culmination of parallel succession of both hanging gardens and alcoves.

GENERALIZED CLASSIC ALCOVE OR ALCOVE-PLUNGE BASIN GARDEN

The alcove features such a generalized garden will contain are as follows:

Hanging Wall. The hanging wall will be well developed, and it will provide shade for the alcove for some portion of the day. A pour-point will be at or near the midpoint of the upper lip of the alcove. The hanging wall will commonly be devoid of higher plants, but in some gardens this wall will be occupied by one or more species of clinging herbaceous plants, and rarely by dwarfed specimens of woody plants.

Face-Wall. The face-wall will be arching in both a horizontal and a vertical plane, or the face-wall will be almost or quite perpendicular. Plants of the clinging type will occupy the face-wall. They will be widely spaced plants of one or more of the following species: *Primula specuicola, Mimulus eastwoodiae, Adiantum capillus-veneris, Petrophytum caespitosum, Lobelia cardinalis; Mimulus cardinalis, Dodecatheon pulchellum,* and *Zigadenus vaginatus.* In some gardens the face-wall is the substrate for scattered specimens of grass and sedge species. Where the face-wall is wet, the surface is clothed by a mat of algae of many different kinds.

Foot-Wall. The foot-wall will be well below the angle of repose and will be covered by detrital colluvium. Where the colluvium is wet constantly it will be grown over with numerous plants. Some of the species of clinging plants will occur on the detrital slope, and many other species will occur there also. Some of the species that are important on the moist colluvium are: *Cirsium rydbergii, Calamagrostis scopulorum, Muhlenbergia curtifolia, M. andina, Carex bicolor* var. *androgyna, C. curatorum, Cladium californicum, Panicum lanuginosum, Zigadenus vaginatus, Habenaria sparsiflora, Epipactis gigantea, Primula specuicola, Celtis reticulata, Quercus gambelii, Q. undulata, Ostrya knowltonii, Cersis occidentalis, Rubus neomexicanus, Rhamnus betulaefolia, Juniperus osteosperma, Pinus edulis, Baccharis emoryi, Rhus trilobata, Shepherdia rotundifolia, Fraxinus anomala, Ephedra viridis, Toxicodendron rydbergii,* and *Yucca toftiae.*

There is a tendency for the vegetation on the foot-wall portion of the garden to be stratified. The more mesophytic plants crowd along the line of contact of the colluvial slope and the face-wall. Here the maidenhair fern *(Adiantum capillus-veneris)* forms a line of vegetation, with the orchid species and sometimes with others competing for space. The mat of marscescent leaf bases of the fern frequently forms a dense layer from which protrudes the green foliage of the current year. Down slope the ferns and other plants give way, except locally, to less mesophytic grasses, forbs, and low shrubs. Near the margin of the detrital slope, and sometimes in the slope proper, the vegetation gives way to tree and shrub species, which further protects the alcove from sun, wind, and rain. The species of trees and shrubs are those listed above, but sometimes there are species of willow *(Salix exigua* and *S. amygdaloides)* and the poplar or cottonwood *(Populus fremontii)* growing on wet colluvium near the margin of the garden.

Plunge Basin (Type IV Gardens).   The plunge basin will be unvegetated where the scouring effect of falling water sweeps alluvial material away. In deep plunge basins there tends to develop a complex community of a hydrophytic nature. Submersed aquatics such as *Zanichellia palustris* and numerous species of algae support an abundance of aquatic micro- and macro-organisms. Where the plunge basin is surrounded by an alluvial terrace, the terrace tends to be occupied by species that are characteristic of both colluvial slopes and of the stream margins in the region. Cattails grow in some plunge basins, especially those which are shallow, or which have a shallow margin. The alluvial terraces or bars associated with plunge basins support the following kinds of plants: *Eleocharis rostellata, Juncus* species, *Panicum lanuginosum, Cladium californicum, Imperata brevifolia, Andropogon glomeratus, Oenothera longissima, Elymus canadensis, Sorghastrum nutans, Panicum virgatum, Salix exigua, Baccharis emoryi, Quercus gambelii, Q. undulata, Cersis occidentalis, Celtis reticulata,* and *Populus fremontii.*

There is a tendency for plants to be aligned along a moisture gradient in and near plunge basins also. The most hydrophytic plants grow in the plunge basin where water is available always. *Panicum* and the *Juncus* species grow in the wet margin of the pond and on the wet terrace sands. The remainder of the species grow in drier portions of the sites where water is available, but not in such great supply. The plunge basin species are transitional down the drainage with the stream course, riparian vegetative type.

Stream Course.   The drainages below Types III and IV gardens vary from dry to wet, with some of them occupied by permanent streams. Density of vegetation and its diversity appears to depend on the gradient of the stream channel, on the accumulation or lack of alluvial terraces, on the nature of the water supply (whether single source or with multiple sources marginal to the main channel) and on the physical nature of the drainage channel. In some of the channels below gardens the vegetation is restricted mainly to pockets of alluvium or to crevices in the underlying sandstone, but in others the vegetative growth is lush, reminiscent of a streamside in the deciduous summer forest of the eastern United States. Most of the species listed above as being characteristic of the margins of plunge basins occur also within well-developed stream-course vegetation. Additional plants are present, too, including such climbers as *Parthenocissus inserta* and *Clematis ligusticifolia*. Both of these plants tend to festoon the woody vegetation along the courses, and sometimes they spread upwards onto the detrital slopes along the margins of the drainages.

It is likely that Powell (1895) had this kind of stream course and garden complex in mind when he described the "oak glen" of his 1869 trip through Glen Canyon.

Drier margins of the drainages and openings along them tend to support plants that are characteristic of the prairies and plains of the Great Plains grasslands. The more hydrophytic plants, such as *Eleocharis, Juncus, Panicum,* and *Muhlenbergia* give way up slope or along the dry side of the moisture gradient to *Panicum virgatum, Sorghastrum nutans, Andropogon hallii,* and *Schizachyrium scoparium*. The ubiquitous plant of moist sites, *Phragmites australis,* can be expected along with these plants or quite by itself as the most common grass of seeps throughout the region.

Where free moisture from gardens, seeps, or streams becomes limiting, the vegetation gives way at once to that characteristic semidesert shrub or grassland community typical for the region surrounding the gardens. Drought becomes the main controlling factor. Ecotonal differences between the mesophytic or hydrophytic communities of gardens, seeps, or streams can be very sharp, or they can be broadly transitional. In these latter instances, it is difficult to classify species clearly as being characteristic of gardens or of the semidesert shrub communities.

GEOGRAPHIC AFFINITIES OF HANGING GARDEN SPECIES

Despite the problems involved with determination of what is a species characteristic that makes it a hanging-garden plant, it seems that those most consistent plants of hanging gardens represent species with divers affinities. Mostly, the gardens appear to be relictual refugia, and represent portions of floras that are currently much better known elsewhere. The gardens represent microcosms of genera and species of prairies and plains grasses, of woody genera of deciduous summer forest trees and shrubs, of herbaceous plants of boreal affinities, and of still others with either Mexican or warm temperate affinities. F. E. Clements (1936), in his "The origin of the desert climax and climate," discussed the disjunctions in geographic distribution of numerous examples of southwestern American plants. Many of the plants which occur in hanging gardens and the mesophytic communities associated with them belong to those genera designated by Clements as "transads." They are those plants that exist on both sides of the desertic communities, and consequently must have extended through those communities in some portion of the previous history. While this appears to be true for some species, especially for the prairie grasses and the summer deciduous forest genera, it does not appear to be true for those plants with boreal affinities and only partially true for the plants of southern affinities. These latter two groups of plants seem to be the result of long-distance dispersal into habitats suitable for survival, reproduction, and dispersal rather than mere remnants of a once more widespread flora. It does not seem likely that the boreal elements were ever directly tied to a widespread flora.

Plants of those species with temperate east-west relationships flower and produce fruits within the time frame that is characteristic of temperate floras. Plants which represent more southern elements tend to produce flowers at seasons of the year that are in keeping with long warm periods. The boreal plant *Primula specuicola* flowers and produces fruit very early in the season, with some flowers opening in January, in the southern gardens, and with climax of flowering time being in March and April. The early appearance of flowers in this beautiful plant has led to the application of the name "Easter flower" to it in southeastern Utah.

Thus, the assemblage of plants which occupies hanging gardens appears to have been derived from many sources. The margins of gardens support such prairie representatives as *Andropogon hallii, Panicum virgatum, Sorghastrum nutans, Schizachyrium scoparium*, and *Andropogon barbinodis*. On the drier margins of the grassland type *Stipa comata, Oryzopsis hymenoides*, and *Hilaria jamesii* occur; there they are transitional into the mixed semidesert shrub-grassland. Seldom do all of these grasses exist in or adjacent to a single garden, but one or more are found associated with most of the better developed ones. All the genera of grasses noted above belong to transad examples, according to the interpretation of Clements.

Woody plants of genera characteristic of deciduous summer forests, and found mostly along stream courses in the southwestern United States, are likewise transads. They include *Baccharis emoryi, Berberis fendleri, Celtis reticulata, Cersis occidentalis, Clematis ligusticifolia, Ostrya knowltonii, Quercus gambelii, Q. undulata, Parthenosissus inserta, Populus fremontii, Rhamnus betulaefolia, Rhus trilobata, Rubus neomexicanus, Salix exigua* (and other *Salix* species),

Petrophytum caespitosum, Symphoricarpos longiflorus, and *Toxicodendron rydbergii.*
Plants with apparent boreal affinities include *Adiantum capillus-veneris, Carex bicolor* var. *androgyna, C. curatorum, Dodecatheon pauciflorum, Epipactis gigantea, Habenaria sparsiflora, Mimulus cardinalis, M. eastwoodiae,* and *Primula specuicola.* Probably it was with reference to this group of plants that Eastwood (1896) made the comparison of "a boreal oasis in a Sonoran Desert."

Species with uncertain but apparently Mexican and/or warm-temperate southeastern affinities include *Andropogon glomeratus, Cladium californicum, Cirsium rydbergii, Eleocharis rostellata, Imperata brevifolia, Panicum lanuginosum,* and *Zigadenus vaginatus.* Clements (1936) noted that both *Andropogon glomeratus* and *Imperata brevifolia* (as *I. hookeri*) are subtropical in nature and in derivation. *Cladium californicum* and *Zygadenus vaginatus* both have affinities to the south, especially toward the subtropics. Indeed, both of these entities have been treated by some previous authors as synonyms of other species; *C. californicum* as a synonym of *C. jamaicense* Crantz (Correll and Johnston, 1970), and *Z. vaginatus* as a synonym of *Z. volcanicus* Benth. (Preece, 1956). *Cladium jamaicense* is cited as being widespread in the Caribbean region and north to the Gulf States and Virginia, with a variety in China and Japan. The distribution of *Zigadenus volcanicus* is mainly Mexican. *Panicum lanuginosum* (including *P. huachucae* Ashe) is related to the Dichanthelium subgenus which is best represented in the eastern United States, and especially in the southeastern portion. The relationship of *Cirsium rydbergii* to other species in the southwest is apparently obscure, but the similarity to some southeastern taxa seem to provide the best alternative in searching for a near congener. *Eleocharis rostellata* is a plant of broad distribution in Mexico, Central America, and South America.

RARE OR UNUSUAL PLANTS

Most of the species belonging to the category described as clinging plants are common to many of the gardens. This is especially true of *Mimulus eastwoodiae* and *Primula specuicola.* These two plants are rare and unusual only outside of hanging gardens. Others of the clinging plants are widespread outside of gardens. The heleborine orchid *Epipactis gigantea* is an example of this latter type.

Plants that are truly rare or unusual in hanging gardens represent only a very small number of the relatively large number of species known from gardens. Rare plants are those which are known to occur in only a small number of the gardens. Some might prove, upon further investigation, to be more common than reported here. Examples of rare or unusual plants include curator sedge *(Carex curatorum),* sawgrass *(Cladium californicum),* Knowlton ironwood *(Ostrya knowltonii),* Fendler barberry *(Berberis fendleri),* New Mexico raspberry *(Rubus neomexicanus)*, satintail *(Imperata brevifolia)*, shooting star *(Dodecatheon pulchellum)*, scarlet monkey flower *(Mimulus cardinalis)*, and death camas *(Zigadenus vaginatus)*.

The sawgrass *Cladium californicum* is known from only a few localities along Lake Powell. Previously to the damming of the Colorado River, this sawgrass was collected in a small garden near the mouth of Kane Creek. That site is now covered by several hundred feet of water. The present study revealed the existence of sawgrass in Driftwood Canyon, Hidden Passage Canyon, and along Wilson Creek. Only the first site remains above the surface of Lake Powell, and that site in Driftwood Canyon is at or near the 3,700-foot maximum elevation of Lake Powell. It is hoped that the plant is present in sites not visited by the present investigators.

The Knowlton ironwood *Ostrya knowltonii* is a rare plant in Utah generally, with demonstrated distribution outside hanging gardens only in limited portions of Grand and San Juan counties. Even in hanging gardens the plant is not common; few are known to support this plant. Surprisingly, it is important in Ribbon Garden near the mouth of Ribbon Canyon, along the east side of Lake Powell. Knowlton ironwood is a codominant in that garden with western redbud and the New Mexico raspberry. Otherwise, the distribution of this ironwood in hanging gardens is limited to a small garden east from Hole-in-the-Rock and one in a tributary of the Escalante River.

A visit to Ribbon Garden in mid to late April is surprising because of the profusion of large white rosaceous flowers with white petals. The flowers are one to two inches broad, and stand out sharply with dark vegetation of the huge, shaded alcove. Flowers of most species in hanging gardens are small, but the exceptions rival the beauty of flowers from the region generally. Those of the New Mexico raspberry result in the display at Ribbon Garden. Of the many gardens investigated, only those near the mouth of Ribbon Canyon are known to support this plant, and this is the only known location for that raspberry in Utah.

Gardens at the base of the Navajo Sandstone, along the margins of Island-in-the-Sky, support stands of Fendler barberry *(Berberis fendleri)*. In Utah, these gardens are unique in occurring at so high an elevation (about 6,000 feet), and the alcoves are often obscured by stands of Douglas fir, Rocky Mountain maple, and other montane plants. They are the only known localities for *Berberis fendleri* in Utah.

The silky panicles of satintail *(Imperata brevifolia)* are not displayed until late summer. Possibly because of this fact, the grass has been collected in Utah only rarely. It is known from the mouth of Forbidding Canyon, at a site now submerged beneath Lake Powell, and at Wilson Creek along the San Juan

Arm of that lake. The latter site was inundated in the spring of 1974, and it now seems probable that *Imperata* is extinct in the Lake Powell region.

The weeping cliffs of Zion support both *Mimulis cardinalis* and *Dodecatheon pulchellum*. The former plant is not known from other hanging gardens in Utah; apparently this species is restricted in Utah to the wet walls in Zion National Park. The latter species, *D. pulchellum,* is present in some of the gardens in the Escalante member of the Entrada formation in Little Valley Canyon, and in one garden in the Escalante Canyon below its confluence with Lake Powell. The latter site was inundated in 1974. Both of these attractive plants occur as clingers on vertical walls and to some extent along the drainages below the gardens.

The particular phase of the death camas known from the hanging gardens, i.e., *Zigadenus vaginatus,* was first described from collections taken from Natural Bridges National Monument (as *Anticlea vaginata* Rydberg). Later, it was noted in the gardens in Arches National Park where it was mistaken for the similar, boreal *Z. elegans* Pursh. The distribution of *Z. vaginatus* in the gardens is disjunct. It is important in some gardens, both as a clinger and as a plant of the foot-wall vegetation, but nearby gardens will not support this plant at all. The reason for the disjunct pattern of distribution is not understood, but disjunctions are not uncommon among other species of clingers either. Those of this sheathed death camas are merely more pronounced.

PLANT SUCCESSION

Succession of plant communities in hanging gardens is tied to the sequence and type of alcove and garden development. Types I and II in the alcove sequence support mainly pioneer species which cling to the cliff face for a time, and then fall free. This is also true for the clinging plants on hanging and face walls in the classic Type III gardens. These plants are capable of reoccupying the bare wall which is exposed by the loss of mature plants of these same species.

Similar removal of vegetation and soil mantle, followed by a cyclic renewal, is to be observed in advanced Type II gardens and in terrace gardens where the plant assemblage and its soil mass slips from the foot-wall or down slope from one terrace to another. Clingers and crevice dwellers then accumulate organic materials and trap alluvium and colluvium. This allows the re-establishment of the complex plant communities on the detrital slopes or along the terraces.

Plant species which finally occupy the fully developed alcove type of gardens seem to depend on such factors as exposure, temperature, amount of water, and accessibility, within the limits of altitude and latitude. When these latter two features become important, then accessibility alone is not sufficient to determine which plants will dominate. Size of alcoves is apparently not directly controlling with regard to which plants occupy them, nor is size controlling with regard to complexity of development and succession, but rather, the size appears to be important in regard to species diversity. Diversity includes more than just number of species; it also includes the character of the unusual plants found in the gardens. For example, the huge alcove of Ribbon Garden contains some of the most unusual of all hanging-garden species. The reason for this diverse flora, however, might be attributed to other features besides size. Much additional work is indicated.

REFERENCES

CLEMENTS, F. E.
  1936.   The origin of the desert climax and climate. *In* "Essays in Geobotany in Honor of William Albert Setchell," 379 pp., T. H. Goodspeed, ed.   University of California Press, Berkeley.
CORRELL, D. S., and JOHNSTON, M. C.
  1970.   Manual of vascular plants, 1, 881 pp.   Texas Research Foundation, Renner, Texas.
EASTWOOD, A.
  1896.   Report of a collection of plants from San Juan County, in southeastern Utah.   Proc. California Acad. Sci., ser. 2, vol. 6, pp. 271-329.
GREGORY, H. E.
  1938.   The San Juan country: A geographic and geologic reconnaissance of southeastern Utah.   U. S. Geol. Surv. Prof. Pap. 188, 123 pp.
HARRISON, B. F.; WELSH, S. L.; and MOORE, G.
  1964.   Plants of Arches National Monument.   Brigham Young Univ. Sci. Bull., biol. ser., vol. 5, no. 1, 23 pp.
POWELL, JOHN W.
  1895.   Canyons of the Colorado, 400 pp.   Chautauqua-Century Press, Meadville, Pennsylvania.
PREECE, S. J.
  1956.   A cytotaxonomic study of the genus *Zigadenus* (Liliaceae), 167 pp.   Ph.D. dissertation, Washington State University.
WELSH, STANLEY L., and MOORE, G.
  1968.   Plants of Natural Bridges National Monument.   Proc. Utah Acad. Sci., Arts and Letters, vol. 45, pp. 220-248.

STANLEY L. WELSH
CATHERINE A. TOFT

Pyrotechnological Studies in Europe and the Middle East

Principal Investigator: Theodore A. Wertime, Research Associate in Archeology, Smithsonian Institution, Washington, D. C.

Grant No. 1123:   For a study of man's uses of fire to shape earths and metals.

From June 30 to July 26, 1973, I pursued further (under this grant, made the previous year) the subject of man's earliest industrial uses of fire. Members of this year's team were: Prof. Ronald Tylecote of the University of Newcastle-upon-Tyne in England (metallurgist and historian); Prof. James Muhly of the University of Pennsylvania (ancient historian, cuneiformist, and expert on ancient tin and bronze); Prof. George Rapp of the University of Minnesota (geologist, archeologist, and expert in neutron activation analysis); Prof. Alan McPherron of the University of Pittsburgh (archeologist-anthropologist, who has excavated Vinča-period Divostin in Yugoslavia); Vincent Pigott (graduate student in Iranian archeology at the University of Pennsylvania); and myself.

Our schedule of work was as follows:

1. July 1-3 inclusive.

Intensive investigation of the Rudna Glava mines of Yugoslavia dating to the Vinča period, or 4th-3d millennia B.C. This was undertaken with generous guidance from their excavator Borislav Jovanovič and help from the Yugoslav Institute of Archeology. We also inspected the Roman-age and Turkish-age smelting sites in the general vicinity of Bor. All team members were present.

2. July 9-14 inclusive.

Intensive study of the metallurgical artifacts excavated by John Caskey and John Coleman at Ayia Irini and Kephala on the Greek island of Kea. These excavations have been carried on since the early 1960's and have yielded evidences of late Neolithic smelting at Kephala and a rich treasure of crucibles, metallic artifacts, and metals, and pieces of presumably Cyprus oxide ingots at Ayia Irini. The metallurgy of Ayia Irini is associated with the flourishing of Kea as an entrepot in Minoan-Mycenean trade toward the mid-2d millennium B.C. Team members were Tylecote, Muhly, Pigott, and Wertime.

3. July 16-21 inclusive.

A survey of ancient smelting and archeological sites on Cyprus. Tylecote had already conducted extensive reconnaissance on Cyprus and plans to excavate there. We were aided by George Maliotis of the Hellenic Mining Company, by Yangos Hadjistavrinou, Director of Geological Services in Cyprus, and by Vassos Karagheorgis,

Director of Antiquities on Cyprus. Team members were Tylecote, Muhly, Pigott, and Wertime.

4. July 23-25 inclusive.

A tour of Alaca Hüyük and Bogazköy in Turkey to collect samples of copper-iron from the Kültepe period in the museum in Alaca Hüyük. Team members were Tylecote, Muhly, Pigott, Wertime, and Ahmet Coskun of the Turkish Minerals Organization, MTA. The team broke up at this point, Wertime and Pigott continuing on to Tehran.

5. July 26-August 8.

Conversations by Wertime and Pigott with Nasratollah Khadem, Director of the Geological Survey of Iran, and by Wertime with Saman Buravas, Director of the Department of Mineral Resources of Thailand concerning sources of tin for the ancient world.

The summer was successful beyond our largest expectations. The three goals of our work were:

1. To continue explorations in the earliest history of copper by studying the new evidences of Vinča period copper along the Danube; and to gain new vantage points on the issue of the independent invention of copper metallurgy on the Danube versus diffusion of copper technology up the Danube from the Black Sea.

2. To broaden our knowledge of the industrial phase of metallurgy and of the concomitant penetration of the sulphide zone of ores. This appears to have begun during the Kültepe period in Turkey (2000-1800 B.C.) when Assyrian merchants organized copper production in Anatolia and the tin trade from Assyria to Anatolia, yielding a new level of bronze production. This was the point to our returning to Alaca Hüyük for samples from the furnace of Maden Corüfü, which seems to have indicated both copper and iron production. From current studies of early Cyprus copper, it now appears that little malachite, cuprite, or azurite existed there and that sulphide ores were in use about 1600 B.C. Hence our week in Cyprus, with plans for Tylecote to undertake futher excavations there in the future.

3. To continue to comb all possible geologic sources for the supply of early tin. Our contacts were renewed with the Geological Survey of Iran, usefully in view of the new discovery of tin traces near Meshed; and were established with the Geological surveys of Thailand and Malaysia. Contacts with the U. S. Geological Survey were broadened.

Yugoslavia

With the excavations by Borislav Jovanović of the Yugoslav Institute of Archeology at Rudna Glava, near Bor, a new era began for the study of early metallurgy in Yugoslavia. Jovanović's findings were published in 1971 (see References). The excavations were equivalent to those carried on in the native copper deposits of the Old Copper Culture of the American Indians in the Great Lakes area of the United States; for Jovanović had found Vinča pottery of the 4th-3d millennium at the bottom of his shafts.

Simultaneously, Alan McPherron and D. Srejovič were excavating some 140 artifacts made of copper ores and copper metal at Divostin (McPherron and Srejovič, 1971). McPherron made some of these artifacts available to Tylecote and Rapp for analysis. Analogy could be found not only to the Old Copper Culture but also to the Braidwood finds at Cayönü Tepesi in Turkey, where one sees a transition from the making of copper artifacts from ores to the making of copper artifacts from metal.

With Jovanovič's and the Institute of Archeology's kind invitation to visit Rudna Glava, possibilities existed to join forces with Jovanovič and McPherron to launch a dual attack on early metallurgy there—to carry out analysis of McPherron's materials by both metallography and neutron activation of trace elements; to get samples of ores in the area of Bor for simultaneous fingerprinting through trace elements; and to compare the context of early copper metallurgy in Yugoslavia to that in southwestern Asia. We seized these possibilities. We hoped also to put to the test the thesis of C. Renfrew (1969) of the independent discovery of metallurgy along the Danube. This thesis has been taken over by Ruth Tringham in her *Hunters, Fishers, and Farmers of Eastern Europe* (1971). Indeed it preoccupied much of the Eighth Congress of Pre- and Proto-history in Belgrade during September, 1971.

I was one of the few persons to take issue with Renfrew at the conference in 1971 and have leveled a major attack on the thesis in two 1973 articles.

After a most pleasant trip by a gasoline-powered railroad car belonging to the mining company of Bor, we found ourselves at Bor on the evening of July 1. Jovanovič and the Archeological Institute in Bor had kindly laid on several jeeps, making it possible for us to begin our archeological reconnaissances at once on the morning of July 2.

The Bor area is a zone of green mountains and valleys, cradled in the elbow of the Danube near the Iron Gates and watered by small tributaries of the Danube. We discovered in our several days there that the metallurgical history of the Bor area is varied and ancient, beginning with the Danubian workings of the Vinča period at Rudna Glava, running through the Roman epoch at Kraku-Lu-Jordan, and continuing in the bloomeries of the Ottoman period, whose slag lies around Maidanpek. In my *Coming of the Age of Steel* (1962) I mention the invasion of Eastern Europe in the 13th century by German miners or "Sassi." The "Saška" River flows through Rudna Glava. The long and massive mining of both copper and iron ore is attested to by slags spread around the landscape.

The pits, as described by Jovanovič (1971), lie well above the village on the mountainside, at a site opened for small commercial mining of magnetite during the early 20th century. In fact, the area is a familiar one of a contact zone, with gossans protruding over a rather steep mountain slope intermingled with slightly marbled limestone. Gossans represent the oxidized iron (limonite-goethite) cap on a sulphide deposit of former pyrites and chalcopyrites. There was enough malachite and azurite about to persuade us that early metalworkers were attracted by blue and green outcrops denoting copper. They made their entry a few meters down into the limestone crevices for the chosen ores, leaving enough pottery, notched deer antlers, and 12-inch gabbro or diorite pounders to establish an unmistakable presence and provenance. The finds are an exciting landmark in the history of mining. Most such sites in Iran, Turkey, or Cyprus are empty of or denuded of their pottery. These seven small shafts were uncovered in the course of magnetite mining, their burden of artifacts fortunately still intact. Jovanovič has done a superb job of excavation.

The metallurgy remains to be established, of course. To jump from the working of native copper (a Stone Age technology) to the smelting of malachite and azurite was to enter a new domain of the technology of fire. The Bor area may have witnessed both this jump and that gradual step that took men through the isolated pockets of azurite and malachite into the sulphides such as chalcocite. The materials lay ready and waiting in the known strata of the earth; men needed only to be ready psychologically and technically.

The museum of Bor exhibits both the mining implements of Rudna Glava and copper axheads (nonsocketed) from the Zlotska cave. These axheads, which appear to be of cast copper (native coppers), fit within the rich tradition of axheads of the late Neolithic Danube. With proper trace-element and macro-element analysis, one could cross-reference them to the ores of the Bor area. This region offers fertile ground for the study of early copper metallurgy and particularly of the thesis that native copper was of such plentitude here and in Hungary that a tradition of casting objects of it arose, possibly coterminous with the advent of smelting. Jovanovič shares our belief that early metallurgists moved through the sequence of cold working native copper, then hot working and casting it, both as a prelude to proceeding fully into the intricacies of smelting the ore.

But there was more to be seen than the history of copper. Iron made its appearance around Bor during the 8th to 6th centuries B.C., presumably an importation from the Black Sea region, since one in Yugoslavia sees few of these interacting effects of copper-cum-lead-silver working that marked the coming of iron in southwestern Asia. We looked at a 6-inch iron dagger and razor blades and horse bits.

Kea (Greece)

Two significant metallurgical sites occupy the island of Kea, southeast of Athens and closest of the Cyclades to the mainland. One is Kephala, a promontory peninsula close to the northern tip of the island. On this windswept point, late Neolithic artisans (early 3d millennium) undertook the smelting of copper from its ores, judging from the remnant slag heap we found at a high point in the windward northeast slope of the peninsula. The slags seemed to have been broken up for their prills.

Excavated by John Coleman, Kephala has yielded a number of small grave and camp sites on limestone escarpments set cavelike on the lee side of the island. A number of small copper artifacts accompany these late Neolithic-early Helladic locations. This is possibly the earliest known extractive copper metallurgy in Greece. Copper artifacts at Kitsos Cave on the Lavrion Peninsula are older, but may be of native rather than smelted copper. We collected samples of both slags and coppers, which are undergoing analysis by Tylecote and Rapp.

In Early-Helladic II-B (19th century B.C.) the port of Ayia Irini was founded opposite the present village of Vourkari within the gloriously sheltered bay of Ayia Nikolao. Kephala may still have had operable settlements at that time. In the 15th century B.C., the buildup of Ayia Irini as a settlement and entrepot began, with strong evidences of Minoan influence. In the 14th century B.C., following an earthquake, Minoan influence had largely given way to Mycenaean. The temple goes back to mid or early Bronze Age. At this site John Caskey has excavated significant numbers of tilting crucibles encrusted with bronze and evidently used for the melting of Cyprus copper with tin to produce axes, arrowheads, chisels, and presumably other artifacts for the trade with Minoan-Mycenaean Greece.

The numerous bronze crucibles and crucible fragments are not the only evidences that persuaded Caskey to invite our team to Kea. Present in the debris were pieces of lead and slag that may attest to early smelting of lead on Kea. But of larger importance are pieces of oxide ingots, presumably from Cyprus and presumably the source of copper for the crucibles and cast bronze artifacts.

I shall not try to recapitulate the data from Kea, artifact by artifact, since this will enter a report prepared for publication with Caskey's materials in *Hesperia*. Suffice it to say that the Kea data, it is hoped, will enable us to see Minoan-Mycenaean metallurgy in a fuller light and to zero in on the difficult question of Aegean-Mediterranean trading patterns in copper and tin.

Cyprus

Surprisingly, no one has verified that the famous oxide bars or their predecessor (planoconvex) bars do actually stem from Cyprus. Most have been
found in Crete or mainland Greece (Euboia). Large ancient traditions of extractive metallurgy are associated with the Cyclades Islands, Crete, Euboia,
and Macedonia, coming to a focus in Lavrion lead. Copper ore is scarce in
Greece. Cyprus must be given futher scrutiny as an early source of copper.
One must look intensively at archeology and mining on Cyprus, as well as the
record in ancient tablets.

Fortunately, Tylecote for some seasons has been well ensconced in the
metallurgy of the old slag heaps of Cyprus, and Muhly has reviewed the extensive ancient written record about "Alashia" (Muhly, 1972). Their work, my
own work, and the more recent archeometallurgical studies of Arthur Steinberg and Frank Koucky (1974), give evidence that Cyprus began to blossom
metallurgically in the Middle Minoan period, or about the time Kea was expanding as an entrepot (1600 B.C.). The enlarging exploitation of Cyprus
copper was not a matter of linear growth of old technologies of smelting, but
appears to have brought men into the sulphide zone of ores—a major departure. No other conclusion can be reached from observation of the peculiar geology of the pillow lavas and gossans of Cyprus and Tylecote's studies of slags.
Despite an evident tradition of roasting, the slags in some cases (particularly
Ora) show unmelted pieces of golden-yellow sulphide. There are few oxides
and carbonates to be found in the pillow lavas of Cyprus. We therefore suspect
that its entry into the international metals market followed the development
of industrial smelting of sulphide ores in Anatolia of the Kültepe period (Wertime, 1973). As in Anatolia, the "industrial" phase of bronze metallurgy in
the Aegean also witnessed the appearance of new supplies of tin, first from the
East, later from as far away as Cornwall (Muhly, 1973).

In Cyprus, we owed much to George Maliotis, exploration geologist with
the Hellenic Mining Co., who escorted us for two days to old mining sites
about Kalavassós and Mitseró.

Our schedule was as follows:

July 18—Mazokampos, near Pareklisha, an area mainly of Roman slags.
   Plateías—an area of Phoenician slags.
   Spéle—a Roman-age site.
July 19—Mitseró—Roman-age slags.
   Kokkinóyia—The Phoenician slags at Kokkinóyia look exactly like gossans, and
   can be told only from the copper prills and charcoal inclusions within them. At
   Kokkinóyia, the Hellenic Mining Co. discovered through geophysical means an

ancient mine that was completely concealed, yet from which more than a million tons of ore had been removed.

Toumba Tou Skourou—Archeological site dug by Emily Vermeule. Little, if any, influence of metals.

July 20—Visited Cytechno company and saw collection of old mining artifacts— rope, baskets, wooden shovel, and a mining winch. All these were from Peristerka, in the Kambia mining area.

July 21—Kition—We visited the archeological site, noting the black slag near the temple wall.

Hala Sultan Tekke—We were given samples of slag by Paul Aström dating from 1200-1250 B.C. This much resembled the red slags at Kokkinóyia.

Athienou (Trude Dothan site)—This had no activity, so there was no chance of inspecting the copper finds.

In these intensive investigations it became clear that there was not entire agreement as to what constituted "Phoenician" slags and what "Roman" slags. I myself have contended that they are more properly "Minoan-Mycenae-an" and "Greek." But the more basic issue is the underlying technology of the Phoenician slags and their connection to the evolution of iron smelting. In most cases the Phoenician slags are so high in iron as to suggest a gossan flux (Steinberg and Koucky, 1974). The early finding of iron on Cyprus is not an accident; it is related to the smelting of sulphide copper; even as the early derivation of iron in Anatolia bears a connection to the advanced techniques of smelting both copper and lead to be found at Kültepe. The Iron Age is the capstone of precedent metallurgies and pyrotechnologies. These observations were our main reason for a brief return to Turkey.

I pay a word of tribute to Vassos Karageorghis, Director of Antiquities on Cyprus, for our last accomplishment. Through his generous collaboration we were able to take drilling samples from a variety of Cyprus's earliest copper artifacts, in the National Museum, for neutron activation by Rapp. Gradually the various studies of slags, artifacts, oxide bars, data on Aegean trade, and early tablets will place Cyprus in its proper and important niche in ancient metallurgy.

Turkey

Scientific study of metals thrives only as it has a base in interested humans. Once again we were indebted to Dr. Satrettin Alpan of the Turkish minerals exploration organization and Dr. Raci Temizer of the Hittite Museum in Ankara for our lightning foray to Alaca Hüyük to gather slags from the copper-smelting furnace of Maden Corüfü, now ensconced in the museum there.

I had twice visited the museum to see this small example of possibly pre-Hittite smelting practice, with its clay fragments, slags, and planoconvex copper ingots, fitting it almost surely into the role of supplying the *Karum* at Kültepe with copper. One anomaly, however, was arresting: a typical fayalite slag "bun" (4 inches in diameter) from an iron-smelting furnace. It is not coincidental that my analyses of Alaca swords show them to have been of terrestrial origin, even though the fayalite is of undetermined date. In any event, we now have iron- and copper-smelting relics in analysis for the light which they will throw on the Kültepe phase of early industrial copper metallurgy and especially of linkages in sulphide smelting of iron and copper.

Iran and Thailand

Thanks again go to Nasratollah Khadem, Director of the Iranian Geological Survey for the attention he has paid in recent years to the search for tin. Vossoughzadeh, his geologist and our teammate in the 1966 expedition to Tal-i-Iblis, has now discovered significant evidences of tin in the granites near Meshed. This region of the possibly pre-Cambrian shield of the eastern Dashte Lut was visited by the pyrotechnological team of 1968 but without serious sampling. It fits with the Greek geographer, Strabo's, description of one source of ancient tin.

In Iran and eastward I was traveling on USIA business. I did, however, stop in Bangkok to talk with Saman Buravas, Director of the General Department of Mineral Resources of Thailand about the tin deposits of Thailand and their relationship to Ban Chiang bronzes, which may now bear a 4th-millennium date. Thai tin has been fabricated into tin objects for 1,500 years. How it was drawn into copper smelting will presumably be explicated by University of Pennsylvania scholars now digging in Thailand. Buravas believed that any trade overland westward must have been by land routes rather than by sea routes, though the richest source, Phukit, lies on the Gulf of Siam.

REFERENCES

Jovanović, Borislav
    1971.   Metalurgija Eneolitsnoc Perioda Jugoslavije, 119 pp.   Archeological Institute, Belgrade.
McPherron, Alan, and Srejović, D.
    1971.   Early farming culture in central Serbia, 14 pp.   National Museum of Kragajevac.
Muhly, James D.
    1972.   The land of the Alashiya.   Pp. 201-219 *in* "Praktikon tou Protou Diethnous Kiprologicou Synedrion." Lefkosia, Cyprus.
    1973.   Tin trade routes of the Bronze Age.   Amer. Sci., vol. 61, pp. 404-413, illus.

RENFREW, C.
1969. The autonomy of the east European Copper Age. Proc. Prehist. Soc., vol. 35, pp. 12-47.
STEINBERG, ARTHUR, and KOUCKY, FRANK
1974. Preliminary study of ancient metallurgy and mining on Cyprus. Pp. 149-178 *in* "American Expeditions to Idalion, Cyprus." Supplement to the Bulletin of the American School of Oriental Research.
TRINGHAM, RUTH
1971. Hunters, fishers, and farmers in eastern Europe, 6000-3000 B.C., 240 pp. Hutchinson University, London.
WERTIME, THEODORE A.
1962. The coming of the age of steel, 330 pp. University of Chicago Press.
1973a. The beginnings of metallurgy: A new look. Science, vol. 182, pp. 875-887, illus.
1973b. Pyrotechnology: Man's first industrial uses of fire. Amer. Sci., vol. 61, pp. 67-682, illus.
1976. National Geographic Society–Smithsonian Institution pyrotechnological reconnaissance of Afghanistan, Iran, and Turkey, 1968. Nat. Geogr. Soc. Res. Rpts., 1968 Projects, pp. 483-492, illus.

THEODORE A. WERTIME

The Late-Postglacial Vegetational History of the Argolid Peninsula, Greece

Principal Investigators: Donald R. Whitehead and Mark C. Sheehan, Indiana University, Bloomington, Indiana.[1]

Grant Nos. 1114,   For a study of the postglacial environmental history of the
1191.   Argolid Peninsula, Greece.

Since 1959, the Hermionid, an eparchy of Argolis in eastern Peloponnesus, has been under archeological investigation, first by M. H. Jameson, then of the University of Pennsylvania, and subsequently by Jameson and T. W. Jacobsen of Indiana University. This cooperative investigation (known as the Argolid Exploration Project) has been responsible for extensive excavation and archeological surveying in the Hermionid. The two foci of the Project's work have been the classical town of Halieis, at Porto Kheli, and the Franchthi cave, about 9 kilometers northwest of Halieis, near the village of Koiladha (see fig. 1).

Remains at Halieis have been dated between about 2,750 years B.P. and 2,250 B.P. (Jameson, 1976), embracing nearly the entire duration of the Classical Greek civilization.

The sediments preserved in the Franchthi cave are unique in Greek archeology. Radiocarbon dates and artifact assemblages indicate that the deepest excavated levels are of Upper Paleolithic age; above them is a series of occupation levels spanning the Mesolithic and Neolithic in a nearly unbroken chronological sequence (Jacobsen, 1973, 1976).

Obviously both of these sites hold great potential for increasing our knowledge of the entire period of human occupation in the Aegean region. It was evident to Jameson and Jacobsen that the long sequence of prehistoric remains could be well understood only if seen in a broad ecological perspective. Most human actions, especially those of prehistoric humans, are, directly or indirectly, interactions with the natural environment. Environmental change influences the behavior of the human population; the human population may itself induce environmental change. To understand the human populations of the past, the archeologist must also understand the environments of the past.

---

[1] This report, in much greater detail, constitutes Dr. Sheehan's doctoral dissertation at Indiana University and is being published elsewhere.

To help fill this need, we were invited by the project's leaders to provide such paleoecological information as might be extracted from the fossil pollen record. In the summer of 1971 we took samples from the trenches excavated in the Franchthi cave and cores of sediment from the bay at Porto Kheli; we also cored three salt lagoons along the southern coast of the Hermionid. Because, as paleoecologists, we must work backward from systems we can observe and understand to systems whose natures we can only infer, we spent part of the summer of 1971 studying the contemporary vegetation of the Argolid and that of surrounding Peloponnesus. We surveyed the vegetation in many different life zones, from coastal brushland (maquis) to coniferous forests in the Taygetos Mountains. We collected moss polsters in several localities to analyze the modern pollen rain in the various vegetational zones.

Unfortunately, summer is a poor time for vegetational surveying in Greece. At this season the Mediterranean climate is dry and most of the herbaceous vegetation has died by the end of June. For this reason and because our opportunities to travel within Greece were limited by time and money, we left Greece with gaps in our understanding of the modern environment.

In 1972 we applied to the National Geographic Society for funds to carry on our research. Through grants 1114 and 1191 we were enabled to: (1) process the samples of cave, bay, and lagoon sediment we had collected in 1971, (2) process the surface samples taken for modern pollen rain analysis, (3) obtain radiocarbon dates for some of the sediment cores, and (4) return to the Hermionid in April 1973 to complete our modern vegetational survey and collect another, more wide-ranging suite of surface samples.

Results

The Surface Samples.   Twenty-three surface samples, from nine different vegetation types, were analyzed. Pollen concentrations were generally good. Although space does not permit a detailed presentation of the results of the analyses, some generalizations drawn from them and relevant to the discussion of the fossil pollen studies must be made.

Several important taxa seem to be underrepresented in the modern pollen rain; that is, they produce pollen in quantities smaller than one would expect, given their frequency in the vegetation. Fir, or *Abies,* pollen is present only in small quantities even when fir is the dominant tree in a forest. The same is true of *Juniperus,* which often dominates the shrubby hillside maquis but whose pollen is very seldom found in the surface samples. It has been known for some time that the *Pistacia*s (*P. lentiscus* and *P. terebinthus*) produce less than their proportion of pollen (Van Zeist, 1967). Our data show this to be

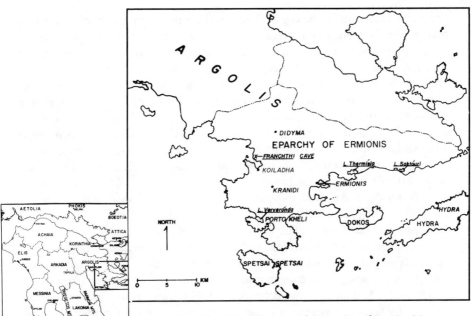

FIG. 1.   The Hermionid (Eparchy of Ermionis).

true except in the vicinity of *P. lentiscus* shrubs at anthesis. With increased distance from the pollen source, or with increased exposure to oxidative mechanisms, the *Pistacia* pollen concentration decreases sharply. Bottema (1974) observed that pollen of *Abies* and *Pistacia* as well as that of *Castanea* (chestnut) and *Acer* (maple) are poorly represented in the pollen rain. Our work confirms these findings. Bottema further observes that deciduous oak species, unlike evergreen oaks, do not flower readily as degraded (browsed or cut) shrubs. He therefore suggests that a degraded deciduous oak forest will produce a pollen spectrum poor in deciduous oak.

Not surprisingly, many taxa are overrepresented. From our results, pine seems to be very much overrepresented in the pollen rain. Samples from forests, both montane and coastal, in which pine is dominant nearly always yield over 90 percent pine pollen, although pine is seldom present at so high a percentage. Olive *(Olea)* produces and disperses pollen well and is overrepresented in some of our maquis samples. The liguliflorous composites (chickory, dandelion, etc.) are generally insect-pollinated species, but they appear in large quantities (up to 25 percent) in most of our maquis samples. They were never this abundant in the vegetation near the sampling sites. Bottema (1975) blames the frequent overrepresentation of this taxon in soil samples to the toughness of the grain, its unique sculpturing (hence easy identification), and to the activity of burrowing bees, which may collect it and bury it in the soil. He also observes (Bottema, 1974) that in deforested areas where the production of arboreal pollen is limited, values for the Liguliflorae, Tubuliflorae (thistles, sunflowers, etc.), and Umbelliferae (the parsley family) increase by default. The coastal maquis of Peloponnesus is a fine example of deforested land, and our surface samples from it always contained these taxa in quantity. In samples from forested regions, except the montane deciduous forest, we found little or no pollen of these herbs.

The results of our modern pollen rain analyses will be dealt with further in the discussion of fossil pollen data.

The Franchthi Cave. The pollen data from the Franchthi Cave (trench F/A) are illustrated in figures 2 and 3. Of the three trenches' samples, only F/A yielded pollen in quantities worth reporting. The samples upon which the figures are based were collected in the summer of 1973 by members of the project staff. The samples we collected in 1971 were mostly barren, despite our use of several different techniques for concentrating fossil pollen. The cultural phase designations were provided by T. W. Jacobsen.

At all levels sampled we encountered very low pollen concentrations.

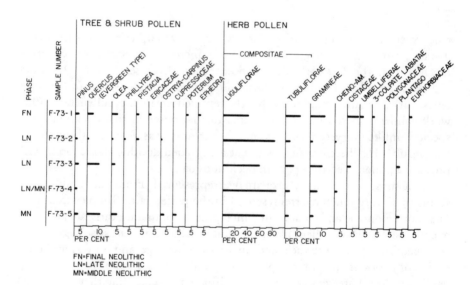

FIG. 2.　Pollen diagram, Franchthi Cave, part I: Middle Neolithic to final.

Only samples F-73-1, 2, and 4 (fig. 2) yielded more than 50 pollen grains after many hours of laborious microscopy. Sample F-73-2 is the only sample to yield over 100 grains (163). Below the Middle Neolithic pollen preservation as well as concentration presents problems; most grains are fragmented,

| | | | COMPOSITAE | | |
PHASE	SAMPLE NUMBER	PINUS	LIGULIFLORAE	TUBULIFLORAE	GRAMINEAE
MIDDLE NEOLITHIC	F-73-6		7	1	2
MIDDLE NEOLITHIC	F-73-7	1	1	1	
EARLY NEOLITHIC	F-73-8				
EARLY NEOLITHIC/ ACERAMIC NEOLITHIC	F-73-9		1	1	
ACERAMIC NEOLITHIC	F-73-10		4		
MESOLITHIC	F-73-11		5		
MESOLITHIC	F-73-12		1		
MESOLITHIC	F-73-13		3		

NUMBER OF GRAINS

FIG. 3.   Pollen diagram, Franchthi Cave, part II: Mesolithic to Middle Neolithic.

crushed, or corroded beyond recognition. Low concentrations of pollen and consequent low pollen sums mean that the samples may be statistically unreliable. In addition, poor preservation indicates that a second source of error must be evaluated: the selective destruction of fragile pollen types. Special care must therefore be taken in interpreting these older samples.

Franchthi samples F-73-1 through F-73-5 have several features in common. All are dominated by liguliflorous composite pollen; *Pinus* (pine), *Quercus* (oak), and *Olea* (olive) pollen are fairly consistently present, as are grains of tubuliflorous composites and the Gramineae (grasses). Several other taxa of herbs, shrubs, and trees are present, their diversity generally decreasing in the lower strata. The two samples least like the others in terms of their tree pollen percentages (especially pine and oak) are F-73-2 and F-73-4. But their differences may be easily explained on the basis of their extraordinarily high percentages of Liguliflorae pollen, which "swamp out" the values of the other taxa. In other words, if the Liguliflorae were excluded from the pollen sums at all levels, the percentages of the remaining taxa would be very similar throughout the diagram.

The modern pollen assemblages to which the F/A assemblages are most directly comparable are those from the coastal maquis. Except for their much higher percentages of Liguliflorae pollen and their slightly higher percentages of grass pollen, the F/A samples are nearly identical to modern samples taken only a few kilometers east of the cave. In general, the higher the pollen sum, the more maquis-like is the pollen assemblage.

It is nevertheless difficult to believe that the vegetation surrounding the cave was like it is now throughout the latter half of the Neolithic. Such a hypothesis requires that nearly total deforestation of the hillsides in the southern Argolid had been carried out by a presumably small population using stone tools, and that the vegetation was kept from regeneration by some means as effective as the widespread grazing practiced there now. Fire might have kept the vegetation degraded throughout this period, but no positive evidence for fires of the necessary extent and regularity is recorded in the literature.

The presence of *Olea* pollen in the F/A sediments is also problematical. It is probably not pollen of wild olive (J. Waddington, personal communication 1974), but no macrofossil remains of cultivated olives are found in the Neolithic sediments (Jacobsen, 1973). It seems improbable that olives were cultivated in the region but not incorporated into the cave sediments.

The most plausible solution to the problems presented by the pollen spectra in the F/A samples is that they have been contaminated with modern pollen. Although we were assured that during sampling all reasonable precautions were taken to avoid sampling contaminated sediments and to avoid their contamination after sampling, some unknown, unforeseen agency may have introduced modern pollen into the trench walls from which the samples were removed. Bottema's (1975) burrowing bees seem likely candidates.

Samples F-73-6 through F-73-11 contain very little pollen; nearly all of it is of the Liguliflorae type. These samples, too, may be contaminated with modern pollen, but in any case their pollen contents have been largely destroyed and they are of no palynological value.

The Bay and Lagoon Sediments: The Cores. Porto Kheli Bay was cored in two places: (1) on the north side, 25 meters west of the 1971 Halieis excavation diving platform, and (2) on the south side, over the ancient harbor of Halieis (see Jameson, 1969, map, p. 316). Three lagoons were cored: Limni Ververonda, L. Thermisia, and L. Saktouri (see fig. 1). Pairs of parallel, offset-overlapping cores were taken from several locations at each lagoon, and at the indicated locations at Porto Kheli Bay.

The L. Ververonda sediments were predominantly evaporites, undoubtedly oxidized. For this reason and because the upper levels of the cores may have been contaminated with spoils from a dredging operation in the lagoon, we elected not to process material from this site.

The longest pairs of cores from L. Thermisia and L. Saktouri and the pairs of cores from Porto Kheli Bay were prepared for pollen analysis following the KOH, HF, acetolysis procedure outlined by Faegri and Iversen (1964).

Radiocarbon Dates. Two radiocarbon dates for the L. Thermisia cores and one date each for the L. Saktouri and Porto Kheli Bay (north) cores were obtained from Teledyne-Isotopes, Inc. A fifth date, for the cores from the south side of Porto Kheli Bay, was obtained but was discarded because the cores from that site (only) were improperly stored and were probably contaminated with modern carbon.

The following tabulation lists the depths and radiocarbon data for the cores from each site:

Site	Maximum sediment depth (in meters)	Depth of dated segment (in meters)	Radiocarbon age (years B.P.)
L. Thermisia	5.35	1.95-2.28	1985±80
L. Thermisia	5.35	4.86-5.25	4375±90
L. Saktouri	2.65	2.00-2.31	2280±80
Porto Kheli Bay	1.80	1.40-1.75	3135±205

Because the lagoon sediments are poor in organic carbon, each date had to be based on 850 grams of sediment, equivalent to a 60-centimeter core segment. Rather than trying to accurately date so long a segment, we combined two 30-centimeter segments from identical depths in two adjacent cores and submitted them as a single sample. The dates are therefore average ages for the dated segments and must not be considered precise.

The Pollen Stratigraphy.   Because the cores from L. Thermisia contain the longest record, we chose the L. Thermisia pollen diagram to represent the pollen stratigraphy of the region. It is presented in figures 4 and 5. Pollen percentages at each level are based on a pollen sum that includes all tree, shrub, and herb pollen, but excludes spores and the pollen of aquatic plants. Data are presented in histogram form to indicate which levels had adequate pollen sums (more than 50 arboreal pollen grains—portrayed by solid bars), and which did not (dashed bars). Asterisks in the *Pinus* and Liguliflorae columns denote levels whose pollen data are derived from counts of two samples, one from each core, taken from exactly the same depth. Data for all other levels are based on a single sample from one or the other of the cores. The top of the sediment column at L. Thermisia was 0.57 meter below the surface of the water in the lagoon.

Pollen diagrams are normally divided into pollen assemblage zones, each zone usually being comprised of series of pollen spectra characteristic of a par-

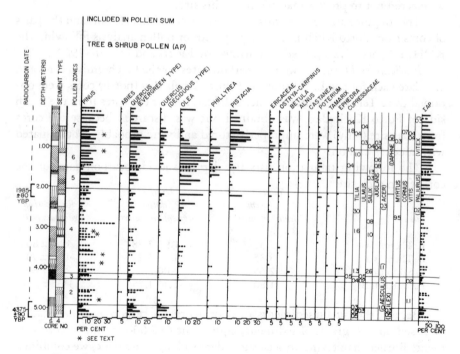

FIG. 4.   Pollen diagram, Limni Thermisia, part I: Arboreal pollen.

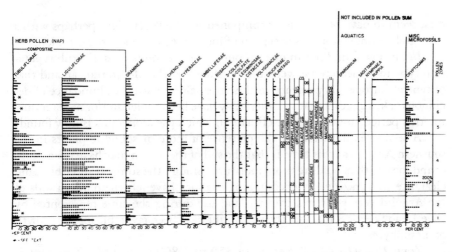

FIG. 5.   Pollen diagram, Limni Thermisia, part II: Herb pollen, etc.

ticular vegetational complex or of a vegetational event of interest to the investigator. We have divided the L. Thermisia diagram into seven zones, some of the boundaries delimiting pollen assemblages and some of them separating levels with poorly preserved and/or very sparse pollen (zones 2 and 4) from the levels richer in remains. These zones are intended only as guidelines for discussion of the pollen stratigraphy and not for comparison with pollen zones described in diagrams published by other authors.

Zone 1 (5.35 to 4.92 meters) (4,550 to 4,350 years B.P.). This zone correlates chronologically with part of the Early Helladic period of the Greek Bronze Age. It contains relatively large percentages of deciduous oak pollen as well as pollen of *Ilex* (holly) and such deciduous tree taxa as *Tilia* (linden), *Ulmus* (elm), *Betula* (birch), and others. Only two grains of olive pollen were found in the zone. The herb flora, dominated by the liguliflorous composites, is abundant (cf. the ΣAP column) and diverse, but the taxa are all typical of maquis vegetation (though not limited to it).

Except for the quantity of deciduous oak pollen and that of holly and the deciduous trees, the pollen spectra in this zone are much like those from the modern coastal maquis. This need not imply, however, that the vegetation of this period was maquis-like. Turrill (1929) describes the maquis type of "brushwood" vegetation as comprised of the understory species from the common forest types of the eumediterranean vegetation belt.

The low values for pine pollen in this zone suggest that pine was not abundant in the area at this time. Rather, the oaks, especially deciduous species, seem to have been a major component of the vegetation, perhaps with a maquis-like understory, as is typical of modern pine woods in the region.

Ilex is now found not in maquis but in the pseudomaquis, a scrub vegetation type intermediate between the brushland of the Mediterranean and that of central Europe. Its presence in this zone, along with the abundance of deciduous oak, suggests that summers may have been cooler and/or moister during this period, much like the climate in which pseudomaquis is now found.

A second explanation for the presence of more mesophytic plants in the southern Argolid at this time is that the soil of the region may have been deeper and looser, thus holding more moisture through the summer months. Land clearance and grazing, by encouraging erosion, have left the modern soils of the Argolid very poor and thin. If land use during the time represented by zone 1 had been less intense, the soil might have been favorable for the growth of mesophytes.

Zone 2 (4.92 to 4.30 meters) (4,350 to 3,800 years B.P.). This zone is characterized by very low pollen concentrations. Small pollen sums and the probability of selective deterioration of some pollen types make the pollen data from zone 2 very unreliable.

There are several possible reasons for the sudden drop in pollen concentrations seen in Zone 2: (1) An increased rate of sedimentation would "dilute" the pollen; an increase in sedimentation could be caused by land clearance or altered trophic status. (2) Because of sea level fluctuations (probably really tectonic activity) (Flemming, 1968, 1969), the water level in the lagoon may have gone down, exposing the sediments to oxidation down to the level of the water table: presumably what is now the top of zone 1. There may well have been any number of water level oscillations during the zone 2 period. If this explanation is valid, there could be significant depositional breaks in the column. Such breaks would, or course, invalidate the age extrapolations based on the two rather widely separated radiocarbon dates (themselves based on samples that may have contained gaps). And (3) shallow water may have permitted wave action to mix the upper layers of sediment with oxygenated water, exposing recently precipitated pollen to the degradation common in aerobic environments. This explanation need not imply any fluctuation in the sedimentation rate.

Sedimentological studies, not yet performed on the lagoon sediments, might provide some insight into the causes of the poor pollen preservation in this zone and others.

Zone 3 (4.30 to 4.15 meters) (3,800 to 3,650 years B.P.). This zone contains sediments deposited during part of the Middle Helladic, a period during which Crete began to rise as a major power in the Aegean. Its pollen is 5 to 10 times as concentrated as that of zone 2.

The arboreal pollen spectrum, dominated by pine and oak (mostly evergreen), contains some olive, elm, and linden. It also contains pollen of the Cupressaceae (the cypress/juniper family), important plants in the modern maquis, but drastically underrepresented in the pollen rain.

Grasses and chenopods, two of the dominant herb types, are typical plants of disturbed ground. Grasses are most common as weeds of arable and waste land; the chenopods are common weeds, but they are also often halophytes, growing in dry and/or salty habitats. The Cyperaceae (sedges), the third dominant herb type, are seldom weeds, being most common in aquatic or salt-marsh habitats (Turrill, 1929).

An explanation for the abundance of these herb taxa may be that the previous zone (2) represents, as we have suggested, a time of low water level in the lagoon. The exposed muds, very salty until leached by fresh water, may have supported a large population of grasses and chenopods, one which diminished as the water level rose again during zone 3. As the habitat surrounding the lagoon changed from dry to moist it may have been colonized by the more hydrophyllic sedges. Further change in the values of these herb types may have occurred above zone 3, but if so no reliable pollen record of it survives.

The arboreal pollen record in this zone, though its percentages are swamped out by the abundant herb pollen, seems to indicate a pine and evergreen oak community with little deciduous oak (perhaps attributable to grazing, a practice which prevents deciduous oak, but not evergreen oak from flowering) (Bottema, 1974). Except for evidence of a few more deciduous taxa than occur in the modern samples, the arboreal vegetation during this period may have been much like that of today.

Zone 4 (4.15 to 2.04 meters) (3,650 to 1,950 years B.P.). This zone is characterized by sparse pollen, although scattered levels have moderate to high pollen sums. It is by far the longest of the seven zones, embracing all of Minoan times, the Greek Dark Ages, and virtually all of the Greek Classical Age.

The few levels with higher pollen concentrations have pollen spectra closely resembling those of modern coastal maquis, except that pine is less abundant and *Olea* is more common (especially in the upper levels). Pine percentages in these samples appear still lower than those in previous zones if the swamping-out of pine values by the local herbs in zone 3 is considered. Among the reliable samples the values for olive pollen appear to increase from the bottom to the top of the zone. *Pistacia,* a common maquis shrub, also becomes generally more abundant toward the top of the zone. The top two reliable samples of zone 4 are the first in the core whose arboreal pollen sums exceed 50 percent.

From what we can confidently extract from zone 4, it appears that toward the end of the "Golden Age" of Greece, olive cultivation became increasingly important, probably following major clearing of the pine forests of the previous centuries. *Pistacia*'s general increase through the zone is, as are the increases of the other arboreal types, at the expense of the herb flora, perhaps because less land was allowed to go to weeds, perhaps because cultivation shifted from field to orchard crops.

Zone 5 (2.04 to 1.52 meters) (1,950 to 1,550 years B.P.). Sediments in this zone were deposited during part of the time that Greece was under Byzantine rule. The pollen record shows a pair of surges in the pine pollen values, one at the bottom and one at the top of the zone. Between them is a brief peak in olive percentages, paralleled by a minor peak of evergreen oak. Among the herbs, the liguliflorous composites are dominant.

Pine forests seem to have been a major part of the vegetation early in this period, perhaps having regenerated somewhat in the latter, poorly documented part of zone 4 (where pine is virtually the only arboreal pollen type encountered). Later in the period, as pine values decrease, olive becomes more important, though it gives way again to pine-dominated spectra above. The sharp drop in olive values at the end of zone 5 and the sharp increase in pine percentages suggest that once more the pine forests were allowed to regenerate. It is possible that one or the other of the pine forest regenerations in this period is attributable to the occupation, by Slavic "barbarians," of Peloponnesus between 1,320 and 1,340 years B.P., during which time the region is said to have been uninhabitable by agrarian people. Such an interpretation would require an offsetting of the radiocarbon time scale by only 200 to 250 years.

The pollen data from Limni Saktouri (figs. 6 and 7) become relevant in zone 5, the first entire zone identifiable in that lagoon's sediments. Pine values there are greatest lower in the zone, decrease above, but do not rebound toward the top as at L. Thermisia; nor do olive values fall dramatically at the top of the zone as they do at L. Thermisia. *Phillyrea,* an evergreen shrub of the olive family, is abundant at both the bottom and the top of the zone in the L. Saktouri cores, while it is abundant only at the top of the zone at L. Thermisia.

The radiocarbon date for L. Saktouri brackets the zone 4/5 boundary with an age of 2,280 years B.P., putting the bottom of zone 5 at about 2,300 years B.P., 350 years older than at L. Thermisia, 870 years before the Slavic occupation.

These data suggest that the pine regeneration recorded at L. Thermisia

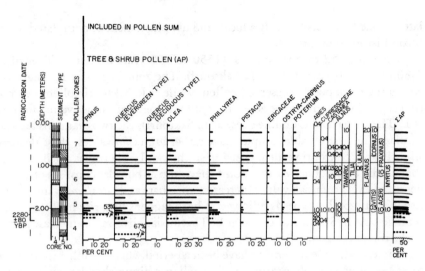

FIG. ·6. Pollen diagram, Limni Saktouri, part I: Arboreal pollen, cores 4 and 5.

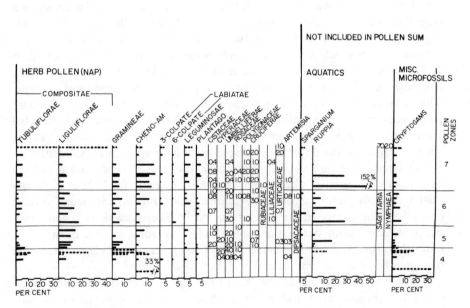

FIG. 7. Pollen diagram, Limni Saktouri, part II: Herb pollen, etc.

late in zone 5 is probably only a local land use phenomenon, not related to any broad historical events.

Zone 6 (1.52 to 0.94 meters) (1550 to 950 years B.P. at L. Thermisia; 1,800 to 1,000 years B.P. at L. Saktouri). The zone begins at L. Thermisia with a region of poorly preserved pollen, while at L. Saktouri pollen preservation is good throughout the zone. Except for somewhat higher values for pine at L. Thermisia (about double those at L. Saktouri), the two diagrams are very similar. The first reliable samples have rather high *Olea* values; these decrease slightly at L. Saktouri while increasing slightly at L. Thermisia until just past the middle of the zone. At this point they drop at both lagoons. As olive values drop, evergreen-oak values increase somewhat, as do *Phillyrea* values. This rise in shrub pollen types is followed at both lagoons by a rise in *Pistacia* percentages. At L. Saktouri, but not at L. Thermisia, olive values increase briefly at the top of the zone.

In general, zone 6 seems to have been a period when the inhabitants came to rely heavily upon olive farming. This reliance diminished later in the period. As olive became less important it was replaced by evergreen shrubs typical of the modern maquis.

Zone 7 (0.94 to 0 meter) (950 to 0 years B.P.). This zone begins at L. Saktouri with a sharp increase in pine pollen values and a sharp drop in olive values. Pine values increase slightly at the base of the zone at L. Thermisia and olive values are very low. Evergreen oak and *Pistacia* values at both sites are high at the beginning of the zone, but while oak values decline later, *Pistacia* increases rather steadily in the first third of the zone. After reaching a peak at L. Thermisia, *Pistacia* values decline steadily toward the top of the zone. At L. Saktouri they oscillate and finally disappear in the uppermost sample. Throughout the lower portion of the zone olive values decrease steadily at both sites. Past midzone the olive values at L. Saktouri increase and then fall abruptly in the uppermost (unreliable) sample. At L. Thermisia olive values are very low until the uppermost sample in which they increase suddenly.

During this period the important olive orchards of zone 6 seem to have been almost completely abandoned until very recently (at least at L. Thermisia). Maquis plants, especially evergreen oaks and *Pistacia,* seem to have taken over dominance in the vegetation. At L. Thermisia there is some evidence of regeneration of the pine forests late in the zone, but the most recent sample suggests that the regeneration has been reversed and olive cultivation has again become very important.

Pollen concentrations in the cores from Porto Kheli Bay are alternately very low and rather high. Except for this fluctuation in concentration the pollen stratigraphy from the north side of the bay is almost uniform. No pollen zones can be delimited within the cores. Pine values are generally very high (50-70 percent). Olive pollen values are smaller below and somewhat greater above. *Pistacia* values are uniform. An explanation for the uniformity of the pollen values at this site, despite its rather old radiocarbon date, might be the activity of tube-dwelling worms or other marine animals that might have reworked the sediments after they were deposited, effectively homogenizing them. The fossilized carbonate tube of such a worm was found in one of the cores from the north side of the bay at a depth of about 1.4 meters. Wave action at times of low sea level stands and possible dredging activities are alternate explanations for the homogeneity of the pollen stratigraphy.

The south side of the bay yielded sediments with slightly more variability. The lower meter of the 2-meter cores has low pine values and high evergreen oak, *Olea,* and Ericaceae (heath family) values. The upper meter has much higher pine values. It has abruptly lowered oak, olive, and Ericaceae values, all of which increase again toward the top of the cores. *Pistacia,* too, becomes relatively more abundant near the top of the cores while olive values drop in the uppermost reliable sample.

The one meter point in the Porto Kheli Bay (south) cores is then probably the equivalent of the zone 6/7 boundary in the lagoon cores and may, by analogy to them, be dated at about 1,000 years B.P.

Conclusions

The Franchthi Cave samples are considered too poor in pollen to provide information on past environments. Further work may reveal special microenvironments within the cave sediments in which pollen is well preserved, but no such results have yet been achieved.

The pollen record preserved in the lagoon and bay sediments suggests the following vegetational history.

Zone 1, 4,550-4,350 years B.P. Mixed oak forest with some pine, linden, elm, and holly implies possibly moister and cooler summers than at present, and/or greater retention of soil moisture, perhaps because of less intensive land use (deforestation and grazing).

Zone 2, 4,350 to 3,800 years B.P. Conditions were not suitable for pollen preservation.

Zone 3, 3,800 to 3,650 years B.P. Forests were of pine and evergreen oak; olive agriculture began to be important. The herb flora is dominated by grasses, sedges, and the Chenopodiaceae-Amaranthaceae group.

Zone 4, 3,650 to 1,950 years B.P. Conditions were poor for pollen preservation. In the scattered reliable samples, pine forest seems scarcer than in previous zones. Olive agriculture increased in importance, especially later in the zone. Scrub vegetation similar to the modern maquis developed.

Zone 5, 1,950 to 1,550 years B.P. Pine forests regenerate somewhat, are cleared and again regenerate (at least at L. Thermisia). Destruction of the pine forest is accompanied by expansion of olive cultivation.

Zone 6, 1,550 to 1,000 years B.P. Olive cultivation reaches a peak accompanied by the destruction of pine forest and maquis.

Zone 7, 1,000 to 0 years B.P. Olive cultivation is abruptly curtailed but pine forest does not regenerate immediately as in zone 5. Instead, maquis expands until midzone when pine forest is briefly and locally reestablished. Later, olive farming is reestablished in the region.

REFERENCES

BOTTEMA, S.
  1974.   Late Quaternary vegetation history of northwestern Greece.   Dissertation, Rijksuniversiteit te Groningen, Netherlands.
  1975.   The interpretation of pollen spectra from prehistoric settlements (with special reference to Liguliflorae).   Palaehistoria, vol. 17, pp. 18-35.
FAEGRI, KNUT, and IVERSEN, J.
  1964.   Textbook of pollen analysis, 295 pp.   Hafner Publishing Co., New York.
FLEMMING, NICHOLAS C.
  1968.   Holocene earth movements and eustatic sea level change in the Peloponnese.   Nature, vol. 217, pp. 1031-1032.
  1969.   Evidence for eustatic change of sea level and earth movements in the western Mediterranean during the last 2,000 years.   Geol. Soc. Amer. Spec. Pap. no. 109, 125 pp.
JACOBSEN, THOMAS W.
  1973.   Excavation in the Franchthi Cave, 1969-1971, pt. 1.   Hesperia, vol. 42, pp. 45-88.
  1976.   17,000 years of Greek prehistory.   Sci. Amer., vol. 234, no. 6, pp. 76-87, illus.
JAMESON, MICHAEL H.
  1969.   Excavations at Porto Kheli and vicinity, preliminary report, I: 1962-1968. Hesperia, vol. 38, pp. 311-381.
  1976.   A Greek countryside: Reports from the Argolid Exploration Project. Expedition, vol. 19, pp. 2-4.
TURRILL, WILLIAM B.
  1929.   The plant-life of the Balkan Peninsula, 490 pp. illus.   Oxford University Press.
VAN ZEIST, W.
  1967.   Late Quaternary vegetation history of western Iran.   Rev. Paleobot. Palynol., vol. 2, pp. 301-311.

MARK C. SHEEHAN
DONALD R. WHITEHEAD

Expedition to the Center City

Principal Investigator: William H. Whyte, Associate, American Conservation Association, New York City, New York.

Grant Nos. 1064, 1140. For a study of the way people use the streets and open spaces of the city.

In 1972 a small group of observers began studying the way inhabitants of a densely crowded island used their open spaces. We had been given a grant by the National Geographic Society's Committee for Research and Exploration and I was registered, to my great pleasure, as "Expedition Leader." Since the island was Manhattan the term might seem inappropriate, but it was not. For many years anthropologists had used the techniques of direct observation to study far-off peoples in far-off places. Rarely, however, had the techniques been applied to the study of people in cities. There had been much research on crowding, high density behavior, and the like, but most of it was vicarious; survey research on questionnaire responses, studies of animals in analogous situations—much of it valuable, to be sure, but with the researcher once or twice removed from that which he was studying.

We thought that firsthand observation of the people themselves—in their everyday life—might be of benefit. We started with parks and playgrounds and such informal recreation areas as city blocks and street corners. We used a variety of tools. With time-lapse cameras mounted on windowsills or rooftops we tracked round-the-clock patterns of key areas. For closer study of peoples' movements, the choreography of street corners, for example, we used telephoto lenses and slow-motion photography. But the most useful tool by far was a notebook and pencil. Observing, and mapping, what is going on hour after hour can be very tedious but if you stick at it you are bound to see what you never did before.

So it was with playgrounds. The conventional image is of jammed playgrounds. We saw jammed playgrounds. The more we observed, however, the more we were struck by the relative absence of people. More playgrounds were empty than full, and they included playgrounds of all types. Many of the empty places, furthermore, were in areas that ranked as high density by the usual people/space indices. Such physical measurements can be very misleading. Social factors are more difficult to quantify, and are easily overlooked. But they are far more important.

It is often assumed that children play in the streets for lack of playground space. We found that they played in the streets because they liked to. And often with very good reason. The East Harlem block we studied provided an environment with all the basics of a fine recreation area. The street itself was the playground; the adjoining stoops and fire escapes were a sitting and watching area highly functional for the mothers and the older people; the chairs and makeshift game tables in front of the social clubs functioned well as the men's preserve. The block had its problems but as an example of urban space use it had more lessons in it than any playground we studied. (One of the problems, dope, caused us some methodological difficulties. We had mounted a time-lapse camera to study the social life on the stoops and fire escapes. Before long it became apparent that we were also recording unusual activity going on around a cellar entrance, with big Cadillacs bearing out-of-state licenses stopping there periodically. We concluded the surveillance.)

This was a high density block. By contrast, some other blocks in the area had considerably lower densities, and more problems. There would be very overcrowded tenements in one part, empty lots and burnt-out buildings in another. Overall, there were not enough people to sustain the network of small stores and activities that give cohesion to a neighborhood.

The most challenging space problem in the city, it was becoming clear, was not over-use but under-use—inefficient use. And as we moved closer to the core, the more pronounced was the imbalance.

We were especially interested in the office building plazas of the central business districts. Since 1961 the city had been allowing builders to go up higher if they would provide plazas at the base. Many acres of high cost open space were provided by this stimulus. Unfortunately, most of the space remained surprisingly empty. A few plazas were very well used; most were near empty. At lunch hour on a beautiful day, the number of people to be found sitting on the plazas averaged four per thousand square feet of open space.

This was an appalling under-use of space for so populous an area. We put the matter to the City Planning Commission. We would study the plazas to determine the principal denominators of the successful ones, of the unsuccessful ones, and propose guidelines for future design. The Planning Commission said that if we could buttress the recommendations with solid documentation it would use them as the basis for a new zoning code.

We set to work. First we studied the social life of the spaces—in all, 16 plazas and 3 small parks. In good weather and bad weather, at peak and off-peak hours we tracked the flow of people, where they sat, how long, what they did. We interviewed people to find where they came from, where they worked, how frequently they used the plaza. On any one plaza, we found, patterns of use were very consistent. Some spots are heavily favored, others not, and though the absolute number of people using the plaza may vary considerably, the relative distribution from sector to sector remains quite uniform. Men tend to the front locations, women to the rear. The most favored spots for both are those which afford a full view of the action up front, but which are also somewhat protected—such as a slightly recessed area under a canopy of leaves. The way men stand and talk—"schmoozing," in New York parlance—is also quite regular. Not often will a group of men stay long in the middle of a large space. They gravitate to edges and objects. They are strongly attracted by pillars and flagpoles, obeying a primeval instinct, perhaps, to have something solid at their backs. Whatever the reason, they like defined places. You will see them in a straight line parallel to and just inside a portico or along the curb of a sidewalk, facing inward.

The most important space for a plaza is not on the plaza. It is the street corner alongside. Watch the activity on one closely and you will note that much of it is satellite to that of the plaza. This is particularly the case when a food vendor is to be found there. He will generate traffic between the corner and the plaza, and this traffic will in turn attract additional people. Activity begets activity.

Street corner behavior provides a fascinating documentation. In one of our early studies we had focused our time-lapse cameras on a number of corners to test several hypotheses. One was that people who encountered each other, or paused to talk, would move out of the pedestrian traffic stream. They didn't. Quite the contrary, they stayed there or moved into it, and the longer the conversation, the more apt it was to be right in the middle. Whatever they may say, people are attracted to other people.

This shows very clearly in comparisons of plaza usage. The most heavily used plazas are the most sociable. They have a higher than average proportion of people in twos and threes. They also have a higher proportion of females, and of females in pairs. Lovers favor the most heavily used places, and are usually to be spotted on the most conspicuous spots on them. Not so paradoxically, the sociable plazas also attract, in absolute numbers, more singles than other plazas do. If one is going to be the amused spectator, a place with the passing parade is best.

Let me jump ahead of our story a moment. The research described in this report was done in 1972 and 1973 and was concentrated largely in New York City. Our hypothesis was that we were essentially studying human beings and that the patterns we discerned in New York would be similar to those in other cities. Since then we have made comparison studies in other cities and have found our hypothesis borne out. The principal variable is size of city. In smaller cities densities tend to be considerably lower, pedestrians move at a slower pace, and there is less of the social activity characteristic of high traffic areas. In most other respects, pedestrian patterns are similar.

But the greatest similarities are to be found in very large metropolitan centers; the people in them tend to behave more like their counterparts in other metropolitan centers, whatever the country, than their fellow nationals in smaller cities. Tokyo, for example: a study we made in the spring of 1977 revealed that pedestrians' proclivity for stopping and talking in the middle of department store doorways, busy corners, and the like is just as strong as in New York. Sitting patterns in parks and plazas are very much the same. Similarly, "schmoozing" patterns in Milan's Galleria are remarkably like those in New York's garment center. Modest conclusion: given the basic elements of a center city—such as high pedestrian volumes, concentration, and mixture of activities—people in one place tend to act very much like people in another.

Back in 1973, however, our universe was New York City and we had to come up with some specific recommendations. What, in sum, distinguished the successful plazas from the unsuccessful? To determine the key physical variables we measured the spaces this way and that, tracked the sun angles, pedestrian flows, nearness to mass transit, enclosure afforded by adjacent buildings. As we piled up the data, overlay by overlay, one conclusion became clearer and clearer: *People tend to sit most where there are places to sit.* This may seem an unusually obvious point to make but it was certainly not clear at the time to many architects and planners, a number of whom believed that the aesthetics of design was what most attracted people. Some still do.

Other factors are indeed important, but the key variable is sittability. In some cases it is inadvertent: the plaza of the Seagram Building (fig. 1), one of the best of all, was not intended as a sitting place. But because the architects didn't gussy up the ledges with railings or shrubbery, it was in fact sittable and so people found it. The element most important was choice: generous-sized benches and long ledges let people sort themselves out. In all too many cases, however, benches are short, mean little affairs and they are placed in isolation from one another. Their function is to punctuate architectural photographs.

Obviously, then, a major recommendation was going to be the provision of plenty of sitting space. But this conjured up another question. How much was too much? How many people were too many? If the new zoning promised to attract many more people to a space might not the numbers crowd out the very amenity being sought? The Planning Commission hoped our research could give some answers.

FIG. 1. Typical time-lapse setup, with camera focused on north section of Seagram Plaza and clock placed so it will show in lower corner of film.

To get at the question of effective capacity we did a series of close-up studies of the most used places on the most used plazas. From place to place peak usage was fairly similar. Per 100 feet of linear sitting space the average number of people at any time during the lunch period would be about 28 and the maximum 40. This yields a rough rule of thumb for architects; to determine the effective capacity of a prime sitting area, divide the number of feet by three.

This is not physical capacity. The kind of use being studied is voluntary use. Were choice more forced—as on a bus, for example—capacity would be somewhere around 66 people per 100 feet. That it is considerably less in free choice situations is due to many factors. One is supply. Many people must pass by a place to provide the fraction who will stop and sit. (In his studies of Copenhagen Jan Gehl has found a consistent ratio between the number of people walking on the city's main pedestrian way and the number of people sitting on its benches.)

But the main determinant of capacity is human instinct. This was best demonstrated by our study of the north front ledge at Seagram's. Through time-lapse photography (see fig. 1) we recorded a typical day in the life of the ledge and charted it minute by minute from 9 a.m. until 6 p.m. On a long chart looking very much like a piano player roll we recorded each sitter, where he sat, and for how long. There was much turnover of people, but during the peak hours the overall number remained quite steady, running between 18 and 21 persons.

Good spacing, one might surmise. To a point, yes, but the amount of available space does not really explain the consistency. At no time were the people evenly spaced out over the ledge, like starlings on a phone wire. In some spots people would be bunched closely together; in others there would be enough empty space for 8 or 10 more people. Some other factor seems to be at work. It is as if people had some visceral sense of what is the norm for a place and were cooperating to maintain it that way, obligingly leaving or sitting down to keep the density within range. Of course, there is no such compact, but the effect is the same and the patterns are similar in other high-use places. Happenstance is at work too—the four friends who squeeze into space left by three, the chance arrival of three loners—but over the long run happenstance is quite regular, too.

Usage, in sum, tends to be self-leveling. There are exceptions; even the most delightful parks, such as Paley and Greenacre, sometimes get a bit too busy. At their most pleasant, however, they have an astonishingly high density—45 to 60 people per 1,000 square feet. The carrying capacity of a well-planned space is much greater than most assume. The prerequisites, furthermore, are a set of basics and they do not require elaborate expense or design acrobatics.

In sum, the proposed guidelines for plazas and similar urban spaces require that they—

1. Be sittable—minimum requirement: one linear foot of sitting space for every 30 square feet of open space. Maximize sittability of ledges and walls; make them low and, where possible, two backsides deep. Extra incentive for provision of movable chairs.

2. Maintain a close relationship to the street—no more than 3 feet above or below sidewalk grade, and except for a compelling reason, no sunken plazas.

3. Provide food—for example, open-air cafes, food kiosks, pass-through windows for snack bars.

4. Provide more trees—in addition to more along the sidewalk, more should be planted within the space and, where possible, in groves.

5. Provide for the needs of the handicapped—clear walkways, ramps, easy steps, which is to say, easier access and movement for all.

And, finally, require a performance bond to be posted by the developer to insure proper provision and maintenance of the facilities provided.

It seemed like being for motherhood and the flag, and we were glad the work was done, for we had other research to do. But the proposals stirred a surprising amount of controversy and we spent a fair amount of time presenting our findings to planning boards, officials, civic groups, and developers. The mills ground slowly, but at length, in May 1975, the zoning was finally enacted by the City's Board of Estimate.

The results have been encouraging. Two years later a companion measure was enacted for residential buildings mandating, in effect, small neighborhood parks in exchange for extra floor space. A number of new office building plazas have already been designed to meet the guidelines. More important, developers have been stimulated to re-do existing plazas and have been adding such previously unpermitted uses as open-air cafes. Many more benches have been provided, on streets as well as on plazas. In their own way, other cities have been rediscovering the benefits of such basic amenities. We like to think our expedition to the center city did come up with something of value and, not least of all—a place to sit.

The work summarized here has been more fully described in my new book *The Social Life of Small Urban Spaces,* published in 1980 by The Conservation Foundation, 1717 Massachusetts Avenue, N.W., Washington, D. C.

WILLIAM H. WHYTE

Pelagic Primary Production in Lake Titicaca

Principal Investigator: Carl Widmer, Elbert Covell College, University of the Pacific, Stockton, California.

Grant No. 1091:   To provide basic ecological information toward elucidating the problem of the trout-fishery failure in Lake Titicaca and to contribute to knowledge of tropical limnology.

Lakes are transitory features of the landscape. Few examples date from the early Tertiary. Lakes mature and finally dry up (Hutchinson, 1957). Titicaca, like many of the world's better-known and larger lakes, was formed by processes associated with mountain building (Moon, 1939; Newell, 1949; James, 1971, 1973). Löffler (1964) suggests that it might be the oldest of the tropical high-mountain lakes, derived from precursors which existed in the Miocene. It is believed, however, to have been formed by the melting of Pleistocene glaciers and to have been deepened to the present 281 meters by downfaulting.

Lake Titicaca (lat. 16° S., long. 69° W., 3,812 meters above sea level) lies in a broad intermontane basin, the *altiplano,* isolated from ocean drainage since the Miocene. This long isolation may explain the unique lacustrine biota. The altiplano is typified by *puna,* a cool tropical steppe of *Festuca, Stipa* and *Calamagrostis* bunchgrasses containing some areas of drought- and frost-resistant shrubs and small trees. The fauna is somewhat reminiscent of cooler semi-desert regions of western North America. In general, the species diversity of the fauna and flora appears to be moderately low.

The average daily temperature range is greater than the seasonal range of daily mean temperatures (Gilson, 1964). At higher elevations night frost occurs during all months of the year. While sunny midday winter temperatures may be comfortably warm, ice often remains unmelted in the shade. Humidity is low over the greater part of the year. The three summer months provide three-quarters of the annual rainfall. Hail commonly falls during violent summer thunderstorms, and summer snow frequently occurs above 4,500 meters altitude. Although average monthly wind velocities are moderate (Monheim, 1956), high winds, 10 to 14 meters per second, are occasionally observed. During 1973 tornadoes occurred at about 0300 on January 30 at the university campus in Puno, and at 0700 on July 14 in midlake. The first-mentioned caused some damage to buildings.

717

The dour climate of the puna is softened by the presence of the large lake (volume: 820 cubic kilometers, surface: 7,600 square kilometers; Gilson, 1964). Maize and passion-fruit are found growing in certain sheltered places near the lakeshore and on islands. The extensive marshes of *Scirpus tatora* in the Bahia de Puno and Lago Pequeño (Huinamarca) have received little or no attention from ecologists. Gilson (1964) estimates the marsh area of the Bahia de Puno to be about 300 square kilometers. It includes an abundant and varied avifauna, but mammals, with the exception of man and his symbionts, are not well represented. The natives of the marshes are called Urus. Their settlement of the lake region is said to antedate that of the predominant native American groups. Droughts in the early 1940's caused an ecologic crash in the marshes, which forced many of the Urus to emigrate. Those remaining made cultural changes (Monheim, 1956). The boatwright has recently appeared as a specialized carpenter, and wooden boats have replaced the traditional reed craft in commercial transportation. Reed craft are still widely used by subsistence fishermen for economic reasons.

Commercial fishing is becoming more important with recent introductions of silversides (*Basilichthys bonariensis*) from Argentina and rainbow trout (*Salmo gairdneri*) from western North America (Everett, 1967, 1971). Subsistence fishing contributes significantly to the nutrition of the lakeshore people, whose population has become rather dense. Local rural people are quite poor in some localities, and the margin above subsistence is nowhere very great.

Submerged macrophytes in some inshore waters make up an important source of cattle forage, especially during the dry season when grass pastures produce poorly. Wurtsbaugh (1974) has pointed out the importance of amphipods in these waters as a source of food for fish. The offshore waters of the main lake basin, Lago Grande (Chucuito), provide habitat for a moderate variety of planktonic forms. The population of one of these, *Boekella titicacae*, is by all standards very large. Cyprinodontid fishes of the genus *Orestias* and the catfish *Trichomycterus rivulatus* make up the indigenous ichthyofauna (Tchernavin, 1955). Some local people report that at least one of the larger species of *Orestias* has become extinct since the introduction of exotic species. Piscivorous, completely aquatic frogs of the genus *Telmatobias* inhabit the lake and the influent streams (Parker, 1940).

Considering the region as whole, the Andes have a north-south orientation, cutting across great latitudes. Weberbauer (1945), in his discussion of the origins of the Peruvian flora, points out the important contributions of the Mexican-western North American and austral regions. Löffler (1964) suggests that these cordilleras, abundant in waterfowl, serve as an avenue of penetration for south-temperate plankton species. The genus *Boekella* consists of fresh-water calanoid copepods and is well represented in Patagonia, New Zealand, and Australia. Species of this genus are widely distributed in lakes of the central Andes.

The work reported here was done by myself and my associates, Peter J. Richerson and Timothy Kittel of the University of California (Davis), with the generous help of Antonio Landa and his coworkers of the Instituto del Mar del Perú, the rector and faculty members of the Universidad Nacional Técnica del Altiplano, Roger Smith of the California State University at Humboldt, Victoria Valcárcel, and many others. Dr. Charles R. Goldman at the University of California, Davis, provided material help in several phases of the work. I am especially indebted to Dr. Richerson for suggesting Lake Titicaca as a subject for research and for his invaluable advice and critical judgment throughout the progress of the work. I am grateful for the financial aid provided by the National Geographic Society, the fellowship granted me by the Organization of American States, and contributions made by the University of the Pacific, the University of California, and the Foresta Institute for Ocean and Mountain Studies.

Materials and Methods

Details of the methodology used in this research are reported elsewhere (Widmer et al., 1974; Richerson et al., 1974; Richerson, et al., 1977). The first thermistor temperature measuring device (February-May) was made at the University of California (Davis). Owing to its loss at the bottom of the lake, a Ruttner (Lunz) water-sampling bottle with a calibrated mercury thermometer was used for determining water temperatures between June and August. This was superseded by a commercially available thermistor used during the remaining months. A silk net (No. 3 bolting), 23 threads per centimeter, with hoop diameter of 25 centimeters was used to capture zooplankton. Water samples were filtered through 0.45-micron membrane filters, which were cleared and mounted on slides in order to enumerate phytoplankton. Meteorological data were obtained from Engineer Eleodoro Aquise J., chief of the meteorological office in Puno. Heat-budget calculations were made according to the method described by Hutchinson (1957). Water transparencies were measured with a Secchi disc.

Carbon-14 primary production, which probably approximates the difference between gross photosynthesis and respiration, was assayed by adding accurately measured amounts of ^{14}C labeled sodium carbonate to known volumes of lake water and incubating these in situ for a measured length of time around midday (Steeman-Nielsen, 1952; Goldman, 1963). Compensation for dark reactions was made by simultaneous incubation of opaque control bottles. The rate of ^{14}C uptake corrected for the dark control was taken as a measure of the increase in phytoplankton biomass, or net primary production. Incubations were done at several depths in, and somewhat below, the euphotic zone.

Chemical determinations of dissolved oxygen, silica, and various inorganic ionic substances were made with the Hach Engineers Field Laboratory DR/EL since convenient laboratory facilities were not available. The accuracy of the nitrate and phosphate determinations in the microgram-per-liter range is doubtful. However, variations in an order of magnitude are given some credibility.

Phytoplankton biovolume was estimated from average measurements of cell dimensions made with the use of a micrometer scale and a phase contrast microscope. Biomass was computed according to the method of Mullin et al. (1966) and expressed in units of carbon. Zooplankton biomass was estimated in a similar manner, assuming the carbon content of wet zooplankton to be 4.5 percent. Collections of zooplankton were made by 100-meter vertical hauls with the zooplankton net previously described.

The results reported here are from 21 data-gathering excursions into Lago Grande directly east of Capachica.

Results

Temperature data confirmed earlier reports (Gilson, 1964) of a thermocline between 50 and 70 meters depth (fig. 1). Homothermy was established by the end of July (winter), and chemical data showed that mixing had occurred to a depth below 100 meters (Richardson et al., 1974). Stratification began in late September (spring) as surface waters were warmed and was well developed by the end of October. The lake remained stratified for the remainder of the year. Between the time of maximum heat content in February and that of the minimum in July, 19 kilocalories of heat were lost per square centimeter of lake surface (Richerson et al., 1974, 1977; Kittel and Richerson, 1978). This heat exchange is higher than that of Lake Victoria (table 2) with approximately 10 kilocalories per square centimeter (Talling, 1966) and is in reasonable accord with the heat budget of the outer-tropical highland Lake Atitlán with 22 kilocalories per square centimeter (Deevey, 1957). Large heat budgets are characteristic of temperate-zone lakes. For example, Hutchinson (1957) lists values for lakes Baikal, Michigan, and Tahoe as 66, 52, and 35 kilocalories per square centimeter, respectively. The intermediate quantity of

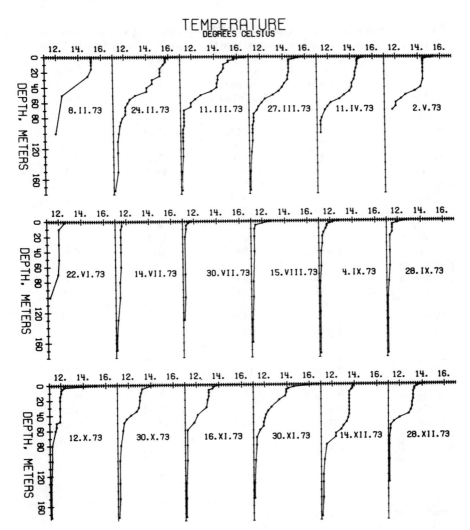

FIG. 1.   Changes in thermal stratification during 1973 shown by temperature-depth profiles.

19 kilocalories per square centimeter for Lake Titicaca should probably be interpreted as indicative of a moderate degree of seasonality in an otherwise tropical lake.

Atelomixis, or limited vertical mixing associated with wind action on the epilimnion during general warming trends (Lewis, 1973), was observed in

TABLE 1.   Summary of Data Obtained for Phytoplankton Production Rates and Biomass. Biomass is Based on Counts from 0-, 7-, and 15-Meter Depths Only

Date	Primary production (g C/m²·day)	Insolation (Kcal/m²·day)	Phytoplankton biomass (mg C/m³)	Silica (5 m) (mg/1)
Summer:				
26 Jan.	1.345	3363	17.40	0.82
8 Feb.	1.177	3382	30.81	1.10
24 Feb.	1.041	3630	27.71	1.05
11 Mar.	1.189	5017	36.75	1.14
Autumn:				
27 Mar.	1.320	5431	22.02	1.10
11 Apr.	1.174	5798	23.47	0.84
2 May	1.395	4666	22.54	0.67
18 May	1.544	4093	39.27	0.49
2 June	1.614	4630	32.46	0.47
Winter:				
22 June	1.673	4557	29.32	0.13
14 July	1.264	3818	29.25	0.06
30 July	1.701	5140	26.91	0.32
15 Aug.	2.014	5480	29.26	0.11
4 Sept.	1.391	5571	19.14	0.20
Spring:				
28 Sept.	1.004	5526	14.28	0.20
12 Oct.	0.756	4948	13.11	0.23
30 Oct.	0.720	5908	13.89	0.17
16 Nov.	0.985	6868	12.71	0.23
30 Nov.	1.579	6715	17.60	0.22
14 Dec.	2.711	6939	27.76	0.25
Summer:				
28 Dec.	2.861	5317	28.18	0.25
Average	1.450	5086	24.47	0.48

Annual primary production: 529 grams C/m²
  Main basin (Lago Grande): 3.1×10^6 metric tons.
  Total lake: 4.0×10^6 metric tons.

temperature profiles (fig. 1) for the months of March, April, and December. This phenomenon appears to be important in maintaining the relatively high primary productivity of tropical lakes, through frequent recycling of nutrients into the upper illuminated layers of the epilimnion (Lewis, 1974).

On April 10 the yellowish-gray flood waters of the Ramis River were seen from a point some 40 kilometers distant in the form of a sharply defined floating plume, several kilometers in length along the northeast shore of Lago

TABLE 2.   Comparison of Selected Limnological Parameters of Several Large Lakes

Lake	[1]*Annual primary production* (*g C/m²· yr*)	[2]*Heat budget* (*Kcal/cm²*)	[3]*Maximum Secchi depth* (*meters*)	[4]*Hypolimnetic temperature* (*°C*)
Tahoe, U.S.A.	52	35	40	4.5
Michigan, U.S.A.	130	52	6	4.3
Atitlán, C.A.	296	22	22	19.5
Titicaca, S.A.	529	19	11	10.9
Lanao, Philippines	620	6	6	24.6
Victoria, Africa	7.12	10	8	23.5

[1]*Annual primary production:*
  Tahoe: Goldman, 1974.
  Michigan: Vollenweider et al., 1974.
  Atitlán: Weiss, 1971.
  Lanao: Lewis, 1974.
  Victoria: Talling, 1965.

[2]*Heat budget:*
  Tahoe: Hutchinson, 1957.
  Michigan: Hutchinson, 1957.
  Atitlán: Deevey, 1957.
  Lanao: Lewis, 1973.
  Victoria: Talling, 1966.

[3]*Transparency (maximum Secchi depth):*
  Tahoe: Goldman, 1974.
  Michigan: Schelske and Roth, 1973.
  Atitlán: Weiss, 1971.
  Lanao: Frey, 1969.
  Victoria: Worthington, 1930.

[4]*Hypolimnetic temperature:*
  Tahoe: Goldman, 1974.
  Michigan: Hutchinson, 1957.
  Atitlán: Weiss, 1971.
  Titicaca: Gilson, 1964.
  Lanao: Lewis, 1973.
  Victoria: Talling, 1966.

Grande. The specific gravity of the lake water is about 1.0021. The river water during autumn originates primarily in runoff and in the melting of summer snow in the regions around the Cordillera de Carabaya. The specific gravity of this water would be expected to be much closer to unity. Therefore, the river water would tend to layer over the lake surface until wind action and cold weather mix it into the lake. Considering the large size of the catchment area relative to the lake surface (ratio: 8 to 1) and the semiarid climate of the region, allochthonous sources of mineral nutrients are probably quite important in maintaining the lake's phytoplankton populations. More work needs to be done in evaluating riverine nutrient contributions to the lake.

The waters of Lake Titicaca are rather transparent and immediately give the impression of oligotrophy. Several other studies of tropical lakes have also noted remarkably transparent water notwithstanding high rates of primary production (Talling, 1965, 1966; Lewis, 1974). Depths at the limit of visibility of the Secchi disc in Lake Titicaca ranged from 4.5 to 10.8 meters, intermediate between measurements reported for Lake Lanao (Frey, 1969) and Lake Atitlán (Weiss, 1971) of 6 and 22 meters, respectively (table 1). Lower transparency coincided with the rainy season and was probably partly due to inorganic seston in the influent water.

Because of lower temperatures, decomposition of organic seston is probably slower in Lake Titicaca than in the warmer tropical lakes (Talling, 1966), and oxygen concentrations remain quite high (2.4 to 4.8 mg/liter) at 140 meters depth and below. This concentration is about half that found in the surface waters. Lower decomposition rates would result in reduced rates of inorganic nutrient recycling and greater incorporation of organic matter into the bottom mud than would be expected in tropical lakes enjoying higher mean temperatures. Nutrient concentrations were found to be generally low and probably limit primary production at certain times of the year.

Primary production depth profiles are presented in figure 2. These profiles may be integrated to give values of primary production per hour per square meter of lake surface. Multiplying these by the ratios of full day insolation with respect to incubation-time insolation gives daily primary production rates. These quantities are listed in table 1. It is clear that significant photosynthesis takes place throughout the year, but a strong decrease occurred in early spring. The reasons for this decrease are not entirely evident. A combination of nutrient depletion followed by deep mixing and dilution of the phytoplanktonic biomass well below the euphotic zone during the homothermic period would seem to be a plausible explanation. With the reestablishment of thermal stratification, atelomixis became important in the control of nutrient availability for phytoplankton growth. Upwelling, detected in the form of changes in the shape of the temperature profile on November 30, and an increase in rainfall during this season, might be responsible for the high rates of primary production during December.

The yearly ^{14}C primary production of 529 grams of carbon per square meter was computed on the basis of an average daily production of 1.45 grams of carbon per square meter. Since the area of Lago Grande is 5,880 square kilometers, the yearly primary production was approximately 3.1 million metric tons of photosynthetically fixed carbon in new phytoplankton biomass. Similarly, the annual primary production of the entire lake was computed to be 4.0 million metric tons of carbon fixed. This figure is probably conservative, since the more shallow waters may be expected to be more productive than the offshore waters. This is because the euphotic zone of the shallow water is in contact with the shoreline and with sediments containing minerals and decomposing organic matter.

Assuming that amphipods and zooplankton are the principal herbivores, and assuming a trophic efficiency of 10 percent (Ryther, 1969), the annual production of these small animals may be estimated roughly at about 400,000

PRIMARY PRODUCTION
MG C/M³/HR

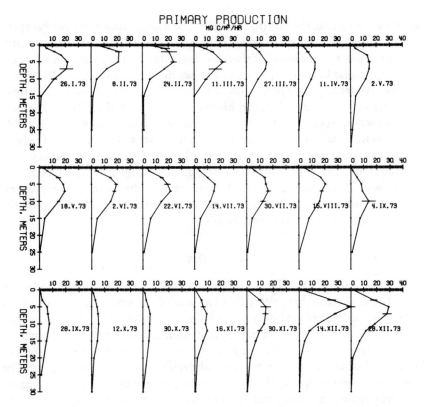

FIG. 2.   Profiles of primary production. Hourly values are averages for the incubation period.

metric tons carbon, or 8.9 million metric tons wet weight. Trophic efficiencies of 15 percent may be used to estimate production at the carnivore levels. The very numerous "ispi," *Orestias mooni* (length: 6 centimeters), other species of *Orestias* of intermediate size, and the smaller silversides (under 20 centimeters), are first-stage carnivores (Wurtsbaugh, 1974). Annual production of these smaller fish is probably around 600,000 metric tons, and annual production of the larger trout and silversides (second-stage carnivores) could be as much as 90,000 metric tons. Everett (1971) reports the maximum annual trout catch in the year 1965 as 500 metric tons. After 1965 the trout fishery declined rapidly.

Stephanodiscus astrae, a large diatom, dominated the phytoplankton during the winter months, whereas *Anabaena sphaerica* var. *attenuata* Bharadwaja was abundant during the humid summer. The disappearance of *S. astrae* at the spring crash might be explained by inadequate concentrations of silica (table 1). *Lyngbya vacuolifera* Skuja became dominant during the spring. A more extensive phytoplankton list appears in a paper by Richerson, et al. (1977).

The zooplankton is strongly dominated by *Boekella titicacae* and accounts for 90 percent of the zooplankton biomass (Widmer et al., 1974). The next most numerous species is the much larger *B. occidentalis,* which probably suffers preferential predation by the smaller fishes (Brooks and Dodson, 1965). Diversity among the zooplankton is low, and populations remain more or less constant with time. Since the phytoplankton biomass is high relative to that of the zooplankton during much of the year (Richerson et al., in preparation), zooplankton are probably limited by fish predation rather than by the amount of algal biomass available as food.

Discussion

A comparison of Lake Titicaca with other large lakes is summarized in table 2. The data strongly suggest that tropical lakes, when compared to temperate lakes of like transparency, are much more productive. The absence of winter stagnation and a period of very low insolation in the tropics is obviously an important factor contributing to higher productivity. Primary production is well distributed over the annual cycle in lakes of the tropics. The higher water temperatures enhance the decomposition of dead organic material, thereby increasing transparency and facilitating the recycling of nutrients. Even in Lake Titicaca, deep temperatures are warmer, and the epilimnetic mixed layer, thicker than in the usual temperate zone lake. The operation of atelomixis in the much thicker epilimnia of tropical lakes affords a more efficient mechanism for the support of high levels of primary production than one finds in temperate lakes with shallow epilimnia. Gilson (1964) concluded that Lake Titicaca is an oligotrophic lake on the basis of its transparency. However, the lake tends toward oligotrophy only when taken in the context of tropical lakes in general. Compared to temperate lakes, Titicaca might reasonably be classified as mesotrophic or somewhat eutrophic on the basis of its relatively high annual net primary production.

Seasonality is expressed in the parameters affecting the Lake Titicaca ecosystem to a greater extent than in the case of the equatorial lakes, which is to be expected. However, seasonal differences in humidity are probably of equal or greater importance to the ecology of the phytoplankton than temperature. None of the data presented here as primary production depth profiles (fig. 2) suggest that solar energy flux might limit primary production at any season of the year.

In conclusion, the evidence presented supports the contention that Lake Titicaca could probably support a higher level of human exploitation in terms of food resources than that which is actually occurring. It is quite clear that the failure of the trout fishery is not due to inadequate primary production. Wurtsbaugh (1974) indicates that it is probable that competition from silversides is of major significance in the curtailment of the trout population, and emphasizes that introduction of exotic species must be done with extreme caution. In the past these introductions have been made haphazardly and with no basis in research.

REFERENCES

BROOKS, JOHN L., and DODSON, STANLEY I.
  1965. Predation, body size, and composition of plankton. Science, vol. 150, pp. 28-35, illus.
DEEVEY, EDWARD S., JR.
  1957. Limnologic studies in Middle America with chapter on Aztec limnology. Trans. Connecticut Acad. Arts Sci., vol. 39, pp. 213-328.
EVERETT, G. V.
  1967. Lake Titicaca and its fisheries. Peruvian Times, vol. 27, no. 1360, pp. 5-8.
  1971. The rainbow trout of Lake Titicaca and the fisheries of Lake Titicaca, 180 pp. Report to the Government of the Republic of Perú.
FREY, D. G.
  1969. A limnological reconnaissance of Lake Lanao. Verhandlungen Internationale Vereinigung für Theoretische und Angewandte Limnologie (Stuttgart), vol. 17, pp. 1090-1102.
GILSON, H. CARY
  1964. Lake Titicaca. Verhandlungen Internationale Vereinigung für Theoretische und Angewandte Limnologie (Stuttgart), vol. 15, pp. 112-127.
GOLDMAN, CHARLES R.
  1963. The measurement of primary productivity and limiting factors in freshwater with carbon-14. Proc. Conf. Primary Productivity Measurement, Marine and Freshwater, M. S. Doty, ed. U. S. Atomic Energy Commission, TID-7633, pp. 103-113.
  1974. Eutrophication of Lake Tahoe emphasizing water quality, 408 pp. Environmental Protection Agency, 660/3-74-034.
HERTING, G.
  1967. Lake Titicaca fisheries resources. Problems and possibilities. Peruvian Times, vol. 27, no. 1389, pp. 10-13.
HUTCHINSON, G. EVELYN
  1957. A treatise on limnology, vol. 1, 1015 pp. John Wiley & Sons, New York.

JAMES, DAVID E.
    1971.   Plate tectonic model for the evolution of the central Andes. Bull.
             Geol. Soc. Amer., vol. 82, pp. 3325-3346.
    1973.   The evolution of the Andes. Sci. Amer., vol. 229, no. 2, pp. 61-69,
             illus.
KITTEL, TIMOTHY, and RICHERSON, PETER J.
    1978.   The heat budget of a large tropical lake, Lake Titicaca (Peru-Bolivia).
             Verhandlungen Internationale Vereinigung für Theoretische und
             Angewandte Limnologie (Stuttgart), vol. 20, pp. 1203-1209.
LEWIS, W. M., JR.
    1973.   The thermal regime of Lake Lanao (Philippines) and its theoretical im-
             plications for tropical lakes. Limnol. Oceanogr. vol. 18, pp. 200-217.
    1974.   Primary production in the plankton community of a tropical lake.
             Ecol. Monogr. vol. 44, pp. 377-409.
LÖFFLER, H.
    1964.   The limnology of tropical high-mountain lakes. Verhandlungen Inter-
             nationale Vereinigung Limnologie, vol. 15, pp. 176-193.
MONHEIM, F.
    1956.   Beitrage zur Klimatologie und Hydrologie des Titicacabeckens.
             Selbstverlag des Geographischen Instituts der Universität Heidelberg,
             152 pp.
MOON, H. P.
    1939.   The geology and physiography of the altiplano of Peru and Bolivia.
             Trans. Linnean Soc. London, ser. 3, vol. 1, pt. 1, pp. 27-43. (Percy Sla-
             den Trust Expedition to Lake Titicaca in 1937 [H. Cary Gilson].)
MULLIN, MICHAEL M.; SLOAN, P. R.; and EPPLEY, R. W.
    1966.   Relationship between carbon content, cell volume and area in phyto-
             plankton. Limnol. Oceanogr., vol. 11, pp. 307-311.
NEWELL, NORMAN D.
    1949.   Geology of the Lake Titicaca Region, Peru and Bolivia. Geological
             Society of America, Memoir 36.
PARKER, H. W.
    1940.   Amphibia. Trans. Linnean Soc. London, ser. 3, vol. 1, pt. 2, pp. 203-
             216. (Percy Sladen Trust Expedition to Lake Titicaca in 1937 [H. Cary
             Gilson].)
RICHERSON, PETER J.; WIDMER, CARL; and KITTEL, TIMOTHY
    1977.   The limnology of Lake Titicaca (Peru-Bolivia). A large, high-altitude
             tropical lake. Institute of Ecology Publications no. 14 July 1977,
             Univ. of California, Davis, pp. 1-78.
RICHERSON, PETER J.; WIDMER, CARL; KITTEL, TIMOTHY; and LANDA C.,
    ANTONIO
    1975.   A survey of the physical and chemical limnology of Lake Titicaca.
             Verhandlungen Internationale Vereinigung Limnologie, vol. 19, pp.
             1498-1503.
RICKER, W. E.
    1969.   Food from the sea. Pp. 87-108 *in* "Resources and Man," P. Cloud,
             ed. W. H. Freeman, San Francisco.

SCHELSKE, C. L., and ROTH, J. C.
  1973.   Limnological survey of Lakes Michigan, Superior, Huron, and Erie.   Univ. Michigan, Great Lakes Res. Div. Publ. 17, pp. 11-18.
STEEMAN-NIELSEN, E.
  1952.   The use of radioactive carbon (C^{14}) for measuring organic production in the sea.   Journ. Cons. Perm. Int. Explor. Mer., vol. 18, pp. 117-140.
TALLING, J. F.
  1965.   The photosynthetic activity of phytoplankton in East Africa lakes.   Int. Rev. Ges. Hydrobiol., vol. 50, pp. 1-32.
  1966.   The annual cycle of stratification and phytoplankton growth in Lake Victoria (East Africa).   Int. Rev. Ges. Hydrobiol., vol. 51, pp. 545-621.
TCHERNAVIN, V. V.
  1955.   Pisces.   Trans. Linnean Soc. London, ser. 3, vol. 1, pt. 3, pp. 217-218.(Percy Sladen Trust Expedition to Lake Titicaca in 1937 [H. Cary Gilson].)
VOLLENWEIDER, R. A.; MUNAWAR, M.; and STADELMANN, P.
  1974.   A comparative review of phytoplankton and primary production in the Laurentian Great Lakes.   Journ. Fisheries Res. Board Canada, vol. 31, pp. 739-762.
WEBERBAUER, A.
  1945.   El mundo vegetal de los Andes Peruanos.   Ministerio de Agricultura, Lima, Peru.
WEISS, C. M.
  1971.   Lake Atitlán.   Univ. North Carolina, Environmental Sciences and Engineering Publ. no. 274, pp. 1-175.
WIDMER, CARL; KITTEL, TIMOTHY; and RICHERSON, PETER J.
  1974.   A survey of the biological limnology of Lake Titicaca.   Verhandlungen Internationale Vereinigung für Theoretische und Angewandte Limnologie (Stuttgart), vol. 19, pp. 1504-1510.
WORTHINGTON, E. B.
  1930.   Observations on the temperature, hydrogen ion concentration, and other physical conditions of the Victoria and Albert Nyanzas.   Int. Rev. Ges. Hydrobiol. und Hydrogr., vol. 24, pp. 328-357.
WURTSBAUGH, W. A.
  1974.   Biología y Pesquería del Pejerrey (*Basilichthys bonariensis*) en el Lago Titicaca.   Instituto del Mar del Perú, Dirección de Investigaciones Pesqueras en Aguas Continentales, Lima, Peru.

CARL WIDMER

APPENDIX

List of Grants for Research and Exploration Made by the National Geographic Society in 1979

1975: To Dr. Ronald Singer, The University of Chicago, Chicago, Illinois, for a search for the earliest humans in Great Britain at Swanscombe.

1976: To Dr. Lawrence G. Straus, University of New Mexico, Albuquerque, New Mexico, for an archeological reconnaissance of Guipuzcoa Province, Spain.

1977: To Mr. Richard M. Leventhal, Cambridge, Massachusetts, for an archeological reconnaissance in southern Belize.

1978: To Ms. Joan S. Gardner, Arlington, Virginia, for a study of Pre-Columbian textiles from Los Rios Province, Ecuador.

1979: To Dr. William M. Hurley, University of Toronto, Toronto, Ontario, Canada, for a study of the social dynamics and subsistence of the Yagi Site, Japan.

1980: To Dr. Rene E. Van Grieken, University of Antwerp, Belgium, for a study of chemical composition of marine aerosols sampled worldwide from a sailing boat.

1981: To Dr. Ralph W. Brauer, University of North Carolina, Wilmington, North Carolina, for a study of the physiology of abyssal freshwater fauna in Lake Baikal, U.S.S.R.

1982: To Dr. Alwyn H. Gentry, Missouri Botanical Garden, St. Louis, Missouri, for a survey of plant distribution and diversity patterns in Amazonian Peru.

1983: To Dr. Eric R. Pianka, University of Texas, Austin, Texas, for a study of desert lizard ecology in Western Australia.

1984: To Dr. John M. Melack, University of California, Santa Barbara, California, for a study of the ecology of Mono Lake, California.

1985: To Mr. Albert E. Sanders, The Charleston Museum, Charleston, South Carolina, for a study of an undescribed cetacean from the Oligocene of Russia.

1986: To Dr. Larry D. Agenbroad, Northern Arizona University, Flagstaff, Arizona, for an excavation of a Late Pleistocene mammoth locality in South Dakota.

1987: To Dr. Charles C. Porter, Fordham University, Bronx, New York, for a study of biosystematics of North Chilean and Peruvian desertic Ichneumonidae.

1988: To Dr. Carl D. Hopkins, University of Minnesota, Minneapolis, Minnesota, for a study of species recognition and neuroethology of electric fish from Gabon.

1989: To Dr. Hannon B. Graves, Pennsylvania State University, University Park, Pennsylvania, for a study of mating and parent-offspring behavior of the crested tinamou.

1990, 2101: To Dr. Roger S. Payne, New York Zoological Society, Bronx, New York, for a study of migration, behavior, and songs of North Pacific humpback whales.

731

1991: To Mr. Richard E. F. Leakey, National Museums of Kenya, Nairobi, Kenya, for paleontological research in the Plio/Pleistocene of the Lake Turkana Basin.

1992: To Dr. Mary D. Leakey, Nairobi, Kenya, for continued exploration and recording of Pliocene tracks at Laetoli, Tanzania.

1993: To Dr. Marvin J. Allison, Medical College of Virginia, Richmond, Virginia, for a study of Pre-Columbian disease.

1994: To Dr. Robert J. Sharer, University Museum, University of Pennsylvania, Philadelphia, Pennsylvania, for archeological investigations at Quirigua, Guatemala.

1995: To Ms. Olga Soffer, Hunter College, New York, New York, in support of an excavation of the Upper Paleolithic site of Mezhirich, Ukrainian S.S.R.

1996: To Dr. Richard M. Gramly, Peabody Museum, Harvard University, Cambridge, Massachusetts, for archeological investigations at the Mt. Jasper mine, northern New Hampshire.

1997: To Dr. Richard F. Townsend, Washington, D. C., in support of mapping the ritual hill of Tetzcotzingo, Mexico.

1998: To Dr. Ehud Netzer, Institute of Archaeology, Jerusalem, Israel, for excavation of the Hasmonean and Herodian winter palace complexes of Jericho.

1999: To Dr. Sterling P. Vinson, The University of Arizona, Tucson, Arizona, in support of an archeological project in Lucania, Italy.

2000, 2020: To Dr. Patricia E. Brown, University of California, Los Angeles, California, for study of echolocation development and communications in neotropical bats.

2001: To Dr. Douglas W. Morrison, Rutgers University, Newark, New Jersey, for a study of cooperative foraging and harem evolution in fruit bats.

2002: To Dr. Kenneth E. Campbell, George C. Page Museum, Los Angeles, California, for studies of vertebrate paleontology in southeastern Peru.

2003, 2081: To Dr. Paul W. Sherman, University of California, Berkeley, California, for a study of the effects of kinship on mammalian social behavior.

2004: To Dr. Howard E. Evans, Colorado State University, Fort Collins, Colorado, for a study of biosystematics of Australian solitary wasps.

2005: To Mr. Walter F. Morris, Jr., Warren, New Jersey, for a project, "A Textured Script, Classic and Modern Maya Textile Designs."

2006: To Dr. Peter I. Kuniholm, Cornell University, Ithaca, New York, for a study of tree ring chronologies for the Aegean and adjacent areas.

2007, 2098: To Dr. Robert H. Smith, The College of Wooster, Wooster, Ohio, in support of archeological investigations at Pella, Jordan.

2008: To Dr. William B. Saunders, Bryn Mawr College, Bryn Mawr, Pennsylvania, for a study of long-term growth and movement of *Nautilus* in Palau.

2009: To Dr. Ted J. Case, University of California, San Diego, California, for a study of behavioral ecology of the insular gigantic sauromalus in the Gulf of California.

2010: To Dr. Louis H. Emmons, Smithsonian Institution, Washington, D. C., for a study of palms as a key to neotropical mammal abundance.

2011: To Dr. Minard L. Hall, Escuela Politecnica Nacional, Quito, Ecuador, for a study of subaerial origin of Espanola Island and the age of terrestrial life, Galapagos.

2012: To Dr. Mitsunobu Tatsumoto, Lakewood, Colorado, in support of isotopic tracer studies of the genesis of calcalkaline rocks.

2013: To Dr. Renato Rimoli M., Universidad Central del Este, Dominican Republic, for a study of paleofauna from caves in the Dominican Republic.

2014: To Dr. Karel L. Rogers, Adams State College, Alamosa, Colorado, for paleontological investigations of the Alamosa Formation.

2015: To Dr. William J. Mader, Brigham Young University, Provo, Utah, for a study of ecology and breeding behavior of the savanna hawk in Venezuela.

2016: To Dr. Lewis T. Nielsen, The University of Utah, Salt Lake City, Utah, for comparative taxonomic and distributional study of Holarctic *Aedes* mosquitoes.

2017: To Dr. Robert E. Dewar, The University of Connecticut, Storrs, Connecticut, in support of an archeological survey in southwest Madagascar.

2018: To Dr. Richard L. Burger, University of California, Berkeley, California, in support of studies at Callejon de Huaylas, Peru.

2019: To Mr. Edward J. Dixon, Jr., University Museum, University of Alaska, Fairbanks, Alaska, for an archeological survey and testing of cave deposits along the Porcupine River, Alaska.

2021: To Dr. S. David Webb, University of Florida, Gainesville, Florida, for a study of systematics and zoogeography of fossil and Recent pocket gophers.

2022: To Dr. Bradford Washburn, The Museum of Science, Boston, Massachusetts, for final revision of the Grand Canyon map manuscript.

2023, 2064: To Dr. Robert F. Dymek, for field studies of metamorphosed Archaean-age supracrustal rocks in west Greenland.

2024: To Dr. Herbert E. Wright, Jr., University of Minnesota, Minneapolis, Minnesota, for a study of glacial and vegetational history of southeastern Labrador.

2025: To Dr. Richard R. Montanucci, Clemson University, Clemson, South Carolina, for a study of hybridization between two species of collared lizards.

2026: To Dr. Kenan T. Erim, New York University, New York City, New York, for continuation of study, investigations and research of archeological material excavated at Aphrodisias, Turkey.

2027: To Dr. Christy G. Turner II, Arizona State University, Tempe, Arizona, in support of a study of the origin of the first Americans: the dental evidence.

2028: To Dr. Payson D. Sheets, University of Colorado, Boulder, Colorado, in support of a geophysical survey for ancient Maya housing.

2029: To Dr. S. Jeffrey K. Wilkerson, Florida State Museum, Gainesville, Florida, for a study of cultural ecology of the Mexican Gulf Coast.

2030: To Dr. Michael H. Jameson, Stanford University, Stanford, California, for an archeological and environmental survey of the southern Argolid, Greece.

2031: To Dr. Robson Bonnichsen, University of Maine, Orono, Maine, in support of the Pryor Mountain Archeological Research Project.

2032: To Dr. Robert E. Ackerman, Washington State University, Pullman, Washington, in support of Southwest Alaska Archeological Survey II: Kagati Lake, Kisaralik-Aniak Rivers.

2033: To Dr. Roger H. Hildebrand, The Enrico Fermi Institute, The University of Chicago, Chicago, Illinois, for exploration of interstellar molecular clouds of submillimeter polarimetry.

2034: To Dr. Paul W. Hodge, University of Washington, Seattle, Washington, for publication of the Atlas of the Andromeda Galaxy.

2035: To Dr. Richard S. Blanquet, Georgetown University, Washington, D. C., for a study of zooxanthellae contribution to respiration in the mangrove jellyfish.

2036: To Dr. Gary E. Belovsky, The University of Michigan, Ann Arbor, Michigan, for a study of comparative competition and diversity of herbivores in Great Plains locations.

2037: To Dr. John R. Flenley, University of Hull, Hull, United Kingdom, for a re-survey of the flora of the island of Krakatoa.

2038: To Dr. Stanley A. Temple, University of Wisconsin, Madison, Wisconsin, for a study of hook-billed kites.

2039: To Dr. Matthew J. Greenstone, University of California, Irvine, California, for a study of web spider resource-partitioning along temperate and tropical elevational gradients.

2040: To Dr. Tracy S. Carter, Oklahoma State University, Stillwater, Oklahoma, for a study of armadillos of Brazil: habitat utilization and food habits.

2041: To Dr. Richard L. Hay, University of California, Berkeley, California, for a study of the stratigraphy of the Laetoli area in northern Tanzania.

2042: To Dr. Charles W. Naeser, U. S. Geological Survey, Denver, Colorado, for study of the geochronology of the Plio-Pleistocene boundary in southern Italy.

2043: To Dr. Louis L. Jacobs, Museum of Northern Arizona, Flagstaff, Arizona, for a study of small vertebrate fossils from the Chinle Formation near St. Johns, Arizona.

2044: To Dr. Mary R. Dawson, Carnegie Museum of Natural History, Pittsburgh, Pennsylvania, for a study of Tertiary terrestrial floras and vertebrate faunas, Canadian High Arctic.

2045: To Dr. Francoise Dowsett-Lemaire, The Livingstone Museum, Zambia, for study of ecological distribution of montane forest birds of the Nyika Plateau.

2046: To Dr. Frank P. Saul, Medical College of Ohio, Toledo, Ohio, for a study of Maya skeletons from Cozumel, Mexico.

2047: To Mr. Augusto R. Cardich, Universidad Nacional de La Plata, Argentina, for study of fluctuation of the upper limits of cultivation in the Andes.

2048: To Dr. John R. F. Bower, Iowa State University, Ames, Iowa, for a study of ecology of the Middle Stone Age, Serengeti National Park, Tanzania.

2049: To Dr. Walter E. Rast, Valparaiso University, Valparaiso, Indiana, for a study of Bronze Age life patterns along the southeastern Dead Sea, Jordan.

2050: To Dr. Carl E. Gustafson, Washington State University, Pullman, Washington, in support of the Manis Mastodon Archeological Project.

2051, 2082: To Mrs. Rae N. P. Goodall, Tierra del Fuego, Argentina, in support of research on the natural history of Tierra del Fuego.

2052: To Dr. Grahame J. W. Webb, University of New South Wales, Kensington, N.S.W., Australia, for a survey of pristine crocodile populations in northern Australia.

2053: To Dr. Henry O. Whittier, University of Central Florida, Orlando, Florida, for a study of comparative biogeography of Society Island mosses.

2054: To Dr. Dale M. Lewis, State University of New York, Albany, New York, for a study of determinants of population structure in the white-browed sparrow weaver.

2055: To Dr. Michael E. Brookfield, Guelph University, Guelph, Ontario, Canada, in suppoort of radiometric dating of rocks along the Indus suture and Karakorums.

2056: To Dr. Robert W. Schmieder, Walnut Creek, California, in support of the Cordell Bank Expedition.

2057: To Mr. Charles R. Schaff, Harvard University, Cambridge, Massachusetts, for a study of Paleocene mammals from the Bear Tooth region of Wyoming and Montana.

2058: To Dr. Robert M. Hunt, Jr., University of Nebraska, Lincoln, Nebraska, for study of paleontology and geology of the Patrick Buttes, Goshen County, Wyoming.

2059: To Dr. Michael R. Voorhies, University of Nebraska, Lincoln, Nebraska, in support of a continuing study of a Miocene rhinoceros herd buried in volcanic ash.

2060: To Dr. Edwin O. Willis, Silver Spring, Maryland, for a study of behavior of *Pithys castanea* (Aves, Formicariidae) in northeastern Peru.

2061: To Dr. Robert S. Kennedy, Pullman, Washington, for a field study of the Philippine eagle.

2062: To Mr. Pepper Trail, Cornell University, Ithaca, New York, for a study of the lek mating system of the cock-of-the-rock *(Rupicola rupicola)*.

2063: To Dr. John L. Hoogland, Princeton University, Princeton, New Jersey, for a study of the sociobiology of the black-tailed prairie dog.

2065: To Dr. Naguib Kanawati, Macquarie University, Sydney, Australia, in support of excavations at Akhmim, Upper Egypt.

2066: To Dr. George F. Bass, Institute of Nautical Archaeology, College Station, Texas, in support of an excavation and analysis of a medieval Islamic shipwreck.

2067: To Mr. Stanley South, University of South Carolina, Columbia, South Carolina, in support of a sixteenth-century research program in South Carolina.

2068: To Mr. James H. Fullard, Erindale College, University of Toronto, Ontario, Canada, for a study of behavioral ecology of East African moths and bats.

2069: To Dr. Knut Schmidt-Nielsen, Duke University, Durham, South Carolina, for a study of water conservation in desert animals.

2070: To Dr. Jared M. Diamond, University of California Medical Center, Los Angeles, California, for a study of visual mimicry in birds.

2071: To Dr. Everett H. Lindsay, The University of Arizona, Tuscon, Arizona, for a study of magnetostratigraphy of selected Late Cenozoic vertebrate sites in Europe.

2072: To Dr. William L. Crepet, The University of Connecticut, Storrs, Connecticut, in support of an investigation of Tertiary angiosperm flowers from east Texas.

2073: To Dr. Timothy C. and Mrs. Janet M. Williams, Swarthmore College, Swarthmore, Pennsylvania, in support of a radar study of transpacific bird migration.

2074: To Dr. Charles van Riper III, University of Hawaii, Hawaii, for a study of the *Palila* in Hawaii.

2075: To Dr. Alan Lill, Monash University, Clayton, Victoria, Australia, for a study of socioecology of five species of Australian bowerbirds.

2076: To Dr. Mehmet C. Ozdogan, University of Istanbul, Istanbul, Turkey, in support of a surface survey for prehistoric and early historic sites in northwestern Turkey.

2077: To Dr. Norman Hammond, Rutgers University, New Brunswick, New Jersey, in support of the archeological excavations and radiocarbon datings at the Cuello Site.

2078: To Dr. Janice M. Stargardt, Cambridge, England, in support of studies in South East Asia.

2079: To Dr. Jay M. Pasachoff, Williams College, Williamstown, Massachusetts, in support of coronal heating studies at the 1980 solar eclipse.

2080: To Dr. James A. Simmons, Washington University, St. Louis, Missouri, for a study of echolocation of prey by mouse-tailed bats.

2083: To Dr. Kendall W. Corbin, University of Minnesota, Minneapolis, Minnesota, for a study of genetic variation in the rufous-collared sparrow (*Zonotrichia capensis*).

2084: To Dr. Walter R. Siegfried, University of Cape Town, Rondebosch, South Africa, for a study of seasonal and geographical variation in the diet of jackass penguins.

2085: To Dr. Tomas Feininger, Universite Laval, Quebec, Canada, for a study of geology of the eastern Andean slope near Quito.

2086: To Dr. Norman Herz, The University of Georgia, Athens, Georgia, for a study of stable isotopic signatures applied to problems of classical Greek marble.

2087: To Dr. C. Vance Haynes, The University of Arizona, Tucson, Arizona, in support of study of Quaternary geochronology of the Western Desert.

2088: To Dr. David W. Steadman, The University of Arizona, Tucson, Arizona, for a study of vertebrate paleontology of the Galápagos Islands.

2089: To Dr. Jose F. Bonaparte, Ministerio de Cultura y Educacion, Buenos Aires, Argentina, for study of Jurassic and Cretaceous vertebrates of South America.

2090: To Dr. Francine G. Patterson, Stanford University, Stanford, California, in support of a continuing study of the lowland gorilla: linguistic and cognitive abilities.

2091: To Dr. John B. Heppner, Smithsonian Institution, Washington, D. C., in support of biological research and survey of microlepidoptera of Peru.

2092: To Dr. David L. Pearson, Pennsylvania State University, University Park, Pennsylvania, for a floral and faunal survey of the Tambopata Reserve, Peru.

2093: To Dr. Thomas B. Thorson, University of Nebraska, Lincoln, Nebraska, for a study of freshwater adaptation in the Niger-Benue stingray *Dasyatis garouaensis*.

2094: To Dr. Birute M. F. Galdikas, Tanjung Puting Reserve, Kalimantan Tengah, Indonesia, for a study of orangutan adaptation at Tanjung Puting Reserve, Indonesia.

2095: To Dr. Anthony G. Coates, The George Washington University, Washington, D. C., for a study of Cretaceous coral/rudist reefs from Turkey, Iran, Afghanistan, and Israel.

2096: To Mr. Robin C. M. Piercy, American Institute of Nautical Archaeology, College Station, Texas, in support of the Mombasa wreck excavation.

2097: To Dr. Janet H. Johnson, Oriental Institute, University of Chicago, Chicago, Illinois, in support of the Quseir Project.

2099: To Dr. Gregory O. Boeshaar, University of Oregon, Eugene, Oregon, for a study of disk characteristics of Sc I galaxies.

2100: To Dr. Marea E. Hatziolos, Washington, D. C., for a study of stomatopod predation on prawns in the Gulf of California.
2102: To Dr. Julian V. Minghi, University of South Carolina, in support of a study, "Franco-Italian Borderland: Impact of Two Decades of Integration."
2103: To Dr. Kraig Adler, Cornell University, Itahaca, New York, for a study of orientation and navigation of desert reptiles.
2104: To Dr. Alexander H. Harcourt, University of Cambridge, Cambridge, England, in support of a mountain gorilla study.
2105: To Dr. Merlin D. Tuttle, Milwaukee Public Museum, Milwaukee, Wisconsin, for a study of the impact of frog-eating bats on frog calling and courtship behavior.
2106: To Dr. John A. Graham, University of California, Berkeley, California, in support of archeological investigations at Abaj Takalik, Guatemala.
2107: To Dr. Michael J. Walker, University of Sydney, Sydney, N.S.W., in support of an archeological excavation of caves near Jumilla, Yecla, and Villena in southeastern Spain.
2108: To Dr. Geoffrey M. O. Maloiy, University of Nairobi, Kabete, Kenya, in support of research, "Have Pastoral Nomads of Northern Kenya Any Special Desert Physiology?"
2109: To Dr. Robert K. Trench, University of California, Santa Barbara, California, for a study of the influence of Zooxanthellae metamorphosis in *Tridacna*.
2110: To Dr. Philip S. Gipson, University of Alaska, Fairbanks, Alaska, for a study of ecology of wolverines in an Arctic ecosystem.
2111: To Dr. Jennifer U. M. Jarvis, University of Cape Town, Rondebosch, South Africa, for a study of the influence of ecological factors on sociality in *Heterocephalus glaber*.
2112: To Dr. Raphael Herbst, Lavalle, Argentina, in support of paleontological and stratigraphical researches in Paraguay.
2113: To Dr. John A. Endler, University of Utah, Salt Lake City, Utah, for a study of color pattern convergences between Brazilian and Trinidadian poeciliid fishes.
2114: To Dr. Gordon W. Frankie, University of California, Berkeley, California, for a study of chemical aspects of territorial and mating behavior in *Centris* bees.
2115: To Dr. Bert Hölldobler, Harvard University, Cambridge, Massachusetts, for a study of social behavior and communication in Australian ants.
2116: To Dr. Randall L. Susman, State University of New York at Stony Brook, Long Island, New York, in support of a pygmy chimpanzee study in Zaire.
2117: To Dr. John Craighead, Missoula, Montana, for two further publications on the grizzly bear study: "Evaluation of Grizzly Bear Food Habits, Food Plants, and Habitat and of Landsat-1, Multispectral Imagery and Computer Analysis of Grizzly Bear Habitat."
2118: To Dr. Robert C. Bailey, Harvard University, Cambridge, Massachusetts, for a study of life history patterns of Mbuti Pygmies in the Ituri Forest of Zaire.
2119: To Mr. Gregory A. Waselkov, Auburn University, Auburn, Alabama, in support of a study of shell midden archeology: coastal adaptation in the lower Potomac valley.
2120: To Dr. Milla Y. Ohel, University of Haifa, Haifa, Israel, for a study of prehistory and paleoecology of the upper Dishon Basin, Israel.

2121: To Drs. Raymond T. Matheny and Bruce N. Dahlin, Brigham Young University, Provo, Utah, in support of Project El Mirador.

2122: To Dr. David W. MacDonald, Oxford University, Oxford, United Kingdom, for a study of nursing coalitions and infanticide in farm cats.

2123: To Dr. Richard P. Blakemore, University of New Hampshire, Durham, New Hampshire, in support of a search for magnetic bacteria in the Southern Hemisphere.

2124: To Dr. Mason E. Hale, Smithsonian Institution, Washington, D. C., in support of an investigation of biological fouling on monuments at Tikal, Guatemala.

2125: To Dr. Lytton J. Musselman, Old Dominion University, Norfolk, Virginia, for a study of fertility patterns and floral biology in three species of witchweed.

2126: To Dr. Ronald H. Petersen, The University of Tennessee, Knoxville, Tennessee, in support of a botanical expedition to Tibet.

2127: To Dr. John T. Emlen, University of Wisconsin, Madison, Wisconsin, in support of a study of behavioral divergence in bird populations on two Bahama islands.

2128: To Dr. Margaret B. Shepard, Cornell University, Ithaca, New York, for a study of feeding ecology and social behavior of the Stewart Island kakapo.

2129: To Dr. Stuart H. Hurlbert, San Diego State University, San Diego, California, for a study of flamingo breeding, ice islands, and lacustrine permafrost in the Andes.

2130: To Mr. Steven L. Swartz, San Diego, California, in support of a study of the gray whale in Baja California, Mexico.

Index